Y0-DVD-180

# PHYSICAL DESIGN OF ELECTRONIC SYSTEMS

*Volume I*
DESIGN TECHNOLOGY

*Volume II*
MATERIALS TECHNOLOGY

*Volume III*
INTEGRATED DEVICE AND CONNECTION TECHNOLOGY

*Volume IV*
DESIGN PROCESS

PRENTICE-HALL ELECTRICAL ENGINEERING SERIES
William L. Everitt, *Editor*

PRENTICE-HALL INTERNATIONAL, INC., *London*
PRENTICE-HALL OF AUSTRALIA, PTY. LTD., *Sydney*
PRENTICE-HALL OF CANADA, LTD., *Toronto*
PRENTICE-HALL OF INDIA PRIVATE LTD., *New Delhi*
PRENTICE-HALL OF JAPAN, INC., *Tokyo*

*Volume I*

# DESIGN TECHNOLOGY

*Prepared by members of the technical staff,*
*Bell Telephone Laboratories, Incorporated,*
*under the general direction of:*

**D. Baker**          **D. C. Koehler**

**W. O. Fleckenstein**          **C. E. Roden**

**R. Sabia**

PRENTICE-HALL, INC., Englewood Cliffs, N.J.

© 1970 *by* BELL TELEPHONE LABORATORIES, INCORPORATED.
*All rights reserved. No part of this book may be reproduced in
any form or by any means without permission in writing from
the publisher.*

PRENTICE-HALL, INC.
*Englewood Cliffs, N.J.*

Current printing (last digit):

10  9  8  7  6  5  4  3  2  1

13-666354-0

*Library of Congress Catalog Card Number 74-76873*

PRINTED IN THE UNITED STATES OF AMERICA

# PREFACE

The physical design of electronic systems encompasses such a range of technology and background that any attempt to write about it raises difficult questions of content. The material in the four volumes of this series has been chosen to emphasize the importance of drawing on fundamental technology in the physical sciences in achieving the physical realization of these systems. Before reviewing the plan for the series, however, it is useful to review some of the trends that have been taking place in electronic systems and the implications of these on physical design. It is convenient to divide such a review into three phases: first, the pre-solid-state electronics era; second, the solid-state electronics era through the early 1960's; and, finally, the trends that appear unmistakable in the period just ahead.

If one looks at the period prior to the solid-state era, the situation might be characterized as follows: Designers were dealing with systems operating at slow to medium speeds, and components were comparatively bulky. Thus, speed did not place a limitation on space, equipment was less susceptible to electrical interference, heat concentration was not a crucial problem, and structures could be overengineered with relatively little penalty.

As the technology moved into the solid-state electronics era, a number of things happened. In a large segment of the system design area, speeds moved from the millisecond to microsecond regions; smaller components and higher-density configurations were required; and, consequently, problems of heat dissipation, noise interference, and more compact and efficient structures became more important. In addition to these system design problems, a host of new materials and devices, with which the physical designer must be familiar, has come into being. The use of the computer as an aid to the physical design and documentation of the design has advanced to the point of having a significant impact in some areas.

It is now clear that we are entering another new phase in the technology being applied to electronic systems, and it seems equally clear that this new technology will have major implications on physical design. Circuit operating speeds are continuing to increase—designers are frequently concerned with nanosecond rather than microsecond speeds. Such circuitry imposes fundamental limitations on maximum spacing of elements and, at the same time, extends the range of susceptibility to electrical interference. Microminiaturization has developed to the point where major application of thin-film and semiconductor integrated circuits is being made in a new generation of systems. These speeds and new devices put a new importance on the understanding of materials, devices, and interconnection means. The higher-density construction required imposes new heat, electrical interference, and structural problems. Finally, the field of computer aids in design and preparation of manufacturing information, and the continuing move to automation in manufacture have now matured to the point where they are having a major impact on design and on the design process.

The plan for the series is to provide basic material that the physical designer needs in order to keep pace with the changes and advances in technology. This volume covers four areas of physical design technology which relate to the interactions among basic parts of an electronic system: Statics and Dynamics of Structures, Thermal Design, Electrical Interaction, and Human Factors. The first chapter serves as an introduction to the series and highlights the nature of physical design. Part I, Statics and Dynamics of Structures, considers the design of structures to withstand static loads as well as the rigors of shock and vibration environments. Thermal design, which is covered in Part II, deals with heat transfer by conduction, convection, and radiation as a means of controlling device temperatures to ensure satisfactory device operation and life. Part III considers the interaction between the physical form and the circuit function of electronic systems  This includes two things: first, the transmission of signals with minimum delay and distortion between elements of the system; and second, the avoidance of mutual interference between signal paths to ensure satisfactory operation. Part IV concludes Volume I with a treatment of human factors in design. An introduction to human characteristics is given, and then human factors are related to design for installation, use, maintenance, and appearance.

Volume II deals with engineering materials that represent the basic ingredients with which the physical designer works. A number of topics in materials technology are covered which are intended to provide the designer with a reasonable understanding of the structure and properties of materials frequently encountered in design. Volume III covers new devices (thin-film and semiconductor integrated circuits) and contact and connection technology. New devices are emphasized since, as noted, they are beginning to have a heavy impact on the next generation of electronic systems. Contacts and connections are of ever-increasing importance as new designs are evolved for miniaturized equipment and as the use of plug-in packages increases. Volume IV, the final volume of the series, considers the system design process. The material presented is intended to improve the efficiency of the design process and give an approach to the physical realization of systems.

The material in this series was prepared for a four-semester graduate level course for members of the technical staff of Bell Telephone Laboratories who are concerned with the physical design of communication systems. The material covered in each semester of the course corresponds roughly to the contents of one volume of the series. Parts of the series can and have been used for single-semester courses for those who have more limited interests. Because of the interdisciplinary nature of physical design, an attempt has been made throughout the series first, to review the fundamentals of each area of technology, and second, to apply these fundamentals to specific physical design problems. It is believed that this treatment makes the series attractive for both university and industrial courses, as well as to the practicing engineer for self-study.

This undertaking was stimulated by Messrs. W. A. MacNair and M. B. McDavitt, former vice presidents of Bell Telephone Laboratories, and it was started under the general direction of Mr. C. H. Elmendorf. In addition to those listed as authors, contributions were made by people from almost every area of Bell Telephone Laboratories. This publication is derived from course text material that was originally edited and printed by members of the Technical Publications organization of the Western Electric Company at Winston-Salem, North Carolina. We are extremely grateful to the many individuals who have made this publication possible.

*Holmdel, New Jersey*

D. BAKER
W. O. FLECKENSTEIN
D. C. KOEHLER
C. E. RODEN
R. SABIA

# CONTENTS

ix

# Chapter 1

# THE NATURE OF PHYSICAL DESIGN

Physical design plays a significant role in almost every aspect of electronic product development and use. It draws upon many disciplines including the materials sciences, device technology, circuit theory, system design, and many areas of mechanical engineering. Other important factors are manufacturing processes, contacts and connections, human factors and styling, reliability and maintenance, economics, and logical and computer aids to design. The aim of this chapter is to emphasize the general nature of physical design by highlighting a variety of these factors. Thus, the following paragraphs will survey briefly the disciplines involved and provide a few selected examples. The chapters in the remainder of this series will then examine various areas of the technology more intensively.

## MECHANICS

The field of mechanics, particularly statics and dynamics, has been one of the classic concerns of the physical designer. Although moving parts are used for many applications in electronic systems (dials, switches and relays, springs, and slides, to mention only a few), most electronic equipment is essentially stationary while it is in service. However, beyond the requirement to withstand

**Fig. I-I** Shock mounted power equipment for a hardened carrier transmission system.

static loads, there is a need to handle dynamic problems. This occurs for many reasons: all equipment must withstand the rigors of shipping and handling; sometimes shock and vibration are encountered due to the operation of nearby equipment; and, in many cases, equipment must be isolated from the shocks resulting from earthquakes or nuclear blasts, Fig. 1-1.

Moreover, there are a variety of mechanisms which are intimately associated with the functioning of some electronic systems. Antenna drives, tracking mechanisms, tape drives, printers, and memory card writers (either the punch or magnetic variety shown in Fig. 1-2) are familiar examples. The design of such mechanisms requires solutions to a wide range of problems of both statics and dynamics.

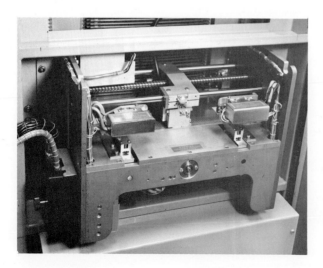

**Fig. I-2** Mechanism used for writing twistor memory cards in an electronic switching system. The multiple writing head in the upper center writes memory cards by selectively magnetizing or demagnetizing each of 2816 tiny magnets "on the fly" as it passes by.[1]

In addition, the trend toward miniaturization is now presenting a whole new set of mechanical problems for the physical designer. New concepts are needed for mounting and interconnecting, and problems of weight concentration are becoming more severe because of the higher component densities. These considerations suggest the need for greater application of fundamental principles, refinement of design tools, and use of improved experimental techniques.

## THERMAL DESIGN

The operation, reliability, and life of circuit components are affected by their operating temperatures. To avoid excessive temperatures, it is important to minimize the energy dissipated and to optimize heat transfer paths from the heat-producing components to the external environment. Even with the advent of relatively low-powered semiconductor devices, the accompanying trend toward miniaturization often results in greater power per unit volume. In addition, structural and electrical constraints may require the use of materials that have poor thermal conductivity, or that components be enclosed in a way that restricts air circulation. Furthermore, the modular "plug-in" concept often results in high thermal resistance at the package-mounting interface. The trend toward miniaturization poses difficult problems in measuring temperatures of devices and equipment for the purpose of evaluating thermal designs. These problems all suggest the need for a more fundamental understanding of heat transfer principles.

As an example, the power supply package shown in Fig. 1-3 illustrates one solution to a heat transfer problem.

## ELECTRICAL INTERACTION

The direct relation between physical design and the operation of high-speed circuits is critically important. This includes two things: first, the device interconnections must be short enough to ensure proper circuit operation; second, the elements must be properly placed to avoid excessive mutual interference. The latter is frequently controlled by proper use of shielding to reduce the effects of stray electric and magnetic fields.

Miniature circuit packages, such as the hybrid integrated circuit substrate shown in Fig. 1-4, permit the short interconnection paths and flexibility in arrangement of the circuit elements required for high-speed operation. They are amenable to batch processing and provide a high degree of reproducibility. The figure illustrates the complex pattern of interconnecting conductors (many as narrow as 125 microns) typical of these circuits. Such circuits require

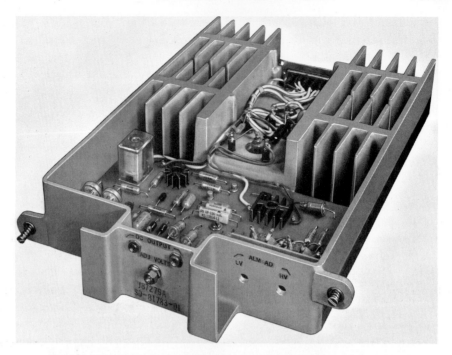

**Fig I-3**  Power supply package for a microwave radio relay communication system. Heat sink fins are integral parts of the chassis. Some heat sinks for individual devices are also shown.

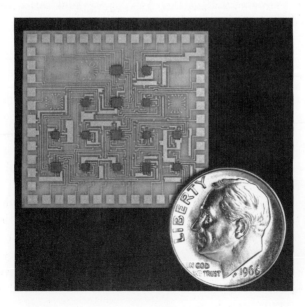

**Fig I-4** Miniature ceramic substrate for logic circuits illustrating complex interconnection pattern. The substrate is shown with 15 beam lead, silicon integrated circuit chips (dark squares) bonded in place.

careful conductor layout and substrate material selection in order to control conductor impedance and capacitive coupling.

The problems of electrical interaction are often even more severe in conventional wiring and cabling arrangements. In many cases, the geometry of interconnecting wires and the segregation of certain groups of cables are important in controlling interference (Fig. 1-5). The importance, then, of under-

**Fig. I-5**  A compartmentalized cable rack at the top of an electronic switching equipment frame. The power, talking, signaling, and control cables are separated and partially shielded to reduce interaction between cable groups.[2]

standing the strong interrelationship between circuit design and physical design is apparent and will undoubtedly become even more so as system speeds increase and as the use of integrated circuits becomes more widespread.

## MATERIALS TECHNOLOGY

Although familiarity with the properties of the materials used in equipment has always been important, the rate at which new materials are being introduced accentuates the need for a more fundamental understanding of their structure

HIGH STRENGTH ALUMINUM
ALLOY FACINGS

SOLID
POLYETHYLENE
CORE

**Fig. 1-6** Laminate (left) formed by bonding aluminum facings to solid polyethylene core is much stiffer than glass-fiber-reinforced plastic (center) or steel (right) strips of equal weight. Laminate can also be postformed as shown by the dish-shaped pieces.

and behavior. As the physicist, chemist, and metallurgist move toward designing new materials or new combinations of existing materials having properties required for specific applications, this need will surely be magnified.

An example of a new combination of materials designed to provide high flexural strength and very low weight is the aluminum-polyethylene laminate shown in Fig. 1-6. This polymer-metal combination is based on new concepts of polymer wetting. The comparison shown is with a polyester glass-reinforced plastic and cold-rolled steel. In this figure, the strips have the same dimensions except for thickness, which is adjusted to provide equal weight; they support equal loads. The aluminum-polyethylene composite can be welded, bent, and punched; it also may be postformed by applying moderate heat and pressure. Compared with steel, the laminate provides a 60 percent weight saving for equal stiffness or flexural strength.

Another example is the complex materials system used for thin-film devices. Figure 1-7 illustrates the variety and sequence of the precise deposition of thin-film layers used in forming resistors, capacitors, and conductors. As an example of the precision that can be achieved, the thickness of the tantalum nitride resistive film, typically 500 Å, can be readily adjusted to achieve a precision of 0.01 percent in resistance value.

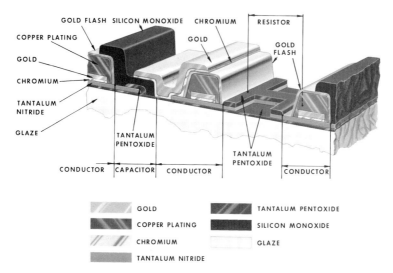

**Fig. 1-7** Cutaway view shows how resistors, capacitors, and conductors are formed by deposition of thin films. Resistors are trimmed to desired value by electrolytic anodization, which is also used for forming a thin layer of tantalum pentoxide as a first dielectric on the lower capacitor electrodes. The conductor areas are five layers deep, but most conduction is in the layer of electroplated copper.

## DEVICE TECHNOLOGY

The physical design of a system should take into account the capabilities and limitations of all of the devices and components that the system uses. Therefore, the physical designer of systems must have a background in device and component technology.

The impact of new technology in the areas of thin-film and semiconductor integrated circuits has already been mentioned. To use such devices effectively requires a fundamental understanding of the structure, methods of fabrication, and properties of the devices. This will not only aid in the proper usage but will also encourage selection of mutually compatible components. Figure 1-8 shows an integrated circuit which is typical of the kind that might be attached to the substrate of Fig. 1-4. The silicon chip is about 1.6 mm square and has 16 beam leads for connections to the substrate. These leads are approximately 100 microns wide and 13 microns thick.

## CONTACTS AND CONNECTIONS

Electrical connections are fundamental to electronic systems, and their production rate, measured in billions per year, is continually increasing. These

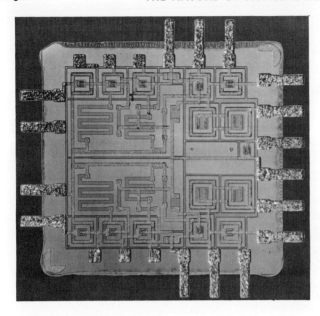

**Fig. I-8** This beam lead, silicon integrated device performs a circuit function equivalent to that of 10 transistors, 4 diodes, and 12 resistors.

connections differ widely in permanency, varying from the temporary, intermittent switching contacts used on relays and switches, to infrequently operated, plug-in contacts, to more permanent pressure connections (as obtained by screwing, crimping, or wedging), and finally to permanently bonded and welded connections. All of these types depend upon electrical conduction through a critical contacting region, often microscopic in size; yet the tremendous numbers in use demand that all types be extremely reliable. Many of the factors which control connection quality are common to all, but different ones of these factors may be dominant according to the desired degree of permanency.

Although contacts and connections have been used since the first experiments with electricity, the ever-increasing demands for reliability and small size are continuing to produce new techniques such as sealed contacts, hot work ultrasonic bonding, and laser welding. Again, the factors which affect connection quality are similar to those for conventional connections, but with new problems arising from the new ranges of application. An understanding of these factors and the principles by which they control quality are obviously important to the physical designers of both components and systems.

## HUMAN FACTORS AND STYLING

The suitability of a product for installation, operational use, and flexibility for growth and maintenance stems almost entirely from the physical design. One of the most familiar examples, the telephone set, provides maximum usefulness to the user through careful physical design of each of its parts, Fig. 1-9. The handset is light, comfortable to hold, and resists turning in the hand. The cradle for the handset is designed to increase the likelihood that it will fall into the proper position (to disconnect the call) when the user intends to hang up. The ringer is designed so that its volume may be easily adjusted by the user. The basic design has the flexibility to accommodate other arrangements such as the use of additional buttons to permit selective connection to several lines, and special features to assist the hard of hearing. Installation and maintenance are simplified by good accessibility, which is assured by mounting the electrical components on a base plate and providing for easy removal of the plastic housing.

**Fig. I-9**  TOUCH-TONE® telephone set illustrating access to components by removing housing.

The location and arrangement of alarm indicators and controls, fuses, and designation strips greatly influence the ease of installation and maintenance of electronic systems. Also, the ability to adapt a basic design to fit varying applications by use of easily installed, simple interconnections is often a fundamental requirement. In addition, many systems include built-in test facilities. The design and placement of this test equipment requires adequate attention to human factors in order to provide for fast and accurate use by maintenance personnel, Fig. 1-10.

In many cases, styling is a key element in the design; each item should be attractive and fit with the user's decorative theme. Examples of telephone products serving different needs are shown in Fig. 1-11. In each case, the styling was chosen to blend harmoniously with a wide variety of surroundings.

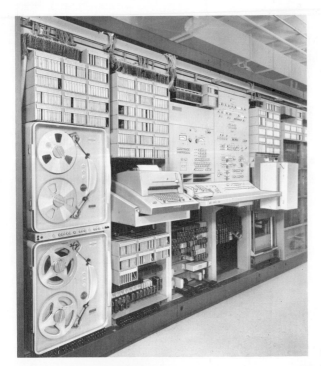

**Fig. 1-10** Master test and control center for an electronic telephone switching system, illustrating arrangement of test controls.[2]

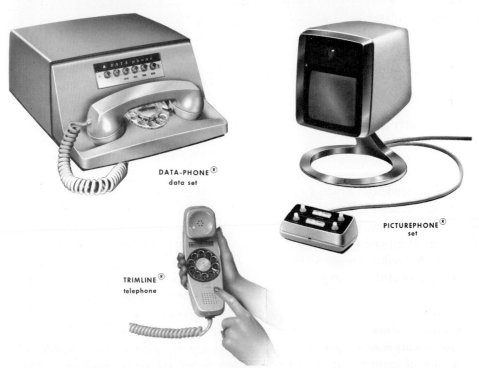

DATA-PHONE®
data set

PICTUREPHONE®
set

TRIMLINE®
telephone

**Fig. 1-11** Styling effects achieved with three types of telephone sets.

Finally, assuring that a system can be operated safely in terms of fire and other physical hazards is a most important human factors consideration. The carbon block protector connected to each telephone line and installed on the user's premises is provided to prevent possible injury to the user and to prevent fires which might result from lightning striking that telephone line. The types of plastic chosen for printed wire board connectors and meter housings, for example, will not support combustion. This was not always the case. At one time, dripping of melted plastic from a meter housing caused a spreading of fire, a condition that has since been corrected by a proper choice of material.

## RELIABILITY AND MAINTENANCE

To a substantial degree, system reliability and durability result directly from physical design choices. These choices cover the gamut of design problems, and the objectives are: minimizing deterioration due to environment, ensuring that ambient conditions within the equipment will allow devices to operate within design limits, selecting appropriate materials, applying proper structural and thermal design techniques, and assuring that adequate operating margins are not degraded through adverse electrical interactions.

The proper balance between reliability and maintainability varies greatly, depending on the requirements for continuous service, redundancy in the equipment, location of the product, and accessibility for repair. Different maintenance philosophies are needed for equipment located in the user's home, in an office building, or in an inaccessible location such as underseas or in a satellite.

## MANUFACTURING PROCESSES

The close coupling between physical design and the methods used in manufacturing a product makes it essential that the physical designer have a thorough knowledge of the technical and economic implications of the manufacturing processes. Although familiarity with the traditional methods is certainly necessary, new and substantially different techniques are continually emerging. High-energy forming processes and electrical and chemical machining methods are relatively new; however, it seems reasonable to expect them to play an important part in product manufacture. The fact is, that with the new materials and device technology, the coupling between design and process is tightening. Also, automation in manufacture, including the use of numerically controlled machine tools, is having an increasing influence on design.

An example of a significant payoff resulting from the physical designer's knowledge of manufacturing methods is the design of the printed wire board carrier for a relatively small electronic telephone switching system to be located on the user's premises.  Originally, a sheet metal carrier fabricated by punching, bending, and spot welding had been proposed, Fig. 1-12. After discussions with manufacturing engineers and a review of preliminary cost estimates, it was decided to design the carrier around the use of die cast parts. Such parts provide the dimensional accuracy required for easy assembly, without special fixtures, and require few subsequent machining operations.  In the new design,

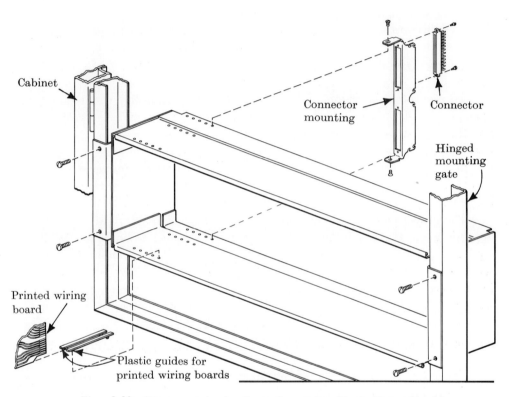

**Fig. 1-12** Sheet metal circuit pack carrier illustrating assembly operations required.

Fig. 1-13, the identical top and bottom plates are cast with card guide slots, ventilation holes, and mounting bosses for snap-in parts—adding little to the cost. The new carrier is self-supporting and eliminates the hinged mounting gate required in the original design. Other assembly costs were substantially reduced by using snap-in, molded plastic parts for mounting the printed wire board connectors to the carrier. As a result of these various measures, the manufactured cost of the completely assembled and mounted printed wire board carriers was reduced nearly 50 percent, compared to the equivalent gate-mounted sheet metal units.

Cabinet

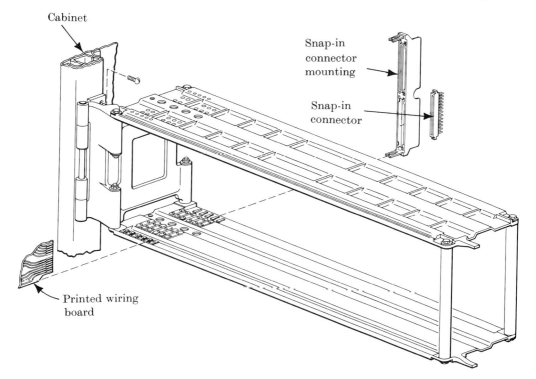

Snap-in
connector
mounting

Snap-in
connector

Printed wiring
board

**Fig. I-13**  Circuit pack carrier using die cast parts shows ease of
assembly.

In this series, manufacturing processes are not treated as a separate
subject, but are discussed in connection with materials fabrication and the
design of devices and systems, with which they are intimately associated.

## ECONOMICS

Throughout the design process, the designer must study the economic
consequences of alternative design decisions. It is not unusual for most of the
total cost of an electronic system to be attributable to, or influenced by,
physical design decisions. A proper economic study should include the total
expenditure required to provide the system installed and ready for use, and all
other expenses incident to keeping the system in service. Frequently, this total
expenditure is expressed as total annual cost. The principal components of
annual cost are depreciation, interest, taxes, insurance, maintenance, and
operation. Of these components, interest and depreciation are in a special
category, since they are the annual cost counterparts of first cost. The remaining components have no direct counterpart in the first cost and, in a sense,
are expenses incident to keeping the system in use. There are many other

recurring expenses such as administration, accounting, and advertising, which are often neglected in preliminary engineering cost studies.

It is a responsibility of the designer to study each aspect of annual cost in order to appraise the total cost of the equipment he designs. Often, low first-cost designs can have expensive long-run consequences when other cost factors are considered. For example, recurring maintenance costs can be reduced by a higher initial investment in more reliable components, built-in features to facilitate testing, plug-in arrangements, etc. This interaction between maintenance cost and the annual equivalent of first cost is illustrated qualitatively in Fig. 1-14. It emphasizes the importance of considering the trade-offs between various components of total annual cost.

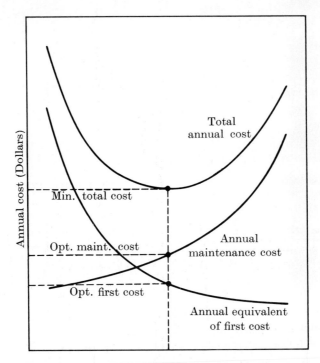

**Fig. I-14**  Influence of first cost and maintenance cost on total annual cost.

## COMPUTERS

The rapidly increasing sophistication and variety of electronic systems makes urgent the use of the computer as a tool to increase the efficiency of the design process. As such, computers are already used in the solution of a wide variety of engineering problems. Their application in the physical design field poses a new and exciting challenge. An obvious use is to relieve the designer of much of the routine portion of his task. A more far-reaching goal is to provide new approaches in design.

The design of equalizer circuit modules for an underwater communication system is a good example of the effective use of computers in the design process. The circuit module shown in the center of Fig. 1-15 is a network that compensates for manufacturing deviations in submarine cable repeaters. After

**Fig. I-I5** Compensation network module for submarine cable amplifier. Computer generates punched tape that directs numerically controlled machining of plastic blanks, each tailored for an individual network.

manufacture of other parts of the system, the individual equalizer circuits must be designed and produced rapidly so as not to delay system installation. To avoid normal drafting delays associated with detailing parts, a common structure was designed for the entire family of networks. Computer subroutines were written to generate a punched tape for directing a numerically controlled production machine to produce the parts. This procedure reduced the design and manufacturing interval by a factor of about five.

The growing capability of computers is making many physical design problems more tractable. These problems include device placement and inter-connection, production of art masters, thermal and structural stress analysis, and problems in fluid mechanics.

## SYSTEM DESIGN CONCEPT

The interdisciplinary aspects of physical design discussed in this section certainly suggest the need for an overall system point of view on the part of the physical designer. In addition, as the technology has advanced, there has been an increasing need for overlap between the traditional areas of development (i.e., device, circuit, and equipment) and the manufacturing process. Since the physical design of the system culminates the development process, the re-sponsibility rests with the physical designer to understand fully the objectives and problems of the other design and manufacturing areas. He must work closely with these areas in determining the overall equipment layout, the size of units, the choice of devices, the degree of standardization feasible in circuit and mechanical design, and in providing the flexibility to cope with changes in demand for space, access, and interconnections. It is also important that the maintenance philosophy (module repair versus throw-away, for example) be planned in advance, so that appropriate arrangements can be integrated into the design from the beginning.

An example of the importance of this kind of system overview is found in the redesign of a widely used telephone central office terminal equipment for long distance circuits. The existing design had created problems of central office space and cable congestion. With the use of miniaturized components, it became evident that, if the traditional separation of functions were retained, the volume of connecting cables would exceed the volume of equipment. Stopgap measures, including the use of smaller cables, were considered but fell short of the objective. However, a satisfactory solution was achieved by taking a broader viewpoint of the equipment configuration and combining functions in such a way as to reduce interconnections. In this way, much of the cabling between bays of equipment was eliminated and a substantial reduction in size achieved in spite of increased complexity.

In addition to the technologies mentioned previously, there is a body of theory developing in the general area of functional and logical aids to design. Some of these include: utility and decision theory, project planning and con-trol methods such as PERT (Program Evaluation and Review Technique) and CPM (Critical Path Method), design optimization techniques, aspects of scientific (statistical) inference, and design of experiments. Some considerations of this nature can be helpful in various phases of a design project, and they appear to have significant potential as an aid to the physical designer in seeking a more systematic and formalized approach to system design.

## REFERENCES

1. Ault, C. F., et al., "No. 1 ESS Program Store," *Bell Sys. Tech. J.*, **43,** 2097–2146, American Tel. and Tel. Co., Sept., 1964. Fig. 1-2 by permission.

2. Ferguson, J. G., et al., "No. 1 ESS Apparatus and Equipment," *Bell Sys. Tech. J.*, **43,** 2355–2439, American Tel. and Tel. Co., Sept., 1964. Figs. 1-5, 1-10 by permission.

In discussing stresses at a point, it is useful to consider an elemental volume within the larger body of material. Such an element is shown in Fig. 2-1 with forces aligned with a particular $x$, $y$, $z$ coordinate system. It will be shown that if the stresses are known on the planes perpendicular to three orthogonal axes, the stresses acting on any other plane through the point can be found. The stresses shown on the three visible faces of the rectangular parallelepiped of material under consideration in Fig. 2-1 follow the usual sign and

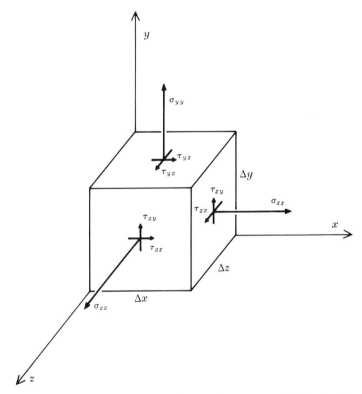

**Fig. 2-1**   Stresses acting at a point on planes perpendicular to the orthogonal axes.

subscript convention. That is, the first subscript denotes the plane on which the stress acts, while the second subscript denotes the direction of the stress in that plane. The stress is considered positive on planes with outward normals in the positive coordinate directions when the stress vector points in a positive coordinate direction; since action and reaction are equal and opposite, the stress is also positive on planes with outward normals in the negative coordinate directions when the stress points in a negative coordinate direction. Of course, the stress vector arrows indicate the directions of the forces applied to the parallelepiped by the material outside. Normal (tensile or compressive) and shear stresses are usually represented, as they are here, by $\sigma$ and $\tau$,* respectively. The usual assumption is made that the material element is small enough for the indicated stresses to represent accurately the average stresses acting on each face, i.e., the variation of stress across the face is too small to introduce significant moment.

To examine the stresses acting on other planes in the body, a tetrahedron as shown in Fig. 2-2 will be analyzed. The stress on the oblique face in any

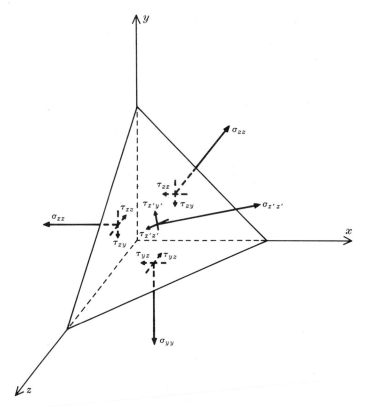

**Fig. 2-2**  Stresses acting on a tetrahedron with one face oblique to the coordinate axes.

direction can be determined as a function of all the stresses on the three orthogonal faces by a simple static force balance. That is, the sum of the forces resulting from the stresses on the orthogonal faces must exactly counterbalance the forces acting on the oblique face. However, the resulting relationships are

---

* A list of principal symbols, units, subscripts, and physical constants is given in Appendix C near the end of this volume.

perfectly valid for dynamic situations, as well as those with body loadings, because the acceleration and body forces, which depend on the volume, are of higher order in the dimensions of the tetrahedron and thus disappear in the limit as the size of the tetrahedron gets small.

Figure 2-2 shows stresses on the oblique plane of normal direction $x'$ corresponding to coordinate axces $x'$, $y'$, $z'$. Six more stresses are associated with the $x'$, $y'$, $z'$ coordinate system, namely those stresses acting on the planes perpendicular to the $y'$ and $z'$ directions. This simple consideration results in three rather lengthy equations for the stresses on the oblique plane, as follows:

$$\sigma_{x'x'} = \alpha^2_{x'x}\sigma_{xx} + \alpha^2_{x'y}\sigma_{yy} + \alpha^2_{x'z}\sigma_{zz} + 2\alpha_{x'x}\alpha_{x'y}\tau_{xy}$$
$$+ 2\alpha_{x'y}\alpha_{x'z}\tau_{yz} + 2\alpha_{x'z}\alpha_{x'x}\tau_{zx} \quad (2\text{-}1a)$$

$$\tau_{x'y'} = \alpha_{x'x}\alpha_{y'x}\sigma_{xx} + \alpha_{x'y}\alpha_{y'y}\sigma_{yy} + \alpha_{x'z}\alpha_{y'z}\sigma_{zz} + (\alpha_{x'x}\alpha_{y'y} + \alpha_{x'y}\alpha_{y'x})\tau_{xy}$$
$$+ (\alpha_{x'y}\alpha_{y'z} + \alpha_{x'z}\alpha_{y'y})\tau_{yz} + (\alpha_{x'z}\alpha_{y'x} + \alpha_{x'x}\alpha_{y'z})\tau_{zx} \quad (2\text{-}1b)$$

$$\tau_{x'z'} = \alpha_{x'x}\alpha_{z'x}\sigma_{xx} + \alpha_{x'y}\alpha_{z'y}\sigma_{yy} + \alpha_{x'z}\alpha_{z'z}\sigma_{zz} + (\alpha_{x'x}\alpha_{z'y} + \alpha_{x'y}\alpha_{z'x})\tau_{xy}$$
$$+ (\alpha_{x'y}\alpha_{z'z} + \alpha_{x'z}\alpha_{z'y})\tau_{yz} + (\alpha_{x'z}\alpha_{z'x} + \alpha_{x'x}\alpha_{z'z})\tau_{zx} \quad (2\text{-}1c)$$

where the $\alpha$'s are the direction cosines between the coordinate directions indicated by the subscripts. The equations for $\sigma_{y'y'}$ and $\sigma_{z'z'}$ may be obtained by substituting $y'$ and $z'$, respectively, for $x'$ throughout the equation for $\sigma_{x'x'}$. Similarly, expressions for $\tau_{y'x'}$, $\tau_{y'z'}$, $\tau_{z'x'}$, and $\tau_{z'y'}$ may be found by substituting corresponding primed coordinates in the expression for either $\tau_{x'y'}$ or $\tau_{x'z'}$. For example, $\tau_{y'z'}$ may be found from the expression for $\tau_{x'z'}$ by substituting $y'$ for $x'$ throughout. The regularity of the subscripts in equations of this type makes it easy to detect errors. For simplicity of presentation, the foregoing results have assumed that $\tau_{ij} = \tau_{ji}$ for $i, j = x, y, z$, which is almost universally true. More comments on this will appear during derivation of the momentum equations, but, except for Eqs. (2-2) and (2-3), this assumption will be made throughout the following discussion.

A simple way of presenting the whole system of stress transformation equations in terms of matrices may be written:

$$[\sigma'] = [\alpha]^T[\sigma][\alpha] \quad (2\text{-}2)$$

where

$$[\sigma] = \begin{bmatrix} \sigma_{xx} & \tau_{xy} & \tau_{xz} \\ \tau_{yx} & \sigma_{yy} & \tau_{yz} \\ \tau_{zx} & \tau_{zy} & \sigma_{zz} \end{bmatrix} \quad (2\text{-}3a)$$

and

$$[\alpha] = \begin{bmatrix} \alpha_{xx'} & \alpha_{xy'} & \alpha_{xz'} \\ \alpha_{yx'} & \alpha_{yy'} & \alpha_{yz'} \\ \alpha_{zx'} & \alpha_{zy'} & \alpha_{zz'} \end{bmatrix} \quad (2\text{-}3b)$$

$[\sigma']$ is of the same matrix form as $[\sigma]$ but with primed subscripts, and $[\alpha]^T$ is the transpose of $[\alpha]$.

These relations imply that, once all the stresses are known relative to one coordinate system, they can be found uniquely for any other coordinate system at the same point by simply requiring that the material element at the point be in equilibrium. These relationships say nothing about how the stresses vary with change of position in the body. Thus, the state of stress at a point is known when all the stresses acting on three mutually perpendicular planes are known.

## TENSOR NATURE OF STRESS

A tensor is a mathematical quantity whose values at a point in one coordinate system are strictly related to its values at the same point referred to another coordinate system by a transformation rule. Only Cartesian tensors (that is, those described in rectangular coordinates) will be discussed. A scalar, or zero order tensor, always has the same value in any system. The vector components, which describe a vector, or first order tensor, vary from one coordinate system to another according to the vector projections on the various coordinate axes. Stress is represented by a second order tensor simply because the transformation rule presented previously is the same as that defining second order tensor transformations. The important consideration here is not the term applied, but that stress is a physical quantity which may be represented by a mathematical quantity with specific well-known properties. The remainder of the section on stress will be used to develop some of the more useful stress relations in terms of tensors. As will be shown, infinitesimal strains are also second order tensors, and the following results will be useful to the understanding of strains as well.

## PRINCIPAL STRESSES

Since the stresses vary with the plane on which they act, it is of real interest to find those planes which are acted on by maximum stresses. Principal stresses are defined as those values of the normal stress which are stationary (i.e., do not change in magnitude) with respect to small variations of the direction cosines. One of the principal stresses must therefore be the maximum normal stress. Equation (2-1) gives $\sigma_{x'x'}$ as a function of three direction cosines $\alpha_{x'x}$, $\alpha_{x'y}$, and $\alpha_{x'z}$.

By requiring that

$$\frac{\partial \sigma_{x'x'}}{\partial \alpha_{x'x}} = \frac{\partial \sigma_{x'x'}}{\partial \alpha_{x'y}} = 0$$

and remembering that when the $x$, $y$, and $z$ directions are mutually orthogonal,

$$\alpha_{x'x}^2 + \alpha_{x'y}^2 + \alpha_{x'z}^2 = 1$$

three sets of $\alpha$'s can be determined, each of which corresponds to a stationary value of $\sigma_{x'x'}$, i.e., $\sigma_{x'x'}$ has zero slope on these three planes relative to changes in the direction of $x'$. (Particulars of this development are given in any of the elasticity books listed under References at the end of this chapter.) It is also discovered that, on the plane defined by each such set of $\alpha$'s, all shear stresses are zero and, further, that the three planes defined by the three sets of $\alpha$'s are mutually orthogonal. In matrix terminology, the matrix of direction cosines, which transforms a given stress matrix into the matrix of principal stresses, diagonalizes the given matrix and yields a maximum, a minimum, and an intermediate stationary value for the $\sigma$'s as the diagonal elements. Throughout this chapter, these three principal stress values will be denoted $\sigma_1 \geqq \sigma_2 \geqq \sigma_3$ with their corresponding sets of cosines $(\alpha_{1x}, \alpha_{1y}, \alpha_{1z})$, $(\alpha_{2x}, \alpha_{2y}, \alpha_{2z})$, and $(\alpha_{3x}, \alpha_{3y}, \alpha_{3z})$. The three sets of $\alpha$'s with their corresponding $\sigma$'s are found from the following equations which are the culmination of the mathematical process of determining the stationary values of stress:

$$\alpha_{ix}(\sigma_{xx} - \sigma_i) + \alpha_{iy}\tau_{xy} + \alpha_{iz}\tau_{xz} = 0 \tag{2-4a}$$

$$\alpha_{ix}\tau_{xy} + \alpha_{iy}(\sigma_{yy} - \sigma_i) + \alpha_{iz}\tau_{yz} = 0 \tag{2-4b}$$

$$\alpha_{ix}\tau_{xz} + \alpha_{iy}\tau_{yz} + \alpha_{iz}(\sigma_{zz} - \sigma_i) = 0 \tag{2-4c}$$

and again

$$\alpha_{ix}^2 + \alpha_{iy}^2 + \alpha_{iz}^2 = 1 \tag{2-4d}$$

where $i = 1$, 2, 3. The $\sigma_i$'s are found by considering the stresses in Eqs. (2-4a, b, c) to be the coefficients and by setting the determinant of the coefficients to zero. This operation gives a cubic equation in $\sigma_i$ which yields three values, $\sigma_1$, $\sigma_2$, and $\sigma_3$:

$$\sigma_i^3 - I_1\sigma_i^2 - I_2\sigma_i - I_3 = 0 \tag{2-5}$$

where

$$I_1 = \sigma_{xx} + \sigma_{yy} + \sigma_{zz} \tag{2-6a}$$

$$I_2 = -(\sigma_{yy}\sigma_{zz} + \sigma_{zz}\sigma_{xx} + \sigma_{xx}\sigma_{yy}) + \tau_{yz}^2 + \tau_{xz}^2 + \tau_{xy}^2 \tag{2-6b}$$

$$I_3 = \sigma_{xx}\sigma_{yy}\sigma_{zz} + 2\tau_{yz}\tau_{xz}\tau_{xy} - \sigma_{xx}\tau_{yz}^2 - \sigma_{yy}\tau_{zx}^2 - \sigma_{zz}\tau_{xy}^2 \tag{2-6c}$$

Substitution of any of these principal stresses into all parts of Eq. (2-4) will yield the corresponding direction cosines. If two of the principal stresses are equal, then any two perpendicular planes which are parallel to the third principal stress may be considered as principal planes, and the normal stresses on all such planes will be equal. If all three $\sigma_i$'s are identical, then any mutually perpendicular set of planes is considered principal, the normal stress is the same in all directions, and there are no shear stresses acting on any plane, i.e., the state of stress is hydrostatic.

If the reference coordinate axes of Eq. (2-1) are the principal axes, then transformation equations are simplified (by the fact that the shear stresses are zero) to

$$\sigma_{x'x'} = \alpha_{x'1}^2 \sigma_1 + \alpha_{x'2}^2 \sigma_2 + \alpha_{x'3}^2 \sigma_3 \qquad (2\text{-}7a)$$

$$\tau_{x'y'} = \alpha_{x'1}\alpha_{y'1}\sigma_1 + \alpha_{x'2}\alpha_{y'2}\sigma_2 + \alpha_{x'3}\alpha_{y'3}\sigma_3 \qquad (2\text{-}7b)$$

## INVARIANTS OF THE STRESS TENSOR

Since the state of stress at a point has so much physical significance, particularly with regard to the amount and nature of the mechanical duress the material experiences, some way of describing the state of stress without reference to a particular coordinate system should be found. The principal stresses in a given situation must be the same regardless of the initial coordinate system from which they were calculated; therefore, the $I$'s in Eq. (2-5) must be independent of the initial coordinate system as well. These quantities are called the three principal invariants of the stress tensor. Equations (2-5) and (2-7) show that the invariants prescribe the entire state of stress since the principal stresses can be determined from Eq. (2-5), and from these, all stresses on any other plane through that point can be determined by Eq. (2-7). The precise orientation of the stress tensor is not available from the invariants alone, but the physical duress of an isotropic material particle hardly depends on the orientation of the local internal loading. That is one of the reasons why yield and failure criteria are so frequently formulated in terms of the invariants. Any combination of these invariants is also, of course, invariant under coordinate transformation.

## MAXIMUM SHEAR STRESS

Some theories about yielding of elastic materials propose that the maximum shear stress is the dominant parameter and that the yield point in three-dimensional stress fields can be predicted in terms of maximum shear stress alone. The resultant shear stress across a plane perpendicular to the $x'$ direction can be found from the vector addition of $\tau_{x'y'}$ and $\tau_{x'z'}$, determined from Eq. (2-7), in terms of the principal stresses as

$$\tau^2 = (\sigma_1 - \sigma_2)^2\alpha_{x'1}^2\alpha_{x'2}^2 + (\sigma_2 - \sigma_3)^2\alpha_{x'2}^2\alpha_{x'3}^2 + (\sigma_3 - \sigma_1)^2\alpha_{x'3}^2\alpha_{x'1}^2 \qquad (2\text{-}8)$$

which is a function of the direction cosines of the $x'$ direction alone. Determining the stationary values of $\tau$ as a function of these cosines, in a manner similar to determining the principal stresses, yields the fact that the shear is stationary on planes whose normals bisect the angles between the principal axes and have the value of $(\sigma_i - \sigma_j)/2$ when the principal directions bisected are the $i$ and $j$ directions. The normal stress on the same plane would be $(\sigma_i + \sigma_j)/2$. With the assumed convention on principal stress magnitudes, the maximum shear stress existing at a point may then be written

$$\tau_{\max} = \tfrac{1}{2}\,(\sigma_1 - \sigma_3) \tag{2-9}$$

## 2-2. EQUATIONS OF MOTION

Section 2.1 discussed the variation of stress at a point as the coordinate system describing a given situation changes. The results are valid whether or not the stresses change with time or space, and they have the derived form as long as the coordinate system is orthogonal at the point in question. This section will discuss the laws governing the variation of stress in time and space. The resulting equations will depend on which coordinate system is being used; however, again, only orthogonal systems will be discussed. It will be assumed that the displacements of the mass particles are small. Otherwise, a discussion of material (Lagrangian) or spatial (Eulerian) descriptions would have to be presented. Very flexible structural members might undergo large displacements while remaining elastic, and theories, such as the elastica[2] for thin beams, have been developed for them.

Figure 2-3 shows all the loadings, except internal body forces and torques, on the limitingly small material volume. Summing all resulting forces in the $x$ direction and equating them to the mass times the acceleration of the material element in the $x$ direction gives

$$\frac{\partial \sigma_{xx}}{\partial x} + \frac{\partial \tau_{yx}}{\partial y} + \frac{\partial \tau_{zx}}{\partial z} + \rho F_x = \rho \frac{\partial^2 u}{\partial t^2} \tag{2-10}$$

upon canceling $dx\,dy\,dz$ from both sides, where $\rho$ is the mass density, $u$ is the $x$ displacement of the material element, and $F_x$ is the component of the body force per unit mass in the $x$ direction.

Similar equations are obtained when the forces are summed in the $y$ and $z$ directions:

$$\frac{\partial \tau_{xy}}{\partial x} + \frac{\partial \sigma_{yy}}{\partial y} + \frac{\partial \tau_{zy}}{\partial z} + \rho\, F_y = \rho \frac{\partial^2 v}{\partial t^2} \tag{2-11a}$$

$$\frac{\partial \tau_{xz}}{\partial x} + \frac{\partial \tau_{yz}}{\partial y} + \frac{\partial \sigma_{zz}}{\partial z} + \rho\, F_z = \rho \frac{\partial^2 w}{\partial t^2} \tag{2-11b}$$

where $F_y$ and $F_z$ are the $y$ and $z$ components of the body force, respectively, and $v$ and $w$ are the $y$ and $z$ displacements, respectively.

Summing moments about an axis which is parallel to the $z$ axis and which passes through the center of mass, and equating them to the product of the

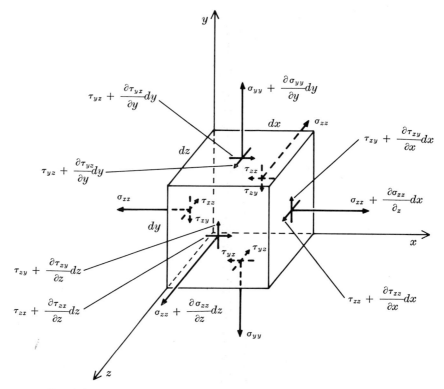

**Fig. 2-3**  Stresses acting on an elemental volume of material.

moment of inertia and the angular acceleration about this axis, gives

$$\left(2\tau_{xy} + \frac{\partial \tau_{xy}}{\partial x}\,dx\right) dy\, dz\, \frac{dx}{2} - \left(2\tau_{yx} + \frac{\partial \tau_{yx}}{\partial y}\,dy\right) dx\, dz\, \frac{dy}{2} + \rho\, M\, dx\, dy\, dz$$

$$= \frac{1}{12}\, \rho\, (dx^2 + dy^2)\, \frac{\partial^2 \Omega}{\partial t^2}\, dx\, dy\, dz$$

where $M$ is the body moment and $\Omega$ is the angle of rotation about this axis. Dropping terms of fourth or higher degree in the differential quantities gives

$$\tau_{xy} - \tau_{yx} + \rho\, M = 0$$

In the usual case, in which body torques are nonexistent,

$$\tau_{xy} = \tau_{yx}$$

This is the important result, previously referred to, that allows the stress tensor to be symmetric in almost all cases.

Equations (2-10) and (2-11) are the equations which allow a spatial description of the stresses in a Cartesian coordinate system. In cylindrical coordinates they become

$$\frac{\partial \sigma_{rr}}{\partial r} + \frac{1}{r}\frac{\partial \tau_{r\theta}}{\partial \theta} + \frac{\partial \tau_{rz}}{\partial z} + \frac{\sigma_{rr} - \sigma_{\theta\theta}}{r} + \rho \, F_r = \rho \, \frac{\partial^2 u}{\partial t^2} \qquad (2\text{-}12a)$$

$$\frac{\partial \tau_{r\theta}}{\partial r} + \frac{1}{r}\frac{\partial \sigma_{\theta\theta}}{\partial \theta} + \frac{\partial \tau_{\theta r}}{\partial z} + \frac{2}{r} \, \tau_{r\theta} + \rho \, F_\theta = \rho \, \frac{\partial^2 v}{\partial t^2} \qquad (2\text{-}12b)$$

$$\frac{\partial \tau_{rz}}{\partial r} + \frac{1}{r}\frac{\partial \tau_{\theta z}}{\partial \theta} + \frac{\partial \sigma_{zz}}{\partial z} + \frac{1}{r} \, \tau_{rz} + \rho \, F_z = \rho \, \frac{\partial^2 w}{\partial t^2} \qquad (2\text{-}12c)$$

where $u$, $v$, and $w$ are the displacements in the $r$, $\theta$, and $z$ directions, respectively, and $F_r$, $F_\theta$, and $F_z$ are the components of any body force. Again it may be assumed that $\tau_{ij} = \tau_{ji}$. Love[1] shows how to obtain these equations in general orthogonal curvilinear coordinate systems. The two systems just discussed are the most commonly used, but, in many cases, other systems are more convenient to match unusual boundary configurations.

## 2-3. STRAIN

While stresses describe the forces acting on a material element, strains indicate the relative distortion of its parts. And just as stress at a point must satisfy certain transformation laws to satisfy static or dynamic equilibrium, so must strain at a point satisfy a transformation law, in fact the same law, but not for the same reason. Strain is a purely geometrical quantity, describing relative displacement of mass points, and purely geometrical considerations require that strain also be a second order tensor.

### STRAIN DISPLACEMENT EQUATIONS

Equations will be derived here for only classical infinitesimal strain, since the more general descriptions provide no commonly useful tool for the design analyst. The theory of infinitesimal strain assumes that products and squares of spatial derivatives of the displacements are negligible compared to these derivatives themselves. To reduce the geometrical complexity, distortions of a body in the $x$, $y$ plane only will be examined to develop the basic strain relationships. In Fig. 2-4, two lines parallel to the coordinate axes are drawn to represent lines of material particles before distortion. After distortion, these same particles are redistributed in space along the other two obliquely intersecting lines. Defining $\epsilon_{xx}$, the strain in the $x$ direction, to be the extension in the $x$ direction of the line of length $dx$, originally lying parallel to the $x$ axis, divided by the line's original length, then $\epsilon_{xx}$ can be found in terms of the displacement field in the following way. If $u$ is the $x$ displacement of the intersection of the

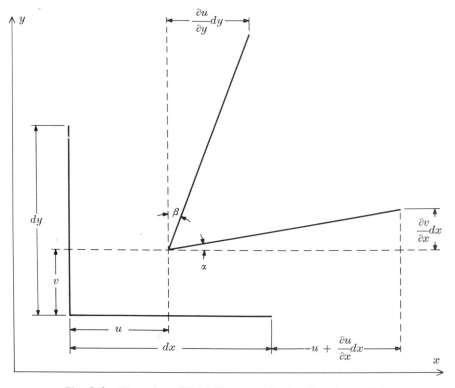

**Fig. 2-4**  Distortion of initially perpendicular lines in a solid.

material lines, then the other end of the horizontal line will have the $x$ displacement:

$$u + \frac{\partial u}{\partial x}\,dx$$

The extension of the line of initial length $dx$ in the $x$ direction is then just

$$\frac{\partial u}{\partial x}\,dx$$

so that

$$\epsilon_{xx} = \frac{\partial u}{\partial x}$$

Defining the shear strain $\gamma_{xy}$ to be the reduction in angle between two perpendicular material lines initially parallel to the $x$ and $y$ directions yields

$$\gamma_{xy} = \alpha + \beta \approx \tan\alpha + \tan\beta = \frac{\partial u}{\partial y} + \frac{\partial v}{\partial x}$$

for small angles, i.e., small shear strains.

**Cartesian Coordinates.** In three-dimensional Cartesian coordinates, all the strain-displacement equations are:

$$\left.\begin{array}{ccc} \epsilon_{xx} = \dfrac{\partial u}{\partial x}, & \epsilon_{yy} = \dfrac{\partial v}{\partial y}, & \epsilon_{zz} = \dfrac{\partial w}{\partial z} \\[2ex] \gamma_{xy} = \dfrac{\partial u}{\partial y} + \dfrac{\partial v}{\partial x}, & \gamma_{yz} = \dfrac{\partial v}{\partial z} + \dfrac{\partial w}{\partial y}, & \gamma_{zx} = \dfrac{\partial w}{\partial x} + \dfrac{\partial u}{\partial z} \end{array}\right] \qquad (2\text{-}13)$$

where $u$, $v$, and $w$ are the displacements in the $x$, $y$, and $z$ directions, respectively.

**Cylindrical Coordinates.** Since the strain-displacement equations depend on spatial variations of the displacements, they take different forms in different coordinate systems. The same relations in cylindrical coordinates are

$$\left.\begin{array}{ccc} \epsilon_{rr} = \dfrac{\partial u}{\partial r}, & \epsilon_{\theta\theta} = \dfrac{u}{r} + \dfrac{1}{r}\dfrac{\partial v}{\partial \theta}, & \epsilon_{zz} = \dfrac{\partial w}{\partial z} \\[2ex] \gamma_{r\theta} = \dfrac{1}{r}\dfrac{\partial u}{\partial \theta} + \dfrac{\partial v}{\partial r} - \dfrac{v}{r}, & \gamma_{\theta z} = \dfrac{1}{r}\dfrac{\partial w}{\partial \theta} + \dfrac{\partial v}{\partial z}, & \\[2ex] \gamma_{zr} = \dfrac{\partial u}{\partial z} + \dfrac{\partial w}{\partial r} & & \end{array}\right] \qquad (2\text{-}14)$$

where $u$, $v$, and $w$ are the displacements in the $r$, $\theta$, and $z$ directions, respectively. Love[1] gives a good presentation of the method of determining the infinitesimal strains in general orthogonal curvilinear coordinate systems.

## STATE OF STRAIN AT A POINT

To examine the state of strain at a point, the same question arises as in the study of stress: How does the selection of a particular set of orthogonal coordinate axes through a point affect the representation of the strain at that point? The geometrical discussion of this question will be limited to the two-dimensional case to reduce the complexity and expose more clearly the underlying geometrical principle.

If the strains $\epsilon_{xx}$, $\epsilon_{yy}$, and $\gamma_{xy}$ are given for the $x$, $y$ directions, can the strains of material lines originally lying parallel to the $x'$ and $y'$ axes be determined?

As shown in Fig. 2-5(a), line AB of length $dx'$ lying initially along the $x'$ axis moves to A′B′ after deformation. If point A moves the distance $v$ in the $y$ direction, then point B will move a distance

$$v + \frac{\partial v}{\partial x}\,dx + \frac{\partial v}{\partial y}\,dy$$

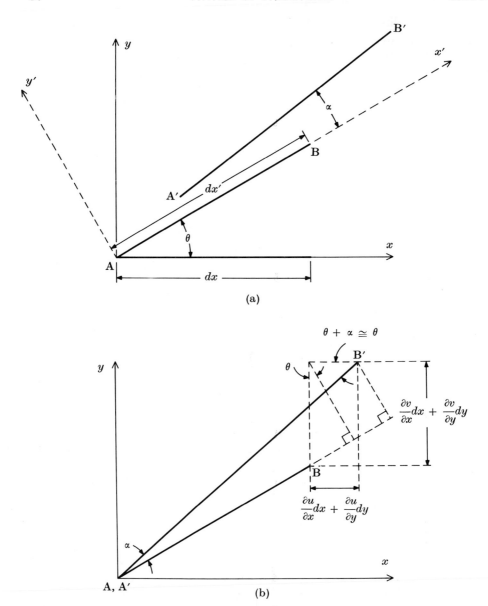

**Fig. 2-5**  Displacement of a material line in a two-dimensional system.

in the $y$ direction, so that point B moves

$$\frac{\partial v}{\partial x}\, dx + \frac{\partial v}{\partial y}\, dy$$

farther in the $y$ direction than does point A. Similarly, point B moves

$$\frac{\partial u}{\partial x}\, dx + \frac{\partial u}{\partial y}\, dy$$

farther in the $x$ direction than does point A. From the geometry of Fig. 2-5(b), where A$'$B$'$ is moved in translation until A and A$'$ coincide for clarity, the extension of AB is thus shown to be

$$\sin\theta\left(\frac{\partial v}{\partial x}\,dx + \frac{\partial v}{\partial y}\,dy\right) + \cos\theta\left(\frac{\partial u}{\partial x}\,dx + \frac{\partial u}{\partial y}\,dy\right)$$

Using the direction cosines for this two-dimensional case of $\cos\theta = \alpha_{x'x} = \alpha_{y'y}$ and $\sin\theta = \alpha_{x'y} = -\alpha_{y'x}$, and with the fact that $dx = \alpha_{x'x}\,dx'$ and $dy = \alpha_{x'y}\,dx'$, the strain in the $x'$ direction is

$$\epsilon_{x'x'} = \frac{1}{dx'}\left[\alpha_{x'y}\left(\frac{\partial v}{\partial x}\,\alpha_{x'x}\,dx' + \frac{\partial v}{\partial y}\,\alpha_{x'y}\,dx'\right) + \alpha_{x'x}\left(\frac{\partial u}{\partial x}\,\alpha_{x'x}\,dx' + \frac{\partial u}{\partial y}\,\alpha_{x'y}\,dx'\right)\right]$$

$$= \alpha_{x'x}^2\epsilon_{xx} + \alpha_{x'y}^2\epsilon_{yy} + \alpha_{x'x}\alpha_{x'y}\gamma_{xy} \qquad (2\text{-}15)$$

upon canceling $dx'$ and replacing the displacement derivatives by the appropriate strains referred to the $x$, $y$ directions.

The angle $\alpha$ may be seen to be approximately

$$\tan^{-1}\left\{\frac{1}{dx'}\left[\left(\frac{\partial v}{\partial x}\,dx + \frac{\partial v}{\partial y}\,dy\right)\cos\theta - \left(\frac{\partial u}{\partial x}\,dx + \frac{\partial u}{\partial y}\,dy\right)\sin\theta\right]\right\}$$

which becomes for small $\alpha$, i.e., small shear strain,

$$\alpha = \frac{\partial v}{\partial x}\,\alpha_{x'x}\alpha_{y'y} + \frac{\partial v}{\partial y}\,\alpha_{x'y}\alpha_{y'y} + \frac{\partial u}{\partial x}\,\alpha_{y'x}\alpha_{x'x} + \frac{\partial u}{\partial y}\,\alpha_{y'x}\alpha_{x'y}$$

Similarly, $\beta$, the angle between the initial and final positions of a material line originally lying parallel to the $y'$ axis, may be found to be

$$\beta = \frac{\partial v}{\partial x}\,\alpha_{y'x}\alpha_{x'y} + \frac{\partial v}{\partial y}\,\alpha_{x'y}\alpha_{y'y} + \frac{\partial u}{\partial x}\,\alpha_{y'x}\alpha_{x'x} + \frac{\partial u}{\partial y}\,\alpha_{x'x}\alpha_{y'y}$$

The shear strain, previously defined as $\alpha + \beta$, becomes

$$\gamma_{x'y'} = 2\alpha_{y'x}\alpha_{x'x}\epsilon_{xx} + 2\alpha_{x'y}\alpha_{y'y}\epsilon_{yy} + (\alpha_{x'x}\alpha_{y'y} + \alpha_{y'x}\alpha_{x'y})\gamma_{xy} \qquad (2\text{-}16)$$

Comparison of Eqs. (2-15) and (2-16) with Eq. (2-1) shows that the equations just derived are two-dimensional versions of the same basic form and, therefore, are subject to the tensor transformation law. In the more general three-dimensional case, it is known that the infinitesimal strains also satisfy precisely the same transformation laws as stresses, and these relations may be obtained by substituting $\epsilon_{ij}$ for $\sigma_{ij}$ and $\frac{1}{2}\gamma_{ij}$ for $\tau_{ij}$ in Eq. (2-1) or any of the other proper equations obtained from Eq. (2-1) by the cyclic subscript permutations discussed in the section on stresses.

Strains are therefore tensors and have the same properties as stresses with respect to principal values and axes, invariants, and maximum shear values.

## LARGE STRAINS

The infinitesimal strain components of Eqs. (2-13) and (2-14) are not adequate measures of relative distortion when the displacement derivatives have products too large to neglect. Strains usually become large when materials flow as in fluids and plastics. However, for real engineering materials in the elastic region, the area in which most stress analysis is pursued, strains remain small enough for the previous expressions to be used.

## COMPATIBILITY EQUATIONS

One very interesting question arises from the material discussed so far in this section. Equation (2-13) shows that, if the three displacements, $u$, $v$, and $w$, are known, the six strains may be determined uniquely by simple differentiation; on the other hand, if a strain field is known, Eq. (2-13) provides six equations for the determination of only three unknowns, the displacements. Mathematically, then, the strains cannot be entirely independent of each other, and some further requirement must be met by the strains before they can prescribe a unique set of displacements. These requirements are that the resulting displacements be single-valued and continuous. That is, displacements are not acceptable if gaps open in the material, if more than one mass point ends up occupying the same position in space, or if two positions refer to a single mass point. These requirements are expressed in the form of equations, called compatibility equations, which the strains must satisfy. These equations, in Cartesian coordinates, are[3]

$$\frac{\partial^2 \epsilon_{xx}}{\partial y^2} + \frac{\partial^2 \epsilon_{yy}}{\partial x^2} = \frac{\partial^2 \gamma_{xy}}{\partial x \, \partial y}, \qquad 2\frac{\partial^2 \epsilon_{xx}}{\partial y \, \partial z} = \frac{\partial}{\partial x}\left(-\frac{\partial \gamma_{yz}}{\partial x} + \frac{\partial \gamma_{zx}}{\partial y} + \frac{\partial \gamma_{xy}}{\partial z}\right) \qquad \text{(2-17a)}$$

$$\frac{\partial^2 \epsilon_{yy}}{\partial z^2} + \frac{\partial^2 \epsilon_{zz}}{\partial z^2} = \frac{\partial^2 \gamma_{yz}}{\partial y \, \partial z}, \qquad 2\frac{\partial^2 \epsilon_{yy}}{\partial z \, \partial x} = \frac{\partial}{\partial y}\left(\frac{\partial y_{yz}}{\partial x} - \frac{\partial \gamma_{zx}}{\partial y} + \frac{\partial \gamma_{xy}}{\partial z}\right) \qquad \text{(2-17b)}$$

$$\frac{\partial^2 \epsilon_{zz}}{\partial x^2} + \frac{\partial^2 \epsilon_{xx}}{\partial z^2} = \frac{\partial^2 \gamma_{zx}}{\partial z \, \partial x}, \qquad 2\frac{\partial^2 \epsilon_{zz}}{\partial x \, \partial y} = \frac{\partial}{\partial z}\left(\frac{\partial \gamma \epsilon_{yz}}{\partial x} + \frac{\partial \gamma_{zx}}{\partial y} - \frac{\partial \gamma_{xy}}{\partial z}\right) \qquad \text{(2-17c)}$$

In cylindrical coordinates they become

$$\frac{\partial^2 \epsilon_{rr}}{\partial \theta \, \partial z} = \frac{r}{2}\frac{\partial}{\partial r}\left(\frac{1}{r}\frac{\partial \gamma_{rz}}{\partial \theta} - \frac{\partial \gamma_{\theta z}}{\partial r} - \frac{1}{r}\gamma_{\theta z}\right) + \frac{1}{2r}\frac{\partial}{\partial r}\left(r^2 \frac{\partial \gamma_{r\theta}}{\partial z}\right) \qquad \text{(2-18a)}$$

$$r\frac{\partial}{\partial r}\left(r\frac{\partial \epsilon_{\theta\theta}}{\partial z}\right) = r\frac{\partial \epsilon_{rr}}{\partial z} + \frac{1}{2}\frac{\partial}{\partial \theta}\left(r\frac{\partial \gamma_{\theta z}}{\partial r} + \gamma_{\theta z} - \frac{\partial \gamma_{rz}}{\partial \theta} + r\frac{\partial \gamma_{r\theta}}{\partial z}\right) \qquad \text{(2-18b)}$$

$$r\frac{\partial}{\partial r}\left(\frac{1}{r}\frac{\partial \epsilon_{zz}}{\partial \theta}\right) = \frac{r^2}{2}\frac{\partial}{\partial r}\left(\frac{1}{r}\frac{\partial \gamma_{\theta z}}{\partial z}\right) + \frac{1}{2}\frac{\partial}{\partial z}\left(\frac{\partial \gamma_{rz}}{\partial \theta} - r\frac{\partial \gamma_{r\theta}}{\partial z}\right) \qquad \text{(2-18c)}$$

$$\frac{\partial}{\partial r}\left(r\frac{\partial \gamma_{r\theta}}{\partial \theta}\right) = r\frac{\partial^2}{\partial r^2}(r\epsilon_{\theta\theta}) + \frac{\partial^2 \epsilon_{rr}}{\partial \theta^2} - r\frac{\partial \epsilon_{rr}}{\partial r} \qquad \text{(2-18d)}$$

$$r \frac{\partial \gamma_{\theta z}}{\partial \theta \, \partial z} = r^2 \frac{\partial^2 \epsilon_{\theta \theta}}{\partial z^2} + \frac{\partial^2 \epsilon_{zz}}{\partial \theta^2} + r \frac{\partial \epsilon_{zz}}{\partial r} - r \frac{\partial \gamma_{zr}}{\partial z} \qquad (2\text{-}18e)$$

$$\frac{\partial^2 \gamma_{rz}}{\partial r \, \partial z} = \frac{\partial^2 \epsilon_{zz}}{\partial r^2} + \frac{\partial^2 \epsilon_{rr}}{\partial z^2} \qquad (2\text{-}18f)$$

These equations are virtually never used in the full three-dimensional display given above, but from them, the equations for the plane polar case ($\partial / \partial z = 0$) and the axially symmetric case ($\partial / \partial \theta = 0$) are easily obtained.

## 2-4. MATERIAL PROPERTIES

In the previous sections of this chapter, the simple concepts of equilibrium of forces and geometry have been developed into descriptions of the behavior of stresses and strains. None of these discussions has involved any important physical property of the material under consideration. The two material properties of principal interest to the structural analyst are stiffness and failure characteristics.

### STRESS-STRAIN RELATIONS

Stiffness is described by stress-strain equations which show how a material resists distortion under a given state of stress. In general, these equations are necessary to the solution of stress-analysis problems. It might be thought that some problems could be solved without ever using the stress-strain relations. For example, in the static case when the accelerations in the equations of motion [Eq. (2-12)] are all zero, and when all the boundary conditions of a problem are specified in terms of the stresses, the stress distribution throughout the body would seem to be determined by using only the equation of motion and the boundary conditions. Unfortunately, the strains caused by such a solution might not be such as to yield continuous, single-valued displacements, so that the compatibility equations are not satisfied. Since the compatibility relations must initially be derived in terms of strains, the relationship between stress and strain must be known. While many simple, statically determinate problems can be solved by conventional strength-of-materials analysis without direct use of the stress-strain relations, the solutions are valid only because the results of such analysis, when properly applied, satisfy the compatibility equations as well as the boundary conditions. There is no analogous solution which bypasses the stress-strain relations for the more general, statically indeterminate case.

The stress-strain relations for any real material are purely empirical. There is no way to predict these relations at present from knowledge of the microscopic material constituents. Because structural materials exhibit an approximately linear relationship between load and deflection throughout the commonly used region of stress, a linearly elastic model (that is, one which obeys Hooke's law with stress proportional to strain) is used in almost all structural analyses. These characteristics of an elastic material are represented by the ubiquitous stress-strain relations.

In the most general stress-analysis problem, temperature variation through a material can cause stresses even without applied mechanical loads. This is because the hotter parts of a material with a positive thermal expansion coefficient will attempt to expand more than surrounding cooler regions. One proper place for this effect to be introduced into the general equations is in the stress-strain relations which will then contain a term representing the strains that would be thermally generated at a point if the surrounding material were not there. In most thermal-stress problems in which both mechanical and thermal loadings are applied, a solution is most easily obtained by solving the mechanical and thermal problems separately and adding the two results. As long as the theory used is linear, which can be determined by examining the equations describing the problem, such superposition is permissible. The stress-strain equations which follow contain the thermal-stress term. The solutions to many thermal-stress problems are available in the literature.[4]

**Isotropic Materials.** Many structural materials are nearly isotropic, i.e., the stiffness is about the same in any direction. The linearly elastic stress-strain-temperature relations for this case are

$$\epsilon_{xx} = \frac{1}{E}\left[\sigma_{xx} - \nu(\sigma_{yy} + \sigma_{zz})\right] + \alpha T, \qquad \gamma_{xy} = \frac{1}{G}\tau_{xy}$$

$$\epsilon_{yy} = \frac{1}{E}\left[\sigma_{yy} - \nu(\sigma_{zz} + \sigma_{xx})\right] + \alpha T, \qquad \gamma_{yz} = \frac{1}{G}\tau_{yz} \qquad (2\text{-}19)$$

$$\epsilon_{zz} = \frac{1}{E}\left[\sigma_{zz} - \nu(\sigma_{xx} + \sigma_{yy})\right] + \alpha T, \qquad \gamma_{zx} = \frac{1}{G}\tau_{zx}$$

where $E$ is Young's modulus, $\nu$ is Poisson's ratio, $T$ is the temperature measured from the reference state, $\alpha$ is the linear coefficient of expansion, and $G$ is the modulus of rigidity, or shear modulus of elasticity. The material constants, $E$, $\nu$, and $G$ are not independent but are related by the equation $E = 2G(1 + \nu)$.

The inverses of Eqs. (2-19) are just as useful. They are

$$\sigma_{xx} = \frac{\nu E e}{(1+\nu)(1-2\nu)} + \frac{E\epsilon_{xx}}{1+\nu} - \frac{\alpha E T}{1-2\nu}, \qquad \tau_{xy} = G\gamma_{xy}$$

$$\sigma_{yy} = \frac{\nu E e}{(1+\nu)(1-2\nu)} + \frac{E\epsilon_{yy}}{1+\nu} - \frac{\alpha E T}{1-2\nu}, \qquad \tau_{yz} = G\gamma_{yz} \qquad (2\text{-}20)$$

$$\sigma_{zz} = \frac{\nu E e}{(1+\nu)(1-2\nu)} + \frac{E\epsilon_{zz}}{1+\nu} - \frac{\alpha E T}{1-2\nu}, \qquad \tau_{zx} = G\gamma_{zx}$$

where $e = \epsilon_{xx} + \epsilon_{yy} + \epsilon_{zz}$.

Equations (2-19) may be determined by inspection for linear systems from the definition of the constants if it is assumed that the $x$, $y$, $z$ planes are principal planes and the $\sigma$'s are principal stresses. It can be shown, however, that the relationships of Eqs. (2-19) and (2-20) also hold true for any orthogonal coordinate system. The equations show that the off-diagonal terms in the strain tensor, $\gamma_{ij}$, are proportional to the off-diagonal terms in the stress tensor, $\tau_{ij}$, so that when one of these tensors is diagonal, i.e., when it is written in terms of the principal directions, then the other tensor is diagonal also. Thus, the principal strain directions are always aligned with the principal stress directions. Furthermore, it is easily shown that $\epsilon_1 \geqq \epsilon_2 \geqq \epsilon_3$ when $\sigma_1 \geqq \sigma_2 \geqq \sigma_3$ if $\nu > -1$.

The elastic constants $E$, $\nu$, and $G$, obtained in the laboratory under nearly isothermal conditions, approximate very closely the corresponding adiabatic elastic constants which should be used under dynamic conditions when the strain varies too rapidly to allow heat flow. Thus, in physical design, no distinction need usually be made between the two.

Other constants are frequently used in the stress-strain relations, and the most common will be defined here. The Lamé parameters, frequently encountered in theoretical work, are

$$\lambda = \frac{E\nu}{(1 + \nu)(1 - 2\nu)}, \qquad \mu = G \qquad (2\text{-}21)$$

The bulk modulus, $K$, which is defined as the ratio of hydrostatic pressure to the dilatation, or fractional volume change it produces, is

$$K = \lambda + \tfrac{2}{3}G = \frac{E}{3(1 - 2\nu)} \qquad (2\text{-}22)$$

The compressibility is defined as $1/K$.

**Anisotropic Materials.** In the most general linear case, a stress is dependent on each of the six strains, and there are 21 independent elastic constants. Wood, fiber glass, and formed metal products also have a degree of anisotropy, although not as complex as the foregoing. However, an isotropic analysis is usually sufficient for structures, even for such materials. Care should be taken, though, to use material constants that are applicable in the direction of major concern, according to the anticipated mode of distortion or failure. For example, Fig. 2-6 shows the effect of grain direction on the modulus of elasticity for a variety of commonly used flat spring materials. If deflection characteristics are to be accurately predicted, it is necessary to specify grain direction and to use the appropriate value of $E$.

**Inelastic Materials.** As has been indicated, the elastic model is only an approximation of a large class of real materials. These materials sometimes, and others always, exhibit inelastic characteristics. This behavior may be

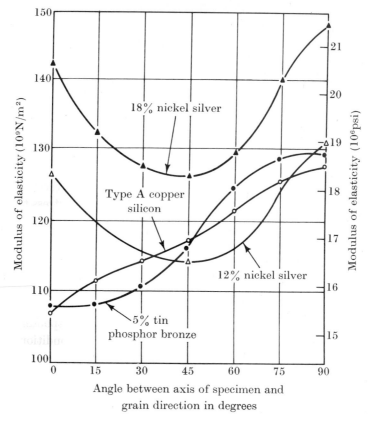

**Fig. 2-6**   Effect of grain direction on the modulus of elasticity—thickness range 0.025 to 0.081 cm.

linear or nonlinear. Most equipment materials act inelastically only after failure, under dynamic loading, or through creep. For the first case, it is enough to know that the part has failed, and this will be discussed later under Modes of Failure. For the other two cases, techniques of viscoelasticity seem appropriate.

Linear viscoelasticity is a particularly useful model because the resulting equations are relatively easy to solve. However, there are few real materials which act in exactly this way, and use of this model has been criticized for this reason. The linear viscoelastic model simply assumes that stress and strain can be related by a linear differential equation which is the same as that which relates the force $\sigma$ and displacement $\epsilon$ in the spring dashpot configuration of Fig. 2-7(a). The two most useful models for simple problems are the Maxwell and Voigt models of Figs. 2-7(b) and (c), respectively.

The Maxwell model is useful in analyses in which creep is important, and

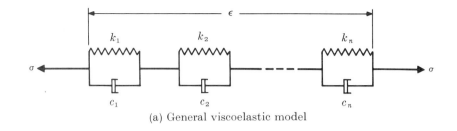

(a) General viscoelastic model

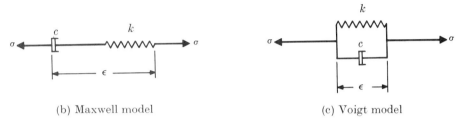

(b) Maxwell model                            (c) Voigt model

**Fig. 2-7**   Mechanical representations of viscoelastic materials.

the Maxwell stress-strain relation becomes

$$\frac{\partial \epsilon}{\partial t} = \frac{\sigma}{c} + \frac{1}{k}\frac{\partial \sigma}{\partial t} \qquad (2\text{-}23)$$

where $c$ is the coefficient of viscosity and $k$ is the spring constant. The Voigt model is used to introduce some damping into otherwise basically elastic models (usually in vibration analysis), and the resulting stress-strain equation is

$$\sigma = k\epsilon + c\frac{\partial \epsilon}{\partial t} \qquad (2\text{-}24)$$

A good idea of the characteristics of these models can be developed by assuming that step loads and displacements are applied to the models in Fig. 2-7 and by determining the resulting displacements or loads. A general discussion of three-dimensional viscoelasticity is also available.[5]

## MODES OF FAILURE

The equations developed thus far in this chapter are sufficient to determine the stresses, strains, and displacements in a typical design problem. And if it is known that the stiffness, elastic distortion, or displacement of a piece of equipment is the limiting design parameter, then enough has been said for determination of these effects. If, however, fracture or yield may be of importance, then some consideration must be given to these modes of failure and to the criteria by which such failure may be predicted.

**Failure by Yielding.** Many designs require that the completed structures remain essentially within the elastic limit, i.e., that the loadings be insufficient to produce appreciable permanent distortion of ductile materials. Unfortunately, the elastic limit is usually not a well-defined point, and a yield stress corresponding to an allowable amount of permanent set is generally used. Yield stresses corresponding to 0.01 to 0.20 percent offset are frequently used for design limits  Since these stresses may be appreciably different, a yield-stress value should always be quoted with reference to the corresponding permanent set.

While yielding occurs immediately upon application of excessive load, continued application of loads near or above the yield stress may cause progressive yielding in the form of creep for constant loads, or in the form of stress relaxation for constant strain. The criteria by which such failures may be predicted depend strongly on the stress, temperature, and material properties. Books like the *Metals Handbook*[6] and the *Metals Reference Book*[7] provide a great deal of this kind of information about a large number of useful metals.

A rapidly applied and released stress can be withstood by most ductile steels more easily than a static load. The allowable stress for high strain rates can be 5 to 10 percent higher than for the static case. The amount of benefit gained here, like creep characteristics, is very much dependent on the particular material, and dependable references or experts should be consulted.

**Failure by Fracture.** Materials like glass and quenched high carbon steel exhibit a mode of failure quite different from that of ductile materials. Examination of the fractured surface of such brittle materials shows no evidence of ductile deformation at all. Griffith's famous theory explains brittle fracture by assuming no yielding is possible, so that minute internal and surface cracks within the material cause large stress concentrations. These concentrations are not relieved, as they are in ductile materials, by local yielding at the crack apex. In brittle materials, the cracks grow once the stress exceeds some value there. This further increases the stress by reducing the load-carrying areas and causes, finally, catastrophic failure. The usefulness of this theory is qualitative only, but the understanding of the brittle failure mechanism is essential to the effective use of such materials.

Brittle fracture can also occur at low temperatures, with the same catastrophic results, in many materials that are ductile at room temperatures. An indication of whether a material will be subject to ductile or to brittle failure is obtained from impact tests and from the percent of elongation at rupture in tensile tests. Large impact energy absorption or elongation indicates ductility.

In predicting brittle fracture, it is necessary to consider the effects of stress concentrations which may be associated with the design of the part or with the method of applying the load. These concentrations are usually associated with discontinuities such as small holes, sharp reentrant corners, grooves, etc. Determination of the appropriate concentration values usually requires reference to test data or expert consultants.

In some applications where yielding is not important, ductile materials may be used satisfactorily provided they do not fracture. The criteria to predict ductile fractures are not as well developed as those for yield, and they are of less use to the equipment designer since he can seldom tolerate the appreciable yielding which precedes fracture for such materials.

Under conditions of dynamic, oscillating loads, fracture may occur in either brittle or ductile materials if the combination of range of stress and average stress exceed allowable values. Failure predictions are generally based on endurance limits determined from specimens subject to complete reversals of stress (zero average stress) for large numbers of cycles, often $10^8$ cycles or greater. The predictions must also include allowance for differences in method of loading for the designed part as compared with the test specimens, differences in surface characteristics, effect of stress concentration, effect of corrosion, and number of stress cycles required during life.

## FAILURE CRITERIA

As will be shown, it is often not sufficient to know the stress at a point in a single direction, or even the maximum tensile stress, to predict failure. More generally, the state of stress or at least an invariant of the stress tensor at the point must be known.

Simple tensile tests will show the uniaxial stress at which failure occurs for various materials, but the point at which failure occurs in a two- or three-dimensional state of stress is not so well known. Several criteria have been used to relate failure under three-dimensional stress to that which occurs under simple, uniaxial loading. These criteria permit material characteristics determined from simple tests to be used meaningfully for design purposes where the state of stress is more complex. The value of any failure criterion is determined by the accuracy with which it represents the behavior of materials under conditions of use. It appears that pure hydrostatic pressure can produce no significant yielding of metals. It is desirable, therefore, that any general-use yield criterion should be independent of the hydrostatic component of the stress field.

**Maximum Normal Stress Criterion.** This criterion, which is attributed to Rankine, assumes that failure will occur at any time that the maximum normal stress on any plane through a point exceeds some limiting value which is constant, regardless of the shear stresses or other normal stresses acting in other directions through that point. If $\sigma_f$ is used to denote the limiting value of normal stress as determined from a simple tensile test, then this criterion may be expressed by saying that failure will occur when $\sigma_1 = \sigma_f$, where $\sigma_1$ is the maximum principal stress through any point in the designed part.

The maximum normal stress criterion gives reasonably good results for some materials which fail by brittle fracture (e.g., cast iron) in stress systems for which the normal stresses of greatest magnitude are positive (tensile). Application to systems with larger compressive stresses is limited, at best, because of the asymmetric behavior of the material. For example, fracture occurs readily under conditions of equal triaxial tension but not at all under hydrostatic compression. The criterion is not suitable for ductile materials.

**Maximum Shear Stress Criterion.** This criterion, also known as the Tresca yield criterion, assumes that the material at a point begins to fail by yielding when the maximum shear stress at that point reaches some value, a constant of the material. This material constant is easily found from the tensile test since the principal stresses in this case are $\sigma_1 = \sigma_f$, and $\sigma_2 = \sigma_3 = 0$, where $\sigma_f$ is the maximum allowable tensile stress. Equation (2-9) for the maximum shear stress gives

$$\tau_{\max} = \tfrac{1}{2}\sigma_f$$

The three-dimensional Tresca yield criterion then becomes

$$\sigma_1 - \sigma_3 = \sigma_f \tag{2-25}$$

and the material is assumed to yield by more than the allowable amount at any point at which the difference between the maximum and minimum principal stresses exceeds the yield stress. It is easily seen that for this criterion the hydrostatic component of stress has no effect on yielding since a hydrostatic state of stress can produce no shear stress in any direction (all directions are principal directions).

**von Mises Criterion.** Another yield criterion, which is less easily stated but which is often used, is the von Mises or maximum distortional strain energy criterion. In this case, yielding is assumed to occur at a point when the elastic energy density associated with distortion (neglecting energy associated with volume changes) at that point reaches some value, a constant of the material. Comparing again with the maximum allowable stress from the simple tensile test (in this case the yield stress), yielding under the von Mises criterion occurs when the principal stresses are such that

$$(\sigma_1 - \sigma_2)^2 + (\sigma_2 - \sigma_3)^2 + (\sigma_3 - \sigma_1)^2 = 2I_1^2 + 6I_2 = 2\sigma_f^2 \tag{2-26}$$

where the $I$'s are the stress invariants of Eq. (2-6). Since each of the terms on the left is zero for equal triaxial stresses, it is evident that this criterion also satisfies the condition for hydrostatic pressure.

Both the maximum shearing stress and the von Mises criteria are frequently used to predict failure by yielding of ductile metals. These criteria, together with the maximum normal stress criterion, are represented in Fig. 2-8 by curves which show the limiting combinations of $\sigma_1/\sigma_f$ and $\sigma_2/\sigma_f$ permitted by the

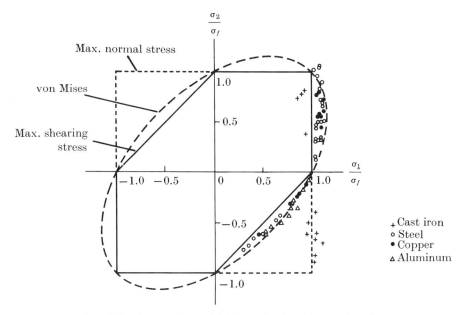

**Fig. 2-8**    Comparison of failure criteria with test data.[8]

various criteria in a two-dimensional stress system for which at least one of the principal stresses is positive. Since maximum stresses and strains nearly always occur at surfaces, comparisons on a two-dimensional basis are quite realistic. In interpreting Eq. (2-25), it should be noted that the first term denotes the maximum principal stress, and the second term is the minimum principal stress. Thus, in the upper right quadrant of Fig. 2-8 where both $\sigma_1$ and $\sigma_2$ are positive, the minimum principal stress is $\sigma_3$, which is always zero in a two-dimensional stress system. In the lower right quadrant, $\sigma_2$ is negative, making $\sigma_3$ an intermediate value that is not used in determining the maximum shear stress.

The data shown for steel, copper, and aluminum indicate that the von Mises theory may be somewhat more accurate in predicting failures of ductile materials, while the maximum shearing stress theory is more conservative. The maximum normal stress criterion appears reasonably good for cast iron, especially for negative values of $\sigma_2$.

**Fracture of Ductile Materials.** In the case of ductile fracture, it is known that the stress values for fracture in tension are much less than they are in compression; therefore, criteria like those for yielding, which give the same results for tension or compression, cannot be used. A modification by Navier of the maximum shear stress criterion states that fracture will occur on a plane on which act a shearing stress, $\tau$, and a normal stress, $\sigma$, when

$$\tau = \tau_f - k\sigma \qquad (2\text{-}27)$$

where $\tau_f$ is the shearing stress for failure by fracture in pure shear as determined from a torsion specimen, and $k$ is a constant of the material, usually found to be close to 1.

Since a compressive $\sigma$ is negative, this criterion increases the shear stress required to cause failure across a plane when there is a compressive stress on that plane. The Navier criterion is used chiefly in a qualitative sense. It shows, for example, that ductile fracture should not ordinarily occur in simple, uniaxial compression since the positive term $(-k\sigma)$ increases more rapidly than $\tau$ as the load is increased. This is even more true under conditions of hydrostatic compression. Since larger shear stresses (and strains) are needed to produce fracture, the material becomes more ductile in its behavior. This is a well-known phenomenon that permits extensive cold-forming of metals under high hydrostatic pressure, and even materials which are normally brittle can often be cold-formed by this technique.

**Fatigue.** The criteria for fatigue failures are usually more difficult to apply than are criteria for static loads because of the large numbers of variables which have a major influence on such failures. For example, most endurance limits that are quoted are based on tests of specimens in flexure, the results of which cannot safely be used for torsion or for axial loading without application of large derating factors. Accurate predictions seem to require that the material in question be tested under representative conditions of loading.

While stress concentrations can usually be ignored for ductile materials under static loads since a small amount of local yielding can serve to distribute the stress, they become of major importance in fatigue. Stress concentrations in the form of tool marks, stamped designations, sharp filets, grooves, threads, and the like usually require derating factors in the range of 2.5 to 10. Even the surface finish of the designed part must be compared with the test specimens to determine relative susceptibility to stress concentration. Much of the published data, based on highly polished specimens, cannot be used directly without derating. Some data are available, however, from flexure tests of strip material with commercial, rolled finishes. Even so, if the designed parts have electroplated finishes, this factor alone will reduce the fatigue strength by as much as 25 to 30 percent, regardless of smoothness. Even mild corrosion during life of the part can similarly degrade the fatigue strength.

Since endurance limits are established for complete reversals of stress, it is often desirable to anticipate the allowable range of stress for various values of average stress. Experience shows that this may be obtained from Goodman type diagrams as shown in Fig. 2-9. These diagrams are constructed with an axis for average stress drawn at 45° and with boundaries for the range of stress which intersect the vertical axis at the plus and minus values of the endurance

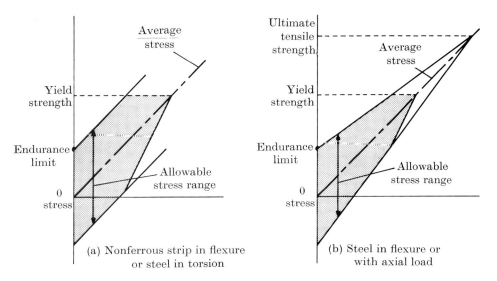

**Fig. 2-9**　Goodman type fatigue diagrams.

limit. In Fig. 2-9(a), these boundaries are parallel to the average stress line, indicating no reduction in permissible range of stress provided the yield strength (usually corresponding to 0.01 percent offset) is not exceeded for these materials. For steel, loaded as indicated in Fig. 2-9(b), the allowable stress boundaries converge on the ultimate tensile stress, indicating some reduction in range as the average stress is increased.

Where only a limited number of cycles are required during life, higher values of the endurance limit may be used where test data so indicate. The extent to which this can be done varies considerably. For example, carbon steels reach a reasonably constant value for the endurance limit after 12- to 20-million operations when protected from corrosion, while aluminum and magnesium alloys typically require 500-million operations with stainless steel and copper alloys intermediate.

Uncertainties concerning the many factors affecting fatigue require careful attention to factors of safety. This is also important since the published endurance limits represent the median value at which a number of specimens have failed, and the spread of failures about this point is likely to be greater than for most material constants obtained under static conditions. When serious questions exist, experts should be consulted.

The tables of Figs. A-1 and A-2 in Appendix A at the end of this volume contain a number of the mechanical properties for some metals and plastics commonly used in the design of electronic equipment. The values shown are typical, but in many cases, the properties will vary widely due to differences in formulation and processing. More detailed and specific data are readily available.[6,7,9]

## 2-5. STATICS AND QUASISTATICS

This section will present a discussion of stress-analysis problems in which the inertial terms in the equations of motion [Eqs. (2-10), (2-11), and (2-12)] are negligible or identically zero. If the inertial terms are zero, no motion takes place, and the problem is a static one. Even when motion exists, it is sometimes so slow that acceleration terms (those containing $\rho\, \partial^2 / \partial t^2$) may be neglected. This is called the quasistatic case. Static and quasistatic cases are usually much more easily solved than their dynamic counterparts; so it is of major importance to be able to distinguish among the various situations.

A little engineering judgment is usually sufficient to make this distinction, but in borderline cases a more involved approach may be necessary. Probably the most direct way is, first, to solve the static problem while carrying the time-variation of the loading throughout the problem, and, second, to substitute the results into the dynamic equations of motion to determine the relative importance of the terms. That is, if the inertial term is small compared to the stress gradients, the inclusion of inertia would not appreciably change the stresses from those calculated statically. Another more easily applied criterion using stress wave propagation times will be presented in Sec. 3.3 on dynamics.

## ELASTICITY AND STRENGTH OF MATERIALS

The previous sections have briefly developed the basic equations of classical elasticity. There are 15 equations contained in Eqs. (2-10), (2-11), (2-13), and (2-20) for the Cartesian system (three equations of motion, six of strain-displacement, and six of stress-strain) in 15 unknowns (the six stresses, six strains, and three displacements). This system of equations is approached in two basically different ways as discussed below.

**Displacements.** If the boundary conditions and loadings can be written simply in terms of displacements, then the stress-strain and strain-displacement relations can be used to rewrite the equations of motion in terms of displacements only. Retaining the dynamic terms, they become

$$(\lambda + G)\frac{\partial e}{\partial x} + G\nabla^2 u + \rho F_x - \frac{\alpha E}{1 - 2\nu}\frac{\partial T}{\partial x} = \rho\frac{\partial^2 u}{\partial t^2} \qquad (2\text{-}28a)$$

$$(\lambda + G)\frac{\partial e}{\partial y} + G\nabla^2 v + \rho F_y - \frac{\alpha E}{1 - 2\nu}\frac{\partial T}{\partial y} = \rho\frac{\partial^2 v}{\partial t^2} \qquad (2\text{-}28b)$$

$$(\lambda + G)\frac{\partial e}{\partial z} + G\nabla^2 w + \rho F_z - \frac{\alpha E}{1 - 2\nu}\frac{\partial T}{\partial z} = \rho\frac{\partial^2 w}{\partial t^2} \qquad (2\text{-}28c)$$

for Cartesian coordinates, where

$$e = \epsilon_{xx} + \epsilon_{yy} + \epsilon_{zz} = \frac{\partial u}{\partial x} + \frac{\partial v}{\partial y} + \frac{\partial w}{\partial z}$$

These three equations in the three unknown displacements form a complete system when loadings and boundary conditions are written in terms of displacements.

**Stresses.** If stresses cannot be eliminated, however, all 15 equations are needed, and if stress solutions are obtained, they must further satisfy the six compatibility equations to assure that the corresponding displacements are continuous and single-valued.

These systems of equations are so complicated that they can seldom be solved in three dimensions for anything like real situations. They are most useful when they can be simplified to one- and two-dimensional problems. More important, they provide a solid basis for understanding the character of an elastic continuum. The numerous mathematical methods devised for solving problems in elasticity, such as stress potentials and complex-number transformations, are presented in books on elasticity.[1,3,10,11] Such techniques are of more use to the specialist in analysis than to the designer.

For design purposes, most of the important problems in stress analysis have been solved by the "strength-of-materials" approach. This misleading name is applied to the art of solving complex problems in elastic structures by paying attention only to those aspects of the elastic distortion which appear to be important. Unfortunately, most strength-of-materials courses are viewed by the student as presenting a series of important results which can be looked up when the need arises, and the development of these results appears to be only a confirmation of their accuracy.

Actually, "strength of materials" is the most powerful tool the design analyst has available. He should come away from such courses, not with beam and spinning disc results at his fingertips, but rather, with a working understanding of how the simplified beam or spinning disc equations were developed and why they give reasonably accurate results. Then, when confronted by a new situation, the analyst should be able to develop his own simplified approach and solution.

Recent investigators have shown that the well-known "strength" solutions can be obtained from the general equations of elasticity by making the appropriate assumptions (see Mindlin[12] for such a discussion on beam and plate vibrations, and Rhines[13] for foundation models). To the design analyst, however, the usefulness of the strength-of-materials approach lies in the fact that it builds up the mathematical model from the simplest but most important considerations.

It should be mentioned here that a large class of problems can easily be solved directly from the equations of elasticity, because the stress or displacement fields are so simple that most of the 21 applicable equations are identically satisfied. The semi-inverse method is used in these cases, in which simplifying assumptions are made regarding the stresses or displacements, so that most of the differential equations are satisfied and those remaining may be easily solved. An example of this method will be presented.

**Example 2.1.** Assume that the spacing between adjacent printed wiring boards is critical in a particular situation and that one of the boards has air at different temperatures blowing across its two faces. Some thermal warpage will result, and the magnitude of this warpage is to be estimated. This kind of situation is very frequently encountered in modern electronic equipment.

Let the board be approximated by the flat plate of Fig. 2-10, and assume that the temperature in the plate has significant variation only through the thickness (in the $z$ direction). The temperature may then be written $T(z)$. As will be pointed out later, the effectiveness of mechanical boundary constraints in any real problem is difficult to evaluate; hence, the worst case for distortion, i.e., free boundaries, will be assumed.

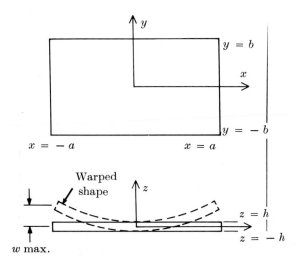

**Fig. 2-10**   Thermally warped plate.

As a first guess assume that $\sigma_{zz} = 0$ because the board is thin and unloaded, and assume that $\sigma_{xx}$ and $\sigma_{yy}$ are the same and vary only in the $z$ direction, as does $T(z)$. The chosen directions may then be seen to be principal directions because of symmetry, so that the shear stresses are all zero. Thus,

$$\sigma_{xx} = \sigma_{yy} = \sigma(z)$$

$$\sigma_{zz} = \tau_{xz} = \tau_{yz} = \tau_{xy} = 0$$

Stresses must be considered here because zero stresses will be needed at the free boundaries. The equilibrium equations, Eqs. (2-10) and (2-11), are identically satisfied by these stresses, but such stress solutions must also satisfy the compatibility equations; therefore, the strains must first be found from Eq. (2-19), or

$$\epsilon_{xx} = \epsilon_{yy} = (1 - \nu)\frac{\sigma}{E} + \alpha T, \qquad \epsilon_{zz} = -2\nu\frac{\sigma}{E} + \alpha T$$

and $\gamma_{xy} = \gamma_{yz} = \gamma_{zx} = 0$. All the compatibility relations, Eq. (2-17), are identically satisfied except the second two, both of which require

$$\frac{\partial^2}{\partial z^2}\left[(1 - \nu)\frac{\sigma}{E} + \alpha T\right] = 0$$

giving simply,

$$\sigma = \sigma_{xx} = \sigma_{yy} = -\frac{\alpha E}{1 - \nu}T + C_1 + C_2 z$$

Stresses of this type cannot satisfy the assumed stress-free boundary conditions, but the two available constants do allow the stress and moment averaged through the thickness to be set to zero, i.e.,

$$\int_{-h}^{h} \sigma_{xx}\,dz = \int_{-h}^{h} \sigma_{xx} z\,dz = 0$$

This relation applies not only along the boundary, but also throughout the plate, since $\sigma$ is independent of $x$ and $y$. Saint-Venant's principle[3] would indicate that the errors in such an approximation would not be felt very far from the boundary. Using these average boundary conditions, the stresses become

$$\sigma_{xx} = \sigma_{yy} = \frac{\alpha E}{1 - \nu}\left(-T + \frac{1}{2h}\int_{-h}^{h} T\,dz + \frac{3z}{2h^3}\int_{-h}^{h} Tz\,dz\right)$$

and the strains are

$$\frac{u}{x} = \frac{v}{y} = \frac{1}{E}\left(\frac{1}{2h}N + \frac{3z}{2h^3}M\right)$$

By integration, the displacement is found to be

$$w = -\frac{3M}{4h^3 E}(x^2 + y^2) + \frac{1}{(1 - \nu)E}\left[(1 + \nu)\,\alpha E\int_0^z T\,dz - \frac{\nu z}{h}N - \frac{3\nu z^2}{2h^3}M\right]$$

where

$$N = \alpha E \int_{-h}^{h} T \, dz, \qquad M = \alpha E \int_{-h}^{h} Tz \, dz$$

and rigid body motions of the origin are set equal to zero. Neglecting the small $z$ displacements due to thickening of the plate indicated by the term in the brackets, the maximum displacement or transverse warpage is

$$w_{max} = -\frac{3M}{4h^3 E} (a^2 + b^2)$$

which becomes

$$w_{max} = \frac{\alpha \theta}{4h} (a^2 + b^2)$$

for a uniform temperature gradient through the plate thickness and with a temperature difference $\theta$ between the faces (lower side hotter).

Assume a board of half-thickness $h = 0.04$ cm (16 mils), a coefficient of linear expansion $\alpha = 20 \times 10^6 /°C$, and dimensions $a = 8$ cm, $b = 5$ cm. The maximum warpage becomes 0.011 cm$/°C$ drop across the board for a linear temperature distribution. The determination of the actual temperature variation is left to the next chapter, but the simplified approach above would indicate the approximate warpage that might be expected. The important result here is that a relatively complex problem has been solved to the extent necessary for design purposes by assuming a situation which is as simplified as possible but which still includes the principal effect.

The remainder of this chapter will emphasize the "strength" approach, in which all the questions raised in the theory of elasticity must still be answered. These are questions of equilibrium of forces, stress-strain relations, and compatible displacements. Example 2.2 will present a real problem from this point of view. References 3, 10, 11, 14, and 15 are useful both for strength-of-materials methods and for results when trying to solve new problems.

## BOUNDARY CONDITIONS

Many of the assumptions made when doing academic problems do not apply in the real case. One such point, important in many structural problems, is the boundary condition. The free or stress-loaded boundary conditions of theory are good approximations of the real cases, but both the clamped and simply supported cases introduce difficulties. If the end of a beam or edge of a plate or shell is built into a relatively massive wall built of a material more rigid than that of the beam or plate, then that boundary may be considered to be clamped. In most cases, however, resilience of the wall or the connecting method causes the actual boundary fixation to be somewhere between clamped and simply supported. Example 2.2, which discusses a moment-loaded frame, will accentuate this specific problem.

The difficulty with simply supported boundaries appears in plate theory. If a rectangular plate is laid over a rigid rectangular frame and a central load is applied to the plate, it will be found that the plate corners lift off the frame. Thus, what might be thought of as a simply supported case is not really so. The simply supported condition assumes zero vertical displacement at the boundary; therefore, no corner lift is possible. The real plate is thus less stiff than the simply supported case would indicate.

**Example 2.2.** In the cabinet for an electronic private branch exchange, most of the electronic equipment is supported on hinged gates mounted with vertical hinge pins attached to the vertical members of the cabinet framework. (See Fig. 2-11.) This arrangement allows the heavy equipment to be swung out for access to the rear. A development model of the cabinet framework was made, and a weight, equivalent to that of the equipment with a person leaning on top of it, was placed at the center of gravity. To approximate a worst condition,

**Fig. 2-11**   Development model of the electronic PBX partially equipped with gates suspended from the left and right uprights.

all this weight was supported by a single hinge at the midpoint of the upright. In this test, deflection of the framework permitted the weight to sag downward so far that the initial design was considered to be unacceptable. The equipment in the actual case would have interfered with the bottom of the cabinet. The question then became: How should the frame be strengthened to accommodate the load?

The frame and its applied load are shown in schematic form in Fig. 2-12(a), where the load is represented by the moment $M_0$. The analysis of such a frame is available in almost any text on indeterminant structures, but the curvature predicted by such texts indicates a deformed shape like the dashed curve, while experiment showed that the supporting upright deflected as represented by the broken line in Fig. 2-12(a). The discrepancy occurs because joints 1, 2, 3, and 4 do not remain right angles under load, as usually assumed. Instead of infinite joint stiffness, some finite stiffness must be assumed.

The next step in the design is an analysis of the frame, including the non-rigid joints. The frame is broken into its component parts, as in Fig. 2-12(b), and the forces and moments existing at each point are written in. When the three basic requirements considered in elasticity are fulfilled, the analysis becomes quite straightforward.

EQUILIBRIUM. As may be seen, vertical and horizontal equilibriums have been assured by the assumed values of the loads applied to each member.

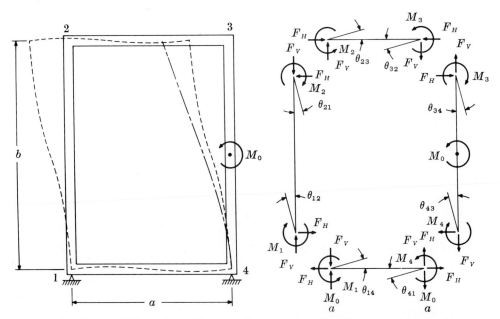

(a) Loading and distortion of framework     (b) Free body diagram of frame elements

**Fig. 2-12** Analysis of cabinet framework with gate suspended at midpoint of right upright.

However, rotational equilibrium for each element requires that the following four equations be satisfied:

$$M_1 + M_2 = F_H b \qquad (2\text{-}29\text{a})$$

$$M_2 = M_3 = F_V a \qquad (2\text{-}29\text{b})$$

$$M_0 = M_3 + M_4 + F_H b \qquad (2\text{-}29\text{c})$$

$$M_0 = M_1 + M_4 + F_V a \qquad (2\text{-}29\text{d})$$

COMPATIBILITY. The requirement of compatibility simply states that the ends of the various members must remain in contact after deformation. Equal angular distortion of adjacent frame members is not required since the joints are only semirigid. We assume small displacements, and we need not consider axial compression of the members. We assume that joints 2 and 3 translate a distance $\delta$ to the left, and, in doing so, each member rotates at its ends to lie tangent to the lines denoted by the corresponding $\theta_{ij}$'s in Fig. 2-12(b).

STRESS-STRAIN RELATIONS. Since our problem is written in terms of forces, we need stress-strain (really force-displacement) relations to allow us to satisfy compatibility. These relations, of course, are the equations for simple beam bending, available in any strength-of-materials book. The most complex member, $\overline{34}$, is shown in detail in Fig. 2-13. For this member, the relations are

$$\frac{2EI}{b}(\theta_{34} - \theta_{43}) = M_0 - 2M_3 - F_H b \qquad (2\text{-}30\text{a})$$

and

$$\frac{EI}{b^2}(\delta - \theta_{43}b) = \frac{3M_0}{8} - \frac{M_3}{2} - \frac{F_H b}{3} \qquad (2\text{-}30\text{b})$$

where $EI$ is Young's modulus times the moment of inertia of the member, assumed in this example to be the same value for each member. Similar equations for the other three members become

$$\frac{2EI}{b}(\theta_{21} - \theta_{12}) = -2M_2 + F_H b \qquad (2\text{-}31\text{a})$$

$$\frac{EI}{b^2}(\delta - \theta_{12}b) = -\frac{M_2}{2} + \frac{F_H b}{3} \qquad (2\text{-}31\text{b})$$

$$\frac{2EI}{a}(\theta_{32} - \theta_{23}) = 2M_3 - F_V a \qquad (2\text{-}31\text{c})$$

$$\frac{EI}{a}\theta_{23} = -\frac{M_3}{2} + \frac{F_V a}{3} \qquad (2\text{-}31\text{d})$$

$$\frac{2EI}{a}(\theta_{41} - \theta_{14}) = 2M_4 + F_V a - M_0 \qquad (2\text{-}31\text{e})$$

$$\frac{EI}{a}\theta_{14} = -\frac{M_4}{2} - \frac{F_V a}{3} + \frac{M_0}{3} \qquad (2\text{-}31\text{f})$$

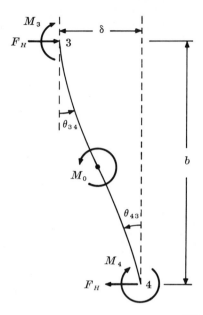

**Fig. 2-13**   Distortions of element $\overline{34}$.

Assume an angular stiffness, $k$, which produces a corner moment reaction, $k\theta$, for a corner angle change, $\theta$. This assumption means

$$M_1 = k(\theta_{12} - \theta_{14}) \tag{2-32a}$$

$$M_2 = k(\theta_{21} - \theta_{23}) \tag{2-32b}$$

$$M_3 = k(\theta_{34} - \theta_{32}) \tag{2-32c}$$

$$M_4 = k(\theta_{43} - \theta_{41}) \tag{2-32d}$$

Apply Eq. (2-29) to Eqs. (2-30), (2-31), and (2-32) to eliminate $M_2$, $M_3$, and $M_4$. Assuming that the corner stiffness is known, this gives a set of 12 equations in 12 unknowns: eight $\theta$'s, $F_V$, $M_1$, $F_H$, and $\delta$. The value of the corner stiffness could be obtained from the previously mentioned experiment by measuring the horizontal deflection of the top member while under load and by inserting this result, along with calculated member stiffness, into the 12 equations solved for $\delta$. Or, a single joint could be set up in the laboratory and the stiffness measured. In any case, the foregoing set of equations allows the designer to obtain the optimum method of stiffening the structure.

The question now is whether stiffening should be obtained by strengthening the frame members or by strengthening the joints. This could be answered by (1) using the equations to find the minimum sufficient joint and member stiffness, (2) running stiffness tests on a few likely joint designs, and (3) comparing the cost of these with that of stiffening the members. It would be difficult to obtain the same kind of information by experiment alone, since the relative influence of member stiffness and joint stiffness on load deflection would be hard to find.

## BUCKLING

Although buckling is a common mode of failure and is frequently catastrophic, the simplified kinds of stress analysis of use to the designer usually assume relatively simple distortion mechanisms and do not yield stability or buckling information. The differential equations of classical linear elasticity are based on Hooke's law and on the omission of nonlinear terms, both in the equations of equilibrium and in the strain-displacement equations. This formulation determines a unique position of elastic equilibrium for every body with prescribed loads and constraints.

In actuality, however, the solution of such a physical problem is not always unique. The same elastic body, under identical conditions of loading and constraint, may have more than one possible position of equilibrium. The incorrect inference to which the classical theory of elasticity leads can be explained by the insufficient accuracy of its formulas.

Buckling generally occurs because one mode of deformation becomes unstable and the structure tends toward another stable mode. There are several different kinds of buckling, and the three most common forms will be described briefly here.

**Bifurcation (or Classical) Buckling.** If the load, $P$, on a structure is sufficiently small, the load-deflection diagram has a single branch (path $OA$ in Fig. 2-14). In this mode of buckling, when the load reaches its so-called *critical value*, a fork or bifurcation point appears in the diagram. The prebuckling mode becomes unstable after the bifurcation point is passed, and the structure passes smoothly from its unbuckled mode to a buckled mode with a continuously positive load-deflection characteristic. After buckling, the structure follows the stable path $AB$ in Fig. 2-14.

The load-deflection diagrams for axially compressed beams and for plates under in-plane compression are similar to the one shown in Fig. 2-14. Line $OA$ corresponds to the unbuckled equilibrium path where the beam or plate is compressed and remains straight. Beyond the critical load, $P_C$, the straight equilibrium position is unstable (represented by the dashed extension of line $OA$), and the beam or plate assumes the buckled shape with lateral deflections.

One basic method of formulating such a classical buckling problem is to write the equilibrium equations for the structural element in the slightly buckled configuration. The value of the load at which a nontrivial solution of these equations exists will be the critical load. A second method is based on the concept that a static, conservative system is in a configuration of stable equilibrium if, and only if, the value of its total potential energy is a relative minimum. The critical load is the load at which such a minimum occurs for some particular small perturbation, and this perturbation then describes the buckled mode shape. Both of these methods may be used to reduce the bifurcation buckling formulation to a linear eigenvalue problem which, when solved, yields the value of $P_C$ and the buckled shape. The energy method is readily extended to yield approximate solutions of many problems of buckling of beams and plates.

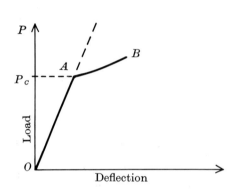

**Fig. 2-14**   Load-deflection curve for classical buckling.

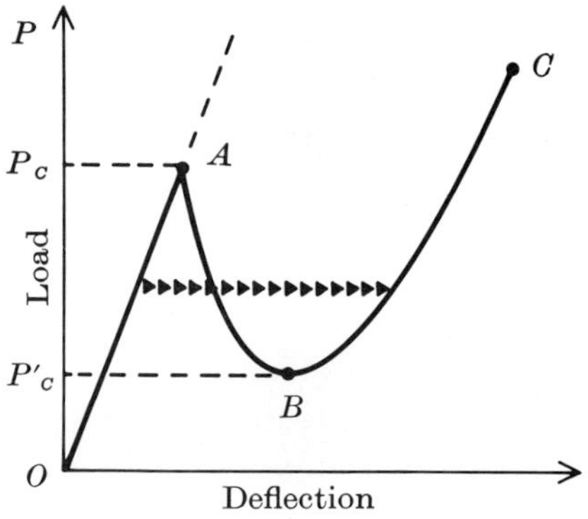

**Fig. 2-15**   Load-deflection curve for finite-disturbance buckling.

**Finite-Disturbance Buckling.** Some structures, like axially compressed, thin-walled cylinders, suffer greatly reduced stiffness after buckling takes place, as shown by the load-deflection diagram in Fig. 2-15. In such a structure, with a sufficiently large finite disturbance, the structure can "jump" from the unbuckled equilibrium state (path $OA$) to a buckled equilibrium state before the classical, calculated buckling load, $P_C$, is reached. This jump can take place at some load between $P'_C$ and $P_C$, as shown by the arrows. The jump at loads below $P_C$ is possible because of perturbations in the practical application of loads and because of imperfections in the material.

An example of this type of buckling in a hollow frame upright formed from a 0.13-cm thick steel sheet is shown in Fig. 2-16. This catastrophic failure resulted from high compressive forces due to bending and, as one would expect, failure occurred in a section that was not reinforced by the heavy brackets used to mount apparatus. Note that, in this case, the load that could be sustained after failure would never again be as great as $P_C$.

The investigation of this type of buckling, including determination of the

**Fig. 2-16** Finite-disturbance buckling of a badly over-loaded framework upright.

critical buckling load, requires a description of the branch $ABC$ of the load-deflection diagram, and a nonlinear formulation is therefore necessary.

**Snap-Through Buckling.** The third or snap-through kind of buckling occurs in structures such as shallow arches whose load-deflection diagram is like those shown in Figs. 2-17 and 2-18. As the load is increased, the stiffness of the structure decreases, and at $P_C$ the structure snaps into a nonadjacent, stable position. A familiar example is the kinking of a venetian blind slat.

The buckling of a very shallow arch in a twistor memory card is shown in Fig. 2-18. The card is an aluminum alloy plate 29 cm by 17 cm by 0.04 cm, with tiny permanent magnets cemented to one side. It is held vertically with the ends confined so that they are simply supported but held straight and parallel. The card is nominally flat, but this test specimen is distorted with a slight spherical curvature, resulting in the characteristic shown, as the center is continuously deflected (confined to prevent snap-through) and the load measured. The four almost identical traces shown where made by an $X$-$Y$ recorder, two for increasing and two for decreasing loads.

As with finite-disturbance buckling, it is possible for snap-through buckling

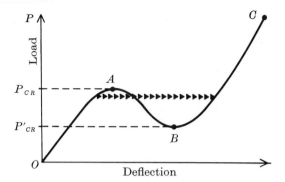

**Fig. 2-17**  Typical load-deflection curve for snap-through buckling.

to take place before $P_C$ is reached.  Again, a nonlinear formulation is required to describe the snap-through phenomenon.  Snap-through buckling will usually take place closer to the theoretical $P_C$ value, however, because the shape of the load-deflection diagram requires greater energy in the perturbations of loading to permit the apparent tunneling to take place.

General discussions of the various buckling phenomena and comprehensive bibliographies are available.[16,17]  Numerous examples of the equilibrium and energy methods applied to classical buckling of beams, plates, and shells are

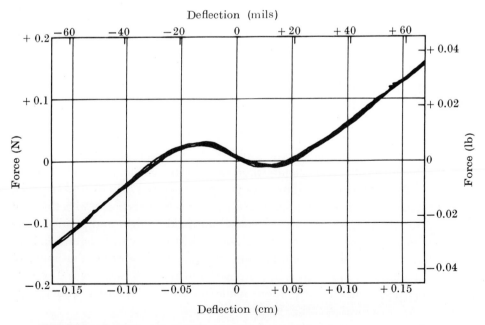

**Fig. 2-18**  Snap-through buckling of developmental twistor memory card.

presented.[18,19,20] Reference 17 also presents some results and further references for finite-disturbance and snap-through buckling.

## STRESS CONCENTRATIONS

Bolt holes, notches, complex structural cross sections, etc., do not greatly affect the stiffness of a structural member. For simplicity, these must usually be left out of basic structural analyses. Once the basic results are obtained, however, it is essential that the local effect of such stress raisers be examined. Brittle materials and materials in fatigue situations are extremely sensitive to stress concentrations, and the design should reduce such effects to the utmost. The usual method of evaluating the effect of a stress concentration is to determine the stress field while neglecting such effects, and then to apply an appropriate stress concentration factor to determine the maximum stress. For design work, this approach should be sufficient. Peterson[21] gives a large number of stress concentration factors. An article with special reference to three-dimensional stress concentration is also available.[22]

## MANUFACTURING TOLERANCES

Manufacturing tolerances must be included in any real design, and they frequently have an important effect on design cost. Unnecessarily close tolerances are a very expensive means of easing the designer's job. On the other hand, such tolerances must be considered when stress analysis is undertaken, simply because the manufactured part will not be the same size or shape as the hypothetical part analyzed. In particular, straightness tolerances on support channels will affect their buckling resistance, and even after parts are made to fit together, tolerances may increase stresses, as shown in the following example.

**Example 2.3.** A cast iron clevis was designed to provide ceiling support for a heavy bay of equipment. The general design is shown in Fig. 2-19. A stringer was to be attached to the clevis by means of a shoulder bolt running through the holes in the clevis. When tightened with its nut, this bolt should allow no clamping load to be applied to the stringer end. The original analysis went as follows.

The total tensile load, $P_1$, of 7100 newtons is applied equally to the two sides of the clevis by the bolt, putting the sides in tension with an average stress of $P_1/2h(w - d)$ at the sides of the holes. Examination of the stress concentration factors appropriate to a hole loaded with a bolt[20] shows that the maximum tensile stress will occur at the sides of the smaller hole of diameter $d_2$, for

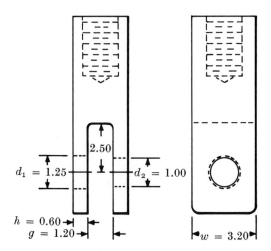

**Fig. 2-19** Cast iron clevis (all dimensions in centimeters).

which the stress concentration factor $K_t$ is 1.55. This gives a maximum calculated stress of

$$\frac{K_t P_1}{2hd_2} = \frac{1.55 \times 7100}{2 \times 0.60 \times 1.00 \times 10^{-4}} = 91.7 \times 10^6 \, \text{N}/\text{m}^2 \quad (13{,}300 \text{ psi})$$

The clevis was thus designed with a safety factor of almost 4, relative to a tensile strength of $345 \times 10^6 \, \text{N}/\text{m}^2$ (50,000 psi).

Tolerances in the final production drawings allowed the head-to-shoulder length of the bolt to be 0.030 cm smaller than the maximum $h + g$ dimensions in Fig. 2-19, because of combined tolerances on bolt and clevis. Some of these assemblies failed in service. Bending of the clevis sides was the cause, resulting in combined bending and axial stresses in excess of the breaking strength. In performing the analysis, the designer failed to recognize that significant bending of the clevis sides would take place.

Consider one side of the clevis as a simple cantilever deflected an amount $\delta = 0.015$ cm under the edge of the bolt head, which is 2.00 cm across flats. The effective clamping point for the cantilever will be some distance above the root since the material in this region will deflect to some degree. This distance will be assumed to equal half the thickness of the cantilever, or 0.30 cm. The effective length of the cantilever is thus assumed to be $l_e = 2.50 + 0.30 - 1.00 = 1.80$ cm. This is probably conservative (short) since some deflection of the bolt will also occur. From simple beam theory, the force to produce the 0.015-cm deflection of the cantilever would be

$$P_2 = \frac{3EI\delta}{l_e^3} = \frac{3 \times 124 \times 10^9 \times 3.20 \times 0.60^3 \times 0.015 \times 10^{-4}}{12 \times 1.80^3} = 5510 \text{ N}$$

$$(1240 \text{ lb})$$

resulting in a moment, at the root, of

$$M = P_2 l = 5510 \times 1.50 \times 10^{-2} = 82.5 \text{ N} \cdot \text{m} \quad (730 \text{ lb in.})$$

Combining bending and axial tensile stresses,

$$\sigma_{\max} = \frac{Mh}{2I} + \frac{P_1}{2hw}$$

$$= \frac{82.5 \times 0.60 \times 12}{2 \times 3.20 \times 0.60^3 \times 10^{-6}} + \frac{7100}{2 \times 0.60 \times 3.20 \times 10^{-4}}$$

$$= 430 \times 10^6 + 18.5 \times 10^6 = 450 \times 10^6 \text{ N} \quad (65,000 \text{ psi})$$

This stress would occur on the outside surface of the clevis at a point opposite the root. The stress at the curved surface of the root is primarily compressive due to the bending load but is diminished by the axial tensile load. Even so, it probably exceeds the maximum tensile stress in magnitude due to the effect of stress concentration. This is not important here, however, since cast iron is much stronger in compression than in tension (see Fig. A-1).

The calculated maximum stress, higher than the breaking strength, indicates that breakage should be expected with this adverse accumulation of tolerances. The importance of attention to tolerances and clearances in design is emphasized here by the fact that a stress 35 times the intended value at this point was inadvertently introduced.

## SIMPLIFIED THEORIES

Plate, beam, and shell theories have been developed because such forms are of great importance and because extensive mathematical simplification can be assumed in these cases when compared to three-dimensional elasticity.

Every structural element is a three-dimensional body, and the exact analysis of the stresses and deformations under applied loads, thermal gradients, etc., presents a formidable mathematical problem. For such flexible bodies as beams, plates, and shells, where one dimension of the body is much smaller than the others, simplifying assumptions may be made which reduce the beam analysis to a one-dimensional problem and the plate and shell analyses to two-dimensional problems. The basic assumption is that points in the body which lie on a normal to the neutral plane (a plane surface passing through the center of the thickness of the undeflected beam, plate, or shell) lie on a normal to this surface in the deformed structure.

**Plates.** For plates, classical small-deflection theory of laterally loaded thin plates assumes, in addition, that

1. the slope of the deflected plate is small, so that its square may be neglected in comparison with unity;

2. the midplane of the plate is a neutral plane, i.e., midplane stresses arising from deflection of the plate into a nondevelopable* surface are ignored.

These assumptions normally restrict the theory to applications where the lateral deflection is small compared to the plate thickness. Solutions for many problems in the classical small-deflection theory of plates are available.[23,24]

When external loads are applied in the plane of the plate, and their order of magnitude is comparable to the critical loads for plate buckling, they may affect the lateral bending appreciably and should be taken into account. The in-plane stress problem is solved under the assumption that membrane stresses arising from lateral deflection of the plate may be ignored. Thus, the in-plane and bending problems are still uncoupled.

When plate deflections are sufficiently large (generally of the order of magnitude of the plate thickness), straining of the middle surface caused by plate deflections into a nondevelopable surface may not be ignored. This more accurate formulation results in a system of coupled nonlinear partial differential equations governing the in-plane and bending problems. They were first derived in 1910 by von Karman, who considered certain quadratic terms in the strain-displacement equations. Solutions in this theory are available[25,26] and many references are given.[23]

**Beams.** The same assumptions about the order of magnitude of the lateral displacements apply in the case of beams. However, the von Karman equations for large deflections reduce to a single linear ordinary differential equation which may be solved for any lateral loading. Also, the *elastica* theory is available for beams, and this theory determines the angle of bending rotation of any beam element exactly in terms of the beam arc length. It thus provides solutions for arbitrarily large deflections of very thin beams. Reference 2 discusses this subject with methods and results.

**Shells.** As remarked previously, the retention of certain quadratic terms in the strain-displacement equations is significant for some problems of flat plates. Flat plates are somewhat exceptional in their behavior, since membrane strains of the middle plane are quadratic functions of the normal deflections. On the other hand, membrane strains due to the normal deflections of the middle surface of a nondevelopable curved shell are ordinarily first-order quantities. Consequently, quadratic terms in the strain-displacement equations

---

* A developable surface is one that can be formed geometrically from a plane without causing stretching of the plane during the transformation, e.g., a cylindrical or conical surface.

are less important for curved shells than for flat plates, and they are frequently ignored. The resulting theory is linear, and problems are often divided into "membrane" and "bending" solutions. Since in-plane stiffness is usually much greater than bending stiffness, the shell is much more efficient when carrying loads in the membrane mode. It also follows that a shell is a more efficient structure for supporting lateral load than is a plate in which membrane action is a second-order effect. Many problems of membrane and bending theory of thin shells have been solved.[27,28]

Although the foregoing discussion cites restrictions on the use of the various simplified theories, the design analyst should not hesitate to make use of them, even when the restrictions are not satisfied. The implications of the violation should be kept in mind, however, so that a judgment can be made about the extent and type of the resulting inaccuracies.

## EXPERIMENTAL TECHNIQUES

Three laboratory methods of determining the strains existing in a structure are particularly useful to the designer. These are strain gauge, brittle lacquer and photoelastic methods.

**Strain Gauges.** The most common and useful form of the strain gauge is the resistance gauge, which changes resistance according to the strain it experiences in one direction. Single gauges of this type can be obtained as small as 0.04-cm square. To use such a gauge, we must know the position on the surface of a body at which the strain is to be measured and also the strain direction of interest. A single gauge can then be attached at that point with the proper orientation to measure the strain. In the most general case, however, the position of maximum strain is not known, and the entire state of strain at the point is necessary for the previously mentioned reasons (particularly yield information). To find the position of maximum strain, the brittle-coating technique, to be discussed next, complements the strain gauge very nicely. This technique shows points of maximum tensile strain, although it is sometimes not very accurate in indicating strain magnitudes. Then, to determine the state of strain, a strain gauge rosette is applied. A rosette consists of at least three individual gauges and gives the complete strain picture in the plane of the surface to which the gauges are attached. Rosettes may be obtained as small as 0.5 cm on a side. Since the surface must be a free surface (unloaded), the stresses normal to the surface are zero, and the shear stresses acting on the surface are zero. The plane of the surface is thus principal, and the state of strain at the point can be determined. The following will illustrate this calculation.

A 60° strain gauge rosette is arranged as shown in Fig. 2-20(a). The plane

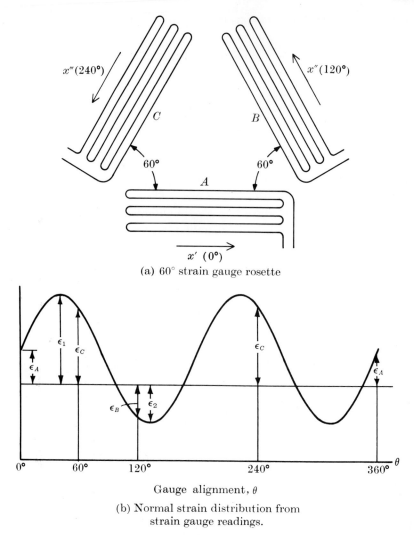

(a) 60° strain gauge rosette

Gauge alignment, $\theta$

(b) Normal strain distribution from
strain gauge readings.

**Fig. 2-20** Geometry and application of 60° strain gauge rosette.

of the surface contains two principal axes, since the normal to this plane is
principal. We write Eq. (2-7a) in terms of strains instead of stresses, since it has
been shown that strains satisfy the same transformation equation. This
produces

$$\epsilon_{x'x'} = \alpha^2_{x'1}\epsilon_1 + \alpha^2_{x'2}\epsilon_2 + \alpha^2_{x'3}\epsilon_3$$

Since we are considering strains in the plane only, one of the angle cosines must
be zero, say, $\alpha_{x'3} = 0$. Then the three measured strains, $\epsilon_A$, $\epsilon_B$, and $\epsilon_C$, may be
written as follows in terms of the two unknown principal strains in the plane of

the surface and the remaining angle cosines:

$$\epsilon_A = \epsilon_{x'x'} = \alpha^2_{x'1}\epsilon_1 + \alpha^2_{x'2}\epsilon_2 \tag{2-33a}$$

$$\epsilon_B = \epsilon_{x''x''} = \alpha^2_{x''1}\epsilon_1 + \alpha^2_{x''2}\epsilon_2 \tag{2-33b}$$

$$\epsilon_C = \epsilon_{x'''x'''} = \alpha^2_{x'''1}\epsilon_1 + \alpha^2_{x'''2}\epsilon_2 \tag{2-33c}$$

where the directions of alignment of gauges $A$, $B$, and $C$ are $x'$, $x''$, and $x'''$, respectively. The six cosines are related as follows, since the principal directions in the plane are orthogonal:

$$\alpha^2_{x'1} + \alpha^2_{x'2} = \alpha^2_{x''1} + \alpha^2_{x''2} = \alpha^2_{x'''1} + \alpha^2_{x'''2} = 1 \tag{2-34}$$

Also,

$$\alpha_{x''1} = -\frac{1}{2}\alpha_{x'1} - \frac{\sqrt{3}}{2}\alpha_{x'2} \tag{2-35a}$$

$$\alpha_{x'''1} = -\frac{1}{2}\alpha_{x'1} + \frac{\sqrt{3}}{2}\alpha_{x'2} \tag{2-35b}$$

since the $x'$, $x''$, and $x'''$ directions change in increments of 120°. Then only one cosine remains unknown, and we have three equations in the three unknowns $\epsilon_1$, $\epsilon_2$, and, say, $\alpha_{x'1}$. An easy way to visualize the result is to plot the three known strains and to fit a sinusoid to the points, as in Fig. 2-20(b). This is an approximate, graphical way of solving Eqs. (2-33), (2-34), and (2-35). It can be shown that the strain, $\epsilon$, has the form $\epsilon = k + \cos(2\theta + \varphi)$, where $\theta$ is the angle of measurement on the physical specimen, and where $k$ and $\varphi$ are constants. Note that $\epsilon_C$ can be plotted at both 60° and 240° for more convenient curve fitting, since $\epsilon$ goes through two complete cycles for a 360° rotation of position on the specimen.

The state of stress (for yield or failure investigations) is then determined from the stress-strain equations, noting that $\sigma_3 = 0$. That is,

$$\epsilon_1 = \frac{1}{E}(\sigma_1 - \nu\sigma_2)$$

$$\epsilon_2 = \frac{1}{E}(\sigma_2 - \nu\sigma_1)$$

can be solved for the two principal stresses in the plane, and the strain normal to the surface can be found from the remaining relation:

$$\epsilon_3 = -\frac{\nu}{E}(\sigma_1 + \sigma_2)$$

The disadvantages of strain gauges are that they give strains averaged over the size of the gauge and that the locations of maximum strain areas must be predetermined. They can, however, give very accurate strain measurements.

**Brittle Lacquer.** Brittle lacquers are used in strain determinations because, after being applied to the surface of an item under study, a brittle lacquer will crack as the item is put under strain. The cracks appear normal to the directions of maximum tensile strain, and the number or frequency of the cracks in a particular area is an indication of the strain level. Tests with such materials can produce very graphic pictures of the strain field at the surface (see Fig. 2-21). Since maximum compressive strains should also be known to get yield information, however, the item may be loaded, then the lacquer applied

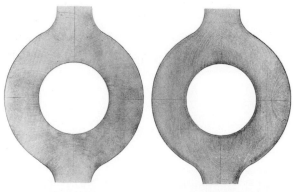

(a) Eyebolt lacquered and     (b) Eyebolt stretched in          **Fig. 2-21** Complementary
    stretched in tension.           tension, lacquered,       brittle-lacquer crack patterns.[29]
                                 and tension removed.

and the load removed. Maximum positive strains in this test correspond to maximum compressive strains in the loaded item. Consequently, a comparison of the results of the two tests with an inverted lacquering-loading sequence will indicate areas of maximum shear stress for yield determination. Regions of maximum shear stress are those which exhibit the largest sum of crack frequencies from the two tests.

"Stresscoat" is the trade name of such a lacquer made by the Magnaflux Corporation, which claims that good quantitative strain information can be obtained with this product when the directions are carefully followed. In any case, the qualitative picture that results from this type of testing indicates the proper positions for the strain gauges used for quantitative measurements.

**Photoelasticity.** Photoelasticity is an experimental stress analysis technique which combines optical principles and the theory of elasticity to provide quantitative solutions for two- or three-dimensional elastic stress distributions in loaded bodies.

*Stress-optic law of photoelasticity.* Plates made of certain crystalline materials (e.g., mica) possess the property that a light wave impinging on them at normal incidence is resolved into two components which are transmitted through the plate with polarizations in planes that are at right angles to each other and to the crystal surface. This phenomenon is referred to as "double refraction" or "birefringence." Furthermore, the optical properties in the two planes of polarization will, in general, be different, so that the two components will be transmitted with unequal velocities. Therefore, when the waves emerge from the plate, there will be a relative phase angle between them that is proportional to the thickness of the plate traversed by the waves.

Photoelasticity is a useful stress analysis technique because almost all transparent materials—such as glass, cellulose nitrate, Bakelite, and many other synthetic resins—temporarily exhibit the property of birefringence to some extent when they are subjected to stress. Thus, consider a flat plate made from a transparent, birefringent material which is subjected to plane stress within the elastic limit. When plane-polarized, monochromatic light impinges normally on the plate, the transmission of light through the plate at a point obeys the following two laws which form the basis of photoelastic stress determination:

1. The light is resolved in the directions of the principal-stress axes and is transmitted only in the planes of principal stress.
2. The velocity of transmission along each principal plane depends on the intensities of both principal stresses.

If the plate is viewed in the field of a polariscope, a series of dark and light bands, called interference fringes, are observed. Experimental and theoretical analyses have established that the points along an interference fringe form a locus of constant principal-stress difference, that is,

$$\sigma_1 - \sigma_2 = \text{constant}$$

along an interference fringe. In particular,

$$\sigma_1 - \sigma_2 = \frac{nf}{h}$$

where:

$n$ = interference fringe number

$f$ = material fringe constant

$h$ = plate thickness.

The material fringe constant is determined by analysis of a calibration specimen of the material. Thus, to compute the principal-stress difference at a point on a stressed plate, when $f$ and $h$ are known, one simply counts the number of interference fringes from a known reference to the point in question. To determine the separate values of $\sigma_1$ and $\sigma_2$, auxiliary techniques are used.

Besides giving quantitative determinations of the individual principal stresses at every point of a stressed plate, the photoelastic method immediately provides the principal-stress directions at every point. From these directions, the principal-stress trajectories can easily be constructed. Figure 2-22 shows a

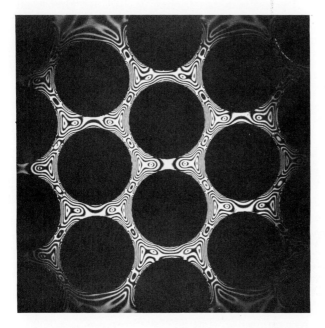

**Fig. 2-22** Photoelastic fringe patterns of a faceplate for a Multifunction Array Radar (MAR) antenna support structure. The plate has uniform tensile loadings of different magnitudes in horizontal and vertical directions.

typical fringe pattern for a perforated plate experiencing in-plane loads. The fringes may be looked at in the same way as profile contours on a map, which points up the difficulty of counting fringes. It is frequently difficult to tell whether some of the regions completely enclosed by fringes are "protrusions" or "depressions" in the profile. The experimentalist can determine this, however, by a general knowledge of the stress field and by watching the way in which the fringes move as the load is increased from zero.

*Three-dimensional analysis.* If three-dimensional stress distributions are required, the "stress-freezing" technique is used. This technique is founded on the diphase property of specific transparent plastics. The diphase theory states that, at room temperature, the solid material is composed of strong and weak molecular networks. At an elevated temperature (the critical temperature), the weak molecular bonds soften, and if a load is applied, the strong molecular bonds are distorted in supporting the load. If the load is now maintained as the temperature is slowly decreased, the distortions will be locked or frozen into the material as the weak molecular bonds resolidify around the strong molecular bonds. Experiments have established that the stresses frozen into the material represent an elastic stress distribution. If thin slices are removed from the material, the stress patterns are not disturbed, and the stress distribution can be analyzed by the conventional photoelastic techniques described earlier. Thus, by means of the stress-freezing technique, internal elastic stress distributions of three-dimensional bodies can be quantitatively evaluated.

*Photostress technique.* If a prototype is available for testing and if surface stresses are required over a large area, the photostress technique is used. This technique furnishes qualitative and quantitative surface stress data and is useful for locating areas of stress concentration.

The method is also based on the property of birefringence, in this case the birefringence of a thin transparent plastic sheet bonded with a reflective cement to the surface of the prototype. A reflection-type polariscope is used in such a way that the polarized light is transmitted normal to the surface of the plastic, reflected at the surface of the prototype, and retransmitted back through the plastic. Interference fringes are formed and can be analyzed as described before.

The advantages of this technique are that it is nondestructive, it is reasonably rapid, data are obtained directly from the prototype, and large areas can be analyzed at one time. Its limitations are that reinforcing effects due to the bonded plastic must be accounted for, large stress gradients will produce quantitative errors if the light does not impinge normal to the plastic, and only surface stresses can be evaluated.

*When photoelasticity should be used.* In general, the stress analyst and designer seek answers to questions such as:

1. Where are the areas of stress concentration?
2. What are the stress concentration factors?
3. What effect will a change of geometry have on the stress distribution and on the stress concentration factor?
4. Where is the point of maximum principal stress and principal-stress difference?
5. What is the magnitude of the maximum principal stress or difference?
6. Is the maximum principal stress a tensile or compressive stress?

While photoelastic techniques are often useful in finding answers to these questions, there are also limitations of which the analyst and designer should be cognizant. They are:

1. It is an indirect method requiring the use of accurate scale models and subsequent interpretation of data for the prototype.
2. Experimental procedures are readily applied to two-dimensional stress problems; three-dimensional problems are much more difficult and require application of carefully developed special techniques.
3. Only elastic stress distributions can be evaluated.
4. The effect of prototype surface conditions such as microscopic corrosion pits and machining scratches cannot be evaluated.
5. Residual stresses or elastic redistribution of stress that occurs after the prototype has undergone some plastic deformation, heat treatment, or welding operations cannot be evaluated.

Being aware of the advantages and limitations of photoelasticity, the analyst and designer can decide whether a particular problem requires photoelastic analysis. However, if any doubt persists, an experienced photoelastician should be consulted.

## REFERENCES

1. Love, A. E. H., *A Treatise on the Mathematical Theory of Elasticity*, 4th ed., New York, Dover Publications, Inc., 1944. A large amount of information on static and dynamic, real and theoretical problems. Difficult notation and organization.

2. Frisch-Fay, R., *Flexible Bars*, Washington, Butterworth & Co. Ltd., 1962. Thorough discussion of the *elastica* theory for thin beams with large deflections.

3. Wang, C. T., *Applied Elasticity*, New York, McGraw-Hill Book Co., 1953. Presents many useful methods of elasticity and strength of materials.

4. Boley, B. A., and J. H. Weiner, *Theory of Thermal Stresses*, New York, John Wiley & Sons, Inc., 1960. Excellent book on the subject, presenting both theory and problem solutions.

5. Hunter, S. C., "Viscoelastic Waves," Chap. 1, *Progress in Solid Mechanics*, **1**, edited by I. N. Sneddon and R. Hill, New York, Interscience, 1960. An understandable yet thorough discussion of three-dimensional viscoelasticity.

6. *Metals Handbook*, 8th ed., Metals Park, Ohio, American Society for Metals, **1**, 1961, **2**, 1964. A compendium of necessary information on metals.

7. Smithells, C. J., editor, *Metals Reference Book*, 3rd ed., Washington, Butterworth & Co., Ltd., 1962. A compendium of necessary information on metals.

8. Murphy, G., *Advanced Mechanics of Materials*, New York, McGraw-Hill Book. Co., 1946. Cites original sources of data on which Fig. 2-8 is based.

9. *Modern Plastics Encyclopedia*, New York, McGraw-Hill Book Co., 1968. A compendium of information on plastics.

10. Timoshenko, S. P., and J. N. Goodier, *Theory of Elasticity*, 2nd ed., New York, McGraw-Hill Book Co., 1951. Presents many useful methods of elasticity and strength of materials.

11. Sokolnikoff, I. S., *Mathematical Theory of Elasticity*, 2nd ed., New York, McGraw-Hill Book Co., 1956. A more mathematical discussion of elasticity than References 3 and 10.

12. Mindlin, R. D., "Influence of Rotatory Inertia and Shear on Flexural Motions of Isotropic, Elastic Plates," *Journal of Applied Mechanics*, New York, American Society of Mechanical Engineers, March, 1951. Examples of the reduction of the general elastic equations to those of a simplified engineering model by proper assumption.

13. Rhines, W. J., "Foundation Models for Continuously Supported Structures," doctoral thesis, School of Engineering, New York University, 1965. Examples of the reduction of the general elastic equations to those of a simplified engineering model by proper assumption.

14. Den Hartog, J. P., *Advanced Strength of Materials*, New York, McGraw-Hill Book Co., 1952. Presents many useful methods of elasticity and strength of materials.

15. Crandall, S. H., and N. C. Dahl, editors, *Introduction to the Mechanics of Solids*, New York, McGraw-Hill Book Co., 1959. Develops a good understanding of the basic concepts of solid mechanics—static, dynamic, rigid and deformable; excellent descriptive figures.

16. Langhaar, H. L., "General Theory of Buckling," *Applied Mechanics Review*, **11**, No. 11, New York, American Society of Mechanical Engineers, 1958. A general discussion of the various buckling phenomena with comprehensive bibliographies.

17. Libove, C., "Elastic Stability," Chap. 44, *Handbook of Engineering Mechanics*, edited by W. Flügge, New York, McGraw-Hill Book Co., 1962. A general discussion of the various buckling phenomena with comprehensive bibliographies.

18. Bleich, F., *Buckling Strength of Metal Structures*, New York, McGraw-Hill Book Co., 1952. Numerous examples of the equilibrium and energy methods applied to classical buckling of beams, plates, and shells.

19. Timoshenko, S. P., and J. M. Gere, *Theory of Elastic Stability*, 2nd ed., New York, McGraw-Hill Book Co., 1961. Numerous examples of the equilibrium and energy methods applied to classical buckling of beams, plates, and shells.

20. Gerard, G., and H. Becker, "Handbook of Structural Stability," *NACA Tech. Notes 3781–3786; NASA Tech. Notes D-162 and D-163, 1957–1959*. Numerous examples of the equilibrium and energy methods applied to classical buckling of beams, plates, and shells.

21. Peterson, R. E., *Stress Concentration Design Factors*, New York, John Wiley & Sons, Inc., 1953. Virtually complete collection of the most useful stress concentration factors.

22. Sternberg, E., "Three-Dimensional Stress Concentrations in the Theory of Elasticity" (review article), *Applied Mechanics Review*, American Society of Mechanical Engineers, **11**, No. 1, Jan., 1958.

23. Timoshenko, S. P., and S. Woinowsky-Krieger, *Theory of Plates and Shells*, 2nd ed., New York, McGraw-Hill Book Co., 1959. Solutions to many problems in the classical small-deflection theory of plates and to problems of membrane and bending theory of thin shells; contains references and some large-deflection theory.

24. Way, S., "Plates," Chap. 39, *Handbook of Engineering Mechanics*, edited by W. Flügge, New York, McGraw-Hill Book Co., 1962. Solutions to many problems in the classical small-deflection theory of plates; contains references and some large-deflection theory.

25. Way, S., "Bending of Circular Plates with Large Deflections," *Trans. of ASME* **56**, No. 8, New York, 1934. Solutions to the large plate-deflection formulation.

26. Levy, S., "Bending of Rectangular Plates with Large Deflections," *NACA Report No. 737*, 1942. Solutions to the large plate-deflection formulation.

27. Flügge, W., *Stresses in Shells*, Berlin, Springer, 1960. Solutions to many problems of membrane and bending theory of thin shells.

28. Flügge, W., "Shells," Chap. 40, *Handbook of Engineering Mechanics*, edited by W. Flügge, New York, McGraw-Hill Book Co., 1962. Solutions to many problems of membrane and bending theory of thin shells.

29. Hetényi, M., editor, *Handbook of Experimental Stress Analysis*, New York John Wiley & Sons Inc., 1950. A compendium of basic information on this subject.

*Chapter 3*

# DYNAMICS OF STRUCTURES

F. T. Flaherty, Jr.

The most serious threats to the structural integrity of most electronic systems arise not from the usual static conditions of normal use, but from dynamic shock and vibration experienced during periods of shipment and installation, or at times of exceptional stress, as during nuclear attack. The situation is called dynamic when the rate of change of loadings is so large that the inertial effects cannot be neglected in Eqs. (2-10) and (2-11). Not only are problems of dynamic loading very common in equipment design, but, as will be shown later, even seemingly innocuous handling of small parts can often result in severe shock damage.

Solving such dynamic problems with the general elastic equations becomes even more difficult than for the static case; therefore, an even greater degree of approximation is needed. While most of the simplified equations for beams, plates, and shells in their dynamic form can be solved, the results are so complicated that their usefulness for design analysis is greatly limited. The results usually appear as an infinite series of modal solutions which converge poorly. Displacements may be obtained with relative ease, but stresses, which correspond to some derivative of the displacements, converge very poorly or not at all.

Two simplifications, however, can give excellent physical insight and good qualitative results; they will frequently give quantitative accuracy as well. We will call these methods the *discrete system* and the *wave propagation* approaches. In the first, a continuous system is transformed into an approximate discrete system. In the second, distortions and stresses are obtained by assuming that one-dimensional stress waves propagate through the structure.

## 3-1. TYPES OF LOADING

Dynamic loadings may be applied to a structure in all of the same ways that static loadings are applied: through the boundaries, over the surface, thermally, or by body loadings. The form of such loadings—that is, the general character of their time variation—dictates the approach to be used. For this reason, the method of representing various dynamic loadings will be discussed first.

### SHOCK LOADING

A shock loading is one which lasts only a short time relative to the damping time constant of the material. In all cases, the distortional response of any real structure to such an input is of finite duration. This is obvious when it is realized that only a finite amount of energy can be introduced by such an input, and that the damping in any real structure will sooner or later transform all of this energy into heat. Then, the mechanical response will have returned to zero. Loadings of this kind are produced by the handling (or mishandling) of equipment, by explosive forces transmitted as a blast wave through the air or as a shock wave through the ground, or by the operation of mechanical devices (closing doors, solenoids, etc.).

Shock loadings may be described in either of two ways. The most common and analytically usable representation is the direct time history. In this case, the force or pressure acting on, or the motion of, some portion of a structure is given directly as a function of time. In practical cases, however, the experimental time histories of loadings may be quite variable, even though tests are run under similar conditions. This is true, for example, in the case of nuclear blast environments. In these cases, the so-called shock spectrum is used to describe the *input* mechanical environment in terms of the *response* of simple mechanical oscillators (i.e., single-degree-of-freedom, mass-spring systems). Experience has shown that, in such complex situations, shock spectra are much more reproducible than are the time histories that generate them. This implies that, for such cases, the distribution of input energy among the frequencies remains unchanged, but that the phase of the various frequencies may change radically from test to test.

Experimentally, these shock spectra are obtained by placing a number of simple mechanical oscillators of different frequencies inside a box. The maximum displacement of each oscillator relative to the box, caused by the input in question, is then measured.

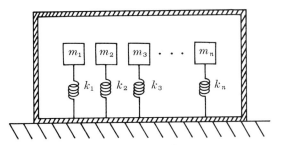

**Fig. 3-1**  Device for measuring shock spectrum.

For example, an ideal drop test in which there is no resilience of the table would give the following results. The box, as shown in Fig. 3-1, would be dropped onto the table. The figure shows the box just as it hits the surface. Assume no motion of the masses $m_1$, $m_2$, . . . , $m_n$ relative to the box during fall. Then, when the box stops instantaneously, mass $m_i$ has a kinetic energy resulting from downward velocity of $gm_ih$, where $g$ is gravitational acceleration and $h$ is the drop distance. The maximum relative displacement, $\delta_i$, of this mass occurs a short time later when the kinetic energy is transformed into potential energy of spring compression, i.e.,

$$\tfrac{1}{2}k_i\delta_i^2 = gm_ih$$

Since the natural angular frequency, $\omega_i$, of the $i$th oscillator is

$$\omega_i = \sqrt{\frac{k_i}{m_i}}$$

then

$$\delta_i = \frac{1}{\omega_i}\sqrt{2gh}$$

But since the maximum velocity of all the oscillators is $V_{\max} = \sqrt{2gh}$, we have

$$\delta_i = \frac{V_{\max}}{\omega_i} \qquad (3\text{-}1)$$

Shock spectra are usually plotted on special log-log paper, and from such plots, maximum accelerations can be found directly. A plotting of $\delta$ versus $f = \omega/2\pi$ from Eq. (3-1) on such paper is shown in Fig. 3-2, where $V = 1.0$ m/s. The peak acceleration experienced by each oscillator may also be read directly from the figure. The lines of constant acceleration are those with $-45°$ slope, and the lines of constant displacement are those with $+45°$ slope.

This log-log paper takes into account the characteristics of the freely vibrating simple oscillator by the way in which the three coordinates intersect.

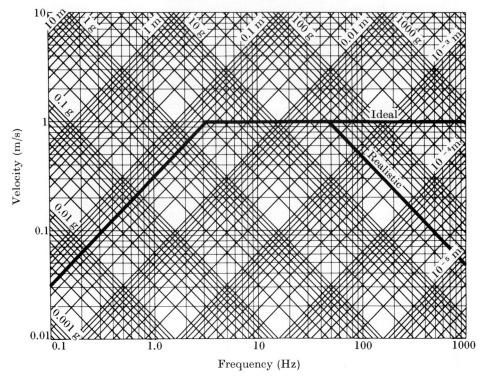

**Fig. 3-2**   Response spectrum for a drop test.

That is, the maximum displacement, velocity, and acceleration amplitudes of a freely vibrating simple oscillator are related by

$$\text{Maximum displacement} = \frac{V_{\max}}{2\pi f}$$

$$\text{Maximum acceleration} = 2\pi f V_{\max}$$

where $f$ is the frequency in Hz.  The shock spectrum paper used throughout this chapter uses the units m, m/s, g, and Hz for the four quantities.  The left-hand or velocity axis has meaning only for a drop test such as the one discussed.  The shock spectrum resulting from impact with an ideal rigid table is a horizontal line, as shown in Fig. 3-2, since all masses are moving with the same velocity at the instant of impact.  A low-frequency, constant-displacement cutoff occurs with a maximum displacement equal to the drop height, $h$.  Also, in a real drop test, the table is found to possess some resilience.  As shown in the figure, an actual shock spectrum follows the ideal result out to an acceleration corresponding to the maximum dynamic load-carrying capacity of the table; then it drops off approximately along a constant acceleration line.

For example, when the drop-test box strikes an ideal, rigid table with an impact velocity of 1 m/s, as shown in Fig. 3-2, the mass of a 100-Hz oscillator would experience a peak acceleration of 63 g's and a displacement of 0.17 cm. In the more realistic case, however, the oscillator mass would see only 30 g's and about 0.075 cm displacement. A fall of 5.1 cm corresponds to an impact velocity of 1 m/s and, since no oscillator will have an amplitude greater than the drop height, there is a constant-displacement, low-frequency cutoff at 0.051 m in Fig. 3-2.

For convenience, a page-size copy of the shock spectrum chart appears as Fig. A-3 in Appendix A. For those more experienced with English units, Fig. A-4 presents a chart for use with this system. The usefulness of these charts, and of a shock spectrum as an input representation, will be discussed more fully later.

## VIBRATORY LOADING

Loadings which persist indefinitely, compared to the time required for the structure to damp out the response of a transient input, are called *vibratory*. Movements during shipping or motion due to rotating machinery are examples. These loadings are either periodic, such as those from rotating machinery, or aperiodic, such as those from shipping. With periodic inputs, the time histories are represented simply by a sum of sinusoidally time-varying terms.

Vibratory loadings are the kind that cause fatigue failures, and a description of the application of fatigue concepts to random excitations is presented thoroughly by Harris and Crede.[1] This reference also discusses statistical vibrations analysis, as does Crandall[2,3] in much more detail.

Shipping, the major cause of aperiodic vibration of electronic equipment, is usually not considered as a statistical problem. Harris and Crede[1] present vibration characteristics of trucks and rail vehicles in terms of peak accelerations and displacements to be expected for various shipping conditions. The implication is that a device being shipped for installation will probably not undergo a sufficient number of stress reversals to produce fatigue failure. However, if the device is to be permanently attached to such a vehicle, the number of stress reversals becomes important, and the device should be designed to operate at stress levels below its fatigue limit.

## 3-2. DISCRETE SYSTEMS

To discuss structural dynamics in any detail, the response of some basic systems must first be presented. A discrete system is the basic vibratory configuration. It is made up of a number of rigid masses separated by finite distances and interconnected with massless resilient members.

## SYSTEMS WITH A SINGLE DEGREE OF FREEDOM

The simplest of such systems is the simple mechanical oscillator, in which a single mass, $m$, is attached to some reference point, $A$, by a linearly elastic spring, $k$ [see Fig. 3-3(a)]. It is assumed that the mass and $A$ can move only in

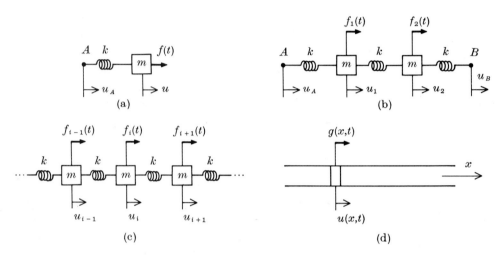

**Fig. 3-3**   Various vibrational systems.

the horizontal direction, and their displacements from the static equilibrium position are given by $u$ and $u_A$, respectively. A force, $f(t)$, may be applied directly to the mass as well. Since the spring force acting to the right is $k(u_A - u)$, a dynamic force balance gives

$$k(u_A - u) + f = m\,\frac{d^2u}{dt^2}$$

or

$$m\,\frac{d^2u}{dt^2} + ku = ku_A + f \qquad (3\text{-}2)$$

Since motion of $A$ and the force $f$ have the same effect on the mass, we will, for brevity, examine $f$ only and assume $u_A = 0$. We will examine $f$ in the form

$$f(t) = F \sin \omega t$$

where $F$ and $\omega$ are constants; any $f$ can be constructed from a combination of such functions by Fourier series or integrals.

The solution to the inhomogeneous equation is obtained by assuming $u_I = U \sin \omega t$, and gives, with Eq. (3-2),

$$-m\omega^2 U + kU = F$$

when $\sin \omega t$ has been canceled; or, solving for $U$,

$$u_I(t) = U \sin \omega t = \frac{F}{k - m\omega^2} \sin \omega t \qquad (3\text{-}3)$$

This is the steady-state solution which neglects the transient response caused by starting the motion. Thus, this solution is assumed to apply when the time at which the motion of the mass is to be examined occurs long after the excitation $f$ was started. Any linear elastic system of finite extent, such as this simple oscillator, loaded by a harmonic system of in-phase forces will respond harmonically and in phase in the steady state. That is, if the forcing functions all have time variation $\sin \omega t$, the response will also have time variation $\sin \omega t$.

If we need information about the response soon after the loading began, the complete solution must be used, and it must satisfy the general initial conditions

$$u \big|_{t=0} = U_0, \qquad \frac{du}{dt} \bigg|_{t=0} = V_0$$

Since the result of Eq. (3-2) will not, in general, satisfy these conditions, the homogeneous solutions must be included, i.e., $u_H$, which satisfies

$$m \frac{d^2 u_H}{dt^2} + k u_H = 0$$

and which has the solution

$$u_H = C_1 \sin \sqrt{\frac{k}{m}} \, t + C_2 \cos \sqrt{\frac{k}{m}} \, t$$

Then the initial conditions and Eq. (3-2) are satisfied by

$$u = u_I + u_H = \frac{F}{k - m\omega^2} \sin \omega t + C_1 \sin \sqrt{\frac{k}{m}} \, t + C_2 \cos \sqrt{\frac{k}{m}} \, t \qquad (3\text{-}4)$$

where

$$C_1 = \sqrt{\frac{m}{k}} \left( V_0 - \frac{F\omega}{k - m\omega^2} \right)$$

$$C_2 = U_0$$

Of course, the reason that the steady-state solution has physical meaning by itself, even though it is not the complete solution, is that every real oscillator has a little damping. If the damping is small enough, the solution will look almost the same as Eq. (3-4), except that $C_1$ and $C_2$ will be multiplied by $e^{-\gamma t}$, where $\gamma$ is very small and positive. Thus, after a long time under the load $f$, those terms would disappear and only the steady-state solution would remain.

When the frequency, $\omega$, of the applied force is equal to the natural frequency, $\sqrt{k/m}$, the denominator of the first term in Eq. (3-4) is zero.

However, the part of the second term $(C_1)$ containing this denominator adds to the first term to produce the indeterminate $0/0$ situation. Applying L'Hospital's rule gives a vibration with amplitude linearly increasing indefinitely with time for the elastic case. This is resonance, of course, and it is a condition to be avoided in practice. A system of any order of complexity should not have any of its natural frequencies near a forcing frequency.

## SYSTEMS WITH MORE THAN ONE DEGREE OF FREEDOM

When more than one mass, or one mass with more than one degree of freedom,* must be considered, the interesting modal concept appears. The simplest two-degree-of-freedom system is shown in Fig. 3-3(b), where the masses and springs are each located by means of a single coordinate dimension. Dynamic equilibrium written for the two masses gives

$$m \frac{d^2 u_1}{dt^2} + 2ku_1 - ku_2 = f_1 + ku_A \qquad (3\text{-}5a)$$

$$m \frac{d^2 u_2}{dt^2} + 2ku_2 - ku_1 = f_2 + ku_B \qquad (3\text{-}5b)$$

Again assuming $u_A = u_B = 0$; $f_1 = F_1 \sin \omega_1 t$; $f_2 = F_2 \sin \omega_2 t$; $u_1 = U_{11} \sin \omega_1 t + U_{12} \sin \omega_2 t$; and $u_2 = U_{21} \sin \omega_1 t + U_{22} \sin \omega_2 t$, the steady-state solution is found to be

$$u_1 = \frac{(2k - m\omega_1^2)F_1}{(2k - m\omega_1^2)^2 - k^2} \sin \omega_1 t + \frac{kF_2}{(2k - m\omega_2^2)^2 - k^2} \sin \omega_2 t$$

$$u_2 = \frac{kF_1}{(2k - m\omega_1^2)^2 - k^2} \sin \omega_1 t + \frac{(2k - m\omega_2^2)F_2}{(2k - m\omega_2^2)^2 - k^2} \sin \omega_2 t$$

The homogeneous solution, for unforced vibration, may be found by assuming that $u_1 = C \sin \omega t$ and $u_2 = D \sin \omega t$ in Eq. (3-5) when the right-hand sides are set to zero. Making this substitution gives

$$-m\omega^2 C + k(2C - D) = 0 \qquad (3\text{-}6a)$$

$$-m\omega^2 D + k(2D - C) = 0 \qquad (3\text{-}6b)$$

For such a solution to be nontrivial, the determinant of the coefficients of $C$ and $D$ must equal zero, or

$$m^2 \omega^4 - 4km\omega^2 + 3k^2 = 0$$

---

* The number of degrees of freedom for a rigid body or for a system of rigid bodies is the minimum number of spatial coordinates (linear and rotational) necessary to describe the position of the body or bodies in space.

Thus, the values of $\omega$ for which the assumed solution exists are

$$\omega = \pm \sqrt{\frac{k}{m}(2 \pm 1)}$$

$$= \pm \sqrt{\frac{3k}{m}}, \qquad \pm \sqrt{\frac{k}{m}} \tag{3-7}$$

Since precisely the same relations would have been obtained had cos $\omega t$ been assumed instead of sin $\omega t$, the general homogeneous solution for $u_1$ may be written as a sum of sine and cosine terms:

$$u_1 = C_1 \sin\sqrt{\frac{3k}{m}}\,t + C_2 \cos\sqrt{\frac{3k}{m}}\,t + C_3 \sin\sqrt{\frac{k}{m}}\,t + C_4 \cos\sqrt{\frac{k}{m}}\,t$$

By substituting Eq. (3-7) in either part of Eq. (3-6), a relationship between $C$ and $D$ for each frequency gives $u_2$ in terms of the $C$'s as

$$u_2 = -C_1 \sin\sqrt{\frac{3k}{m}}\,t - C_2 \cos\sqrt{\frac{3k}{m}}\,t + C_3 \sin\sqrt{\frac{k}{m}}\,t + C_4 \cos\sqrt{\frac{k}{m}}\,t$$

The modal quality of this system now becomes apparent. By the word modal we refer to a motion of the system which can be described by a single frequency. The above solution is the superposition of two modes of vibration. The four $C$'s are determined by the four initial conditions on $u_1$ and $u_2$, but the resulting motion has a peculiar property. For that part of the homogeneous solution oscillating at a frequency $\sqrt{3k/m}$, $u_1 = -u_2$; while for that part oscillating at a frequency $\sqrt{k/m}$, $u_1 = u_2$. This result suggests a transformation of Eq. (2-40) (still assuming $u_A = u_B = 0$). By adding and subtracting Eq. (2-40) and substituting $\zeta = u_1 - u_2$, $\eta = u_1 + u_2$, we obtain

$$m\frac{d^2\zeta}{dt^2} + 3k\zeta = f_1 - f_2 \tag{3-8a}$$

$$m\frac{d^2\eta}{dt^2} + k\eta = f_1 + f_2 \tag{3-8b}$$

The two equations are now independent of each other or "uncoupled" and are in the form of Eq. (3-2) for the simple oscillator. Of course, we solved two coupled equations to obtain the mode shapes (i.e., $C_1 = -D_1$ and $C_3 = D_3$, etc.) necessary to determine the proper substitution to decouple the equations. Even so, this decoupling becomes very helpful for general discussions of a particular configuration and also in obtaining solutions to some complex problems. Furthermore, it is always possible to decouple linearly elastic discrete systems of a finite number of degrees of freedom.

A more straightforward way of decoupling is through use of matrix algebra. In the general case, equilibrium equations corresponding to Eq. (3-5) for $n$ degrees of freedom are:

$$m_{11} \frac{d^2 u_1}{dt^2} + m_{12} \frac{d^2 u_2}{dt^2} + \cdots + k_{11} u_1 + k_{12} u_2 + \cdots + k_{1n} u_n = f_1$$

$$m_{21} \frac{d^2 u_1}{dt^2} + m_{22} \frac{d^2 u_2}{dt^2} + \cdots + k_{21} u_1 + k_{22} u_2 + \cdots + k_{2n} u_n = f_2$$

$$m_{n1} \frac{d^2 u_1}{dt^2} + m_{n2} \frac{d^2 u_2}{dt^2} + \cdots + k_{n1} u_1 + k_{n2} u_2 + \cdots + k_{nn} u_n = f_n$$

These may be rewritten in matrix notations as

$$M \frac{d^2 U}{dt^2} + KU = F \tag{3-9}$$

where

$$M = \begin{bmatrix} m_{11} & m_{12} & \cdots & m_{1n} \\ m_{21} & m_{22} & \cdots & m_{2n} \\ \cdot & \cdot & \cdot & \cdot \\ \cdot & \cdot & \cdot & \cdot \\ \cdot & \cdot & \cdot & \cdot \\ m_{n1} & m_{n2} & \cdots & m_{nn} \end{bmatrix}, \quad U = \begin{bmatrix} u_1 \\ u_2 \\ \cdot \\ \cdot \\ \cdot \\ u_n \end{bmatrix}$$

$$K = \begin{bmatrix} k_{11} & k_{12} & \cdots & k_{1n} \\ k_{21} & k_{22} & \cdots & k_{2n} \\ \cdot & \cdot & \cdot & \cdot \\ \cdot & \cdot & \cdot & \cdot \\ \cdot & \cdot & \cdot & \cdot \\ k_{n1} & k_{n2} & \cdots & k_{nn} \end{bmatrix}, \quad F = \begin{bmatrix} f_1 \\ f_2 \\ \cdot \\ \cdot \\ \cdot \\ f_n \end{bmatrix}$$

Matrix algebra[4] tells us that it is always possible to find a single transformation which will diagonalize two matrices if they are both real and symmetric and if at least one is positive definite. Fortunately, physical considerations always require that these conditions be satisfied for the discrete systems discussed here. If $Q$ is such a transformation matrix, then with $U = QZ$ substituted into Eq. (3-9), it becomes

$$MQ \frac{d^2 Z}{dt^2} + KQZ = F$$

where

$$Z = \begin{bmatrix} \zeta_1 \\ \zeta_2 \\ \cdot \\ \cdot \\ \cdot \\ \zeta_n \end{bmatrix}$$

Premultiplying by $Q^{-1}$ gives

$$\bar{M}\frac{d^2Z}{dt^2} + \bar{K}Z = Q^{-1}F = \bar{F} \tag{3-10}$$

where $\bar{M} = Q^{-1}MQ$, $\bar{K} = Q^{-1}KQ$, and both are diagonalized. That is, the equation has been put into canonical form, and the algebraic equations generated by Eq. (3-10) are all of the form

$$\bar{m}_i\frac{d^2\zeta_i}{dt^2} + \bar{k}_i\zeta_i = \bar{f}_i$$

These may be solved by all of the techniques applicable to the simple oscillator problem. Of course, in general, each $\zeta$ equals a linear algebraic sum of all the $u$'s. The $\bar{f}$'s are also linear sums of the $f$'s. Examples of the usefulness of this development will be presented in the sections on applications. Computation centers normally have a program which will very quickly generate $\bar{M}$ and $\bar{K}$, given $M$ and $K$.

Systems with multiple degrees of freedom are frequently encountered in electronics. An example is shown in Fig. 3-4. The three ferrite sheets in each horizontal row are interconnected with 0.25-mm diameter copper wires with

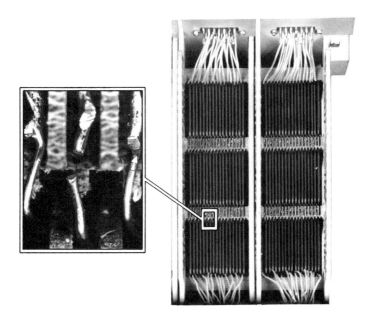

**Fig. 3-4** Partially disassembled ferrite sheet memory showing fatigue failure. Enlarged view of the area in the rectangle illustrates failure of the jumper wire. A crack which appears to be an incipient failure of a second wire is just visible at the point of the arrow.

soldered joints in the centers of the spans. The sheets are supported at the edges in slots which provide about 0.025-cm vertical clearance so that slightly warped sheets will not be strained. During vibration, the sheets can move independently within the limits of the slots, except as restrained by the "springs"—in this case, the interconnecting wires. The design was suspected of weakness after occasional opens had been found following shipment, and tests confirmed that breakage of some wires would occur after vibration at 4 g's in the 55- to 200-Hz range. The design was strengthened by the addition of a rubbery compound at the edges of the sheets to substantially prevent motion without straining them.

## 3-3. CONTINUOUS SYSTEMS

Many structures can be analyzed as discrete systems with reasonable accuracy. Equipment units supported by shock mounts or in resilient packaging to protect against handling shock are often in this category. However, when the distortion of members containing appreciable distributed mass must be examined, a continuum approach is usually necessary. Unfortunately, obtaining solutions to continuous problems for systems more complex than the simple beam and plate solutions available in textbooks usually introduces a great deal of mathematical difficulty. In fact, only recently have the more complex static beam and plate models been investigated dynamically. Young,[5] Chap. 61, gives a good list of references on many aspects of this problem. Nevertheless, a few general comments may be in order. The simple dynamic rod, beam, and plate solutions are reasonably accurate when the wavelengths are long compared to the small dimensions of these items. When these wavelengths approach the same size as the small dimension, as they do under impact loadings or very-high-frequency excitation, significant inaccuracies appear. Also, solutions for stresses become inaccurate in cases for which the displacement solutions appear to be accurate because the stresses depend on derivatives of displacements and are affected more strongly by higher-frequency modes— the modes least accurately represented. However, because high frequencies are usually damped out sooner than lower frequencies, reasonable accuracy from simple solutions is possible when the point of interest is a large distance from the point of impact.

The wave propagation approach can sometimes be of direct use, and this case will be discussed briefly here. The continuous case may always be considered the limiting form of the discrete case. For example, the dynamic equilibrium for horizontal motions of the mass point $i$ in Fig. 3-3(c) may be written

$$m \frac{d^2 u_i}{dt^2} + k(2u_i - u_{i-1} - u_{i+1}) = f_i$$

Using difference notation, this becomes

$$m \frac{d^2u(ih)}{dt^2} - k\delta^2 u(ih) = f_i \qquad (3\text{-}11)$$

where $\delta^2$ is the second central difference operator,[4] and where $h$ is the static equilibrium distance between the masses, assumed uniform. Dividing Eq. (3-11) by $h$ gives

$$\frac{m}{h} \frac{d^2u(ih)}{dt^2} - \frac{kh}{h^2} \delta^2 u(ih) = \frac{f_i}{h} \qquad (3\text{-}12)$$

Referring to Fig. 3-3(d), we now assume that the number of mass points becomes infinitely large and infinitesimally close together. The mass per unit length, $m/h$, remains equal to the constant $\rho A$, and the excitation force per unit length, $f_i/h$, does not change but may now be represented by the continuous function, $g(x, t)$. Equation (2-47) then becomes

$$\rho A \frac{\partial^2 u(x, t)}{\partial t^2} - AE \frac{\partial^2 u(x, t)}{\partial x^2} = g(x, t) \qquad (3\text{-}13)$$

where $AE$ is another arbitrary constant. It is well known[4] that

$$\lim_{h \to 0} \frac{\delta^2 u(ih)}{h^2} = \frac{\partial^2 u(x)}{\partial x^2}$$

The fact that $kh$ is a constant may be seen if we recall that the stiffness of an ideal spring varies inversely with the length when the other spring dimensions do not change.

The choice of the letters for the constants $\rho A$ and $AE$ above was due to the fact that Eq. (3-13) now represents the equation for dynamic longitudinal distortion of a continuous uniform rod. The foregoing derivation of the rod equation was used because it shows (although in the reverse direction) one way of approximating a continuous member by a discrete system; it shows also that the approximation approaches the exact situation as the number of discrete elements increases. More will be presented on this question in the next section.

The form of the solution of Eq. (3-13) to be discussed here may be written

$$u(x, t) = r(x - v_s t) + s(x + v_s t) \qquad (3\text{-}14)$$

which satisfies the homogeneous form, i.e., $g = 0$, or

$$\rho \frac{\partial^2 u}{\partial t^2} = E \frac{\partial^2 u}{\partial x^2} \qquad (3\text{-}15)$$

when

$$v_s = \sqrt{\frac{E}{\rho}}$$

Substitution shows that Eq. (3-14) satisfies Eq. (3-15) when the functions $r$ and $s$ are twice differentiable. A more complicated proof is necessary if $r$ and $s$ are discontinuous, as they frequently are in practice. If $r(x)$ is plotted along the $x$ axis, then $r(x - v_s t)$ becomes a wave of the same shape which propagates in the $+x$ direction with a speed $v_s$; and $s(x + v_s t)$ has the shape $s(x)$ and propagates in the $-x$ direction with speed $v_s$. Thus, the constant $v_s$ is the velocity of elastic (sound) wave propagation. Such solutions most easily represent the displacements of an infinite rod which experiences initial displacement and velocity distributions. It is interesting to note that the stress, $\sigma$, satisfies the same homogeneous equation, since

$$\sigma = \sigma_{xx} = E\,\epsilon_{xx} = E\,\frac{\partial u}{\partial x} \tag{3-16}$$

and since differentiating Eq. (3-15) with respect to $x$ and making the above substitution gives

$$\rho\,\frac{\partial^2 \sigma}{\partial t^2} = E\,\frac{\partial^2 \sigma}{\partial x^2}$$

A stress wave is thus associated with a displacement wave at all points by Eq. (3-16), and it propagates at the same speed.

However, we are interested in structures of finite length, loaded at their ends. First let us examine a rod with its left-hand end forced in such a way that the displacement there has the time history $u_0(t)$ [see Fig. 3-5(a)]. Disregarding

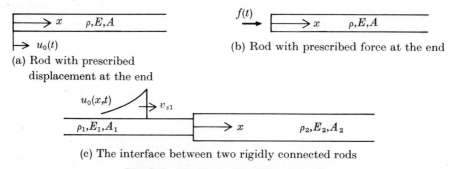

(a) Rod with prescribed
    displacement at the end

(b) Rod with prescribed force at the end

(c) The interface between two rigidly connected rods

**Fig. 3-5**   Mechanical loading of a rod.

interactions at the other end for the moment, the solution is simply

$$u(x, t) = u_0\!\left(t - \frac{x}{v_s}\right) \tag{3-17}$$

for the entire rod. Next, let us examine a rod loaded by a time-varying force $f(t)$ at its left-hand end [see Fig. 3-5(b)]. Again, disregarding interactions at the other end, the solution may be obtained as follows. Function $u$ has the form

$$u = u(x - v_s t)$$

but the external force must equal the internal force at $x = 0$, or

$$EA \left. \frac{\partial u}{\partial x} \right|_{x=0} = EA\, u'\,(-v_s t) = -f(t) = -f\left(\frac{-v_s t}{-v_s}\right)$$

where the prime denotes differentiation of $u$ with respect to the argument, and the minus sign preceding $f(t)$ results from the sign convention for stresses. Then

$$EA\, u'\,(x - v_s t) = -f\left(\frac{x - v_s t}{-v_s}\right)$$

or

$$u(x - v_s t) = \frac{v_s}{EA} \int^{t-x/v_s} f(\eta)\, d\eta + \text{constant} \tag{3-18}$$

The constant can be evaluated if we know how long the loading has been applied. For example, assume

$$f(t) = \begin{cases} 0, & t < 0 \\ \sin \omega t, & t \geq 0 \end{cases}$$

Then

$$u = \frac{v_s}{EA} \int^{t-x/v_s} \sin \omega \eta\, d\eta + \text{constant}$$

$$= \frac{-v_s}{\omega EA} \cos \omega\left(t - \frac{x}{v_s}\right) + \text{constant}$$

Requiring that the displacement at the end be zero for $t \leq 0$ gives

$$u = \begin{cases} 0, & t - \dfrac{x}{v_s} < 0 \\[2mm] \dfrac{v_s}{\omega EA}\left[1 - \cos \omega\left(t - \dfrac{x}{v_s}\right)\right], & t - \dfrac{x}{v_s} \geq 0 \end{cases}$$

In this case, the stress wave generated is, of course, merely

$$\sigma(x, t) = -\frac{1}{A} f\left(t - \frac{x}{v_s}\right) \tag{3-19}$$

Let us now examine what takes place at the other end. Consider the general case of one rod with properties $E_1$, $\rho_1$, and area $A_1$ terminating in another rod of properties $E_2$, $\rho_2$, and area $A_2$ [see Fig. 3-5(c)]. Assume that a displacement wave $u_0(x - v_{s1} t)$ approaches the interface from the left. Two boundary conditions must be satisfied at $x = 0$ (i.e., at the interface): (1) the displacement on both sides of $x = 0$ must be the same, and (2) the forces across $x = 0$ must be in equilibrium. Since the one-dimensional wave equation is being used, no account can be taken of the three-dimensional effects caused by a change in area as shown.

The boundary conditions are satisfied by the assumption that a reflected wave $u_1(x + v_{s1}t)$ travels to the left from the boundary and that a transmitted wave $u_2(x - v_{s2}t)$ travels to the right into the second medium. The displacement on the left of the boundary is the sum of the incident and reflected waves or $u_0 + u_1$, and the displacement boundary condition requires

$$u_0(-v_{s1}t) + u_1(v_{s1}t) = u_2(-v_{s2}t) \tag{3-20}$$

The force condition requires

$$A_1 E_1 \left( \frac{\partial u_0}{\partial x} + \frac{\partial u_1}{\partial x} \right)_{x=0} = A_2 E_2 \left( \frac{\partial u_2}{\partial x} \right)_{x=0} \tag{3-21}$$

Since the argument of each of the $u$'s is of the form $x + v_s t$, then

$$\frac{\partial u}{\partial x} = u'$$

where the prime denotes differentiation of $u$ with respect to the argument. Equation (3-21) becomes

$$A_1 E_1 [u_0'(-v_{s1}t) + u_1'(v_{s1}t)] = A_2 E_2\, u_2'(-v_{s2}t)$$

Differentiating through Eq. (2-55) with respect to $t$ gives

$$-v_{s1} u_0'(-v_{s1}t) + v_{s1} u_1'(v_{s1}t) = -v_{s2} u_2'(-v_{s2}t)$$

Functions $u_1'$ and $u_2'$ may then be found from the previous two equations as

$$u_1'(v_{s1}t) = \frac{z_{12} - 1}{z_{12} + 1}\, u_0'(-v_{s1}t) \tag{3-22}$$

and

$$u_2'(-v_{s2}t) = \frac{v_{s1}}{v_{s2}} \frac{2}{z_{12} + 1} u_0'(-v_{s1}t) \tag{3-23}$$

where

$$z_{12} = \frac{v_{s1}}{v_{s2}} \frac{A_2 E_2}{A_1 E_1} = \frac{A_2}{A_1} \sqrt{\frac{\rho_2 E_2}{\rho_1 E_1}}$$

After multiplying through by $dt$, we may write Eq. (3-23) as:

$$u_2'(v)\, dv = \frac{2}{z_{12} + 1}\, u_0'(w)\, dw$$

where $v = -v_{s2}t$ and $w = -v_{s1}t$. Integrating both sides to the upper limit $t$ gives

$$u_2(-v_{s2}t) = \frac{2}{z_{12} + 1}\, u_0(-v_{s1}t)$$

or

$$u_2(-v_{s2}t) = \frac{2}{z_{12} + 1}\, u_0\left(-v_{s2}t\, \frac{v_{s1}}{v_{s2}}\right)$$

so that

$$u_2(x - v_{s2}t) = \frac{2}{z_{12} + 1} u_0\left[\frac{v_{s1}}{v_{s2}}(x - v_{s2}t)\right] \qquad (3\text{-}24)$$

This shows that the transmitted displacement wave has the same form as the incident wave, but its amplitude is changed. It is stretched out or shrunken in the $x$ direction according to $v_{s1}/v_{s2}$, and it travels at speed $v_{s2}$ (see Fig. 3-6).

Similarly, Eq. (2-57) becomes

$$u_1(x + v_{s1}t) = \frac{1 - z_{12}}{1 + z_{12}} u_0[-(x + v_{s1}t)] \qquad (3\text{-}25)$$

This shows that the reflected wave is also reflected mathematically about the interface relative to the incident wave (because of the minus sign in the argument) and is negative or positive, depending on whether $z_{12}$ is greater or smaller than 1. Figure 3-6 shows displacement waves for two of the possible situations.

Equation (3-16) then allows us to determine stress wave interactions from the preceding results directly. For an incident stress wave,

$$\sigma_0(x - v_{s1}t) = E_1 u_0'(x - v_{s1}t)$$

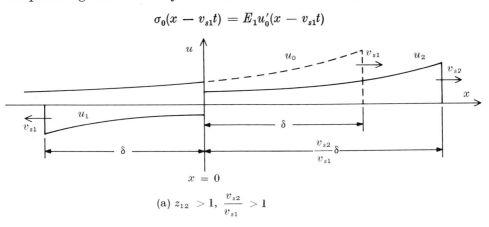

(a) $z_{12} > 1$, $\dfrac{v_{s2}}{v_{s1}} > 1$

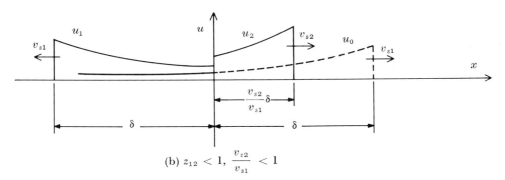

(b) $z_{12} < 1$, $\dfrac{v_{s2}}{v_{s1}} < 1$

**Fig. 3-6**  Displacement wave interaction.

The reflected stress wave $\sigma_1$ is

$$\sigma_1 = E_1 u_1'(x + v_{s1}t) = -E_1 \frac{1 - z_{12}}{1 + z_{12}} u_0'[-(x - v_{s1}t)]$$

$$= \frac{z_{12} - 1}{z_{12} + 1} \sigma_0[-(x + v_{s1}t)] \qquad (3\text{-}26)$$

and the transmitted wave $\sigma_2$ becomes

$$\sigma_2 = E_2 u_2'(x - v_{s2}t) = \frac{2E_2}{z_{12} + 1} \frac{v_{s1}}{v_{s2}} u_0'\left[\frac{v_{s1}}{v_{s2}}(x - v_{s2}t)\right]$$

$$= \frac{2}{z_{12} + 1} \frac{E_2 v_{s1}}{E_2 v_{s2}} \sigma_0\left[\frac{v_{s1}}{v_{s2}}(x - v_{s2}t)\right]$$

$$= \frac{2(A_1/A_2)z_{12}}{z_{12} + 1} \sigma_0\left[\frac{v_{s1}}{v_{s2}}(x - v_{s2}t)\right] \qquad (3\text{-}27)$$

Figure 3-7 shows the stress interactions for the same cases discussed in Fig. 3-6 for displacements. Setting $z_{12} = 0$ or $\infty$ gives results for the free- or

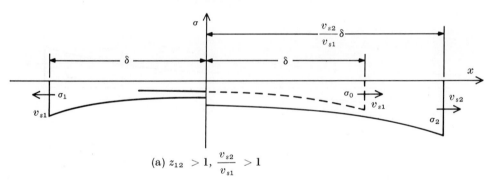

(a) $z_{12} > 1$, $\dfrac{v_{s2}}{v_{s1}} > 1$

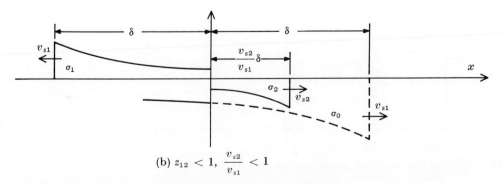

(b) $z_{12} < 1$, $\dfrac{v_{s2}}{v_{s1}} < 1$

**Fig. 3-7**  Stress wave interaction.

fixed-end condition, respectively, for both stresses and displacements. Two interesting conclusions can be drawn from examining Figs. 3-6 and 3-7:

1. From Fig. 3-6(b), the transmitted displacement wave will have greater magnitude when the wave travels from a stiffer to a less stiff material.
2. From Fig. 3-7(a), the transmitted stress wave may have greater magnitude (depending on $A_1/A_2$) when the wave travels from a less stiff to a stiffer material.

An example of the use of one-dimensional wave solutions will now be given.

**Example 3.1.** A solenoid with armature mass $m$ is attached to a structural member in a piece of equipment as shown in Fig. 3-8. It is attached in such a

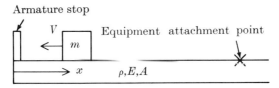

**Fig. 3-8**  Solenoid impact problem.

way that, when the solenoid operates, the armature strikes a stop which is rigidly connected to the structure. Assume that it strikes this stop with velocity $V$. Assume further that some rather delicate equipment is attached to another part of the structure. It is of interest to estimate the motion of this equipment attachment point and the resulting equipment loading due to solenoid operation.

The force time history required to stop the armature is ideally an impulse (very large force $f$ of very short duration $\Delta t$) of value $\int f \, dt = mV$. Equation (3-18) was developed for this case and shown that the displacement wave propagating along the rod is

$$u(x - v_s t) = \frac{-v_s}{EA} \int^{t - x/V_s} f(\eta) \, d\eta + \text{constant}$$

In this case, $f$ is the impulse or

$$f = mV \, \delta(x - v_s t)$$

so that

$$u(x - v_s t) = -v_s \frac{mV}{EA} U\!\left(t - \frac{x}{v_s}\right)$$

where $\delta$ is the unit impulse function and $U$ is the unit step function. The constant is zero because there is no motion prior to wave arrival. This result states that each point in the rod steps to the left a distance

$$v_s \frac{mV}{EA} = \frac{mV}{A\sqrt{E\rho}}$$

as the wave passes. For the case of a 50-gram armature which strikes at a velocity of 2 m/s and a steel structural member with a cross-sectional area of 0.4 cm², the magnitude of this motion is

$$\frac{0.05 \times 2}{0.4 \times 10^{-4}\sqrt{207 \times 10^9 \times 7850}} = 62 \times 10^{-6}\,\text{m} \quad (0.00244\ \text{in.})$$

It is easy to see that a step displacement input appears as a line of constant displacement on shock spectrum paper (because, no matter what the frequency, any simple oscillator will oscillate with the input step amplitude). Figure 3-9 plots these results. If the maximum acceleration the equipment can with-

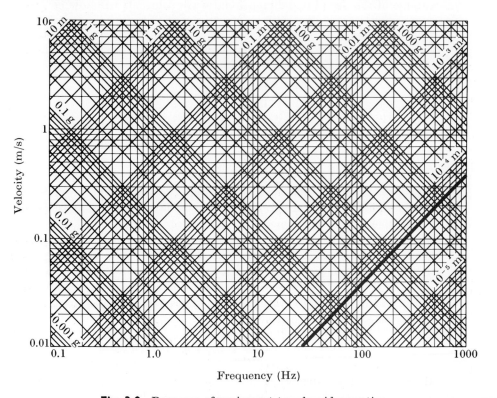

**Fig. 3-9**  Response of equipment to solenoid operation.

stand is 3 g's (a commonly quoted value for electronic equipment), then the shock spectrum shows that the equipment must have a natural frequency less than about 110 Hz. Otherwise, some resilient mounting should be considered for the equipment. This is a conservative analysis since the mass of the equipment may reduce its response; nevertheless, it is a good rough estimate.

Suppose the rod had extended to the left beyond the armature stop in Fig. 3-8. If other conditions remain the same, an impulsive tensile wave of half the magnitude previously discussed would travel to the right, while a compressive wave of the same magnitude would travel to the left. Such a result may be obtained analytically by considering the point $x = 0$ to be an interface and by requiring that the displacements match at the interface, but requiring also that the forces differ by $f$. If there had been joints or changes in the structural cross section or material between the armature stop and the equipment, a change in the magnitude of the wave transmitted to the equipment could be estimated by the results previously calculated for wave interactions at an interface.

While the preceding example involving shock transmission from a solenoid to delicate equipment on a common mounting bar may be met only occasionally in equipment design, it illustrates an approach to the analysis of a class of shock-transmission problems that is quite common. Sources of shock include relays; electrically and manually operated switches; collision with external bodies during maintenance, installation, or shipment; etc.

## DISTINGUISHING BETWEEN DYNAMIC AND QUASISTATIC CASES BY WAVE PROPAGATION TIMES

In Sec. 2.5 we discussed the importance of distinguishing between time-variant problems that must be analyzed dynamically, and those that can be handled statically with time-variant inputs. The method of answering this question is sometimes uncertain since it requires a good estimate of the quasistatic stress field to determine the relative importance of the various terms in the equations of motion. Another, more practical approach to this problem follows.

Physically, a problem is static if the body experiencing a time-variant load can completely adjust itself to each incremental change in the load before the next such increment is applied. If the effects of each incremental load change have been carried throughout the body by stress and displacement waves before the next increment is felt, then the body is able to adjust itself and can maintain static equilibrium.

If, then, we can estimate the time it takes for a stress wave carrying the kind of distortion energy of interest to traverse a body in its longest dimension, we have a way of estimating the time required for a body to reach equilibrium. However, this adjustment cannot be completed by only the first wave, because of this wave's continuing refraction and reflection. For this reason, at least ten wave traversals should be allowed so that static equilibrium can be attained during the load rise time. The time for a stress wave to traverse the structure, estimated from the wave velocities below, gives an order-of-magnitude value for the fundamental period of vibration of uniform structures. If the structures have very much mass attached, so that they cannot be considered uniform, the traverse time of the fundamental wave should be determined by the methods of the section, to follow, on reducing continuous systems to discrete systems. Ten times this value should then be compared to the loading rise time.

**Tension and Compression.** The previous section includes a discussion of the propagation of longitudinal waves in rods, and the speed of propagation was found to be $\sqrt{E/\rho}$. In an infinite medium, the same kinds of waves travel at a speed of $\sqrt{(\lambda + 2G)/\rho}$, where $\lambda$ is the Lamé constant of Eq. (2-21). This speed may be as much as 50 percent greater than $\sqrt{E/\rho}$ because the rod is free to contract transversely, which an infinite medium cannot do. To be conservative (that is, to use the lower speed), $\sqrt{E/\rho}$ should be used to estimate the response times of bodies in which pure tensile and compressional waves are important. These include longitudinally loaded rods, in-plane loads on plates, and loadings on bulky bodies.

**Shear.** Shear waves propagate at a speed of $\sqrt{G/\rho}$. This value may be half $\sqrt{E/\rho}$ for some materials, so the proper expression, $\sqrt{G/\rho}$, should be used in shear problems, such as torsional motion.

**Bending.** The speed of propagation of tensile and shear waves is independent of the wavelength, in first order theory at least, as we have seen. However, the speed of propagation of bending waves decreases with increasing wavelength, even in the simplest bending theories. It then becomes necessary to use the speed of the longest wavelength of importance, which cannot be too much larger than the largest dimension of the body. This argument results in using

$$\frac{\pi h}{l}\sqrt{\frac{E}{12\rho}}$$

for the bending wave speed in estimating bending response times for a solid structure, where $h$ is the structure thickness in the plane of bending and $l$ is the largest dimension. The expression

$$\frac{\pi}{l}\sqrt{\frac{EI}{\rho A}}$$

should be used for beams of complex cross section. Here $I$ is the moment of inertia appropriate to the bending direction, and $A$ is the cross-sectional area.

An example of the use of these velocities will now be presented.

**Example 3.2.** A plate of dimensions 15 by 10 by 0.16 cm, and properties $E = 1.4 \times 10^9 \text{ N/m}^2$, $\rho = 1400 \text{ kg/m}^3$ is supported around the edges and experiences harmonic motion in all three planes at a frequency of 50 Hz. These dimensions and material constants are of the order frequently encountered in printed wire boards and, as indicated previously, the frequency is in a range commonly encountered during shipment. Can the plate vibration be analyzed quasistatically or must it be considered as a dynamic problem?

*Solution.* The rise time of each cycle of the loading is found to be

$$t_r = \frac{1}{4 \times 50} = 0.005 \text{ s}$$

The longitudinal wave speed is

$$V_l = \sqrt{\frac{E}{\rho}} = \sqrt{\frac{1.4 \times 10^9}{1400}} = 1000 \text{ m/s}$$

and the time for a tensile wave to traverse the plate is

$$\frac{0.15}{V_l} = 0.15 \times 10^{-3} \text{ s}$$

Consequently, the in-plane problem is quasistatic. The bending speed is

$$\frac{\pi h}{l\sqrt{12}} \sqrt{\frac{E}{\rho}} = \frac{\pi \times 0.0016}{0.15\sqrt{12}} 1000 = 9.7 \text{ m/s} \quad (380 \text{ in./s})$$

and the traversal time is 0.0155 second, so that the bending problem must be treated dynamically.

## REDUCTION OF CONTINUOUS TO DISCRETE SYSTEMS FOR SHOCK LOADINGS

Because the usual vibration solutions of continuous systems converge poorly and also are frequently difficult to obtain, it is often helpful to approximate the continuous system by a discrete system of one or more masses. Transient loadings are usually generated by handling shock or ground motions caused by earthquakes or, in the case of hardened communications systems, by nuclear blast. In all of these cases, the equipment is loaded through its supports, and the early-time distortion response approximates the fundamental vibration mode. Damping is usually neglected when transient shock response is investigated because maximum displacements occur during the first few cycles and the small damping in structures can have little effect.

By assuming that equipment responds to shock in the first mode only, the problem reduces to that of a simple or single-degree-of-freedom oscillator. In practice, an approximation to the first mode shape will be used. It will be shown that the approximate simple oscillator is related to the continuous system through the kinetic and potential energy integrals which have been shown to be insensitive to the particular mode shape assumed in discussions[6,7] of the Rayleigh method. These mode shapes will be assumed to be as simple as possible. The question remains as to how the parameters of the continuous system can be correlated with the parameters of the simple oscillator.

To make this correlation we will follow two rules: the kinetic and potential energies will be made the same in the two systems, and the displacement of the continuous system relative to its attachment points will be made the same as the displacement of the mass relative to its ground at all times. These two conditions will define the parameters of the simple system.

As Example 3.2 has shown for a specific case, the transverse motion of a plate must often be considered to be dynamic, while the in-plane motions can be considered to be static. The same is usually true of beams. In the following discussion, only plates will be considered, but these results are easily reduced to those for a beam. The same method may be applied to all kinds of structures such as frames, racks, and cabinets. In such cases, for enclosed electronic equipment at least, shock loadings on the plate appear through uniform motion of the plate boundary. For the plate of Fig. 3-10(a), the equations of small

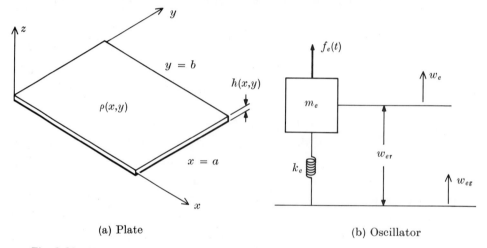

(a) Plate                                (b) Oscillator

**Fig. 3-10**   Nonuniform rectangular plate and the corresponding simple oscillator.

transverse motion may then be written as

$$L(w) = \frac{\partial^2 w}{\partial t^2} = 0 \tag{3-28}$$

$$w = w_g(t) \quad \text{at} \quad x = 0, a; \quad y = 0, b$$

where $w_g$ is the motion of the boundary; $L$ is a linear differential operator in $\partial/\partial x$ and $\partial/\partial y$ without any undifferentiated terms in $w$, and it contains the density variable. If $w_r(x, y)$ is defined as the relative motion between the point $x, y$ in the plate and the boundaries, Eq. (3-28) may be rewritten

$$L(w_r + w_g) + \frac{\partial^2}{\partial t^2} (w_r + w_g) = 0 \tag{3-29}$$

$$w = w_g(t) \quad \text{at} \quad x = 0, a; \quad y = 0, b$$

because $w_g$ satisfies the time-varying boundary conditions. Since $w_g$ is constant in $x$ and $y$, Eq. (3-29) may be rewritten

$$L(w_r) = \frac{\partial^2 w_r}{\partial t^2} = -\frac{d^2 w_g}{dt^2} \tag{3-30}$$

$$w_r = 0 \quad \text{at} \quad x = 0, a; \quad y = 0, b$$

and the ground acceleration appears as a forcing function on the motion $w_r$. The problem is therefore transformed into a force-loaded version, where a plate of motionless boundaries and displacement $w_r$ has applied to it a time-variant pressure loading. We will call this second form the standard version of the problem.

Considering now a simple oscillator excited through motions of the ground, a similar transformation is possible. The equation for motion of the simple oscillator of Fig. 3-10(b) may be written directly in the form of the standard problem by an obvious transformation of the similar system of Eq. (3-2) since $w_{or} = w_e - w_{eg}$

$$m_e \frac{d^2 w_{er}}{dt^2} + k_e w_{er} = -m_e \frac{d^2 w_{eg}}{dt^2} \tag{3-31}$$

Assume that the plate vibration is in one mode only. Then $w_r$ may be written in terms of a mode shape $\phi(x, y)$ with an amplitude $W_r$, that is,

$$w_r(x, y, t) = W_r \phi(x, y) \tau(t) \tag{3-32}$$

The corresponding simple oscillator motion is

$$w_e(t) = W_{er} \tau(t) \tag{3-33}$$

Equating the kinetic energies of the two systems gives

$$m_e = \int_0^a \int_0^b h(x, y)\, \rho(x, y)\, \phi^2(x, y)\, dx\, dy \tag{3-34}$$

since we equate $W_r = W_{er}$ and since the time variations of the two motions are required to be the same. Thus $m_e$ is determined. Equating the stored potential energy of the two systems at any instant gives

$$k_e = \int_0^a \int_0^b D(x, y) \left\{ \left( \frac{\partial^2 \phi}{\partial x^2} + \frac{\partial^2 \phi}{\partial y^2} \right)^2 - 2(1 - \nu)\left[ \frac{\partial^2 \phi}{\partial x^2}\frac{\partial^2 \phi}{\partial y^2} - \left( \frac{\partial^2 \phi}{\partial x \, \partial y} \right)^2 \right] \right\} dx\, dy$$

$$\tag{3-35}$$

where

$$D = \frac{E h^3}{12(1 - \nu^2)}$$

and $k_e$ is determined. The above plate energy equation may be found on page 47 of Ref. 8. The final question is, how should $w_{eg}$ be related to $w_e$?

If a pressure distribution acting on the plate is $p(x, y, t)$, then the power generated by the load is

$$E = \int_0^a \int_0^b p W_r \phi \frac{d\tau}{dt} \, dx \, dy \tag{3-36}$$

The power put into the oscillator by a load $f_e(t)$ is

$$E = f_e W_{er} \frac{d\tau}{dt}$$

and equating the two gives

$$f_e = \int_0^a \int_0^b p\phi \, dx \, dy$$

Then

$$-m_e \frac{d^2 w_{eg}}{dt^2} = -\frac{d^2 w_g}{dt^2} \int_0^a \int_0^b \rho h\phi \, dx \, dy \tag{3-37}$$

since

$$f_e = -m_e \frac{d^2 w_{eg}}{dt^2} \tag{3-38}$$

and

$$p = -ph \frac{d^2 w_g}{dt^2} \tag{3-39}$$

upon comparing Eq. (3-30) with the plate equations (e.g., Ref. 8, p. 82). It may be seen that if $\rho$ and $h$ are uniform (i.e., not functions of $x$ and $y$) then $p$ is also uniform and $k_e$ can be found using the plate energy equation of the form

$$\tfrac{1}{2} k_e W_{er} = \tfrac{1}{2} p W_r \int_0^a \int_0^b \phi \, dx \, dy \tag{3-40}$$

Define the plate resistance, $R$, to be the total plate load, $abp$, required to produce unit maximum displacement, i.e.,

$$abp = RW_r$$

Then Eq. (3-40) becomes

$$k_e = \frac{R}{ab} \int_0^a \int_0^b \phi \, dx \, dy \tag{3-41}$$

$R$ or $R/ab$ is usually given in tabulations of static plate responses.

**Simplified Mode Shapes.** The simplified mode shapes should be formed of the harmonic function of lowest spatial frequency which satisfies the proper boundary conditions and which has the general shape of the first vibration mode. If a plate has simply supported boundaries, the mode shape should then be assumed to be

$$\phi(x, y) = \sin \frac{\pi x}{a} \sin \frac{\pi y}{b} \tag{3-42}$$

so that

$$\phi = 0 \quad \text{at} \quad x = 0, a; \quad y = 0, b$$

$$\frac{\partial^2 \phi}{\partial x^2} = 0 \quad \text{at} \quad x = 0, a$$

and

$$\frac{\partial^2 \phi}{\partial y^2} = 0 \quad \text{at} \quad y = 0, b$$

If the boundaries may be considered to be clamped,

$$\phi(x, y) = \frac{1}{4}\left(1 - \cos\frac{2\pi x}{a}\right)\left(1 - \cos\frac{2\pi y}{b}\right) \tag{3-43}$$

so that

$$\phi = 0 \quad \text{at} \quad x = 0, a; \quad y = 0, b$$

$$\frac{\partial \phi}{\partial x} = 0 \quad \text{at} \quad x = 0, a$$

and

$$\frac{\partial \phi}{\partial y} = 0 \quad \text{at} \quad y = 0, b$$

The reduction of a plate to a built-in beam is accomplished by assuming the plate to be free along $x = 0, a$ and clamped along $y = 0, b$. The mode shape is that of the corresponding beam running in the $y$ direction, i.e.,

$$\phi(x, y) = \frac{1}{2}\left(1 - \cos\frac{2\pi y}{b}\right) \tag{3-44}$$

**Shock Response.** To estimate the response of the continuous structure, it is only necessary to obtain the corresponding simple oscillator and the transformed load. Solving the simple oscillator problem then gives the time history of the point of maximum deflection of the plate. If the stresses in the continuous system are to be obtained, the maximum stresses should be determined from the static deflection curve, using whenever possible the maximum displacement obtained from the simple system. Stresses obtained from the approximate mode shape will probably be more in error because stresses are very sensitive to mode shape. There is an opinion[9] that the static deflection curve more nearly approximates the shock response shape than does the first vibration mode shape, so that stresses obtained in such a way should be fairly accurate.

Some useful charts for estimating the response of a simple oscillator will be presented here. It may be seen that the ratio $\tau/T$ is sufficient to estimate the amplitude of the response, where $\tau$ is the characteristic time of the loading history and $T$ is the period of oscillation of the continuous system; hence

$$T = 2\pi\sqrt{\frac{m_e}{k_e}} \qquad (3\text{-}45)$$

In Fig. 3-11, $K$ is the "dynamic load factor," i.e., the ratio of the peak dynamic displacement to that of the mass if it followed the load quasistatically. The curves plotted in Fig. 3-11 are the envelopes of the actual curves for $K$, since it is usually unsafe to use lower values of $K$ from the precise response curves.

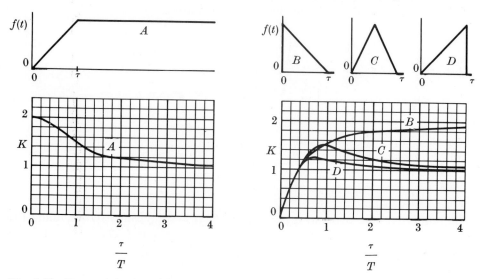

**Fig. 3-11**  Dynamic load factors for response to various functions $f(t)$ versus characteristic time-to-period ratio.

A small error in system frequency or loading time might cause a large under-estimation of $K$.

These dynamic load factors assume that a force $f(t)$ is applied to the mass of a simple oscillator as in Fig. 3-3(a). However, they may also be used with continuous systems experiencing support motions by finding the equivalent force loading and the constants for the equivalent simple oscillator. For example, the previous discussion shows the transformation of a distributed, boundary-motion problem into a simple-oscillator, forcing-function problem. By comparing Eqs. (3-31) and (3-37), it is seen that the apparent *force* loading is

$$f(t) = -\frac{d^2 w_g}{dt^2} \int_0^a \int_0^b \rho h \phi \, dx \, dy$$

where $\phi$ is an assumed mode shape for the shock response. This may be a static deflection curve, a harmonic curve which approximates the shape of the first mode, or some other similar shape.

The maximum deflection of the simple oscillator is its static response to the peak value of $f(t)$ times the appropriate dynamic load factor from Fig. 3-11. Since the various energies have been equated between the oscillator and the plate, the maximum deflection of the plate will be its static deflection under the peak value of $-\rho(d^2 w_g/dt^2)$ times the same dynamic load factor.

**Example 3.3.** Assume that a uniform plate has the configuration shown in Fig. 3-10(a), with simply supported boundaries, except that there is a mass $M$

**Fig. 3-12** A circuit pack used in an electronic switching system.

attached at the point $x_0$, $y_0$. This could be a relatively heavy transformer or inductor on a printed wiring board such as the one shown in Fig. 3-12. Assume that the loading appears as a motion of the boundary, given by

$$w_g = \begin{cases} 0, & t < 0 \\ W \sin \dfrac{\pi t}{\tau}, & 0 \leq t \leq \tau \\ 0, & t > \tau \end{cases}$$

We will first find the corresponding simple oscillator by assuming that the response of the plate has the mode shape of Eq. (3-42), i.e.,

$$\phi(x, y) = \sin \frac{\pi x}{a} \sin \frac{\pi y}{b}$$

From Eq. (3-34),

$$m_e = \rho h \int_0^a \int_0^b \sin^2 \frac{\pi x}{a} \sin^2 \frac{\pi y}{b} \, dx \, dy + M \sin^2 \frac{\pi x_0}{a} \sin^2 \frac{\pi y_0}{b}$$

where $\rho$ and $h$ are the properties of the uniform plate, and the mass $M$ has been introduced as an impulse function in density at the point $x_0$, $y_0$. Thus,

$$m_e = \frac{\rho abh}{4} + M \sin^2 \frac{\pi x_0}{a} \sin^2 \frac{\pi y_0}{b} \tag{3-46}$$

From Eq. (3-35),

$$k_e = \frac{Eh^3}{12(1-\nu^2)}\left(\frac{\pi^2}{a^2} + \frac{\pi^2}{b^2}\right)^2 \int_0^a \int_0^b \sin^2 \frac{\pi x}{a} \sin^2 \frac{\pi y}{b}\, dx\, dy$$

or

$$k_e = \frac{abEh^3}{48(1-\nu^2)}\left(\frac{\pi^2}{a^2} + \frac{\pi^2}{b^2}\right)^2 \tag{3-47}$$

since the terms in the brackets in Eq. (3-35) cancel when integrated between the limits. The period of the oscillator is therefore

$$T = 2\pi\sqrt{\frac{m_e}{k_e}} \tag{3-48}$$

Eq. (3-37) then gives

$$-m_e \frac{d^2 w_{eg}}{dt^2} = \begin{cases} 0, & t < 0 \\ \dfrac{W\pi^2}{\tau^2} \sin \dfrac{\pi t}{\tau}\left(\rho h \displaystyle\int_0^a \int_0^b \sin \dfrac{\pi x}{a} \sin \dfrac{\pi y}{b}\, dx\, dy \right. \\ \qquad\qquad \left. + M \sin \dfrac{\pi x_0}{a} \sin \dfrac{\pi y_0}{b}\right), & 0 \leq t \leq \tau \\ 0, & t > \tau \end{cases}$$

or

$$-m_e \frac{d^2 w_{er}}{dt^2} = \begin{cases} 0, & t < 0 \\ \dfrac{W\pi^2}{\tau^2} \sin \dfrac{\pi t}{\tau}\left(4 \dfrac{ab\rho h}{\pi^2} + M \sin \dfrac{\pi x_0}{a} \sin \dfrac{\pi y_0}{b}\right), & 0 \leq t \leq \tau \\ 0, & t > \tau \end{cases} \tag{3-49}$$

If the forcing function $C$ of Fig. 3-11(b) is assumed to represent the half sine wave of Eq. (3-49) (and it certainly does within the error of the other approximations made here), then, knowing $\tau/T$, the dynamic load factor $K$ can be picked off directly. The result states that the maximum dynamic displacement of the plate is

$$W_r = \frac{K}{k_e}\left[\frac{W\pi^2}{\tau^2}\left(4\frac{ab\rho h}{\pi^2} + M \sin \frac{\pi x_0}{a} \sin \frac{\pi y_0}{b}\right)\right]$$

The maximum stress in the plate would then be determined as follows.

The static pressure load on the plate must include the effect of $M$ and is determined from Eq. (3-39) as

$$p = \frac{\pi^2 W}{\tau^2}\left[\rho h + M\delta(x - x_0, y - y_0)\right]$$

where it must be remembered that $M$ produces a point loading at the point $x_0, y_0$, i.e., $\delta$ here is the two-dimensional Dirac delta function. The maximum static stress in a plate experiencing a uniform load of

$$\rho h \frac{\pi^2 W}{\tau^2}$$

and a point load at $x_0, y_0$ of magnitude

$$M \frac{\pi^2 W}{\tau^2}$$

must then be determined from a static plate analysis, as in Ref. 8, and the resulting value must be multiplied by $K$.

## STEADY-STATE VIBRATIONS

Determining the steady-state response of a continuous system directly from the continuous equations involves about the same degree of difficulty as solving the static problem. A solution is assumed which has the same time variation as one of the harmonic components of the loading. The spatial form of this response is then determined. When all such load components have been treated in this way, the complete response is obtained by summing the responses to all the components. This procedure is relatively simple for beams and rods but is difficult for plates, except for a few special cases.

Other specialized methods are available, such as Ritz's extension of Rayleigh's method which can be used to obtain the higher natural modes. Each mode is then treated as a simple oscillator, as in the previous section, and the responses of all modes are added to get the complete response. Such methods are usually too time-consuming for the designer.

It has been the hope of many investigators in the past that a discrete-element approximation of a plate can be developed which, with a computer, will readily yield vibration solutions, and much work is presently being done in this area. No generally applicable method has as yet been developed, however. Longitudinal vibrations are easily approximated in this way, but they are also easily solved by the direct approach.

Continuous steady-state vibration analysis is, therefore, probably best attacked as follows. Longitudinal rod and bending beam vibrations can usually be handled by the basic methods.[6,7,10] Plate vibrations are best handled experimentally. Equipment and techniques for such investigations will be discussed in a following section.

One more comment on steady-state vibrations should be made. For some reason, vibration texts seldom discuss the problem of vibrations caused by motions at the boundaries of a structure (the most important problem for the designer). However, they all examine the distributed loading case in detail.

A simple boundary-loaded problem will be transformed to standard form here. The equation for the rod, Eq. (3-13), is

$$\rho A \frac{\partial^2 u}{\partial t^2} - AE \frac{\partial^2 u}{\partial x^2} = g \tag{3-50}$$

If we set the distributed load $g = 0$, but require that the ends of the rod move back and forth, i.e.,

$$u = U \sin \omega t \quad \text{when} \quad x = 0, l$$

a special but simple technique is necessary to solve this problem. Assume

$$u = u_1 + u_2$$

where $u_1$ is the quasistatic solution, that is, $u_1$ satisfies

$$\frac{\partial^2 u_1}{\partial x^2} = 0$$

and

$$u_1 = U \sin \omega t \quad \text{at} \quad x = 0, l$$

Function $u_1$ is easily found to be $u_1 = U \sin \omega t$ for all $x$. Then, substituting $u_1 + u_2$ for $u$ in Eq. (3-50), it is seen that $u_2$ must satisfy

$$\rho A \frac{\partial^2 u_2}{\partial t^2} - AE \frac{\partial^2 u_2}{\partial x^2} = \rho A U \omega^2 \sin \omega t \tag{3-51}$$

and

$$u_2 = 0 \quad \text{at} \quad x = 0, l$$

Now the equation for $u_2$ is of the usual distributed excitation form and is solved in the usual way. Much more complicated problems with time-dependent boundary conditions can be reduced to standard form in the same way.

Figure 3-13 shows one corner of a rectangular acrylic plate which failed in fatigue during steady-state vibration near the resonant frequency. In this case, analysis of the design is complicated by the fact that the clamping of the corners is only semirigid and stress concentrations are introduced by the mounting holes.

## 3-4. DESIGN FOR DYNAMIC ISOLATION

Shock and vibration isolation will be discussed here in a rather over-simplified way. The purpose is to give the design engineer a feeling for the goals sought and the methods employed. The specific procedures outlined can and should be used for rough estimates of design parameters; but for critical applications, the final mounting design and testing should be performed by a specialist.

The object of isolation is to separate the equipment from its mechanical environment in such a way as to reduce or remove some unwanted environmental effect. This effect is usually the dynamic overload of a delicate part. It

**Fig. 3-13**  Fracture of an acrylic plastic cover plate on an
early model twistor memory following severe vibration.

is easy to see that a violent acceleration of a piece of equipment can cause
internal parts to fail, since the attachment points of these parts must transmit
the acceleration force from the equipment as a whole to the part.

This acceleration force is easily approximated by $Wa/g$, where $W$ is the
weight of the part in newtons, $a$ is the expected acceleration, and $g$ is the
acceleration due to gravity. The ratio $a/g$ is simply the acceleration in $g$ units.
Thus, a part weighing 2 newtons and accelerated at $2 \times 9.807 = 19.614 \text{ m/s}^2$
experiences a 2-g acceleration from an applied force of 4 newtons. These simple
relationships are the reason why the shock capabilities of equipment are
usually specified by the number of g's the equipment can withstand.

Such specifications are useful if the duration of the loading is short enough
to prevent resonances from building up, but long enough for the shock wave to
be transmitted through the structure without significant attenuation. In other
words, the maximum g representation of the excitation is adequate only if the
shock energy is in a form which couples with the mass to produce a gross,
shock-type response. If the excitation is such as to produce significant internal
distortions or to produce resonant coupling, then a more complete analysis is
necessary. One must always consider what energy form is most dangerous to
the equipment, e.g., high g's at a high frequency will crack a crystal, while large
displacements at a low frequency will cause structural members to yield.

We will examine two cases in which the simple g designation is not
sufficient:

1. Suppose that equipment is mounted on a floor that undergoes ground
   shock. Because of this shock, the floor will oscillate at its natural
   frequency, say around 30 Hz, for a number of cycles. The equipment

will thus see a shock loading with a very strong component at 30 Hz. A quick calculation of a two-degree-of-freedom system—one mass representing the floor and the other the equipment—shows that the equipment sees a shock spectrum of about the same magnitude as if it were attached directly to the outside ground, *if* there are no equipment or shock-mount natural frequencies near the floor frequency. Otherwise, the results of the two-mass problem must be used. Usually, fundamental floor frequencies are between 5 and 30 Hz, shock-mounting frequencies are between 3 and 10 Hz, and lowest equipment resonances are between 10 and 100 Hz.

2. At the other extreme, tapping the support of a piece of equipment produces very high g loadings containing very little energy. The high accelerations, which appear only in very high frequency components, are greatly attenuated by passing through structural joints and may be completely removed by a thin rubber pad. The shock spectrum of Fig. 3-9 for the solenoid impact problem shows a loading of this kind. The curve appears only at the right-hand side of the graph. Although 300 g's would be experienced by an object with a natural frequency of 1000 Hz, actual equipment frequencies are usually much lower, and little acceleration would be felt.

By far the most common method of isolation is to support the equipment on resilient members or materials which will reduce the natural frequency of the equipment and its mount enough so that only acceptable acceleration amplitudes are experienced. Usually, the equipment may be considered rigid compared to the mount, and the simple oscillator solution is sufficient. If the shock spectrum of the loading is available, then the proper mounting frequency for a simple oscillator and the resulting requirement for rattle space (the amount of free motion the mounted equipment will experience) can be read off the graph directly. As will be seen in what follows, rattle space increases as the frequency decreases. In tight quarters, special mounting techniques may be necessary to meet both g and rattle-space requirements. An explanation of the use of damping and nonlinear springs for unusually difficult applications is available.[1]

## SHIPPING AND HANDLING

Some important shipping and handling shock spectra will be discussed here. A spectrum for equipment attached to the floor or walls of the cargo space in trucks is shown in Fig. 3-14. The straight-line portions of the curves for military trucking are adapted from data summarized in Ref. 1, based on vehicles traveling at high speed over very rough terrain. Lower values are

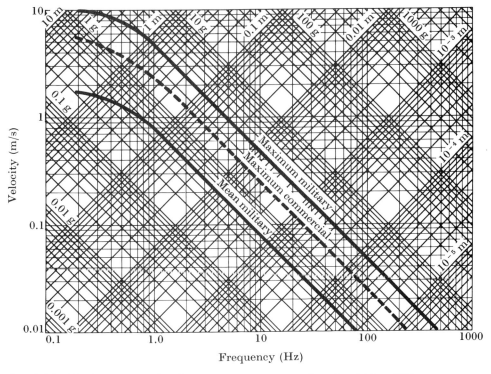

**Fig. 3-14** Shock spectrum for the cargo compartment of road vehicles. Military curves are for speeds on a rough road at which vehicle damage and driver injury are possible.[1]

assumed for commercial trucking on highways. In either case, much larger shocks could occur in case of accident or if the equipment were not tied down. Natural frequencies below 1 Hz are rarely of practical interest, but qualitatively, the curves must drop off, approaching constant velocities as shown.

The vibrations due to normal rail travel are significantly less than those for trucking, except during coupling when two rail cars may come together at fairly high speeds. Figure 3-15 shows the impact speed distribution for a large number of car impacts. The curve is smoothed from the actual data.[1]

Railroad impact of this type can be considered to be a horizontal impact problem in which one car approaches another at a given velocity. The speed of the moving car does not go to zero instantaneously because freight cars are equipped with *draft gear* (essentially buffer springs) which moderate the impact somewhat. Reference 1 shows the action of various draft gear, the worst of which (friction type) is used on most cars in service at the present. The maximum force transmitted by such friction gear is about 5.3 million newtons (1.2 million pounds) for a 12-mph impact. Only about 5 percent of the impacts in Fig. 3-15 are at more than 12 mph. For an empty car weighing around 18,000 kg

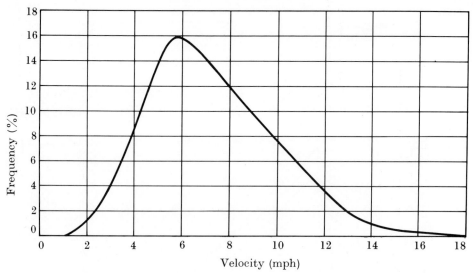

**Fig. 3-15**   Distribution of impact speeds in rail freight switching.[1]

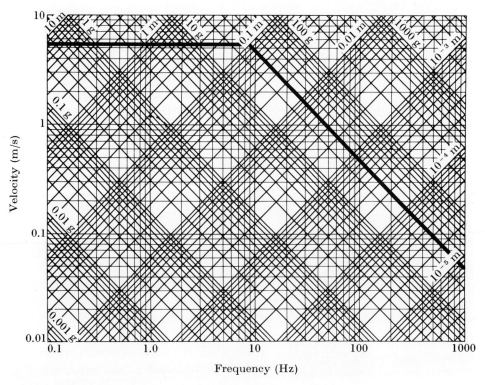

**Fig. 3-16** Shock spectrum for railroad car coupling impact at 12 mph.

(40,000 pounds), this gives deceleration of 30 g's. High-frequency items fixed to the car will experience the same deceleration as the car, and no items will experience more than this; therefore, one boundary on the shock spectrum will be the 30-g line (see Fig. 3-16). On the other hand, the large deceleration still appears to low-frequency items as an ideal impact, so that a velocity bound of 12 mph = 5.4 m/s can also be drawn as shown. This figure, then, gives the rough shock spectrum for railway car impact at 12 mph for equipment fixed to the car; unrestrained cargo will see larger shocks. The curves are for the horizontal direction, of course.

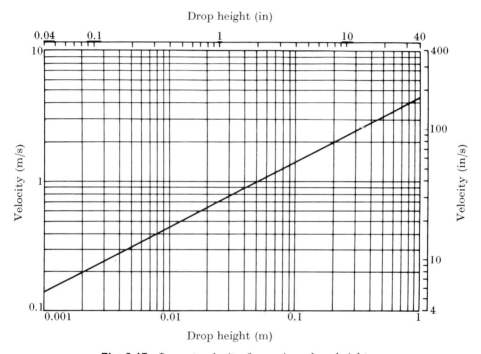

**Fig. 3-17**   Impact velocity for various drop heights.

Handling or loading equipment for all types of transportation may produce the largest shock environment. These shocks result when the package is dropped against an unyielding surface. The velocity of impact versus drop height is plotted in Fig. 3-17. The shock spectrum to be used with such dropping shocks is simply a straight horizontal line drawn on shock spectrum paper at the velocity of impact, with the appropriate amplitude cutoff at the low-frequency end.

**Example 3.4.** A cubical, 20-kg unit may undergo commercial shipping and handling shocks of any of the three types mentioned. It is expected that this unit will not be dropped more than 20 cm. What packaging characteristics must be met if this unit is to be packed for shipment, using linear elastic mounts, to achieve a maximum acceleration of 3 g's?

*Solution.* The composite shock spectrum for these loadings—both horizontal (railroad car coupling) and vertical (handling and trucking)—is plotted in Fig. 3-18. From the figure, the 3-g maximum acceleration requires mounted frequencies of 0.9 and 2.4 Hz horizontally and vertically, respectively.

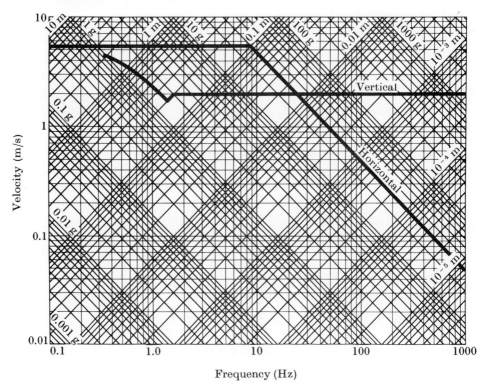

**Fig. 3-18**  Composite shock spectrum.

In practice, it is often impractical to distinguish between vertical and horizontal shock during shipment or handling because of difficulty in controlling the orientation of the equipment. In this case, the more stringent requirement would have to be assumed for any direction. The easily handled, cubic geometry in the preceding example would be especially difficult to control. Orientation of larger units can often be controlled by use of skids on the down side of the shipping crate, plus generous use of "this side up" labels. Even so, the position cannot be guaranteed. For instance, the heavily loaded frame shown in Fig. 3-19 was crated with skids on the far left side. Both the packing and the frame were designed with the expectation that this side would be kept on the bottom during shipment. The damage shown applied only to the

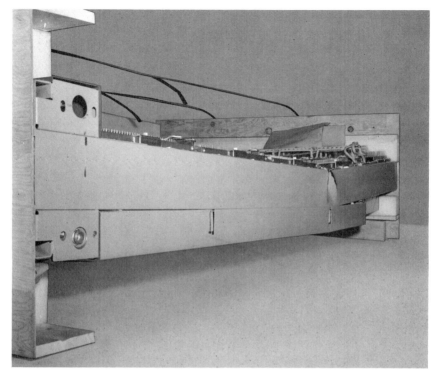

**Fig. 3-19**   Partially uncrated program store frame which was damaged during shipment by truck.

right-hand frame member and is presumed to have resulted from the crate tipping over during shipment. This would subject the right portion of the framework and adjacent equipment to a fall of about 1.4 meters. It is usually uneconomical to design for this kind of abuse, which would have been avoided had the crate been properly lashed in place.

## ON-SITE SHOCK ENVIRONMENTS

Once stationary equipment has been installed, the shock environment to be considered is caused by operation of nearby equipment, collision with test or other maintenance equipment, earthquake, or (in the case of hardened applications) by nuclear attack. The shock caused by the operation of communications equipment is usually a high-frequency shock of the sort discussed in the solenoid-impact problem. These effects damp out quickly and are of importance only to very closely coupled delicate items. However, if operation of the equipment causes continuing vibration, as opposed to shock, then large responses of nearby items can be generated over a period of time.

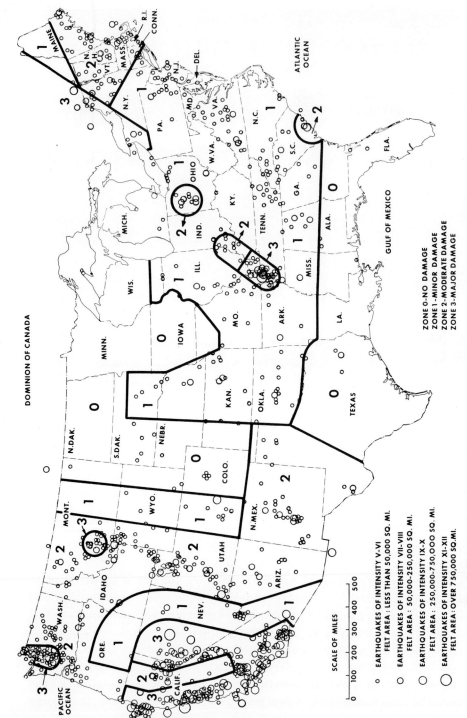

**Fig. 3-20** Earthquakes and seismic zones of approximately equal earthquake suscep-tibility in the United States.[11]

**Earthquake.** Unfortunately, very strong earthquake motions have not been measured accurately. Maximum accelerations measured are around 0.33 g in a horizontal direction at a distance 30 miles from the epicenter (the point on the earth's surface directly above the point of fault motion). However, building code requirements in earthquake-susceptible areas such as Los Angeles, California, require interior structures that are not integral parts of the building framework to be capable of withstanding horizontal accelerations up to 1 g. The Uniform Building Code[11] recommends that nonintegral structures be designed for 1-g horizontal acceleration in all areas of the United States designated zone 3, indicating maximum earthquake susceptibility (see Fig. 3-20). Designs for $\frac{1}{4}$ g and $\frac{1}{2}$ g are recommended for zones 1 and 2, respectively. These recommendations have also been adopted by the American Standards Association. Building architects meet the intent of the code by using construction techniques that have evolved from knowledge of previous failures in strong-motion areas.[9]

While the equipment itself is usually capable of withstanding considerably more than 1-g acceleration, it is also important that the equipment be mounted and braced adequately to prevent damage. Due to penalties in economy, installation, and appearance, it is usually impractical to provide the additional anchorage and bracing needed for maximum protection in all locations. The physical designer must therefore specify alternative arrangements according to the degree of protection required.

**Nuclear Attack.** Ground motion from an above-ground or surface nuclear explosion (the type to be expected in an attack) is caused largely by the coupling of the air-blast wave with the ground. The ground response is strongly affected by the burst height and range and by the soil properties. A typical ground shock spectrum of the type for which hardened electronic equipment is sometimes designed is shown in Fig. 3-21. The corresponding blast increases the air pressure by 170,000 N/m² (25 psi), and the seismic wave travels through moderately firm soil with a speed of 760 m/s (1700 mph) for this case. The ASCE Manual[12] describes a way of estimating such spectra.

## FRAME PROTECTION VERSUS SUBUNIT PROTECTION

In designing for dynamic loads, it is necessary to consider where the structures should be made strong and where protection, if required, should be provided. An insight to this problem is gained by considering the inherent strengths associated with small structures as compared with large ones. Regardless of whether shock or vibration is under consideration, the inertia loadings are forces or moments associated with the acceleration of masses so

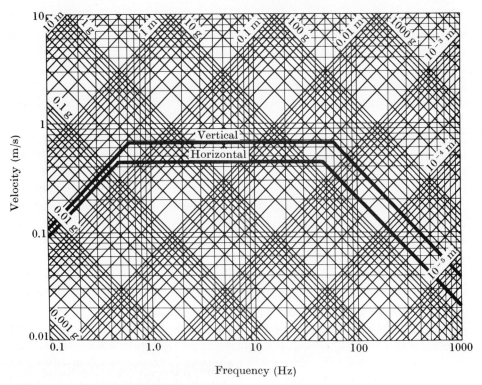

**Fig. 3-21**   Typical nuclear ground shock spectra.

that, for a given acceleration, these forces vary as the cube of the linear dimensions. The areas that resist these forces vary as the square of the linear dimension; thus, for a given acceleration, the stresses in force per unit area are directly proportional to the first power of the scale factor. Small structures are inherently more shock resistant than large ones. Further, for a given material, the natural frequency of a structure varies inversely with scale factor, as can be seen from the relation

$$\omega = \sqrt{\frac{k}{m}} = \sqrt{\frac{E \times \text{length}^2 / \text{length}}{\rho \times \text{length}^3}} = \sqrt{\frac{E}{\rho}} \times \frac{1}{\text{length}}$$

Thus, when small structures (subunits) are mounted inside large ones, they not only tend to be stronger, but also the relatively low natural frequency of the larger structure, plus any shock protection that it enjoys, tend to filter out the potentially damaging, higher frequency portions of any shock or vibration spectrum originating outside the structure. This generalization holds true for components and structures which are appreciably different in size (natural frequency); for comparable sizes, interactions associated with near-resonance may substantially increase the likelihood of damage, as will be discussed later.

The foregoing considerations suggest that shock protection may be needed for the large equipment cabinets and framework structures even though the smaller components may not require it; this is often the case. Even if this were not true, however, and protection were needed only for the subunits, the protection usually would be applied to (or built into) the frame structure for the following reasons.

1.  When the subunits are separately protected, the volume required for rattle space increases significantly for the same level of protection, as shown schematically in Fig. 3-22. Since the natural frequencies of the

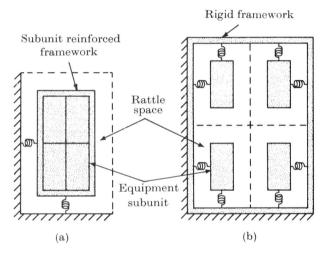

**Fig. 3-22** Space saving when entire frame is shock-mounted (a) as compared with subunit mounts for equal protection (b).

subunits cannot be made exactly the same, it is generally necessary to allow sufficient space between units to accommodate unfavorable motion phasing. When a system consists of several frames or cabinets, the same principle is used to save space by attaching the frames together and protecting them as a group. Illustrations of this procedure will be given later in this section.

2.  The subunits are usually interconnected electrically within the frame as well as between frames. Wiring and cabling designs to accommodate large subunit motions are not only costly but also reduce reliability and electrical performance.

3.  An arrangement of supports that will decouple motions in the three directions of translation and three angles of rotation (not shown in Fig. 3-22) is easier to achieve with a single set of mounts than with

multiple sets; also, access to the mounts for maintenance is generally improved.

4. Frequently, the most severe shocks to be protected against occur during shipment. Temporary, relatively inexpensive protection can be applied to the outside of the structure and discarded after shipment, thereby avoiding need for permanently allocated rattle space.

5. Even though separately protected subunits may be mounted in a very stiff framework stiffly attached to ground, some flexibility always exists with the result that resonance and associated energy transfer between subunits are apt to be difficult to control, particularly under sustained vibration.

Frequently, only a small portion of the equipment within a frame requires shock protection. In such cases, individual protection may be warranted, but the design should be compatible with the shock response characteristics of the

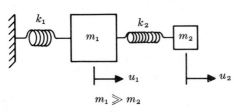

$m_1 \gg m_2$

**Fig. 3-23** Vibrational system with two degrees of freedom.

larger structure. Consider the system shown in Fig. 3-23 in which a small mass $m_2$ is flexibly supported by a much larger mass $m_1$, which is also flexibly supported to ground. Because of the large mass difference, $m_2$ may be neglected in determining the motion of $m_1$. The system can then be viewed as two systems, each with a single degree of freedom, with the response of the first system acting as the forcing function for the second. If the shock is imparted by a free fall with terminal velocity $V$ at $t = 0$, then, from previous discussions of the shock spectrum charts the initial conditions at $t = 0$ may be approximated as

$$u_1 = u_2 = 0; \qquad \frac{du_1}{dt} = \frac{du_2}{dt} = V$$

If damping is neglected, the motion of $m_1$ becomes

$$u_1 = \frac{V}{\omega_1} \sin \omega_1 t; \qquad \frac{du_1}{dt} = V \cos \omega_1 t; \qquad \frac{d^2 u_1}{dt^2} = -\omega_1 V \sin \omega_1 t \quad (3\text{-}52)$$

where $\omega_1 = \sqrt{k_1/m_1}$. The equation of motion for $m_2$ is

$$m_2 \frac{d^2 u_2}{dt^2} + k_2 u_2 = k_2 u_1 = \frac{k_2 V}{\omega_1} \sin \omega_1 t$$

This equation is readily solved by any of several approaches. Using Laplace transforms, and letting $\mathscr{L}(u_2) = U_2$, yields

$$m_2(s^2 U_2 - V) + k_2 U_2 = \frac{k_2 V}{s^2 + \omega_1^2}$$

$$U_2 = \frac{\omega_2^2 V}{(s^2 + \omega_1^2)(s^2 + \omega_2^2)} + \frac{V}{s^2 + \omega_2^2}$$

Taking inverse transforms, with care as to the signs of the terms in brackets, yields

$$u_2 = \frac{V}{1 - (\omega_1/\omega_2)^2}\left[\frac{1}{\omega_1} \sin \omega_1 t - \frac{1}{\omega_2} \sin \omega_2 t\right] + \frac{V}{\omega_2} \sin \omega_2 t$$

$$= \frac{V}{1 - (\omega_1/\omega_2)^2}\left[\frac{1}{\omega_1} \sin \omega_1 t - \frac{(\omega_1/\omega_2)^2}{\omega_2} \sin \omega_2 t\right] \qquad (3\text{-}53)$$

Taking derivatives yields

$$\frac{du_2}{dt} = \frac{V}{1 - (\omega_1/\omega_2)^2} \left[\cos \omega_1 t - (\omega_1/\omega_2)^2 \cos \omega_2 t\right] \qquad (3\text{-}54)$$

and

$$\frac{d^2 u_2}{dt^2} = \frac{V}{1 - (\omega_1/\omega_2)^2} \left[-\omega_1 \sin \omega_1 t + (\omega_1/\omega_2)^2 \omega_2 \sin \omega_2 t\right] \qquad (3\text{-}55)$$

The maximum values of these quantities may be approximated by letting the sine and cosine terms equal $+1$ or $-1$, whichever gives the larger value. This approximation is conservative with errors in $u_2$ or $d^2u_2/dt^2$ which do not exceed 15 percent for $\omega_1/\omega_2 > 1.4$ or $< 0.7$, and which are much smaller over most of this range; further, these maxima occur during the first cycle of the slower frequency so that damping is reasonably neglected. It is convenient to express these maxima as ratios of the motions of $m_2$ as compared with $m_1$. From Eqs. (3-52) through (3-55) they are

$$\frac{|u_2|_{\max}}{|u_1|_{\max}} = \left|\frac{1 + (\omega_1/\omega_2)^3}{1 - (\omega_1/\omega_2)^2}\right| \qquad (3\text{-}56)$$

$$\frac{|du_2/dt|_{\max}}{|du_1/dt|_{\max}} = \left|\frac{1 + (\omega_1/\omega_2)^2}{1 - (\omega_1/\omega_2)^2}\right| \qquad (3\text{-}57)$$

and

$$\frac{|d^2u_2/dt^2|_{\max}}{|d^2u_1/dt^2|_{\max}} = \left|\frac{1 + (\omega_1/\omega_2)}{1 - (\omega_1/\omega_2)^2}\right| \qquad (3\text{-}58)$$

In addition, the ratio of the rattle space for $m_2$ mounted in $m_1$ to the external rattle space for $m_1$ alone becomes

$$\frac{|u_2 - u_1|_{\max}}{|u_1|_{\max}} = \frac{(\omega_1/\omega_2)^2 + (\omega_1/\omega_2)^3}{1 - (\omega_1/\omega_2)^2} \qquad (3\text{-}59)$$

Equations (3-56) through (3-59) are plotted as functions of the frequency ratios in Fig. 3-24. Several points are of interest. When shock protection (spring $k_2$ in Fig. 3-23) is added to protect $m_2$, the maximum acceleration of $m_2$ becomes worse until $\omega_1/\omega_2 \geqq 2$. Even at this break-even point, the displacement of $m_2$ is three times that of $m_1$, and the rattle space required is four times as great. Thus, it is not sufficient to just avoid resonance, but the frequency

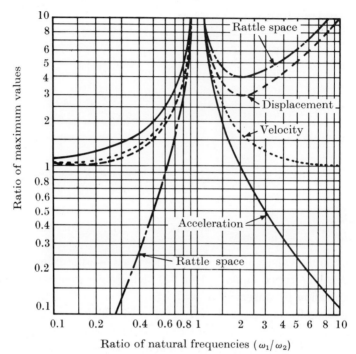

**Fig. 3-24** Ratio of maximum values for motions of $m_1$ as compared with $m_2$ in a system with two degrees of freedom in which $m_1 \gg m_2$, with shock excitation and no damping.

ratio must appreciably exceed 2 to effect an improvement. On the other hand, if $\omega_1/\omega_2$ is increased to 6 by reducing the stiffness of $k_2$, the maximum acceleration (and stresses) of the protected member are reduced by a factor of 5. The maximum velocity is not appreciably different from that for the main mass, but allowance must be made within the structure for a substantial increase in rattle space. Although this discussion relates to spring supports deliberately added for local protection, it applies equally well to compliance that may be introduced inadvertently in the design. Internal supports should be either very stiff or quite flexible in relation to their masses, as compared with the support of the structure as a whole.

Some problems of an internally suspended component are illustrated by the following example. Even this is greatly simplified, however, by considering shock in only the vertical direction and by neglecting tolerances and safety factors.

**Example 3.5.** A large console contains components that are able, in general, to withstand a vertical shock load of 10 g. An exception is a small galvanometer which may be damaged if the shock exceeds 5 g. The most severe shock expected during shipment is a drop from a height of 15 cm. After it is unpacked, the console may be shocked by a drop of 3 cm during handling with a forklift truck, but compliance of the framework limits the internal shock to the 10-g general component requirement. What design features should be incorporated to protect the galvanometer?

*Solution.* The response spectra for the two drops are shown in Fig. 3-25. Each spectrum is bounded at the lower frequencies by diagonal lines of constant displacement and at intermediate frequencies by horizontal lines of constant velocity corresponding to their respective drop heights.

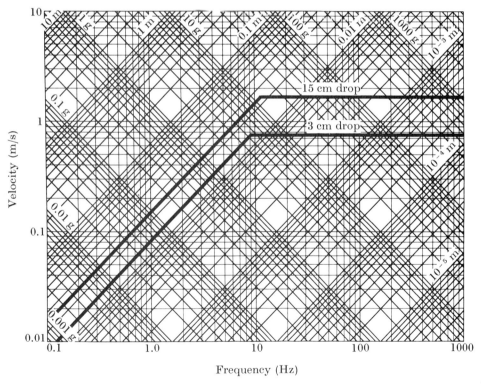

**Fig. 3-25**  Shock response spectra for 3-cm and 15-cm drops.

Considering only the requirements after unpacking, it would be sufficient to spring-mount the galvanometer to reduce maximum acceleration by a factor of 2 (from 10 g to 5 g). From Fig. 3-24, this would require a frequency ratio of

$\omega_1/\omega_2 = f_1/f_2 = 3$, with a rattle-space ratio of 4.5. From the 3-cm drop spectrum of Fig. 3-25, and a shock level of 10 g, the natural frequency of the console framework, $f_2$, is 20 Hz and the displacement is 0.6 cm. Thus, a galvanometer mount with a natural frequency of 6.7 Hz and rattle space of 2.7 cm would just meet requirements after unpacking.

Assume that, during shipment, the console is packed to protect components to the 10-g level. From Fig. 3-25, the console would have a natural frequency of 10 Hz and a displacement amplitude of 2.5 cm. But from Fig. 3-24, for a frequency ratio of $10/6.7 = 1.5$, the galvanometer acceleration becomes $2 \times 10 = 20$ g, with a rattle-space requirement of $4.6 \times 2.5 = 12$ cm. It is therefore necessary to design the galvanometer suspension to protect it during shipment. For a frequency ratio of 3 and a rattle-space ratio of 4.5, the galvanometer suspension should have a natural frequency of $\frac{10}{3} = 3.3$ and rattle space of $4.5 \times 2.5 = 11.2$ cm. This will give more than adequate protection after unpacking, but design for these parameters could present problems of alignment and stability during use. Other possibilities, which might be more desirable, would be to redesign the console base and packing to protect the entire console to the 5-g level or, if possible, to equip the galvanometer with supports or reinforcing members to make it capable of withstanding 10 g, at least temporarily.

## VIBRATION PROTECTION

Although the shock environment is usually controlling from a design standpoint some equipments must be designed to resist vibration damage. This

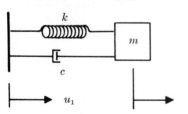

**Fig. 3-26** Vibrational system with a single degree of freedom excited by motion of the foundation.

is frequently true of equipment transported or used on certain types of aircraft and other vehicles. Failures generally result from fatigue, usually after many cycles of stress.

The analysis of a simple, single-degree-of-freedom system excited by sinusoidal motion $\omega_1$ of the support foundation (Fig. 3-26) is similar to that for the small mass $m_2$ of the preceding analysis, except that the transient terms of frequency $\omega_2$ are neglected. This is because, for vibration analysis, only the continuous, steady-state conditions are usually of interest, and terms based on the natural frequency $\omega_2$ are quickly damped out. Damping may also affect the response to the forcing function frequency, $\omega$, in a major way, and its presence is recognized by introducing the coefficient of viscosity, $c$, in a Voigt model representation.

The *transmissibility* of the sinusoidal motion of the foundation to the steady-state, sinusoidal motion of the mass is shown in Fig. 3-27 for various levels of damping and for various ratios of exciting frequency to natural frequency, $\omega_1/\omega_2 = \omega_1/\sqrt{k/m}$. These curves are similar to the ratios of

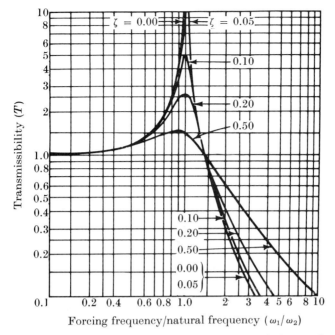

**Fig. 3-27**  Transmissibility of displacement, velocity, and acceleration for a viscous-damped system excited by sinusoidal motion of the support.

maximum values in Fig. 3-24 except that, since only pure sinusoids of the same frequency (though of different phase angle) are being compared, the same curves of Fig. 3-27 represent ratios of maximum displacement, velocity, and acceleration.

The curves are plotted from the relation

$$T = \sqrt{\frac{1 + (2\zeta\omega_1/\omega_2)^2}{[1 - (\omega_1/\omega_2)^2]^2 + (2\zeta\omega_1/\omega_2)^2}}$$

which is derived from the equations of motion, and where the parameter $\zeta = c/(2\sqrt{km}) = c/2m\omega_2$ represents the fraction of critical damping present. Very simple structures have inherent damping which varies, typically, from about $\zeta = 0.01$–$0.02$ for machined or welded construction to perhaps $0.05$ for bolted or riveted construction. Complex structures containing a variety of parts and mounted components generally have higher values.

Comparison of Figs. 3-24 and 3-27 shows the improvements gained for the vibration case by eliminating the starting transients. With reference to the vibration curve for zero damping, the frequency ratios must exceed $\sqrt{2}$, rather than 2, for a reduction in maximum acceleration; also, the rate of improvement is greater as the frequency ratio is further increased by reduction of the natural frequency. A substantial reduction in displacement, rather than an increase, is also experienced. Actual space saving may not be realized, however, because a structure subject to vibration usually has shock requirements also.

## MOTION DECOUPLING

One of the first steps in design for dynamic isolation is to require, if at all possible, that for each coordinate direction, the line of action of the shock mounts should be through the center of gravity (c.g.) of the sprung mass. The

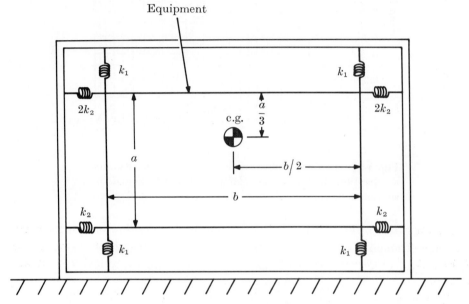

**Fig. 3-28**  Uncoupled vibratory mass.

mounts should also be designed so that rotation of the mass about its c.g. in any direction will cause no resultant translational force. Then the motion of the mass in any of its six degrees of freedom will be uncoupled from all the others, and each such motion satisfies the simple oscillator equation. Figure 3-28 shows a mass with an offset center of gravity. Motions of this mass have been decoupled in the plane of the paper by a suitable choice of spring constants. It is assumed, of course, that the equipment is rigid compared to the shock mount. If this were not so, the amount of isolation introduced by the mount would be small.

The shock spectra for the various linear and rotational directions are examined to determine the frequency needed for the mass-mount combination in order to meet the acceleration limit of the equipment. The appropriate shock mounts for the various directions must then be designed. Each mount must have the stiffness to produce the correct frequency and must be able to withstand the total motion required.

The large rattle space needed to protect some equipment from heavy ground shock can present a serious space problem where units are independently mounted. A common solution to avoid separate rattle spaces between

**Fig. 3-29** Platform-mounted power equipment as used with hardened carrier systems. Shock mounts are just visible along the right edge of the platform.

the various equipment units is to combine a number of units on a single shock-mounted platform, Fig. 3-29, for which rattle space is needed only around the periphery. Another solution is to suspend the equipment from pendulous mounts, again with adjacent units anchored together to prevent individual motion. The frames shown in Fig. 3-30 are suspended from the ceiling by steel rods which contain shock absorbers to protect against vertical shock. These absorbers may be mounted in various offset positions relative to the rods in order to provide various stiffnesses. These stiffnesses can be matched to the weights of the frames to give approximately equal natural frequencies in the vertical direction. Since horizontal motions depend chiefly on pendulum

**Fig. 3-30**  Pendulous-mounted electronic switching equipment in a hardened application (wiring side of frames shown).

action for which frequency is independent of mass, these frequencies are well matched also. This minimizes stress on the interconnecting frame members. The supports at the base of the frames in Fig. 3-30 are weak snubbers which limit swinging under normal conditions.

Both of these commonly used arrangements depart from the "ideal" in that coupling is present between the various degrees of freedom. Two examples illustrating the approach to analysis of these more complex cases are discussed next.

**Example 3.6.** Because of surrounding equipment, the cabinet of Fig. 3-31 must be mounted directly to the floor, without support at the sides. The cabinet has three degrees of freedom in the plane of the paper: translations $u$ and $v$ (measured relative to the ground) and rotation $\theta$. The cabinet has mass $m$ and moment of inertia $I$ about the center of gravity. Each of the two mounting springs has vertical stiffness $k_v$ and horizontal stiffness $k_h$. Assume that the mounting is to provide protection only for translational ground motion (no ground rotation). The equations of motion[6,7,10] of the body may then be

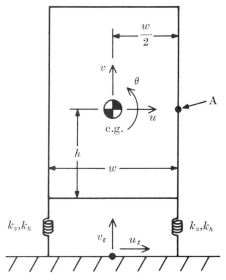

**Fig. 3-31** Floor mounted cabinet.

written

$$I\frac{d^2\theta}{dt^2} + (\tfrac{1}{2}k_vw^2 + 2k_hh^2)\theta + 2hk_hu = 0 \tag{3-60a}$$

$$m\frac{d^2u}{dt^2} + 2k_hu + 2hk_h\theta = -m\frac{d^2u_g}{dt^2} \tag{3-60b}$$

$$m\frac{d^2v}{dt^2} + 2k_vv = -m\frac{d^2v_g}{dt^2} \tag{3-60c}$$

Because the horizontal mount forces do not act through the center of gravity, $\theta$ and $u$ are coupled while $v$ is uncoupled and may be treated independently.

Let us decouple Eqs. (3-60a and b). We do this not by solving the homogeneous equations, as was done for Eq. (3-5) in a previous section, but merely by finding the decoupling transformation. Assume one of the decoupled variables to be

$$\eta = \alpha\theta + u$$

or

$$u = \eta - \alpha\theta \tag{3-61}$$

where $\alpha$ is an as-yet-unknown constant. Substituting Eq. (3-61) into Eqs. (3-60a and b) gives

$$I\frac{d^2\theta}{dt^2} + (\tfrac{1}{2}k_vw^2 + 2k_hh^2)\theta + 2hk_h(\eta - \alpha\theta) = 0 \tag{3-62a}$$

$$m\left(\frac{d^2\eta}{dt^2} - \alpha\frac{d^2\theta}{dt^2}\right) + 2k_h(\eta - \alpha\theta) + 2hk_h\theta = -m\frac{d^2u_g}{dt^2} \tag{3-62b}$$

Multiplying through Eq. (3-62a) by $m\alpha/I$ and adding to Eq. (3-62b) gives

$$m\frac{d^2\eta}{dt^2} + 2k_h\left(1 + \frac{hm\alpha}{I}\right)\eta + 2\left[-\frac{hk_hm}{I}\alpha^2 + \left(\frac{k_vw^2m + 4k_hh^2m}{4I} - k_h\right)\alpha + hk_h\right]\theta$$

$$= -m\frac{d^2u_g}{dt^2} \quad (3\text{-}63)$$

The $\alpha$ which decouples the equation is found by setting the quantity in brackets equal to zero and solving for $\alpha$, i.e.,

$$\alpha = \frac{-I}{2hk_hm}\left[k_h - \frac{k_vw^2m + 4k_hh^2m}{4I} \pm \sqrt{\left(k_h - \frac{k_vw^2m + 4k_hh^2m}{4I}\right)^2 + \frac{4h^2k_h^2m}{I}}\right]$$

$$(3\text{-}64)$$

These two values of $\alpha$ are designated $\alpha_1$ and $\alpha_2$, while corresponding values of $\eta$ are $\eta_1$ and $\eta_2$. The two decoupled equations may then be written as follows from Eq. (3-63) with the coefficient of $\theta$ equal to zero:

$$m\frac{d^2\eta_1}{dt^2} + k_1\eta_1 = -m\frac{d^2u_g}{dt^2} \quad (3\text{-}65a)$$

$$m\frac{d^2\eta_2}{dt^2} + k_2\eta_2 = -m\frac{d^2u_g}{dt^2} \quad (3\text{-}65b)$$

where

$$k_1 = 2k_h\left(1 + \frac{hm\alpha_1}{I}\right)$$

and

$$k_2 = 2k_h\left(1 + \frac{hm\alpha_2}{I}\right)$$

Since Eqs. (3-65a and b) have the form of simple oscillators excited by the ground motion $u_g$, then the solutions can be read directly from shock spectrum paper. For example, if $\omega_1 = \sqrt{k_1/m} = 2\pi(30 \text{ Hz})$ and $\omega_2 = \sqrt{k_2/m} = 2\pi(20 \text{ Hz})$, and if the ground motion gives the shock spectrum of Fig. 3-21, then

$$\eta_{1\max} = 0.0023 \text{ m}, \qquad \left(\frac{d^2\eta_1}{dt^2}\right)_{\max} = 8.4 \text{ g} \quad (3\text{-}66a)$$

and

$$\eta_{2\max} = 0.0034 \text{ m}, \qquad \left(\frac{d^2\eta_2}{dt^2}\right)_{\max} = 5.5 \text{ g} \quad (3\text{-}66b)$$

Note that both the equations of motion [Eq. (3-60)] and readings on shock spectrum charts are in terms of displacement relative to the ground. On the other hand, shock spectrum charts conveniently give total accelerations as needed to determine the forces and stresses developed in the equipment and shock mounts.

A very interesting characteristic of the modes of Eq. (3-66) can now be used to find the maximum values of $u$ and $\theta$ from the above values. It is always possible, in problems like the above, to excite only one of the modes by use of a proper forcing function. Now, if we hypothetically excite, by this means, only the $\eta_1$ mode, then of course $\eta_2 = 0$ for all time. But we must still use the fact that, from Eq. (3-61), $\eta_2 = 0 = \alpha_2\theta + u$ in order to extract the separate values of $\theta$ and $u$ from $\eta_1$. To put this another way, setting all but one mode equal to zero defines the mode shape of that remaining mode. This is true, in general, for problems of this type, even when more degrees of freedom are present. In the above case, the relationship of $\theta$ and $u$ in the $\eta_1$ mode is obtained by setting $\eta_2 = 0$, i.e., for $\eta_1$ vibration, $u = -\alpha_2\theta$ and, similarly, for $\eta_2$ vibration, $u = -\alpha_1\theta$. Then for $\eta_1$ vibration where $u = -\alpha_2\theta$, from Eqs. (3-61) and (3-66), we obtain

$$\theta_{max} = \left|\frac{0.0023}{\alpha_1 - \alpha_2}\right| \text{ rad}, \qquad \left(\frac{d^2\theta}{dt^2}\right)_{max} = \left|\frac{8.4}{\alpha_1 - \alpha_2}\right| \text{ g/m} \qquad (3\text{-}67a)$$

$$u_{max} = \left|\frac{0.0023}{1 - \alpha_1/\alpha_2}\right| \text{ m}, \qquad \left(\frac{d^2u}{dt^2}\right)_{max} = \left|\frac{8.4}{1 - \alpha_1/\alpha_2}\right| \text{ g} \qquad (3\text{-}67b)$$

Similarly for the $\eta_2$ mode,

$$\theta_{max} = \left|\frac{0.0034}{\alpha_2 - \alpha_1}\right| \text{ rad}, \qquad \left(\frac{d^2\theta}{dt^2}\right)_{max} = \left|\frac{5.5}{\alpha_2 - \alpha_1}\right| \text{ g/m} \qquad (3\text{-}68a)$$

$$u_{max} = \left|\frac{0.0034}{1 - \alpha_2/\alpha_1}\right| \text{ m}, \qquad \left(\frac{d^2u}{dt^2}\right)_{max} = \left|\frac{5.5}{1 - \alpha_2/\alpha_1}\right| \text{ g} \qquad (3\text{-}68b)$$

Over a period of several cycles, it is to be expected that these modes may both reach maximum at the same time. Thus, the total maximum for each of the above values is the sum from each mode. For example,

$$\left(\frac{d^2\theta}{dt^2}\right)_{\substack{max \\ total}} = \left|\frac{8.4 + 5.5}{\alpha_1 - \alpha_2}\right| \text{ g/m}, \quad \text{etc.}$$

The decoupled vertical mode has a frequency $\sqrt{2k_v/m}$, which is equal to, say, 10 Hz. This value gives, from the vertical spectrum of Fig. 3-21,

$$v_{max} = 0.012 \text{ m}, \qquad \left(\frac{d^2v}{dt^2}\right)_{max} = 4.4 \text{ g}$$

The maximum acceleration varies throughout the body, since components from both translation and rotation must be added. For example, the maximum vertical acceleration of the point A is

$$4.4 \text{ g} + \frac{w}{2}\left|\frac{8.4 + 5.5}{\alpha_1 - \alpha_2}\right| \text{ g}$$

An illustration of shock mounting similar to that covered in the previous example is shown in Fig. 3-32. The protected equipment is at the left, rigidly attached to a mounting plate whose right end is shown supported by two brackets and shock-absorbing mounts. While these mounts are at right angles

**Fig. 3-32**  A shock-mounted A2A video unit.

and directed toward the center of mass of the supported equipment, the unsymmetrical suspension results in coupling between the degrees of freedom in a manner similar to that just discussed.

**Example 3.7.** Another kind of shock mount in which coupling causes trouble is that in which the coupling is nonlinear. Such a mount is shown in Fig. 3-33. This example has three degrees of freedom: swinging and vertical motions

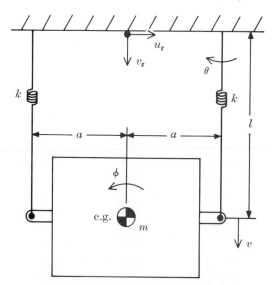

**Fig. 3-33**  Pendulous shock mount.

relative to the mounting surface, and rotation of the mass about its own center of gravity.

The equations governing the motion of the mass can be written in many different forms, depending on the number and complexity of the nonlinear terms retained. Lagrange's equation is most useful in developing the equations for systems of this complexity, if we wish to retain the many types of inertial coupling. The equations themselves are not important; they have not been solved in any of their nonlinear forms for either transient or steady-state motions. Of greater importance is the fact that design parameters can still be easily estimated in such complex situations.

Although the coupling is nonlinear, the equations of motion can be written in an approximate, linearized form which removes all coupling, as follows:

$$\frac{d^2\theta}{dt^2} + \frac{g}{l}\theta = -\frac{1}{l}\frac{d^2u_g}{dt^2}$$

$$m\frac{d^2v}{dt^2} + 2kv = -m\frac{d^2v_g}{dt^2}$$

$$I\frac{d^2\phi}{dt^2} + 2a^2k\phi = 0$$

where $l$ is assumed to be very much larger than $v$. Now the three motions appear to be uncoupled, which, in reality, they are not. If, however, each of the three motions is treated separately to determine its initial response to some input, the energy absorbed by each mode due to a ground shock can be obtained. Then, when important design parameters, such as rattle space or maximum acceleration, must be evaluated, we can assume that the energy initially absorbed by the various modes is distributed later by the nonlinear coupling among the modes in such a way as to maximize the parameter in question. For example, assume that the swinging and vertical frequencies are 0.3 Hz and 0.6 Hz, respectively. If the equipment must withstand the shock spectra of Fig. 3-21, the uncoupled maximum values of $\theta$ and $v$ are $0.15/l$ and $0.18$ m, respectively. The stored spring energy in the vertical mode is $2(\frac{1}{2})k(0.18)^2$, and if we are interested in the horizontal rattle space, we must assume that this energy has been transferred to the swinging mode. The swinging energy due to the maximum angle $0.15/l$ is $(mg/2l)(0.15)^2$ which is the weight times the maximum vertical motion. Therefore, the total energy is

$$\frac{mg}{2l}(0.15)^2 + k(0.18)^2$$

and the total lateral motion, including that due to the energy from both modes, is

$$l\theta_{\max} = \sqrt{(0.15)^2 + \frac{2lk}{mg}(0.18)^2}$$

Since, from the frequency ratio, $\sqrt{2k/m}/\sqrt{g/l} = 2$, then $2kl/mg = 4$, and

$$l\theta_{\max} = \sqrt{(0.15)^2 + 4(0.18)^2} = 0.39 \text{ m} \quad (15.3 \text{ in.})$$

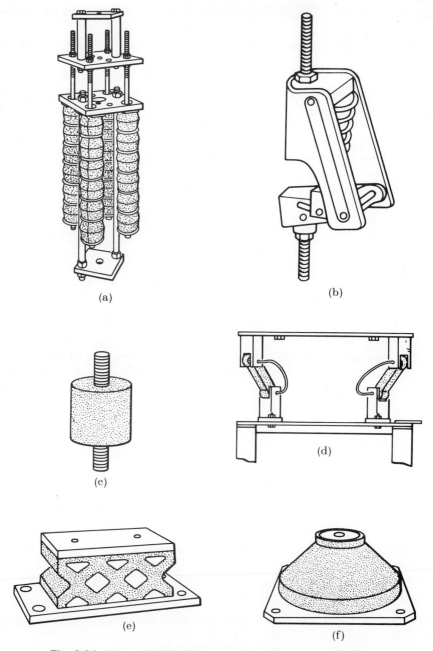

(a)

(b)

(c)

(d)

(e)

(f)

**Fig. 3-34**   Some shock isolators used in electronic equipment.

Thus, the required rattle space is more than twice the value calculated by considering only the swinging mode.

A similar determination of maximum acceleration might require (depending on the geometry) that all the energy be contained in the rotational mode or in the vertical mode, etc.

## ISOLATORS AND CUSHIONING MATERIALS

Shock or vibration protection may be provided by designing the basic structure to have a suitable compliance with relation to its mass, or by using compliant supports such as springs or commercial isolators. Although simple springs are effective, inexpensive, and easily tailored to provide the desired characteristics for a particular application, the commercial isolators are often easier to mount. Inexpensive mounts using rubber (usually in shear) are ordinarily limited to frequencies above 10 Hz and to amplitudes of about 0.3 cm or less. However, special designs are available with larger capacities. Commercial mounts using steel coil springs are usually limited to amplitudes of about 3 cm or less, but relatively expensive models are available with higher amplitudes and with frequencies down to 2 Hz. A few examples of isolators currently used with electronic equipment are shown in Fig. 3-34; their characteristics are given in Fig. 3-35. Examples of specific applications for isolators (c) and (f) have been shown in Figs. 3-32 and 3-29, respectively.

Unlike most springs, commercial isolators using rubber are often non-linear in their deflection characteristics, becoming stiffer (or occasionally less stiff through buckling action) and therefore developing higher acceleration forces as the deflections increase. In addition, these characteristics vary with the rate of loading. It is important, therefore, to use such isolators for their designed conditions. Consider, for example, the last isolator listed in Fig. 3-35. If this isolator supports the average designed load of 815 kg (1800 pounds) and experiences a vertical shock corresponding to a velocity of 0.76 m/s (30 in./s), the unit should oscillate with a natural frequency of 4 Hz. From a response spectrum chart, a maximum acceleration of 2.0 g would be expected. The actual maximum acceleration, however, is 3.1 g, a significant increase as a result of nonlinear deflection that will require greater structural strength. Other precautions, such as a supporting geometry that will decouple motions in the six degrees of freedom (three translational and three rotational) have already been discussed.

A variety of resilient cushioning materials are in common use to provide shock and vibration protection during shipment. These materials are foamed or of fibrous construction to provide a low modulus of elasticity; they are generally used only in compression at relatively low stress levels. Examples are latex-bonded hair, corrugated fiberboard, cellulose wadding, and foams of latex,

| View in Fig. 3-34 | Designation* | Designed load (kg) | | | Natural frequency (Hz) Vert. | Horiz. | Maximum input velocity (cm/s) | Maximum acceleration transmitted at maximum velocity (g) Vert. | Horiz. | Maximum deflection (cm) |
|---|---|---|---|---|---|---|---|---|---|---|
| (a) | Barry 20450 | 70 | to | 140† | 2.50 | 0.25 | 152 | 3.0 | — | 14.2 |
|  |  | 140 | to | 200† | 2.50 | 0.25 | 152 | 3.0 | — | 14.2 |
|  |  | 200 | to | 320† | 2.75 | 0.25 | 152 | 3.0 | — | 14.2 |
|  |  | 320 | to | 450† | 2.75 | 0.25 | 152 | 3.0 | — | 14.2 |
|  |  | 450 | to | 680† | 2.75 | 0.25 | 152 | 3.0 | — | 14.2 |
| (b) | Crown KS20243 | 67 | to | 670‡ | 3.3 | 0.25 | 127 | 2.8 | — | 8.1 |
| (c) | Lord J6984-75 | 1.5 (Shear) | | | 16.8 | 6.9 | 38 | — | 1.7 | 0.86 |
|  | or Royal 302A | 2.0 (Comp.) | | | 14.3 | 5.9 | 30 | 2.9 | — | 0.30 |
| (d) | Barry 17580 | 102 | | | 2.85 | 2.90 | 165 | 2.5 | 2.8 | 9.1 |
|  | Barry 17590 | 280 | | | 2.85 | 4.40 | 165 | 4.2 | 5.0 | 9.1 |
| (e) | Barry 18020 | 730 | | | 6.00 | — | 76 | 3.0 | — | 2.8 |
| (f) | Barry 17975 | 110 | to | 250 | 4.50 | 4.75 | 76 | 2.2 | 2.2 | 3.0 |
|  | Barry 20002 | 250 | to | 500 | 4.30 | 4.50 | 76 | 2.5 | 2.0 | 3.0 |
|  | Barry 20897 | 500 | to | 630 | 4.00 | 4.20 | 76 | 3.0 | 2.9 | 3.0 |
|  | Barry 20336 | 630 | to | 1000 | 4.00 | 4.10 | 76 | 3.1 | 3.0 | 3.0 |

* Barry Controls Division of Barry Wright Corp., Watertown, Mass.; Crown Controls Corp., New Bremen, Ohio; Lord Mfg. Co., Erie, Pa.; U.S. Rubber Co., Rockefeller Center, New York, N.Y.

† Ranges shown apply for 1 to 5 columns, respectively.

‡ Continuously adjustable for any load in this range.

**Fig. 3-35** Physical and electrical characteristics of some shock isolators used in electronic equipment.

polyester and polyether urethane, polyethylene, and polystyrene. These and other materials provide a wide variety of resilience and strength characteristics that have been well evaluated for packing purposes.[1] The following example illustrates a method of analysis that is useful for relatively small shock loadings, for which the velocity of deformation is low.

**Example 3.8.** A program store, used in an electronic switching system, consists of three frames, or shipping units. The heaviest frame, shown in Fig. 3-36, contains eight twistor memories and weighs 810 kg (1800 pounds). In this example, the problem is to estimate the degree of shock which the crated frame can withstand during shipping and handling without damage to the external structural members of the frame. Also, we would like to compare this shock load with the commercial trucking shock spectrum of Fig. 3-14 and with the spectrum for railroad car coupling in Fig. 3-16. The crate supports the frame on its side

**Fig. 3-36**  Program store memory frame, partially uncrated after shipment.

and is provided with skids on the down side to facilitate handling with a forklift truck. It is assumed that this orientation will be maintained during transportation.

VERTICAL SHOCK. As shown in Fig. 3-37, the entire weight of the frame rests on the lower upright which, in turn, is supported by a 5-cm thick section of foam polyethylene. The polyethylene rests on a sturdy wood structure which is assumed to be very stiff in comparison with the polyethylene. The load is applied to the upper surface of the upright through heavy brackets which protect this surface from bowing. The load is assumed to be uniformly distributed along the 214-cm length of the upright.

The first step is to anticipate the mode of failure. In this example, we will assume that, as the shock load increases beyond some limit, the thin lower side of the upright will become bowed concave upward across its width, due to uniform pressure from the polyethylene. While the edges of this surface are not

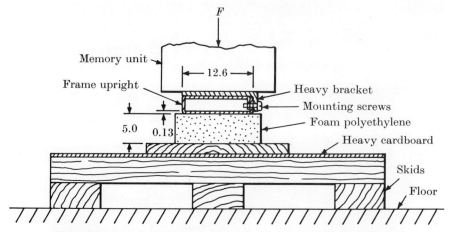

**Fig. 3-37**  Detail of vertical support structure (all dimensions in centimeters).

simply supported, they are more simple than fixed, and simple support will be assumed as a conservative measure. Thus, the lower surface becomes a thin, very wide, and comparatively short, simply supported beam with uniform load.

The upright is of low-carbon steel, $\frac{1}{4}$ hard, and has a yield stress of $280 \times 10^6$ N/m² (about 40,000 psi). The maximum allowable moment, then, is

$$M_f = \frac{\sigma_f I}{c} = \frac{280 \times 10^6 \times 214 \times 0.13^3 \times 10^{-6}}{12 \times 0.13/2} = 169 \text{ N·m}$$

From simple beam theory, for a uniform load,

$$F = \frac{8M_f}{l} = \frac{8 \times 169}{12.6 \times 10^{-2}} = 10,700 \text{ N}$$

where $F$ is the maximum allowable force. Since the frame provides a static weight of 810 kg (or 7940 newtons), only $(10,700 - 7940)/7940 = 0.35$ g shock can be sustained without danger of permanent bowing of the lower surface.

The area of the polyethylene which supports this load is $12.6 \times 214 = 2700$ cm², resulting in a maximum compressive stress of $10,700/(2700 \times 10^{-4}) = 40,000$ N/m². From Fig. 3-38, the corresponding total compression of the polyethylene is about $0.20 \times 5 = 1.0$ cm. For this nonlinear characteristic, the static compressive stress of $7940/(2700 \times 10^4) = 29,400$ N/m² results in a total compression of about $0.10 \times 5 = 0.5$ cm. Thus, the dynamic deflection which corresponds to the dynamic load of 0.35 g is $1.0 - 0.5 = 0.5$ cm. From Fig. 3-14, this shock capability is seen to be well below the maximum commercial trucking spectrum, so that some shipping damage might be expected. Also, from Fig. 3-14, the maximum velocity is roughly 0.13 m/s which, from Fig. 3-17, corresponds to a drop height of only about 0.1 cm.

Notice, from Fig. 3-14, that reducing the stiffness of the polyethylene (reducing the area or increasing the thickness) would have little effect on resistance to

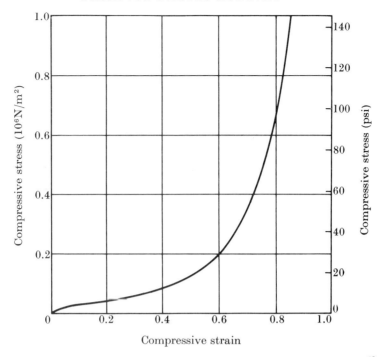

**Fig. 3-38**  Typical stress-strain characteristic of foam polyethylene.[13]

trucking shock. Only increasing the permissible g value helps, such as by reinforcing the side of the upright during shipment with a sheet of heavy plywood. Also, note that this calculation was conservative in the assumptions of simple support at the edges and in uniformly loaded polyethylene. Since the polyethylene deflection is only 1 cm, deflection of the upright may not be negligible by comparison, and even elastic deformation will reduce the load in the center.

END SHOCK. The frame is packed to resist end shock from either direction. Examination of the top channel and base details suggests that the top channel may be slightly weaker and will thus be analyzed. This material is also low-carbon steel, but of a softer grade, with a yield strength of $220 \times 10^6 \text{ N/m}^2$ (32,000 psi).

As shown in Fig. 3-39, the top channel is supported by a sheet of plywood which rests against six strips of foam polyethylene. It is assumed that the heavier gauge metal of the top channel, plus the plywood, will prevent distortion of the kind experienced with the frame upright. Instead, it is assumed that the channel will fail in simple flexure and that the thin plywood offers no reinforcement in the lengthwise direction.

Although the channel is welded to the frame uprights, these supports are not fixed since the uprights and welded joints have some flexibility. Therefore, simple support will again be assumed. If calculations show adequate channel

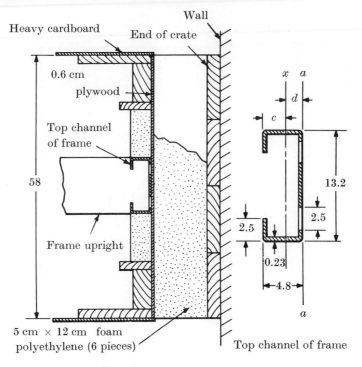

Top view

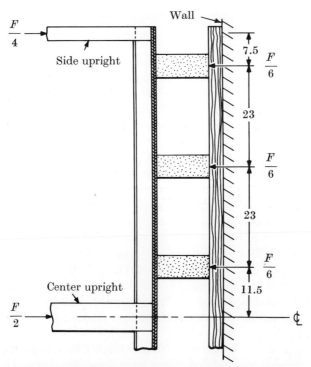

**Fig. 3-39** Detail of end support structure with enlarged view of frame channel (all dimensions in centimeters).

strength under this condition, we are not dependent on the stiffness of the joints to reduce the bending moment in the channel. Even so, the joint might be investigated for stiffness and strength to determine whether joint distortion might constitute another mode of failure.

It is first necessary to locate the centroid of the channel and to calculate $I$. From the enlarged section in Fig. 3-39, the cross-sectional area is found to be 5.04 cm² and the first moment of the area about the $a$-$a$ axis is 10.4 cm³, giving a distance $d$ to the centroid of 2.06 cm. From this, the moment of inertia $I_{xx}$ is calculated to be 18.4 cm⁴. The distance $c$ from the centroid to the outermost fiber is $4.80 - 2.06 = 2.74$ cm. The cross-sectional areas of the 2.5-cm wide holes in the outer surface of the channel are omitted from these calculations. No stress concentration factor is applied, however, since the channel is a ductile material not subject to fatigue failures. Then,

$$M_f = \frac{\sigma_f I}{c} = \frac{220 \times 10^6 \times 18.4 \times 10^{-6}}{2.74} = 1480 \text{ N·m} \quad (13{,}100 \text{ lb- in.})$$

From the lower view of Fig. 3-39 the location of maximum moment is quickly determined to be opposite the polyethylene strip near the center of the span. Summing the moments at this point, we obtain:

$$M_f = \frac{F}{4} (23 + 7.5)10^{-2} - \frac{F}{6} (23)10^{-2} = 0.038 F \text{ N·m}$$

Then,

$$F = \frac{M_f}{0.038} = \frac{1480}{0.038} = 39{,}000 \text{ N} \quad (17{,}300 \text{ lb})$$

and the allowable shock load is

$$\frac{39{,}000}{7940} = 4.9 \text{ g}$$

The area of polyethylene which supports the end shock load is $6 \times 58 \times 5 = 1740$ cm², giving a unit stress of 224,000 N/m². From Fig. 3-38, and with a depth of 12 cm, the deflection of the polyethylene is $0.62 \times 12 = 7.5$ cm.

Since this is a horizontal shock, the railroad coupling spectrum of Fig. 3-16 is of interest. The point for this deflection and shock load is below the recommended curve; moreover, the effective location on the spectrum chart should be even lower, since the curvature of the material characteristic results in less energy absorption at this deflection than for a linearly elastic material. However, failure of these top channels has not been a problem. This suggests that the spectrum may be somewhat higher than optimum for maximum economy. From the area under the curve of Fig. 3-38, it can be readily shown that the frame and packing are protected to a "drop" height of 12.7 cm (5.0 in.)— in an end direction, of course. This is a substantial drop for a unit of this size and, with modern handling methods, should seldom be exceeded.

FRONTAL SHOCK. Frontal shock will be experienced if the frame is shipped transverse to the length of the car, anchored to a bulkhead wall as shown in Fig. 3-40. The two ends of the frame are supported somewhat similarly, but with different pieceparts, to match the frame geometry. The mode of failure assumed is that the uprights, which are supported at the ends but carry a distributed load, will fail in flexure.

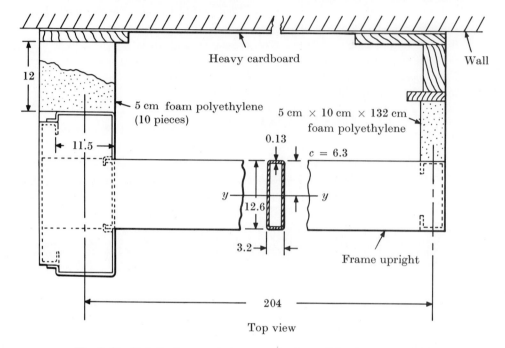

**Fig. 3-40**   Detail of support structure for frontal shock (all dimensions in centimeters).

Since bending is about the $y$-$y$ axis, the screw holes in Fig. 3-37 occur in regions of maximum stress and make the simplified cross section of Fig. 3-40 reasonable. $I_{yy}$ is calculated to be 72.9 cm⁴, and the allowable moment is

$$M_f = \frac{\sigma_f I_{yy}}{c} = \frac{280 \times 10^6 \times 72.9 \times 10^{-6}}{6.3} = 3240 \text{ N·m}$$

Since the top upright supports only one-quarter of the total load,

$$F = \frac{M_f \times 4 \times 8}{l} = \frac{3240 \times 32}{2.04} = 50,800 \text{ N}$$

and the shock capability is

$$\frac{50,800}{7940} = 6.4 \text{ g}$$

Examination shows that the polyethylene support at the right end is slightly stiffer than that at the left, so this will be used for a more conservative calculation of deflection. The stress on the polyethylene is

$$\frac{50,800}{2 \times 5 \times 132 \times 10^{-4}} = 385,000 \text{ N/m}^2$$

From Fig. 3-38, the deflection becomes $0.72 \times 10 = 7.2$ cm. This protection is below the recommended level for railroad car coupling in Fig. 3-16, but the energy absorption corresponds to a 13-cm (5.1 in.) drop—adequate for most handling situations.

It is evident that the shock resistance of the external frame members and shock mounts determines, to a degree, the requirements for the interior structure and components. If the components have greater shock resistance than the structure, which is often the case, failure of the structure can sometimes save the more expensive components. Figure 3-19 illustrates this case.

The preceding example was simplified by neglecting the effect of creep on the thickness of the polyethylene cushion. Such creep, caused by the static load of the frame, can be appreciable over a period of time and should be considered unless shipment immediately follows packing.

Also, in the preceding analysis, shock spectrum charts are used to compare the requirements of specified shock loadings with the capability of package designs using nonlinear materials. To make such comparisons, the dynamic load and deflection are separated from the static values (for vertical loads). Even so, comparisons are only approximate because the motion of the load is not sinusoidal, even for the half-cycle of increasing load on which calculations are based.

It is also important to be sure that the material characteristic represents the material behavior under the conditions of use. Materials with appreciable amounts of damping (such as foamed plastics) exhibit stress-strain characteristics which are sensitive to the strain velocity, particularly when the velocity is high. In such cases, dynamic characteristics simulating the use condition are needed, as illustrated by the following example. Again, the effect of creep will be neglected.

**Example 3.9.** A chassis unit 30 cm high, 30 cm deep, and 50 cm long has a uniformly distributed weight of 180 newtons (about 40 pounds), and can withstand a shock load of 20 g in any direction. It is to be packed to withstand a drop of 76 cm (30 in.). The outside surfaces of the chassis may be considered smooth and strong on all six faces. Find the thickness of polyester urethane, foamed to a density of 35 kg/m³, that may be placed as a continuous sheet on each face to give the required protection. Characteristics for this foam material are given in Fig. 3-41.

(a) Static stress-
strain characteristic
in compression

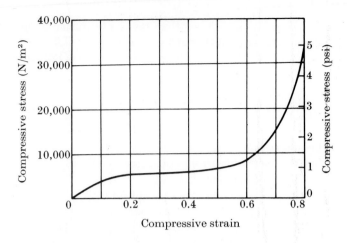

(b) Natural frequency
as a function of
static compressive
stress

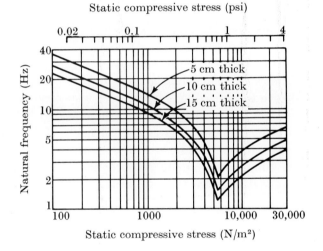

(c) Maximum acceleration
as a function of static
compressive stress
for a 76 cm (30 in.) drop

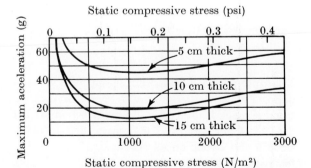

**Fig. 3-41** Characteristics of polyester, urethane foamed to a density
of 35 kg/m³ (2.2 lb/ft³).[1]

*Solution.* A package of these proportions might be dropped on any face. The ends would exert a static load of $180/(0.3)^2 = 2000$ N/m², and the sides, 1200 N/m². From Fig. 3-41(c), the required thickness is 15 cm at the ends and about 10 cm on the sides.

The foregoing solution was simple and direct, using data in the form most appropriate to the application. Consider, for instance, what would happen if the static characteristic of Fig. 3-41(a) had been used to calculate the required thickness of cushioning material at the sides. Neglecting the relatively small effect of static load, the maximum stress on the sides is $20 \times 1200 = 24,000$ N/m², for which the area under the curve is 5200 N/m². Equating energies, $Wh = 5200Ad$, or

$$d = \frac{Wh}{5200A} = \frac{180 \times 0.76}{5200 \times 0.15} = 0.175 \text{ m} = 17.5 \text{ cm}$$

This compares with the 10-cm thickness calculated in the example, suggesting that under dynamic conditions the load is picked up more rapidly, storing more energy for a given maximum deflection.

The effects of the flattened stress-strain relation on the natural frequency of static loads with small superimposed amplitudes of motion are shown somewhat dramatically in Fig. 3-41(b). However, neither chart (a) nor (b), based on essentially static loading, is very useful in this case.

## 3-5. SHOCK SUSCEPTIBILITY OF ELECTRONIC ELEMENTS

Shock can cause either failure or false operation of components. Electromechanical apparatus such as switches and relays can be operated falsely due to the inertia of the armatures or other moving parts when the applied accelerations are in the proper directions. This is seldom a problem in unhardened applications since continuous operation is usually not expected during severe shock conditions. In hardened applications, shock-resistant apparatus may be selected or designed. Shock resistance may be obtained by counterbalancing the moving parts to achieve a static balance of the masses about a pivot. By this means, we avoid rotational moment (and consequent false operation) due to translational shock which is the most prevalent kind.

Electron tubes of the usual sizes are internally quite resistant to shocks below their element frequencies of 500 to 600 Hz. However, the manner in which the tubes are mounted can make them vulnerable to damage or dislocation at lower frequencies. Special mounting techniques should be used in shock environments.[1] Larger tubes such as cathode ray or traveling wave tubes require very special shock mounting attention.

Experience in the field has shown that, during use, structural failures of small electronic devices—transistors, diodes, capacitors, resistors, transformers, etc.—usually occur at their mounts, not internally. Components supported in "pigtail" fashion by their leads are especially vulnerable; yet, even this support is adequate for many applications where shock and vibration are limited. Similarly, connecting wires are vulnerable if they support appreciable weight of associated cable. Where problems of this kind exist, the usual solution is to separately support the masses, thus relieving the connecting leads of this function.

With regard to internal strength, small components are relatively shock resistant, compared to the larger structures in which they are mounted. This is readily evident from scaling considerations, as previously discussed. Further, the relatively low natural frequency of the larger structure, together with its shock protection, effectively filters out the high-frequency portions of the shock spectrum, which are potentially most damaging to the components. Thus, the smaller components are usually more subject to damage during individual handling or manufacturing operations than during shipment or shock of the larger units in which they are mounted. When energy loads are applied directly to the components, breakage can often result because of their small energy-absorbing capacity. This capacity diminishes as the cube of the scale factor and sometimes is responsible for unexpected damage to small components. A few examples are discussed next.

Before assembly in the protective equipment environment, the components are subject to many hazards. For example, dropping or rough handling of semiconductor devices can crack the glass seals, break the semiconductor wafers, or cause the small internal bonds to open. In general, these devices are capable of withstanding shocks up to 2000 g's; but a fall from a bench to the floor can give shocks up to 6000 g's, depending on the device, the position on impact, and the type of floor. Special packing and handling procedures are therefore used with such devices.

When assembled in quantities to larger structures such as printed wire boards, axial-leaded components are frequently preassembled in rolls or strips in which the components are arranged side by side with the ends of the leads taped together. In this form, they can be fed into automatic assembly machines without the hazard of individual, manual handling. As a result of sad experience, the assembly machines are also designed to minimize shock or strain to the component. Strains to the component body are minimized by clamping the leads adjacent to the body during lead-forming operations. Also, trimming leads to length is done by shearing, rather than with the swaging action typical of conventional wire cutters. With the latter, the wire is fractured with a snap which sends a longitudinal shock wave into the component body, often breaking the semiconductor chip in a transistor or diode.

Another failure due to shock energy in small devices is illustrated by the breakage of the ferrod sticks in the ferrod sensor, shown a little larger than actual size in Fig. 3-42. The ferrod stick is of a brittle ferrite material and is weakened by two holes near the center in which single-turn windings are threaded. The ferrod stick is mounted inside the coils and is supported at the

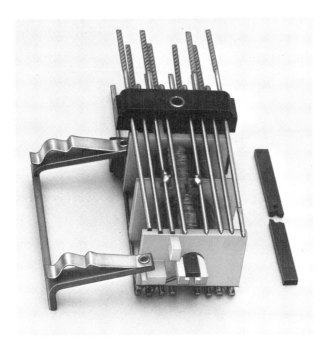

**Fig. 3-42**  Partially  disassembled  ferrod  sensor  and broken ferrod stick.

ends by molded nylon spoolheads as shown. When completely assembled, the legs of the armature, shown at the left, rest against the ends of the ferrod stick and are held in contact with the stick by spring pressure.

Frequent breakage of the sticks was encountered during handling and shipment. This was assumed to be due to the fact that the stick and associated armature were supported in the spoolhead by clearance holes, which could permit some rattling. These clearances were then filled with a soft rubber sealing compound. The problem was solved, however, only after the rubber was replaced with a soft tuft of wool yarn under each end of the stick. While this problem is still not fully understood, the wool yarn appears to absorb the shock energy associated with the relatively heavy armature, thereby protecting the ferrod stick from breakage. The soft rubber was doubly ineffective: not only did its high bulk modulus minimize energy absorption for the geometry in which it was used, but also it anchored the ends of the stick to the nylon spoolheads, thereby promoting breakage as the spacing between spoolheads shrank and expanded with changes in humidity.

Another example of unexpected damage to small parts occurred in the flying spot store, a photographic memory system. In this store, glass code plates 25 cm by 32 cm by 0.23 cm thick are precisely positioned by means of small ball bearings. During use, the ground edges of the plates are held in contact with the outer races of the bearings by light spring pressure. There was no shipping problem here since the plates were disassembled for shipment. During reassembly, however, breakage occurred with alarming regularity as the edges of the plates were brought into contact with the bearings, even though mechanical features were provided to limit the velocity of approach to the order of 3 cm per second. It was not the rugged glass plate that broke—it was the small, steel outer race of the bearing. Eventually, it became necessary to replace the bearings with blocks of energy-absorbing nylon, even though some of the positioning accuracy was thereby sacrificed.

### 3-6. DYNAMIC TESTING

Since accurate dynamic analysis is almost impossible for mechanical systems of any complexity, it is very important to make appropriate dynamic tests for assurance that equipment can survive its dynamic environment. Unfortunately, it is often difficult to design a test which reproduces a given environment with any certainty, even neglecting the fact that specification of the original environment itself is often nebulous.

We are aided, however, by the manner in which the various modes respond to shock spectra. The spectrum gives the response of a simple oscillator to a given excitation, and linear systems can be decoupled into modes, each of which satisfies the simple oscillator equation. It is evident, therefore, that two excitations with different time histories but with the same shock spectrum will both excite all the modes of a linear system to the same maximum amplitudes. It is also true that the phases between the modes in the responses to the different excitations will be different. However, the likelihood that two modes will combine in such a way as to produce maximum distortion during one of these responses is about the same as during the other response. The basic concept in dynamic testing, then, is to test equipment with a shock spectrum that will produce a response spectrum as much as possible like the response spectrum experienced in real life. Exceptions would be those rare cases when the real-life excitation has a known time history which can be reproduced in the laboratory. In such cases the known time history is used.

Historically, dynamic testing of equipment has had only two basic purposes. The first is to determine the allowable acceleration limit which the equipment can withstand without damage. The other is to evaluate the performance of the equipment either by itself or mounted on the shock isolation system it will need, using a simulation of the particular dynamic environment expected. In practice, the acceleration limit of the equipment would first be determined by test. Then the shock spectrum of the expected environment would be examined to determine the frequency of the shock mount required to limit the equipment acceleration to this value. The equipment would then be returned to the testing machine, this time on its shock mounts, and would be tested with the simulated use environment.

Many people now believe that the first of these tests is usually meaningless—that general excitations acting through various shock mounts cannot be represented by a single test series. The latest testing procedure for shock-mounting design is much more straightforward. The equipment is tested as though it were mounted on a shock mount experiencing the expected input for a series of tests in which the stiffness of the mount (and the natural frequency of the mounted equipment) is gradually increased until the equipment fails. A mount giving mounted frequencies somewhat lower than the failure frequency should then be satisfactory. Of course, if the item withstands the input for very high mount frequencies, no isolation is necessary.

The remainder of this section will discuss the types of testing machines available, their usefulness, and the associated testing procedures.

## SHOCK TEST MACHINES

Most mechanical shock test machines are either of two types—drop machines or hammer machines. In the first, equipment is attached to a carriage which is then raised some distance against gravity and dropped onto a table. As mentioned previously, if the impact were rigid (velocity step), the shock spectrum for this test would be a straight horizontal line at the impact velocity on shock spectrum paper. It is often the case that the expected dynamic environment for some equipment has the form of Fig. 3-14 or Fig. 3-16, with acceleration cutoffs at high frequencies—for example, 3 g's in Fig. 3-14 and 30 g's in Fig. 3-16. This cutoff is simulated on a drop machine by causing the drop table to impact against pellets of some malleable material. The pellets are crushed on impact and so limit the peak acceleration. The drop distance is the maximum response displacement, yielding a low-frequency displacement cutoff (see Fig. 3-43). The acceleration of the carriage in a drop test on a lead pellet machine increases approximately linearly from zero, at the moment of initial contact with the pellet, to a maximum; it then drops off abruptly to zero as motion ceases. Some structural ringing at high frequency is superimposed on this waveform. The peak acceleration corresponds to the cutoff value, and the reciprocal of the duration of the acceleration is about $\pi$ times the cutoff frequency in Hertz. If the carriage is dropped on rubber or sand, a rough, half

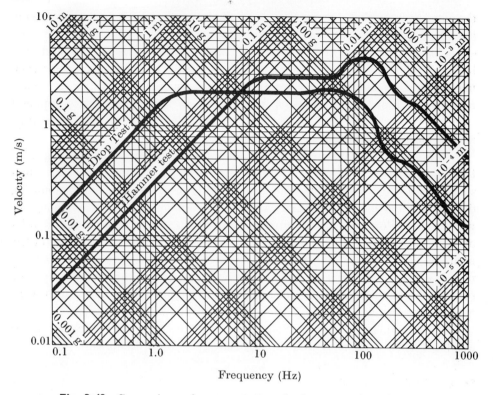

**Fig. 3-43** Comparison of representative shock spectra from hammer and drop tests.

sine wave can be produced. Figure 3-44 shows a typical drop test machine for small equipment. This model has a load capacity of 16 kg (35 lb) and a maximum drop height of 1.5 m (60 in.). The shape of the deceleration curve can be varied by changing the shape and material of the pellet.

Ideally, a hammer test is a drop test in reverse. Figure 3-45 presents the general configuration of such a tester. The hammer picks up energy by dropping through gravity and then strikes the table. If the table were not constrained, it would impulsively pick up some velocity and sail away. However, such tables have stops which limit their travel and produce the low-frequency, displacement cutoff as shown in the spectrum of Fig. 3-43. Hammer machines are more convenient for producing horizontal shocks than are drop machines; hence, they are somewhat more versatile.

Equipment can be attached to either kind of test machine and tested to shock spectra which are closely trapezoidal in shape and which, in turn, represent many real situations quite well. More complex spectral shapes can sometimes be created by spring-mounting the table, thereby causing a resonant frequency to appear as a bump at that frequency in the spectrum.

There are also hydraulic (or gas) driven devices which can produce shocks with a programmed time history by metering the fluid through an orifice. The Hyge shock tester is such a machine.

When unusually long duration of the accelerating force is needed, air gun machines can be used. In these, the equipment is mounted on a carriage in a gun barrel which is sealed at both ends. The equipment and carriage are accelerated and decelerated within the barrel by compressed air.

A large variety of shock machines is available with load capacities varying from 230 gm (0.5 lb), for a small Naval Ordnance Laboratory air gun to 2500 kg (5600 lb) for the Navy machine shown in Fig. 3-45. The latter uses a 1360-kg hammer with a maximum effective drop height of 1.7 meters and has an 1800-kg anvil on which the test equipment is mounted. Maximum accelerations vary from less than 100 g's to 2000 g's for various machines, with as high as 200,000 g's available in the small air gun.

As will be discussed in the next section, the electrodynamic vibration machine, when used with the proper associated equipment, can produce motion time histories of very general form. This means that certain transient loadings can be reproduced very accurately

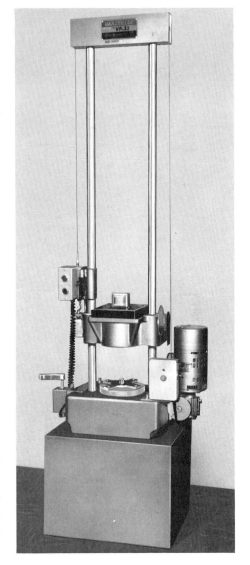

**Fig. 3-44**  Drop test machine with lead pellet between impacting surfaces.

when their time histories are known. Acceleration levels are limited compared to mechanical shock test machines, however.

### VIBRATION TEST MACHINES

The purpose of shock machines is to develop an impact which will give a shock spectrum resembling as much as possible that of the expected shock environment. Vibration test machines can be used in the same way, of course,

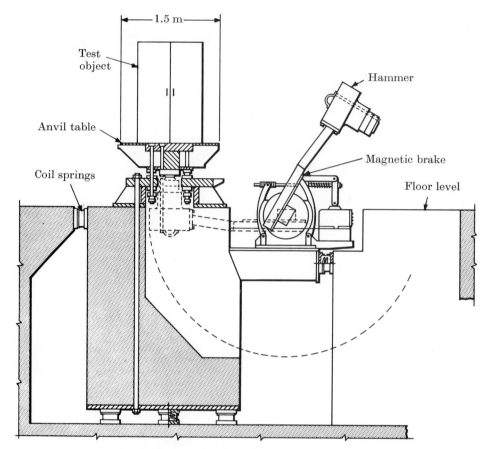

**Fig. 3-45**   High-impact, hammer shock machine.

when the expected environment is vibratory. As stated earlier, the most important dynamic environment for the communications equipment designer is usually the shock environment, whether from handling, ground shock, or transportation. Nevertheless, vibration tests are useful in precipitating fatigue failures of types that can occur under some shipping conditions with equipment that is weak in this respect. The early model memory unit of Fig. 3-4 illustrates this case.

Vibration tests can be of definite use in the investigation of shock responses of shock-mounted equipment or equipment which can be approximated by a simple oscillator. For example, assume that a shock-mounted equipment unit has a vertical mounting frequency of 10 Hz and that it experiences the ground shock of Fig. 3-21. The equipment will be left vibrating with an amplitude of 1 cm after the shock is gone and until mount damping brings the motion to rest. The shock-mounted response of this equipment can therefore be approximated by attaching the equipment directly to a vibration machine (without shock mounts) and vibrating it at 10 Hz and 1 cm displacement.

To go still further in accordance with recent shock-mount design philosophy, consider equipment that is attached directly to a vibration machine and is vibrated at continuously increasing frequencies at amplitudes which are given for each frequency by a particular shock spectrum. Then the proper shock-mounting frequency is somewhat below the frequency at which failure occurs for that equipment in the environment given by that shock spectrum. Care must be taken, however, that such a "search" test is not continued so long as to produce fatigue failures which would not occur in the real shock environment.

All the vibration characteristics of the machines to be discussed depend strongly on the weight of the equipment being tested and on the vibratory characteristics of this equipment. This is especially true when this weight is any appreciable fraction of the machine's maximum load capacity. These relationships are of principal interest to the machine operator and have been worked out in detail.[1]

The electrodynamic vibration machine is the most versatile machine for vibration testing. It utilizes the force generated by an electromagnet to accelerate the load. By applying a voltage of proper time history across the magnet terminals, any time variation of table motion can be achieved within the amplitude and frequency limitations of the machine. If only harmonic vibrations are to be produced, a single-phase alternator driven at various speeds can produce the motive power at the corresponding frequencies. But when more general time histories are required, an electronic amplifier following the output of a magnetic tape recorder may supply this power. Different tapes played through the recorder produce different time histories. Analog circuits may also be used to provide the electronic input. This type of machine is the most convenient for generating random excitation, since all one needs is a properly recorded tape.

More than 25 models of American-built vibration machines of this type are available.[1] These vary widely in capacity. A small machine weighing 16 kg and built by Textron, Inc. develops an accelerating force of 5.3 newtons (1.2 pounds) and is capable of developing 200 g's at resonance with a total amplitude of 0.064 cm. A larger machine built by the same manufacturer weighs 11,000 kg, develops 110,000 newtons (25,000 pounds) accelerating force, and has a maximum 75-g acceleration with a total amplitude of 2.5 cm.

Mechanical vibration machines (sometimes called shake tables) operate on either of two principles—direct-drive or reaction. A direct-drive machine is a positive-displacement device in the sense that the motive source is directly coupled to the vibration table, for example, through a crank and connecting rod. The reaction machine uses the inertial forces generated by one or more unbalanced rotors to excite the table. Most machines of both types can produce oscillations at various frequencies, but only one frequency at a time. By changing the phase of two unbalanced rotors, some reaction machines can cause coupled motions in two directions.

More than 40 varieties of direct-drive and reaction-type machines are available.[1] These provide maximum accelerations varying from 6.5 g's at 0.56-cm total amplitude to 63 g's at 0.32-cm amplitude for light loads. Maximum load capacities vary from 5 kg to 5000 kg. While machines of these kinds are often of higher capacities than the electrodynamic types, frequencies are usually limited to a maximum of 100 Hz, and they are much less flexible for simulating vibration spectra encountered under use conditions.

Hydraulic vibration machines are available which will produce controlled, time-varying forces and motions similar to those produced by electromagnetic machines. The hydraulic machines, however, are designed to be used at frequencies which are low and at motions and forces which are large compared to those of the electrodynamic machines. Piezoelectric vibrators operate at the other end of the frequency range—above 1000 Hz and with displacements less than 0.003 cm.

## REFERENCES

1. Harris, C. M., and C. E. Crede, *Shock and Vibration Handbook*, New York, McGraw-Hill Book Co., 1961. A complete but variable discussion of shock and vibration. Figure 3-41 by permission.

2. Crandall, S. H., and W. D. Mark, *Random Vibrations in Mechanical Systems*, New York, Academic Press, Inc., 1963. Important description of this subject.

3. Crandall, S. H., editor, *Random Vibration*, Cambridge, Mass. M.I.T., **1**, 1958; **2**, 1963. Important description of the subject.

4. Hildebrand, F. B., *Methods of Applied Mathematics*, 2nd Ed., Englewood Cliffs, N.J., Prentice-Hall, Inc., 1965.

5. Young, D., "Continuous Systems," Chap. 61, *Handbook of Engineering Mechanics*, edited by W. Flügge, New York, McGraw-Hill Book Co., 1962.

6. Jacobsen, L. S., and R. S. Ayre, *Engineering Vibrations*, New York, McGraw-Hill Book Co., 1958. General engineering solutions and methods in mechanical shock and vibration.

7. Timoshenko, S. P., *Vibration Problems in Engineering*, 3rd ed., Princeton, N. J. D. Van Nostrand Co., Inc., 1955. General engineering solutions and methods in mechanical shock and vibration.

8. Timoshenko, S. P., and S. Woinowsky-Krieger, *Theory of Plates and Shells*, 2nd ed., New York, McGraw-Hill Book Co., 1959. Solutions to many problems in the

classical small-deflection theory of plates and to problems of membrane and bending theory of thin shells; contains references and some large-deflection theory.

9. Norris, C. H., et al, *Structural Design for Dynamic Loads*, New York, McGraw-Hill Book Co., 1959. Presents, among other things, dynamic-elastic and elasto-plastic design procedures for structures.

10. Den Hartog, J. P., *Mechanical Vibrations*, 3rd ed., New York, McGraw-Hill Book Co., 1947. General engineering solutions and methods in mechanical shock and vibration.

11. *Uniform Building Code*, Pasadena, Calif., International Conf. of Building Officials, 1964. Earthquake code information is contained in Vol. 1, with zone map inside rear cover.

12. *Design of Structures to Resist Nuclear Weapons Effects*, Manual of Engineering Practice #42, New York, American Society of Civil Engineers, 1962. Includes dynamic-elastic and elasto-plastic design procedures for structures.

13. *Military Standardization Handbook—Package Cushioning Design*, MIL-HDBK-304, Department of Defense, Washington, D.C., 1964. Contains information on packaging materials and their applications.

*Part II*

**THERMAL DESIGN**

*Chapter 4*

# FUNDAMENTAL CONCEPTS IN CONDUCTIVE AND CONVECTIVE HEAT TRANSFER

## C. A. Fritsch

The operation, reliability, and life of circuit elements are related to their steady-state (and sometimes transient) temperatures of operation. The governing principles of heat transfer relate temperature directly to power dissipated. Consequently, any device in which an electrical current is flowing requires a heat transfer path from the point where the heat is generated to some heat sink. The optimization of this heat transfer path and, to a certain extent, the minimization of the energy dissipated in the device are the final ends of any thermal design.

The chapters comprising Part II of this volume present an approach to the recognition and solution of thermal design problems—an approach based on the analytical description of heat transfer phenomena. While there are no magic formulas or universal answers to thermal design problems, criteria will be developed that will aid the designer in the recognition of important problem areas and in the exercise of sound engineering judgment. In addition, the complementary use of analytical and experimental approaches will be emphasized. It is hoped that this treatment will provide insight into the applicability of specific techniques and will prepare the reader for greater use of the heat transfer literature.

The three modes of heat transfer are conduction, convection, and radiation. Conduction can be defined as a microscopic phenomenon which is described on a macroscopic scale by a coefficient times a temperature gradient. Convection heat transfer includes the conductive mechanism, but, in the convective mode, the transmission of energy is augmented by the fluid motions which are governed by momentum transfer. Radiation is electromagnetic in nature, and the description of radiative exchanges is based on the fact that photons propagate in straight lines and obey the laws of optics.

In this chapter, the basic equations necessary for solution of conductive and convective heat transfer problems are presented. Subsequent chapters will cover methods in conduction and convection, and radiative heat transfer.

## 4-1. FORMULATION OF THE CONDUCTION AND CONVECTION PROBLEM

The conductive and convective heat transfer problem can be introduced by consideration of a body of some given shape immersed in a fluid having some specified far-field temperature and velocity distribution. The fluid acts, at least temporarily, as the heat sink. Thermal design problems ultimately consist of finding the desired body shape and the optimum fluid characteristics, so that certain components on the body are held within the temperature limits required for effective operation.

In the general problem, two quantities are of interest to the engineer: the heat flux density from a certain body (wall) as given by the Fourier–Biot law

$$q_w = -k \frac{\partial T}{\partial y} \tag{4-1}$$

and the wall shear stress, which is given by Newton's law of viscosity

$$\tau_w = \mu \frac{\partial u}{\partial y} \tag{4-2}$$

where $T$ is temperature, $u$ is velocity, $y$ is a coordinate normal to the wall, $k$ is thermal conductivity, and $\mu$ is dynamic viscosity. The wall shear stress is a measure of the friction losses in a flow and of the drag on a body, while the wall heat flux is related to the temperatures attained in electrical elements.

## 4-2. TRANSPORT PHENOMENA IN GASES, LIQUIDS, AND SOLIDS

Transport properties such as thermal conductivity and dynamic viscosity allow effects actually occurring on a microscopic scale to be described in terms of macroscopic events. These properties can be understood in terms of the type of microscopic carrier active, its speed of transport, and the distance it has to travel to give up the quantity being transported.

Transport in a gas can be associated with the movement of the molecules due to their thermal energy. The molecules, moving in a random manner, interchange energy from more energetic locations to less energetic ones, the net transport being from a higher temperature to a lower one.*

In pure metals, heat conduction is analogous to electrical conduction, since the primary mechanism of transport in both cases is the conduction electrons. Thermal conductivity $k$ can thus be described in terms of an "electron gas," so that a relation between $k$ and the electrical conductivity $\sigma$ can be obtained. This relationship is called the Wiedemann–Franz–Lorentz law:

$$\frac{k}{\sigma T} = 2.44 \times 10^{-8} \ \text{V}^2/{}^{\circ}\text{K}^2 \qquad (4\text{-}3)$$

It is useful in that electrical conductivity measurements are usually easier to obtain than are measurements of $k$.

When a metal is alloyed or impurities are added, the places where electron movement is impeded become more numerous. In the extreme cases, electronic conduction decreases to such an extent that another mode of transport begins to become important. This is called *phonon* conduction, and it is similar to the method by which sound is propagated. In the limiting case, the number of conduction electrons is essentially zero, and the material is a dielectric. Phonon conduction is then the only mode operative, and the associated lattice vibrations can be treated as packets of energy propagated at the sonic velocity. These packets should be considered as a "phonon gas" in which population density, collision rate, and capacity can be predicted by statistical methods. Again, material impurities, lattice imperfections, and, at low temperatures, specimen size all serve to limit phonon movements. As a consequence, thermal conductivity in dielectrics can be very sensitive to crystalline structure.

Thermal conduction in liquids can be predicted from the consideration that liquids act more like solids than gases in that they possess a quasi-lattice structure. The molecules, due to this thermal motion, collide with their neighbors and, in doing so, transport energy according to an elastic-wave type of transport which moves with the sonic velocity $v_s$. This transport of energy can be predicted from Bridgman's equation

$$k = 3k_b v_s \lambda^{-2} \qquad (4\text{-}4)$$

where $k_b$ is Boltzmann's constant and $\lambda$ is the molecular spacing assuming a cubical lattice.

In deriving the conservation equations, we will assume a macroscopic scale on which materials may be treated as continuous. This requirement is also incorporated in the use of such coefficients as $k$ and $\mu$, since the distances for

---

* For more details concerning transport coefficients, see Jakob[1].

exchange interactions of carriers must be very small compared to the dimensions of the system being analyzed. However, in thin films at low temperatures, the assumption of a continuum may not be valid. This is illustrated in Fig. 4-1, in which the aspects of thermal conduction are summarized.

A chart demonstrating the relative values of $k$ for solids, liquids, and gases is given in Fig. 4-2. The thermal properties of design materials and of air and water are tabulated in Appendix B for convenience. While thermal property

| Material | Type of carrier | Speed | Interaction distance dependence | Interaction distance values | Theory |
|---|---|---|---|---|---|
| Gas | Molecules | Thermal velocity | Mean free path | 0.1 $\mu$m at room conditions 0.3 m at 120 km altitude | Kinetic theory (Maxwell–Boltzmann statistics) |
| Dielectric | Phonons | Sonic velocity | Phonon-phonon and phonon-structure interactions | 5 nm at 300°K A few tenths of a cm at 1°K | Phonon model (Bose–Einstein statistics) |
| Conductor | Conduction electrons | Thermal velocity | Electron-phonon and electron-structure collisions | For copper: 40 nm at room temperature; 10 $\mu$m below 10°K | Wiedemann–Franz–Lorentz law (Fermi–Dirac statistics) |
| Liquid | Elastic waves | Sonic velocity | Quasi-lattice spacing | Approximately 0.5 nm | Bridgman equation |

**Fig. 4-1**  Thermal conduction summary.

values for design purposes are available in such heat transfer texts as Eckert and Drake[2] and Hsu[3] and in survey work,[4] the most extensive coverage of property data is provided in the monumental work of the Thermophysical Properties Research Center of Purdue University.[5,6]

## 4-3. DERIVATION OF THE CONTINUITY EQUATION

To derive the conservation equations,* consider first the conservation of mass. We choose an element of volume $\Delta V$ having dimensions $\Delta x$, $\Delta y$, and $\Delta z$, as illustrated in Fig. 4-3. The material has a velocity $\mathbf{w}$ (which can be broken into $x$, $y$, $z$ components of $u$, $v$, $w$) and a density $\rho$. This material moves across the control volume, leaving behind the change in the mass flow rate ($\rho u$) according to

$$\frac{\partial(\rho u)}{\partial x} \Delta x \quad \text{etc.}$$

Assume that the control volume contains no sources or sinks of mass. The time rate of storage of mass within the volume must then be equal to the net rate at

---

* For a more rigorous treatment of this material see Ref. 7.

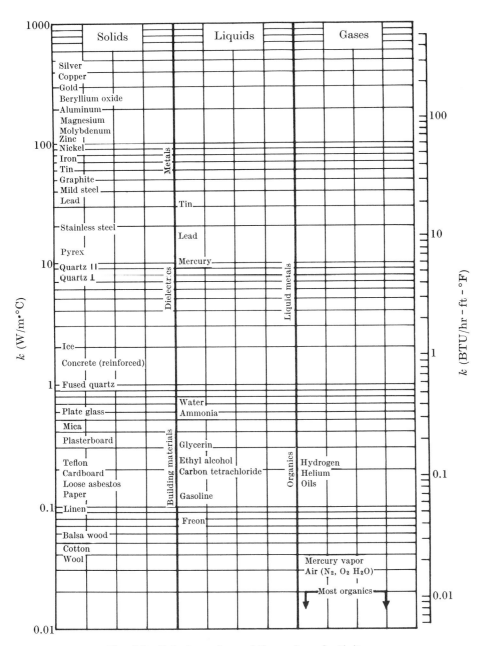

**Fig. 4-2**  Relative values of thermal conductivity.

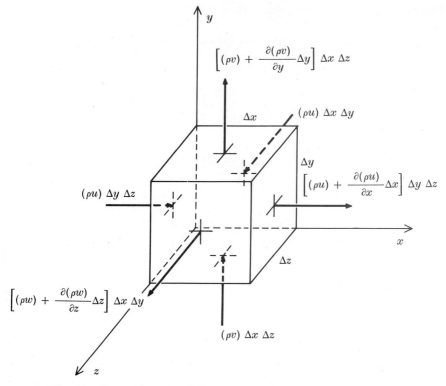

**Fig. 4-3** Convective mass balance on an elemental control volume.

which mass is convected across the bounding faces. Consequently,

$$\frac{\partial \rho}{\partial t} \, \Delta V = (\rho u) \, \Delta y \, \Delta z - \left[ (\rho u) + \frac{\partial (\rho u)}{\partial x} \, \Delta x \right] \Delta y \, \Delta z$$

$$+ (\rho v) \, \Delta x \, \Delta z - \left[ (\rho v) + \frac{\partial (\rho v)}{\partial y} \, \Delta y \right] \Delta x \, \Delta z + \cdots \text{etc.}$$

On canceling like terms and dividing by $\Delta V = \Delta x \, \Delta y \, \Delta z$, this equation reduces to the conservation of mass equation or the *continuity equation*:

$$\frac{\partial \rho}{\partial t} + \frac{\partial (\rho u)}{\partial x} + \frac{\partial (\rho v)}{\partial y} + \frac{\partial (\rho w)}{\partial z} = 0 \qquad (4\text{-}5)$$

which, in vector notation, can be written

$$\frac{\partial \rho}{\partial t} + \text{div} \, (\rho \mathbf{w}) = 0 \qquad (4\text{-}6)$$

Equation (4-5) can be expanded as

$$\frac{D\rho}{Dt} + \rho \left( \frac{\partial u}{\partial x} + \frac{\partial v}{\partial y} + \frac{\partial w}{\partial z} \right) = \frac{D\rho}{Dt} + \rho \, \text{div} \, \mathbf{w} = 0 \qquad (4\text{-}7)$$

where the operator

$$\frac{D}{Dt} = \frac{\partial}{\partial t} + u\frac{\partial}{\partial x} + v\frac{\partial}{\partial y} + w\frac{\partial}{\partial z} \tag{4-8}$$

The capitalized derivative is called the total, substantial, particle, or material derivative, since it represents the change in a property (in this case $\rho$) of a particle of material from the point of view of an observer sitting on the particle having a velocity $\mathbf{w}$. For the case where the fluid is incompressible, the changes in density are all zero; hence, $D\rho/Dt = 0$, so that the continuity equation reduces to

$$\frac{\partial u}{\partial x} + \frac{\partial v}{\partial y} + \frac{\partial w}{\partial z} = 0 \tag{4-9}$$

Again, in vector notation, Eq. (4-9) becomes div $\mathbf{w} = 0$. For the observer seated on the particle, Eq. (4-9) can be interpreted as a change in the shape of the volume of the particle.*

## 4-4. CONSERVATION OF MOMENTUM— THE NAVIER-STOKES EQUATIONS

We next consider a force balance (momentum balance) on the small particle of material with mass $\Delta m = \rho\,\Delta V$. Writing Newton's second law for the particle, we have

$$\begin{array}{c}\text{time rate of} \\ \text{change of momentum}\end{array} = \begin{array}{c}\text{net body force acting} \\ \text{on the material}\end{array} + \begin{array}{c}\text{resultant of the} \\ \text{surface forces}\end{array} \tag{4-10}$$

$$\frac{D}{Dt}(\mathbf{w}\,\Delta m) = \mathbf{F}\,\Delta V + \mathbf{P}\,\Delta V$$

where $\mathbf{F}$ and $\mathbf{P}$ are defined on a per-unit-volume basis.† We note that the mass $\Delta m$ of the particle is constant. Dividing Eq. (4-10) by $\Delta V$ therefore yields

$$\rho\frac{D\mathbf{w}}{Dt} = \mathbf{F} + \mathbf{P} \tag{4-11}$$

We now define a force per unit area $\mathbf{p}_x$, $\mathbf{p}_y$, $\mathbf{p}_z$ acting on the faces normal to the respective axes, as illustrated in Fig. 4-4. The resultant of all the surface forces $\mathbf{P}$ will be

$$\mathbf{P}\,\Delta V = \mathbf{p}_x\,\Delta y\,\Delta z - \left(\mathbf{p}_x + \frac{\partial \mathbf{p}_x}{\partial x}\,\Delta x\right)\Delta y\,\Delta z$$

$$+ \mathbf{p}_y\,\Delta x\,\Delta z - \left(\mathbf{p}_y + \frac{\partial \mathbf{p}_y}{\partial y}\,\Delta y\right)\Delta x\,\Delta z \ldots \text{etc.}$$

---

* This is analogous to the elementary statement of continuity $A_1 u_1 = A_2 u_2$ for flow through a constriction.

† Gravitational, electrostatic, and electrodynamic forces are examples of body forces.

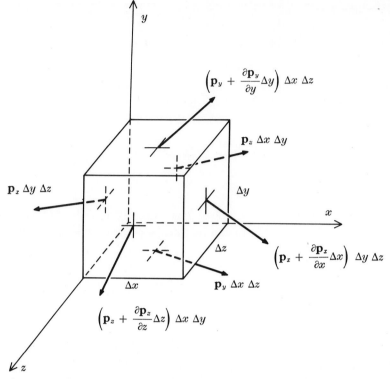

**Fig. 4-4**  Surface forces acting on an elemental particle.

Reducing and dividing by $\Delta V$, this becomes

$$\mathbf{P} = \frac{\partial \mathbf{p}_x}{\partial x} + \frac{\partial \mathbf{p}_y}{\partial y} + \frac{\partial \mathbf{p}_z}{\partial z} \tag{4-12}$$

Now each of the surface forces can be divided into shear forces in the plane of the face and normal forces perpendicular to the faces. On a per-unit-area basis, these are the stresses discussed in Chapter 2. Consequently,

$$\mathbf{p}_x = \mathbf{i}\sigma_{xx} + \mathbf{j}\tau_{xy} + \mathbf{k}\tau_{xz} \tag{4-13a}$$

$$\mathbf{p}_y = \mathbf{i}\tau_{yx} + \mathbf{j}\sigma_{yy} + \mathbf{k}\tau_{yz} \tag{4-13b}$$

$$\mathbf{p}_z = \mathbf{i}\tau_{zx} + \mathbf{j}\tau_{zy} + \mathbf{k}\sigma_{zz} \tag{4-13c}$$

Using Eqs. (4-13) in Eq. (4-12), the three components of the force balance [Eq. (4-11)] become

$$\rho \frac{Du}{Dt} = F_x + \frac{\partial \sigma_{xx}}{\partial x} + \frac{\partial \tau_{yx}}{\partial y} + \frac{\partial \tau_{zx}}{\partial z} \tag{4-14a}$$

$$\rho \frac{Dv}{Dt} = F_y + \frac{\partial \tau_{xy}}{\partial x} + \frac{\partial \sigma_{yy}}{\partial y} + \frac{\partial \tau_{zy}}{\partial z} \tag{4-14b}$$

$$\rho \frac{Dw}{Dt} = F_z + \frac{\partial \tau_{xz}}{\partial x} + \frac{\partial \tau_{yz}}{\partial y} + \frac{\partial \sigma_{zz}}{\partial z} \tag{4-14c}$$

The stresses on a fluid as exerted by the neighboring fluid can be described in terms of pressure and viscous effects. Newton's law of viscosity can be generalized by considering the elongations and angular deformations of our three-dimensional particle.[8] This *constitutive* relation yields a description similar to Hooke's law for elastic bodies, and it is called Stokes' law of friction:

$$\sigma_{xx} = -p + \lambda\left(\frac{\partial u}{\partial x} + \frac{\partial v}{\partial y} + \frac{\partial w}{\partial z}\right) + 2\mu\frac{\partial u}{\partial x} \tag{4-15a}$$

$$\sigma_{yy} = -p + \lambda\left(\frac{\partial u}{\partial x} + \frac{\partial v}{\partial y} + \frac{\partial w}{\partial z}\right) + 2\mu\frac{\partial v}{\partial y} \tag{4-15b}$$

$$\sigma_{zz} = -p + \lambda\left(\frac{\partial u}{\partial x} + \frac{\partial v}{\partial y} + \frac{\partial w}{\partial z}\right) + 2\mu\frac{\partial w}{\partial z} \tag{4-15c}$$

$$\tau_{xy} = \tau_{yx} = \mu\left(\frac{\partial v}{\partial x} + \frac{\partial u}{\partial y}\right) \tag{4-15d}$$

$$\tau_{yz} = \tau_{zy} = \mu\left(\frac{\partial w}{\partial y} + \frac{\partial v}{\partial z}\right) \tag{4-15e}$$

$$\tau_{xz} = \tau_{zx} = \mu\left(\frac{\partial u}{\partial z} + \frac{\partial w}{\partial x}\right) \tag{4-15f}$$

If we add Eqs. (4-15a, b, and c) and define the mean pressure $\hat{p}$ as

$$\hat{p} = -\tfrac{1}{3}(\sigma_{xx} + \sigma_{yy} + \sigma_{zz}) = p - (\lambda + \tfrac{2}{3}\mu)\operatorname{div}\mathbf{w} \tag{4-16}$$

we see that $\hat{p}$ differs from the thermodynamic pressure $p$ by an amount which depends on $(\lambda + \tfrac{2}{3}\mu)$, a quantity called the bulk viscosity. Experience has shown that the bulk viscosity can usually be taken as zero, so that $\lambda = -\tfrac{2}{3}\mu$. Using this consequence, substitution of Eqs. (4-15) in Eqs. (4-14) yields the *Navier–Stokes equations*:

$$\rho\frac{Du}{Dt} = F_x - \frac{\partial p}{\partial x} + \frac{\partial}{\partial x}\left[\mu\left(2\frac{\partial u}{\partial x} - \frac{2}{3}\operatorname{div}\mathbf{w}\right)\right]$$
$$+ \frac{\partial}{\partial y}\left[\mu\left(\frac{\partial u}{\partial y} + \frac{\partial v}{\partial x}\right)\right] + \frac{\partial}{\partial z}\left[\mu\left(\frac{\partial w}{\partial x} + \frac{\partial u}{\partial z}\right)\right] \tag{4-17a}$$

$$\rho\frac{Dv}{Dt} = F_y - \frac{\partial p}{\partial y} + \frac{\partial}{\partial y}\left[\mu\left(2\frac{\partial v}{\partial y} - \frac{2}{3}\operatorname{div}\mathbf{w}\right)\right]$$
$$+ \frac{\partial}{\partial z}\left[\mu\left(\frac{\partial v}{\partial z} + \frac{\partial w}{\partial y}\right)\right] + \frac{\partial}{\partial x}\left[\mu\left(\frac{\partial u}{\partial y} + \frac{\partial v}{\partial x}\right)\right] \tag{4-17b}$$

$$\rho\frac{Dw}{Dt} = F_z - \frac{\partial p}{\partial z} + \frac{\partial}{\partial z}\left[\mu\left(2\frac{\partial w}{\partial z} - \frac{2}{3}\operatorname{div}\mathbf{w}\right)\right]$$
$$+ \frac{\partial}{\partial x}\left[\mu\left(\frac{\partial w}{\partial x} + \frac{\partial u}{\partial z}\right)\right] + \frac{\partial}{\partial y}\left[\mu\left(\frac{\partial v}{\partial z} + \frac{\partial w}{\partial y}\right)\right] \tag{4-17c}$$

In the case of constant density and viscosity, the simplified equations can be put in vector form

$$\rho \frac{D\mathbf{w}}{Dt} = \mathbf{F} - \operatorname{grad} p + \mu(\nabla \cdot \nabla)\mathbf{w} \tag{4-18}$$

where in cartesian coordinates the operator $\nabla \cdot \nabla$ signifies taking the Laplacian $\nabla^2$ of each component of $\mathbf{w}$.

## 4-5. THE GENERAL ENERGY EQUATION

Turning now to the energy balance, we again consider a particle of constant mass $\Delta m$ and volume $\Delta V$. The first law of thermodynamics requires that

rate of increase of kinetic energy of the particle $+$ rate of increase of internal energy $=$ rate at which the body forces do work *on* the particle $+$ rate at which work is done *on* the particle by surface forces

$+$ rate of energy gain due to conduction $+$ rate of generation of energy within the particle (4-19)

We first note that the kinetic energy is $\frac{1}{2}\Delta m\mathbf{w} \cdot \mathbf{w}$ and that the internal energy is $\Delta m\tilde{u}$, where $\tilde{u}$ is the specific internal energy. Thus, for constant mass, the time rate of change on a per-unit-volume basis is $\rho\mathbf{w} \cdot D\mathbf{w}/Dt$ for the kinetic energy and $\rho\, D\tilde{u}/Dt$ for the internal energy. If we take the definition of work as a force moving through a distance, then the time rate of work of the body force $\mathbf{F}$, moving with the particle and having a velocity $\mathbf{w}$, is

$$\mathbf{F} \cdot \mathbf{w} = uF_x + vF_y + wF_z$$

Consider now the rate at which the surface forces do work. As illustrated in Fig. 4-5, each of the surface forces $\mathbf{p}_x$, $\mathbf{p}_y$, and $\mathbf{p}_z$ do work while being moved through a distance at the rate $\mathbf{w}$. The work being done on the plane $x = 0$ tends to decrease the energy of the particle, while the work being done on the plane $x = \Delta x$ tends to increase that energy. Hence, the net rate of work due to the surface forces is the change in the respective components.

Heat is conducted across the faces of the volume element according to the Fourier–Biot law [Eq. (4-1)]. Thus, a diagram similar to Fig. 4-5 can be drawn for heat conduction. Energy crosses the plane $x = 0$ according to $q = -k(\partial T/\partial x)$ and at the rate

$$q = -\left[k\frac{\partial T}{\partial x} + \frac{\partial}{\partial x}\left(k\frac{\partial T}{\partial x}\right)\Delta x\right]$$

at $x = \Delta x$. The net heat flux will then be the difference

$$q_{x=0} - q_{x=\Delta x} = \frac{\partial}{\partial x}\left(k\frac{\partial T}{\partial x}\right)\Delta x$$

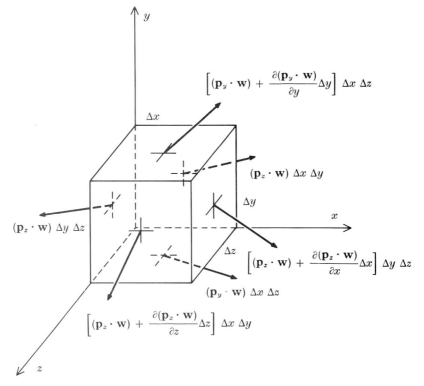

**Fig. 4-5** Net work by surface forces on an elemental particle.

We combine all of the foregoing arguments and define a function of $q'''$ to represent the heat generated per unit volume due to joulean heating, chemical reactions, etc. Then the energy balance statement [Eq. (4-19)], upon division by $\Delta V$, becomes

$$\rho \mathbf{w} \cdot \frac{D\mathbf{w}}{Dt} + \rho \frac{D\tilde{u}}{Dt} = \mathbf{w} \cdot \mathbf{F} + \frac{\partial}{\partial x}(\mathbf{w} \cdot \mathbf{p}_x) + \frac{\partial}{\partial y}(\mathbf{w} \cdot \mathbf{p}_y) + \frac{\partial}{\partial z}(\mathbf{w} \cdot \mathbf{p}_z)$$

$$+ \frac{\partial}{\partial x}\left(k \frac{\partial T}{\partial x}\right) + \frac{\partial}{\partial y}\left(k \frac{\partial T}{\partial y}\right) + \frac{\partial}{\partial z}\left(k \frac{\partial T}{\partial z}\right) + q''' \quad (4\text{-}20)$$

If we substitute the stress components [Eq. (4-13)] for the forces $\mathbf{p}_x$, $\mathbf{p}_y$, and $\mathbf{p}_z$ and perform the indicated differentiation, Eq. (4-20) on regrouping becomes*

$$\rho\left(\mathbf{w} \cdot \frac{D\mathbf{w}}{Dt} + \frac{D\tilde{u}}{Dt}\right) = u\left[F_x + \frac{\partial \sigma_{xx}}{\partial x} + \frac{\partial \tau_{yx}}{\partial y} + \frac{\partial \tau_{zx}}{\partial z}\right] + v\left[\quad\right] + w\left[\quad\right]$$

$$+ \sigma_{xx}\frac{\partial u}{\partial x} + \tau_{xy}\frac{\partial u}{\partial y} + \tau_{xz}\frac{\partial u}{\partial z} + \tau_{xy}\frac{\partial v}{\partial x} + \sigma_{yy}\frac{\partial v}{\partial y} + \tau_{yz}\frac{\partial v}{\partial z}$$

$$+ \tau_{xz}\frac{\partial w}{\partial x} + \tau_{yz}\frac{\partial w}{\partial y} + \sigma_{zz}\frac{\partial w}{\partial z} + \nabla \cdot k\nabla T + q''' \quad (4\text{-}21)$$

* Note that the operator $\nabla$ is equivalent to grad, while $\nabla\cdot$ is equivalent to div.

We note that the terms in the brackets are the three components of the force balance, Eq. (4-14). These terms cancel with the kinetic energy term on the left-hand side, since

$$\mathbf{w} \cdot \frac{D\mathbf{w}}{Dt} = u\frac{Du}{Dt} + v\frac{Dv}{Dt} + w\frac{Dw}{Dt} \tag{4-22}$$

Using Stokes' law of friction [Eq. (4-15)], the remaining stress terms can be replaced by velocity gradients and a pressure term, giving

$$\rho\frac{D\tilde{u}}{Dt} = -p\,\mathrm{div}\,\mathbf{w} + \mu\left\{\left(\frac{\partial u}{\partial y} + \frac{\partial v}{\partial x}\right)^2 + \left(\frac{\partial u}{\partial z} + \frac{\partial w}{\partial x}\right)^2 + \left(\frac{\partial v}{\partial z} + \frac{\partial w}{\partial y}\right)^2\right.$$
$$\left. - \frac{2}{3}(\nabla\cdot\mathbf{w})^2 + 2\left[\left(\frac{\partial u}{\partial x}\right)^2 + \left(\frac{\partial v}{\partial y}\right)^2 + \left(\frac{\partial w}{\partial z}\right)^2\right]\right\} + \nabla\cdot k\nabla T + q''' \tag{4-23}$$

Combining the terms within the braces into one function $\Phi$, where $\mu\Phi$ is called the *viscous dissipation*, Eq. (4-23) can then be written

$$\rho\frac{D\tilde{u}}{Dt} = -p\,\mathrm{div}\,\mathbf{w} + \mu\Phi + \nabla\cdot k\nabla T + q''' \tag{4-24}$$

$$\begin{array}{ccccccc}
\text{change in} & = & \text{work of} & + & \text{work of} & + & \text{net heat} & + & \text{heat generated} \\
\text{internal energy} & & \text{compression} & & \text{friction} & & \text{conducted} & & \text{per unit volume}
\end{array}$$

Note that the potential energy changes were taken into account in the body force term, since $\mathbf{F}$ included gravitational as well as electrostatic and electrodynamic forces—all of which no longer affect the energy equation in the above form.

We wish to convert Eq. (4-24) to a form expressed exclusively in terms of temperature, pressure, and density. To this end, we introduce the relationship of enthalpy $\tilde{h}$ to internal energy $\tilde{u}$, where $\tilde{u} = \tilde{h} - p\tilde{v}$. From thermodynamics,

$$D\tilde{h} = c_p DT + \tilde{v}(1 - \beta T)Dp \tag{4-25}$$

where $c_p$ is the constant pressure specific heat, $\tilde{v}$ is the specific volume, and $\beta$ is called the volumetric coefficient of expansion and is defined as

$$\beta = \frac{1}{\tilde{v}}\left(\frac{\partial\tilde{v}}{\partial T}\right)_p \tag{4-26}$$

Consequently,

$$\rho\frac{D\tilde{u}}{Dt} = \rho c_p\frac{DT}{Dt} - \beta T\frac{Dp}{Dt} + \frac{p}{\rho}\frac{D\rho}{Dt} \tag{4-27}$$

Now, continuity in the form of Eq. (4-7) requires that $D\rho/Dt = -\rho\,\mathrm{div}\,\mathbf{w}$. Thus, Eq. (4-27) substituted in Eq. (4-24) gives

$$\rho\frac{D\tilde{u}}{Dt} = \rho c_p\frac{DT}{Dt} - \beta T\frac{Dp}{Dt} - p\nabla\cdot\mathbf{w} = -p\nabla\cdot\mathbf{w} + \mu\Phi + \nabla\cdot k\nabla T + q'''$$

$$\tag{4-28}$$

which, on simplification, becomes the *general energy equation*:

$$\rho c_p \frac{DT}{Dt} = \beta T \frac{Dp}{Dt} + \mu \Phi + \nabla \cdot k \nabla T + q''' \qquad (4\text{-}29)$$

## 4-6. A SUMMARY OF THE CONDUCTION AND CONVECTION PROBLEM FORMULATION

As mentioned at the beginning of this chapter, the wall heat flux and the wall shear stress are the two items of interest. To determine these two quantities, the velocity distribution and the temperature distribution must be found. The five basic equations available for this task are:

Continuity equation (4-5)
Navier–Stokes equations (4-17a, b, and c)
Energy equation (4-29)

These equations contain seven unknowns—$u$, $v$, $w$, $\rho$, $p$, $c_p$, and $T$. Additional equations, called equations of state, are required. Equations of state in general form could be

$$\rho = \rho(p, T), \qquad c_p = c_p(p, T) \qquad (4\text{-}30)$$

Specifically, for a perfect gas, they take the form of

$$\rho = \frac{p}{RT}, \qquad c_p = \text{constant} \qquad (4\text{-}31)$$

or, for an incompressible fluid,

$$\rho = \text{constant}, \qquad c_p = c_p(p, T) \qquad (4\text{-}32)$$

or a numerical tabulation of experimentally determined values. Thus, at least conceptually, $q_w$ and $\tau_w$ can be found once the transport properties

$$k = k(p, T) \qquad (4\text{-}33)$$

$$\mu = \mu(p, T) \qquad (4\text{-}34)$$

are known.

## REFERENCES

1. Jakob, M., *Heat Transfer*, Vols. I and II, New York, John Wiley & Sons, Inc., 1949. An excellent reference book and historical review of the heat transfer field.

2. Eckert, E. R. G., and R. M. Drake, *Heat and Mass Transfer*, New York, McGraw-Hill Book Co., Inc., 1959. Good introductory text with clear descriptions of basic problems.

3. Hsu, S. T., *Engineering Heat Transfer*, Princeton, N. J., D. Van Nostrand Co., Inc., 1963. Undergraduate text with engineering emphasis. Comprehensive listing of property values for design purposes.

4. Goldsmith, A., H. J. Hirschhorn, and T. E. Waterman, "Thermophysical Properties of Solid Materials," Vols. I–V, Armour Research Foundation, *WADC TR 58-476*, Nov., 1960. A somewhat incomplete but often useful collection of property data.

5. Touloukian, Y. S., editor, *Retrieval Guide to Thermophysical Properties Research Literature*, New York, McGraw-Hill Book Co., Vol. I, 1960; Vol. II, 1963. An index of the literature of the world for finding experimental and analytical work on property values for solids, liquids, and gases.

6. *Thermophysical Properties Research Center Data Book*, **1–3**, Purdue Research Foundation, Lafayette, Ind., 1964. Plots of property data with recommended values noted. Work currently in progress, although some thermal conductivity and viscosity data are available.

7. Thurston, R. N., *Physical Acoustics*, edited by W. P. Mason, Chap. 1, New York, Academic Press, Inc., 1964. A particularly clear development of the basic equations of continuum mechanics.

8. Prandtl, L., and O. G. Tietjens, *Fundamentals of Hydro and Aerodynamics*, New York, Dover Publications, Inc., 1957.

*Chapter 5*

# CONDUCTIVE HEAT TRANSFER

## L. W. Dickey and C. A. Fritsch

The generalized heat transfer problem for conduction and convection, formulated in the previous chapter, reduces to a problem in pure conduction for situations where the velocities are zero. Problems of this type involve both solids and fluids, but the spaces filled by the fluids must be small enough that convection is negligible.*

Conduction problems can be solved by exact or approximate techniques. Exact solutions are treated in many texts such as Arpaci,[1] Schneider,[2] Carslaw and Jaeger,[3] and Grober, Erk, and Grigull.[4] The primary emphasis in this chapter, however, will be placed on the application of approximate techniques in conduction. Criteria will also be developed to aid the designer in determining when the transient part of a problem must be considered and when various boundary conditions must be specified.

## 5-1. FORMULATION OF THE CONDUCTION PROBLEM

Consider a material where the particle velocities are zero and no significant pressure changes are present. Under these conditions, the general energy

---

* Criteria for making such a judgment will be considered in Chapter 6.

equation [Eq. (4-29)] reduces to the transient conduction equation:

$$\rho c \frac{\partial T}{\partial t} = \nabla \cdot k \nabla T + q'''$$ (5-1)

where $c$ is to be interpreted as the specific heat under the conditions of the process. If we assume constant properties, the thermal conductivity can be moved outside the differentiation, and a meaningful system parameter called the *thermal diffusivity* can be defined as

$$\alpha = \frac{k}{\rho c}$$ (5-2)

so that Eq. (5-1) becomes

$$\frac{\partial T}{\partial t} = \alpha \nabla^2 T + \frac{q'''}{\rho c}$$ (5-3)

If we further stipulate a steady-state condition, this reduces to *Poisson's equation*

$$\nabla^2 T = \frac{q'''}{k}$$ (5-4)

which for zero heat generation becomes Laplace's equation. In isotropic bodies, the heat flow lines and the lines of constant temperature must always be orthogonal; hence, the temperature distribution in steady state can always be sketched. (See pages 138 through 146 of Schneider.[2])

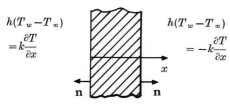

$$h(T_w - T_\infty)$$
$$= k \frac{\partial T}{\partial x}$$

$$h(T_w - T_\infty)$$
$$= -k \frac{\partial T}{\partial x}$$

**Fig. 5-1**   One-dimensional conduction in a plane slab.

The initial and boundary conditions necessary for the solution of any conduction problem could consist of (1) an initial temperature distribution, usually a constant; (2) prescribed temperatures on the boundaries, usually constant across a given face; and (3) prescribed heat flux at the boundaries, usually given in terms of a heat transfer coefficient, $h$.

The heat transfer coefficient is an artifice which allows the wall heat flux $q_w$ to be specified in terms of a temperature difference $(T_w - T_\infty)$, where $T_w$ is the wall temperature and $T_\infty$ is the fluid temperature some distance away from the body. Thus, $h$ is *defined* by the relation

$$q_w = h(T_w - T_\infty)$$ (5-5)

Since the wall heat flux is also given by the gradient of the temperature just inside the body, then

$$h(T_w - T_\infty) = -k\mathbf{n} \cdot \text{grad } T$$ (5-6)

where **n** is the unit normal vector to the surface. This is illustrated for one-dimensional conduction in a slab in Fig. 5-1. Note the difference in sign on the two faces.

The heat transfer coefficient $h$ is assumed to be constant, so that it may be used as a boundary condition for heat transfer calculations. While this is only an approximation, it gives useful engineering information.

Under some conditions, such as exposure to a high radiant heat source, the surface heat flux is practically independent of wall temperature, and a better statement of Eq. (5-5) would be to specify the wall heat flux as

$$q_w = q(x, y, z, t) \qquad (5\text{-}7)$$

In cases where the wall heat flux is insignificant, the surface is *insulated*, so that

$$\frac{\partial T}{\partial x} = 0 \qquad (5\text{-}8)$$

A boundary condition for two bodies in contact requires that the heat flux on each side of the boundary be equal; hence,

$$q_w = -k_1 \frac{\partial T_1}{\partial x} = -k_2 \frac{\partial T_2}{\partial x} \qquad (5\text{-}9)$$

If the two bodies were in perfect contact, the temperatures on each side of the interface would also be equal. However, since real surfaces are never in perfect contact, the temperature difference can be related to the heat flux by the relation

$$q_w = h_c(T_1 - T_2) \qquad (5\text{-}10)$$

where $h_c$ is called the thermal contact conductance. Contact conductance is an important consideration in the thermal design of electronic equipment and, therefore, is considered in more detail in the following section.

Before continuing our discussion of conductive heat flow, however, it will be useful to introduce the concept of thermal resistance and capacitance. When the Fourier–Biot law is applied to heat conduction across a pure resistance (i.e., steady state between two isotherms $T_1$ and $T_2$) the heat flow per unit time $Q$ is proportional to the difference of these temperatures. Thus, we may write

$$Q = (qA)_1 = \frac{1}{R}(T_1 - T_2) \qquad (5\text{-}11)$$

where $R$ is the thermal resistance. The thermal resistance is a function of the thermal conductivity and the geometry of a body. For example, in conduction across a plane wall of thickness $L$ and cross-sectional area $A$, the thermal resistance is $L/Ak$. The term resistance is used because of the similarity between Eq. (5-11) and Ohm's law, where the analogous terms are voltage and temperature difference, and heat flow and current. Since Eqs. (5-5) and (5-10) are of the same form, we may consider $1/Ah$ and $1/Ah_c$ as thermal resistances also.

In bodies or segments of bodies where the internal resistance can be separated from the heat storage nature of the body, a thermal capacitance can be defined as the heat capacity of that volume element in analogy to electrical capacitance. These concepts will be employed in the following discussion while the electrical-thermal analog will be described more completely later in this chapter.

## 5-2. THERMAL CONTACT RESISTANCE

Thermal conduction in electronic equipment almost always involves heat transfer through composite surfaces. The contact resistance at these interfaces may represent an appreciable fraction of the total resistance to heat flow. Although an analytical description of thermal contacts is omitted here for brevity, the general parameters that influence heat transfer across the interface between two solids are known to be:

1. The thermal conductivity of the mating materials.
2. The actual area in contact (only a few discrete points touch when two surfaces are pressed together).
3. The thickness and physical properties of surface films (oxide films are the ones most commonly found on metallic surfaces).
4. The quantity and thermal properties of the substance, usually air, filling the interstices between the mating surfaces.

The first of these parameters, thermal conductivity, is obviously important because the principal mode of heat transfer across a thermal junction is conduction.* To improve the contact conductance, the designer should choose mating materials with as high a thermal conductivity as is consistent with other design criteria.

The number and size of the actual areas in contact must be known before a meaningful prediction can be made of contact conductance. A mathematical analysis of a thermal contact, free of surface films, was first carried out by Fenech and Rohsenow[5] and was later simplified by Clausing and Chao.[6] Both teams of investigators conclude that the actual areas in contact depend upon:

1. The applied pressure (pressure increases the number and size of contact points and improves the conductance of the thermal junction; it does so more noticeably than any other parameter).

---

* Temperature differences are usually such that radiation is negligible.

2. Surface finish and flatness deviation.

3. Material hardness and resistance to plastic flow.

The intimacy of contact between two surfaces is greatly influenced by surface oxide films, which invariably are present on most engineering materials, particularly metals. Clausing and Chao experimentally observed that the thermal contact conductance of a magnesium junction was increased by an order of magnitude after removing a visible oxide film on the surface (Fig. 5-2).

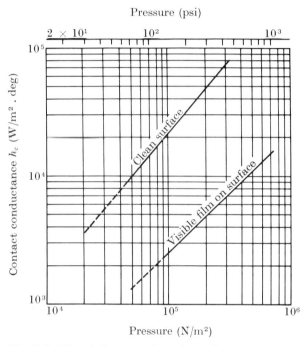

**Fig. 5-2** The influence of surface films on contact conductance.[6]

The improvement in thermal conductance achieved by cleaning the surface is analogous to the improvement in electrical conductance of a contact. However, a definite mathematical analogy does not exist between thermal and electrical contacts because the relating equation, the Wiedemann–Franz–Lorentz law [Eq. (4-3)], does not account for phonon conduction of thermal energy through the dielectric surface films.

A significant improvement of contact conductance may be achieved by inserting a thin layer of soft material having a high thermal conductivity between the mating surfaces. In spite of the additional interface, a higher total conductance results, largely from an increase in contact areas. Investigators have used thin shims[7,8] and surface platings[9,10] of soft materials such as aluminum, lead, copper, etc., and have observed a three- to five-fold improvement in the contact conductance. Ten-fold increases in conductance have been achieved after coating the mating surface with a silicone grease.[6,9]

Many experiments have been carried out to investigate the nature of thermal contacts, but the compilation of the results in a common form is difficult because the measurements were not all made under the same experimental conditions. Realizing the practical value of such a compilation, however, a summary of the results of several investigators is attempted here. Figure 5-3 gives a description of the experimental conditions, and Fig. 5-4 shows, for each material, the relationship between contact conductance and pressure for two contacting bodies of the same material. The curve for each material is a best line-fit through the referenced data and is estimated to be accurate within a factor of two. Where accuracy is critical, design data should be obtained by testing specific samples.

| Material | Ref. | Surface finish, rms ($\mu$m) | Contact pressure (N/m$^2$) | Contact pressure (psi) | Contact conductance (W/m$^2$·deg) |
|---|---|---|---|---|---|
| Aluminum: | | | | | |
| 2024-T3 | 8 | 0.152–1.65 | 13.8–241 | 2–35 | 114–738 |
| 2024-T4 | 6 | 0.305 | 317–6719 | 46–975 | 664–34,600 |
| 2024-T4 | 10 | 0.203–1.27 | 124–8531 | 18–1238 | 1180–21,400 |
| 6061-T6 | 12 | 0.203–1.52 | 67–7870 | 10–1142 | 1560–3230 |
| 6061-T6 | 11 | 0.076–0.228 | 1.38–138 | 2–20 | 284–1830 |
| 7075-T6 | 13 | 0.381–343 | 138–6615 | 20–960 | 340–17,000 |
| Beryllium: | | | | | |
| CR Grade | 9 | 0.051–0.102 | 365–7939 | 53–1152 | 261–14,800 |
| Brass | | | | | |
| | 6 | 0.254–0.762 | 138–6547 | 20–950 | 568–7260 |
| Copper: | | | | | |
| ETP (Hard) | 10 | 0.254–0.762 | 13.8–152 | 2–22 | 227–2270 |
| OFHC | 9 | 0.152–0.203 | 448–8118 | 65–1178 | 1660–90,500 |
| Magnesium: | | | | | |
| | 6 | | 172–5168 | 25–750 | 851–68,100 |
| AZ-31 | 8 | 0.889–1.14 | 13.8–241 | 2–35 | 114–709 |
| Stainless steel: | | | | | |
| 302 | 11 | 0.305–0.508 | 13.8–138 | 2–20 | 74–415 |
| 416 | 14 | 1.57–3.81 | 5513–96,475 | 800–14,000 | 4250–68,100 |
| 17-4 PH | 13 | 0.432–3.43 | 276–6891 | 40–1000 | 170–7380 |
| Steel: | | | | | |
| 4140 | 10 | 0.076–1.98 | 0–6891 | 0–1000 | 2840–79,500 |
| 1020 | 15 | 0.813–42.2 | 1378–20,673 | 200–3000 | 3780–28,400 |
| 1020 | 7 | 1.60–3.18 | 0–2067 | 0–300 | 1290–3690 |

**Fig. 5-3.**  Contact conductances for various contact pressures and surface finishes on some common metals.

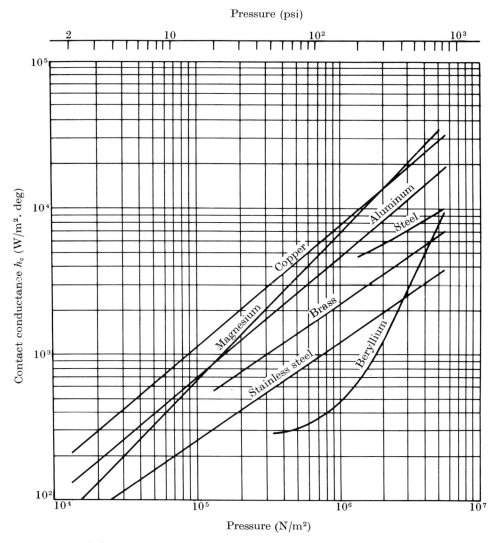

**Fig. 5-4** Summary of dry-joint thermal conductance data for some common materials.

More specialized investigations have been concerned with the nature of heat transfer between two dissimilar materials. Several investigators have observed that, when one of the materials is a pure metal, the conductance varies noticeably with direction of heat flow. This directional effect is less prominent for a junction consisting of metal alloys or dielectrics where heat is transmitted primarily by phonons rather than by conduction electrons. Among the important contributors to this field are Moon and Keeler,[16] who explain thermal directional effects using quantum mechanics. This explanation is similar to that used for the current directivity of a semiconductor junction.

## 5-3. DIMENSIONLESS GROUPS IN CONDUCTION

Consider transient heat conduction in a one-dimensional situation with negligible heat generation per unit volume. Equation (5-3) becomes

$$\frac{\partial T}{\partial t} = \alpha \frac{\partial^2 T}{\partial x^2} \tag{5-12}$$

This equation can be nondimensionalized in terms of a *normalized length* $\xi$ and the *natural time* of the system $\tau$ (sometimes called the *Fourier modulus*)

$$\xi = \frac{x}{L} ; \qquad \tau = \frac{\alpha t}{L^2} \tag{5-13}$$

where $L$ is the thickness of the slab. If the environment temperature is $T_\infty$, Eq. (5-12) can be written in terms of the *temperature excess*

$$\theta = (T - T_\infty) \tag{5-14}$$

as

$$\frac{\partial \theta}{\partial \tau} = \frac{\partial^2 \theta}{\partial \xi^2} \tag{5-15}$$

The energy equation in this form is independent of the slab thickness and its material properties.

Suppose that a slab of thickness $L$ has an initial temperature $\theta_0$ above an ambient temperature $T_\infty$, and that the face $x = L$ is exposed to the ambient while the face $x = 0$ is insulated. These boundary conditions can be stated as

$$\theta(\xi, 0) = \theta_0 \tag{5-16a}$$

$$\frac{\partial \theta}{\partial \xi}(0, \tau) = 0 \tag{5-16b}$$

$$-\frac{k}{L}\frac{\partial \theta}{\partial \xi}(1, \tau) = h\theta(1, \tau) \tag{5-16c}$$

The convective condition, Eq. (5-16c), can be seen to depend on the dimensionless group called the *Biot number*:

$$N_{\mathrm{Bi}} \equiv \frac{hL}{k} = \frac{\text{internal resistance}}{\text{external resistance}} \tag{5-17}$$

Thus, whenever a boundary condition of the type given by Eq. (5-16c) is used, the capacitive nature of the heat transfer system external to the one being considered has been neglected since this external problem has been replaced by a pure resistance $1/Ah$.

In situations where the internal resistance of the body is large compared to $1/Ah$, then $N_{\mathrm{Bi}} \gg 1$. Under this condition, the surface will essentially take on the environment temperature in times corresponding to $\tau \cdot N_{Bi} > 1$, and Eq. (5-16c) can be replaced for later times by a constant-temperature boundary condition (which is equivalent to $N_{Bi} \to \infty$)

$$\theta(1, \tau) = 0 \tag{5-18}$$

For slabs with $N_{Bi} \gg 1$, analytical solutions have shown that the conduction situation is essentially steady-state for times where $\tau \geq 1$. Similarly, since the internal resistance between two spots separated by a distance $L$ is $L/Ak$, then heat generated at any spot is essentially diffused a distance $L$ in the time corresponding to $\tau \geq 1$.

> **Example 5.1.** An example illustrating the use of the Fourier modulus concerns the carbon transmitter used in the telephone handset. A change in transmission occurs during the few seconds after line current begins to flow. It was thought that this effect was due to a variation in electrical resistance as a result of localized heat generation at the contact points between the discrete carbon granules. Since the heat generation then is not uniform, one wishes to know for what time scale the associated temperature variations and discontinuities are important and when the carbon can be treated as a continuum.
>
> Assume that the grain size is 0.02 cm and that the thermal diffusivity of carbon (graphite) is $\alpha = 2.8 \times 10^{-5}$ m²/s. Then $\tau = \kappa t/D^2 \geq 1$ when $t \geq 1.4 \times 10^{-3}$ s. This means that localized heating effects are diffused in a few milliseconds and that, for later time effects, the granular medium can be treated as a continuum. Therefore, the observed effect is not due to localized heat generation in the carbon granules and, indeed, was later determined to have resulted from thermal expansion of the metallic parts of the transmitter.

In situations where $N_{Bi} \ll 1$, the internal resistance is small enough compared to the environmental resistance that the temperature within the body is essentially uniform. Recalling the energy equation for pure conduction [Eq. (5-1)], we indicate an integral over the volume $V$ of the body, assuming zero heat generation, as

$$\iiint_V \rho c \, \frac{\partial T}{\partial t} \, dV = \iiint_V \text{div} \, (k \, \text{grad} \, T) \, dV \tag{5-19}$$

If we replace $k$ grad $T$ with Eq. (5-6) and use the divergence theorem, Eq. (5-19) can be written

$$\iiint_V \rho c \, \frac{\partial T}{\partial t} \, dV = - \oiint h(T_w - T_\infty) \, dA \tag{5-20}$$

Under the condition $N_{Bi} \ll 1$, then $T \approx T_w = T(t)$. Consequently, in terms of $\theta$, Eq. (5-20) becomes

$$\left( \rho c \, \frac{D\theta}{Dt} \right) V = -(h\theta)A \tag{5-21}$$

This, of course, can be integrated directly to give

$$\theta = \theta_0 e^{-hAt/\rho c V} \tag{5-22}$$

where the initial condition of Eq. (5-16a) has been satisfied. Thus, an otherwise complex conduction problem has been reduced to the analog of a simple discharging capacitor with negligible internal resistance.

It can be readily seen from this simple result that a body having the largest value of $A/V$ cools the quickest. Thus, a sphere of a given radius $r$ cools faster than an infinitely long cylinder of the same radius, which in turn cools faster than a slab where $L = r$.

The exponent in Eq. (5-22) can be written in terms of $N_{Bi}$, $\tau$, and a geometric factor

$$\Phi = \frac{AL}{V} \tag{5-23}$$

Thus, even though the response is independent of the thermal conductivity, we can write

$$\theta = \theta_0 e^{-N_{Bi}\Phi\tau}; \qquad N_{Bi} \ll 1 \tag{5-24}$$

so that a *thermal time constant* can be determined by setting $N_{Bi}\Phi\tau$ equal to unity and solving for $t$.

**Example 5.2.** Consider a 3-mm aluminum plate moving on an assembly line which at one stage must be heated from 25°C to at least 95°C by being pressed against a stainless steel heater with $7 \times 10^4$ N/m² (10 psi) pressure. We wish to calculate how long contact must be maintained for a heater temperature of 125°C.

From Fig. 5-4, we have curves of contact conductances of aluminum on aluminum and stainless steel on stainless steel. Picking a value somewhere between the two curves and closer to the aluminum curve (since it is softer), we choose $h_c = 400$ W/m² · °C. Taking $k$ for aluminum (Appendix B, Fig. B-1) as 138 W/m · °C, we calculate

$$N_{Bi} = \frac{hL}{k} = \frac{(400)(3 \times 10^{-3})}{138} = 8.7 \times 10^{-3} \ll 1$$

Consequently, Eq. (5-24) is applicable. If the heater is operating at 125°C, then $T_\infty = 125$°C and the time required for $\theta/\theta_0 = \frac{30}{100}$ can be found from setting

$$e^{-N_{Bi}\Phi\tau} = \frac{30}{100}$$

Thus,

$$N_{Bi}\Phi\tau = -\ln\left(\frac{30}{100}\right) = 1.2$$

For a slab heated on one side, $\Phi = 1$. Thus, if $\alpha = 5.57 \times 10^{-5}$ m²/s

$$t = \frac{\tau L^2}{\alpha} = \left(\frac{1.2}{8.7 \times 10^{-3}}\right)(3 \times 10^{-3})^2 \left(\frac{1}{5.57 \times 10^{-5}}\right)$$

$$= 22.3 \text{ s}$$

## 5-4. TRANSIENT EFFECTS IN SYSTEMS DUE TO PERIODIC INPUTS

In many electronic systems, joulean heating results from a periodic or pulsed electrical current. For equipment enclosures exposed to daily and seasonal weather variations, the thermal response can also be assumed to be periodic. While the analytical treatment of the two types of inputs is similar, the latter case, with the periodic boundary condition, has implications for our treatment of the problem of periodic heat generation. Hence, we will treat it first.

### PERIODIC TEMPERATURES DUE TO HARMONIC SURFACE VARIATIONS

Consider transient one-dimensional heating of a very thick (semi-infinite) solid with a harmonic surface temperature variation. The boundary-value problem for constant properties, in terms of the temperature excess above the average temperature, becomes

$$\frac{\partial \theta}{\partial t} = \alpha \, \frac{\partial^2 \theta}{\partial x^2} \tag{5-25}$$

$$\theta(x, 0) = 0 \tag{5-26a}$$

$$\theta(0, t) = A \cos \omega t \tag{5-26b}$$

$$\lim_{x \to \infty} \theta(x, t) = 0 \tag{5-26c}$$

If we are not concerned with the initial transient response necessary to reach the fluctuating state, then we will not require that Eq. (5-26a) be satisfied. For a periodic temperature boundary condition [Eq. (5-26b)], we are led to assume a separable solution of the form

$$\theta(x, t) = g(x)e^{j\omega t} \tag{5-27}$$

where the complex exponential†

$$e^{j\omega t} = \cos \omega t + j \sin \omega t \tag{5-28}$$

Substituting Eq. (5-27) in Eq. (5-25), we have

$$\frac{d^2 g}{dx^2} = \frac{j\omega}{\alpha} g \tag{5-29}$$

which integrates to

$$g(x) = B_1 e^{-x\sqrt{j\omega/\alpha}} + C_1 e^{x\sqrt{j\omega/\alpha}} \tag{5-30}$$

---

† Note that a simple assumption of $g(x) \cos \omega t$ would not satisfy the energy equation [Eq. (5-25)].

The one-half power of a complex number may be expressed as

$$\sqrt{\frac{j\omega}{\alpha}} = \pm\sqrt{\frac{\omega}{2\alpha}}(1+j) \tag{5-31}$$

Substituting Eq. (5-31) in Eq. (5-30), we have

$$g(x) = B_1 e^{\mp x\sqrt{\omega/2\alpha}\,(1+j)} + C_1 e^{\pm x\sqrt{\omega/2\alpha}\,(1+j)} \tag{5-32}$$

The forms of Eq. (5-32) corresponding to positive exponents are not admissible due to boundary condition, Eq. (5-26c). Consequently, Eq. (5-32) reduces to

$$g(x) = B e^{-x\sqrt{\omega/2\alpha}\,(1+j)} \tag{5-33}$$

Since temperatures must be real, then

$$\theta(x, t) = \text{Re}\,[B e^{-x\sqrt{\omega/2\alpha}\,(1+j)} e^{j\omega t}] \tag{5-34}$$

which expands to

$$\theta(x, t) = B e^{-x\sqrt{\omega/2\alpha}}\,\text{Re}\left[\left(\cos x\sqrt{\frac{\omega}{2\alpha}}\cos \omega t + \sin x\sqrt{\frac{\omega}{2\alpha}}\sin \omega t\right)\right.$$
$$\left. + j\left(\sin \omega t \cos x\sqrt{\frac{\omega}{2\alpha}} - \cos \omega t \sin x\sqrt{\frac{\omega}{2\alpha}}\right)\right] \tag{5-35}$$

Thus, on applying condition Eq. (5-26b) to the real part of Eq. (5-35), we have

$$\theta(x, t) = A e^{-x\sqrt{\omega/2\alpha}}\left[\cos\left(\omega t - x\sqrt{\frac{\omega}{2\alpha}}\right)\right] \tag{5-36}$$

In summary, we note that a wavelength $\lambda$ can be defined as

$$\lambda = \frac{2\pi}{\sqrt{\omega/2\alpha}} \tag{5-37}$$

so that the amplitude of the "thermal wave" $A e^{-2\pi x/\lambda}$ decays exponentially in the slab as a function of $\lambda$. An increase in frequency or a decrease in diffusivity results in a corresponding increase in attenuation. Note that when $x = \lambda/2$, $A$ is reduced to 0.043 of its original value and, at a distance $x = \lambda$, $A$ is reduced by a factor of $e^{-2\pi} = 0.002$. Thus, thermal waves are strongly attenuated for distances in excess of one wavelength.†

If the surface heat flux is a harmonic function of time of maximum amplitude $F_0$, then from operating on Eq. (5-36) as shown in Ref. 3, one finds that

$$\theta(x, t) = \frac{F_0 e^{-x\sqrt{\omega/2\alpha}}}{(k\rho c)^{1/2}\omega^{1/2}}\left[\cos\left(\omega t - x\sqrt{\frac{\omega}{2\alpha}} - \frac{\pi}{4}\right)\right] \tag{5-38}$$

which is attenuated at the same rate as the temperature wave but 45° out of phase. These relations are useful not only to predict the response to thermal

---

† See page 82 of Ref. 4 for a further discussion and graphs of periodic variations.

oscillations but also to estimate how much of a pulsed system can be considered in steady state.

**Example 5.3.** Communication transmission systems such as a buried coaxial cable system require regulating repeaters at certain intervals to compensate for cable temperature variations. For instance, a nominal repeater spacing of 25.8 km is required for acceptable signal-to-noise ratios if the cable is to experience a temperature variation of $\pm 11°C$. If the variations are significantly less than this, an important cost reduction might be possible. Assume that the cable is to be buried to a depth of 1.2 m, and estimate the temperature variations to be expected.

If a harmonic form is assumed for the thermal variation, then Eq. (5-36) is applicable. Considering first the daily variations, and taking a value of $\alpha = 0.054 \times 10^{-5}$ m$^2$/s for the soil (see Appendix B, Fig. B-1), then, for $\omega = 2\pi/86,400$ rad/s,

$$x\sqrt{\frac{\omega}{2\alpha}} = 1.2\sqrt{\frac{\pi}{86,400(0.054 \times 10^{-5})}} = 10$$

and $e^{-10} = 4.5 \times 10^{-5}$, so that the effects of daily variations are negligible. Considering the annual variations, with $\omega = 2\pi/86,400(365)$ rad/s, then

$$x\sqrt{\frac{\omega}{2\alpha}} = 1.2\sqrt{\frac{\pi}{(86,400)(365)(0.054 \times 10^{-5})}} = 0.52$$

so that $e^{-0.52} = 0.595$. If the annual variation of the (averaged daily) temperature is $\pm 14°C$, then at 1.2 m the cable will experience a variation of about $\pm 8°C$.

It is interesting to note the phase lag in this problem. We compute the phase angle in Eq. (5-36) as

$$x\sqrt{\frac{\omega}{2\alpha}} = 0.52 \text{ rad} \approx 30°$$

so that if the coldest surface temperature occurs on February 1, the coldest cable temperature will occur on March 1.

## TRANSIENT EFFECTS IN SYSTEMS WITH PERIODIC HEAT GENERATION

Figure 5-5 illustrates a typical circuit component (a diode) through which a train of periodic pulses is passed in the $x$ coordinate direction. Assuming that the heat is generated uniformly in one layer of the composite structure of the component, we wish to calculate the periodic temperature distribution for the component and the body on which it is mounted. We will further assume one-dimensional conduction with constant properties. The corresponding analytical

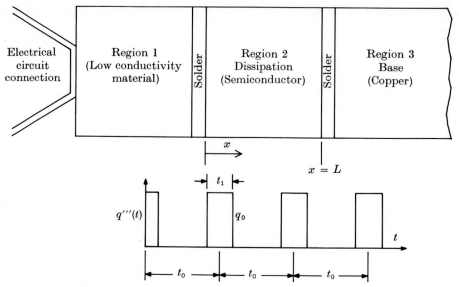

**Fig. 5-5**   Schematic of an electrical component composite.

formulation can be specified as

$$\frac{\partial \theta}{\partial t} = \alpha \frac{\partial^2 \theta}{\partial x^2} + \frac{q'''(t)}{\rho c} \tag{5-39}$$

with the assumed boundary conditions of

$$\frac{\partial \theta}{\partial x}(0, t) = 0 \tag{5-40}$$

$$\theta(L, t) = 0 \tag{5-41}$$

The heat generated for any given period, as illustrated in Fig. 5-5, is

$$q'''(t) = q_0 \left[ U(t) - U\left(t - \frac{t_1}{2}\right) + U\left(t - t_0 + \frac{t_1}{2}\right) \right] \tag{5-42}$$

where the unit step function is defined as

$$U(t - t_i) = \begin{cases} 1; & t \geq t_i \\ 0; & t < t_i \end{cases} \tag{5-43}$$

We nondimensionalize Eq. (5-39) by defining the following quantities

$$\xi = \frac{x}{L}; \qquad \tau = \frac{\alpha t}{L^2}; \qquad \theta^* = \frac{\theta}{q_0 L^2 / k} \tag{5-44}$$

and obtain

$$\frac{\partial \theta^*}{\partial \tau} = \frac{\partial^2 \theta^*}{\partial \xi^2} + f(\tau) \tag{5-45}$$

where $f(\tau)$ is the function contained in the brackets of Eq. (5-42). Expressing $f(\tau)$ in terms of an exponential Fourier series, we write

$$f(\tau) = \sum_{n=-\infty}^{+\infty} C_n e^{j\omega_n \tau} \qquad (5\text{-}46)$$

The coefficients $C_n$ are given by

$$C_n = \frac{1}{\tau_0} \int_0^{\tau_0} f(\tau) e^{-j\omega_n \tau} \, d\tau = \frac{1}{n\pi} \left[ \sin \left( \frac{n\pi\tau_1}{\tau_0} \right) \right] \qquad (5\text{-}47)$$

where $\tau_1$ and $\tau_0$ correspond to $\tau$ at $t_1$ and $t_0$, respectively, and $\omega_n = 2n\pi/\tau_0$. It is convenient to write $f(\tau)$ in the form

$$f(\tau) = f_0 + \frac{1}{\pi} \sum_{n=-\infty}^{+\infty} \left( \frac{1}{n} \sin \frac{n\pi\tau_1}{\tau_0} \right) e^{j\omega_n \tau} \qquad (n \neq 0) \qquad (5\text{-}48)$$

where $f_0$, the average power dissipated, is

$$f_0 = \lim_{n \to 0} \frac{1}{n\pi} \sin \left( \frac{n\pi\tau_1}{\tau_0} \right) = \frac{\tau_1}{\tau_0} \qquad (5\text{-}49)$$

Note that $f_0$ sets the average level of the temperature above the point $x = L$ for any value $0 \leq x \leq L$. We are led to assume a solution of the form

$$\theta^*(\xi, \tau) = \Phi(\xi, \tau) + \psi(\xi) \qquad (5\text{-}50)$$

where $\Phi(\xi, \tau)$ will represent the fluctuations of the temperature above the time-averaged distribution $\psi(\xi)$. The time-averaged temperature satisfies

$$\frac{d^2\psi}{d\xi^2} = -f_0 \qquad (5\text{-}51\text{a})$$

with

$$\frac{d\psi}{d\xi}(0) = 0 \qquad (5\text{-}51\text{b})$$

$$\psi(1) = 0 \qquad (5\text{-}51\text{c})$$

Thus, on integrating and applying the boundary conditions, we have

$$\psi(\xi) = \frac{\tau_1}{2\tau_0} (1 - \xi^2) \qquad (5\text{-}52)$$

As shown previously in this section, we assume that the fluctuating temperature has a solution of the form

$$\Phi(\xi, \tau) = \text{Re} \sum_{n=-\infty}^{+\infty} g_n(\xi) e^{j\omega_n \tau} \qquad (n \neq 0) \qquad (5\text{-}53)$$

On substituting Eq. (5-53) into Eq (5-45), we see that $g_n(\xi)$ must satisfy

$$\frac{d^2 g_n}{d\xi^2} - j\omega_n g_n = -C_n \qquad (n \neq 0) \qquad (5\text{-}54)$$

The general solution of Eq. (5-54) for $n \neq 0$ is

$$g_n(\xi) = A \sinh \sqrt{j\omega_n}\,\xi + B \cosh \sqrt{j\omega_n}\,\xi + \frac{C_n}{j\omega_n} \tag{5-55}$$

Applying the boundary conditions to Eq. (5-55) and taking the real part of the resulting expression in a manner similar to that for the periodic surface temperature problem, we have

$$\Phi(\xi,\,\tau) = 2 \sum_{n=1}^{\infty} \frac{C_n}{\omega_n}\left[ \left(\frac{b\eta - a\zeta}{a^2 + b^2}\right) \cos \omega_n \tau - \left(\frac{a\eta + b\zeta}{a^2 + b^2} - 1\right) \sin \omega_n \tau \right] \tag{5-56}$$

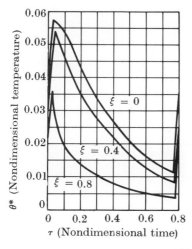
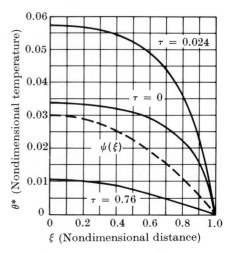

(a) Period $\tau_0 = 0.8$

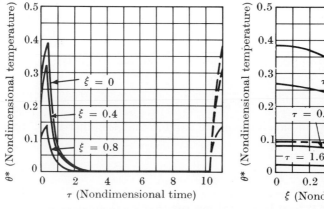
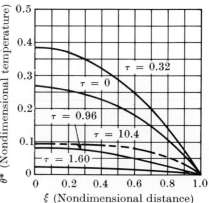

(b) Period $\tau_0 = 10.6$

**Fig. 5-6** Periodic response of electrical component composite with simple boundary conditions.

where

$$a = \cosh \alpha_n \cos \alpha_n; \qquad b = \sinh \alpha_n \sin \alpha_n$$

$$\eta = \cosh \alpha_n \xi \cos \alpha_n \xi; \qquad \zeta = \sinh \alpha_n \xi \sin \alpha_n \xi$$

$$\alpha_n = \sqrt{\frac{\omega_n}{2}}; \qquad\qquad \omega_n = \frac{2n\pi}{\tau_0}$$

$$C_n = \frac{1}{n\pi}\left[\text{ins}\left(\frac{n\pi\tau_1}{\tau_0}\right)\right]$$

The total solution, Eq. (5-56) plus Eq. (5-52), depends on the period $\tau_0$ and the duty cycle $\tau_1/\tau_0$. The resulting nondimensional temperature $\theta^* = \theta k/q_0 L^2$ has been plotted for $\tau_1/\tau_0 = 0.06$ and $\tau_0 = 0.8$ and 10.6 in Fig. 5-6.

**Example 5.4.** Consider the component illustrated in Fig. 5-5 to be a diode. We wish to find out if the foregoing analysis is applicable to a real situation where the diode has the following construction across its axis.†

| Region | Material | Thickness $(10^{-2}$ m) | $k$ (W/m² · °C) | $\alpha$ $(10^{-4}$ m²/s) |
|--------|----------|-------------------------|-----------------|---------------------------|
| 1 | Kovar | 0.051 | 18 | 0.043 |
|   | solder | 0.0038 | 33 | 0.218 |
| 2 | silicon | 0.010 | 95 | 0.533 |
|   | solder | 0.0038 | 33 | 0.218 |
| 3 | copper | 3.0 | 380 | 1.10 |

Then, if the analysis is applicable, we wish to calculate the maximum temperature rise in the diode.

We first ask how far into the solder-copper structure the fluctuating temperatures penetrate for $t_1 = 9$ $\mu$s ($\tau_0 = 0.8$). Characterizing the fluctuating temperature as a sinusoidal input of period $2t_1$ for a factor-of-ten attenuation, Eq. (5-36) requires that

$$e^{-x\sqrt{\omega/2\alpha}} = 0.1$$

$$x = \frac{2.3}{\sqrt{\omega/2\alpha}} = 2.5 \times 10^{-5}\,\text{m}$$

using $\alpha = 0.218 \times 10^{-4}$ m²/s for solder. We see that the fluctuating temperature is limited essentially to the solder during the on-phase of the pulse. The rest of the structure (the copper) can be considered to have only a steady-state temperature distribution.

The other side of the diode is connected into the electrical circuit through the Kovar layer and a copper strap with a contact pressure of $13.78 \times 10^3$ N/m² (2 psi). From Fig. 5-4, $h_c \approx 1.71 \times 10^2$ W/m² · °C so that the

---

† Properties are evaluated at approximately 100°C.

total resistance out of the silicon-solder-Kovar side of the diode (for constant cross-sectional area) is

$$\left(\frac{L}{k}\right)_{\text{solder}} + \left(\frac{L}{k}\right)_{\text{Kovar}} + \frac{1}{h_c} = \frac{0.0038 \times 10^{-2}}{33} + \frac{0.051 \times 10^{-2}}{18} + \frac{10^{-2}}{1.71 \times 10^2} \approx \frac{1}{h_c}$$

The total resistance to heat flow out the positive $x$ direction is

$$\left(\frac{L}{k}\right)_{\text{silicon}} + \left(\frac{L}{k}\right)_{\text{solder}} + \left(\frac{L}{k}\right)_{\text{copper}} = \frac{0.010 \times 10^{-2}}{95} + \frac{0.0038 \times 10^{-2}}{33}$$

$$+ \frac{3.0 \times 10^{-2}}{380} \approx \left(\frac{L}{k}\right)_{\text{copper}}$$

Consequently, a type of $N_{\text{Bi}}$ results from comparing these two resistances, giving

$$\frac{(L/k)_{\text{copper}}}{1/h_c} = h_c \left(\frac{L}{k}\right)_{\text{copper}} = \frac{1.71 \times 10^2 (3 \times 10^{-2})}{380} = 1.35 \times 10^{-2} \ll 1$$

and the assumption that the face $x = 0$ is insulated is certainly a good one.

Experience has indicated that the heat generation within a diode is not uniform since a rather large localization of electrical resistance occurs at the interfaces of the various doped regions. However, these variations for the above diode appear to take place over a distance of about $1 \times 10^{-6}$ m. We then ask how far this localized heating is diffused in times of the order of $t_1 = 9 \times 10^{-6}$ s. On setting the natural time of the system equal to 1, we have $\alpha t_1 / x^2 = 1$, and

$$x = \sqrt{\alpha t_1} = \sqrt{(0.533 \times 10^{-4})(9 \times 10^{-6})} = 2.2 \times 10^{-5} \text{ m}$$

Thus, the high localized heat generation rates are not accompanied by high localized temperatures for this value of $t_1$. Sufficient diffusion occurs during the time $t_1$ so that the heat appears to be generated over a larger segment. Therefore, the assumption of uniform heat generation is adequate.

If we neglect the capacitance effects in the solder, then the previous analysis (as justified by the foregoing discussions) is applicable. To apply the results of Eq. (5-52) with Eq. (5-56), we note that, if $Q$ is the total power dissipated per pulse, then for a diode of radius $a$ the dissipated power per unit volume is

$$q_0 = \frac{Q}{\pi a^2 L}$$

Referring to Fig. 5-6, we see that the peak temperature $\theta^* = 0.057$ occurs at the insulated face ($\xi = 0$) and at the end of the heating pulse ($\tau = 0.024$). For $Q = 200$ W and $a = 5 \times 10^{-4}$ m, $q_0 = 2.54 \times 10^{12}$ W/m$^3$. Then from Eq. (5-44) the maximum temperature rise within the diode is

$$\theta = \frac{0.057 q_0 L^2}{k} = \frac{0.057(2.54 \times 10^{12})}{95} (0.01 \times 10^{-2})^2 = 15.2°\text{C}$$

However, for longer pulses such as $\tau_0 = 10.6$ (Fig. 5-6), the fluctuating part of the temperature rise can be a factor of 6 higher, i.e., 90°C, although the consideration of the transient effects in the solder and copper would tend to somewhat lessen this apparent increase in temperature rise. The more exact solution taking into account these effects can be obtained analytically or by finite differences as demonstrated in Example 5.6.

## 5-5. THE ELECTRICAL-THERMAL ANALOG

Many problems of practical importance in conduction cannot be readily solved by analytical techniques. Thus, the analogy of the response of a resistance-capacitance circuit to transient (and steady-state) conduction is useful. As mentioned earlier, the description by Ohm's law of current flow in an electrical circuit corresponds to the description of heat flow by the Fourier–Biot law. The principle of conservation of charge is analogous to the conservation of energy. Consequently, one might expect the description of the transient electrical potential (voltage) in a region to be similar to the description of the transient thermal potential (temperature) in an analogous region. This is indeed the case, and even though the

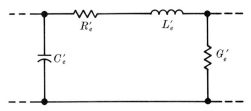

**Fig. 5-7**   Electrical circuit for a unit length of transmission line.

analogy holds for three-dimensional regions, for clarity we will consider a one-dimensional case such as the electrical transmission line illustrated in Fig. 5-7. The differential equation for the voltage $V(x, t)$ can be derived as

$$(R'_e C'_e + L'_e G'_e) \frac{\partial V}{\partial t_e} = \frac{\partial^2 V}{\partial x^2} - C'_e L'_e \frac{\partial^2 V}{\partial t_e^2} - R'_e G'_e V \qquad (5\text{-}57)$$

where the primes denote impedances per unit length. Considering the case of negligible leakage ($G'_e = 0$) and negligible self-inductance ($L'_e = 0$), Eq. (5-57) reduces to

$$\frac{\partial V}{\partial t_e} = \frac{1}{R'_e C'_e} \frac{\partial^2 V}{\partial x^2} \qquad (5\text{-}58)$$

which is analogous to the transient, one-dimensional heat flow equation for constant properties

$$\frac{\partial T}{\partial t} = \frac{k}{\rho c} \frac{\partial^2 T}{\partial x^2} \qquad (5\text{-}59)$$

It is well known that a transmission line can be approximated by an equivalent lumped circuit. By analogy, the heat transfer problem can be broken into a set of nodes with particular *thermal resistances* and *thermal capacitances*. The equivalent variables and the scaling factors necessary to relate the two problems are listed in Fig. 5-8. Note that the scale factors are not all independent but are governed by the interrelations of the variables themselves.

| Quantity | Thermal | Electrical | Scaled relationship |
|---|---|---|---|
| Potential | $T$ (temperature) | $V$ (voltage) | $V = aT$ |
| Flux | $Q = qA$ (heat flow) | $i$ (current) | $i = \dfrac{a}{mn} qA$ |
| Resistance | $R_\theta = \dfrac{\Delta x}{kA}$ (resistance in one-dimensional flow) | $R_e$ | $R_e = mnR_\theta$ |
| Capacitance | $C_\theta = \rho c\, \Delta x\, A$ (heat capacity in one-dimensional case) | $C_e$ | $C_e = \dfrac{C_\theta}{m}$ |
| Time | $t_\theta$ | $t_e$ | $t_e = nt_\theta$ |

**Fig. 5-8**   Electrical-thermal analog.

To complete the analogy of the boundary-value problems, the original boundary conditions must also be carried over. Five different boundary conditions are illustrated in Fig. 5-9.

The conduction problem can be solved by analysis or by building the equivalent electrical circuit. The lumped equivalent circuit is obtained by dividing the region of interest into a network of lumped subvolumes. In essence, this replaces the partial differential equation by an equation in finite differences. The potentials can then be determined at a finite number of individual points rather than in a continuous manner. The electrical network for the subdivided system will consist of series resistors and parallel capacitors connected at the nodal points of the network.

In steady-state situations, only the resistors are needed where thermal resistance for steady flow is defined by

$$Q = (qA)_1 = \frac{1}{R}(T_1 - T_2) \tag{5-60}$$

and where $T_1 - T_2$ represents some characteristic temperature difference. A list of thermal resistances for various geometries is given in Fig. 5-10. Notice that the resistance as defined by Eq. (5-60) consists of the product of $1/k$ (thermal resistivity) and a geometrical factor determined by the geometry of the body.

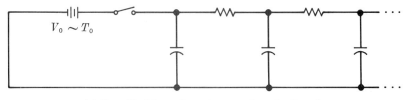

(a) Specified boundary temperature (voltage)

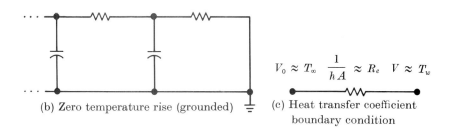

(b) Zero temperature rise (grounded)

$$V_0 \approx T_\infty \quad \frac{1}{hA} \approx R_e \quad V \approx T_w$$

(c) Heat transfer coefficient boundary condition

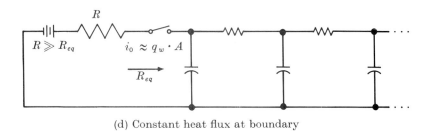

(d) Constant heat flux at boundary

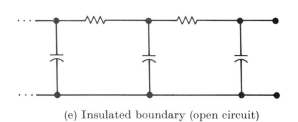

(e) Insulated boundary (open circuit)

**Fig. 5-9**  Electrical-thermal analog boundary conditions.

The electrical analog technique is demonstrated for a steady-state problem in the following example. Analog techniques for representing the conduction problem in a continuous manner are available, particularly for steady-state situations without heat generation so that Laplace's equation is applicable.[2] A field plotter for the latter case is described on page 519 of Ref. 17.

| Geometry | Arrangement | Thermal resistance | Remarks |
|---|---|---|---|
| Plate | | $\dfrac{L}{kA}$ | One-dimensional transfer |
| Hollow cylinder | | $\dfrac{\ln\,(D_o/D_i)}{2\pi kL}$ | Length of cylinder $L \gg D_o$ (one-dimensional transfer) |
| Hollow sphere | | $\dfrac{1/D_i - 1/D_o}{2\pi k}$ | Inner surface uniform temperature $T_1$ while outer surface at $T_2$ |

Body at $T_1$ in region having far-field temperature $T_2$

| | | | |
|---|---|---|---|
| Sphere | | $\dfrac{1}{2\pi Dk_\infty}$ | Infinite space or half-space approximately reached when $L/k_\infty \gg l/k$, where $L$ is some length in the outside region at $T_2$ and $l$ is some length of the inside region at $T_1$. |
| Hemisphere near an insulated surface | | $\dfrac{1}{\pi Dk_\infty}$ | |
| Sphere near an insulated surface | | $\dfrac{1}{2\pi Dk_\infty}\left(1 + \dfrac{D}{4h}\right)$ | |
| Circular disk | | $\dfrac{1}{4Dk_\infty}$ | |

| *Geometry* | *Arrangement* | *Thermal resistance* | *Remarks* |
|---|---|---|---|
| | *Body at $T_1$ in region having far-field temperature $T_2$ (continued)* | | |
| Circular disk on an insulated surface | 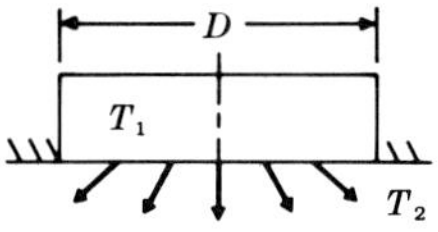 | $\dfrac{1}{2Dk_\infty}$ | Infinite space or half-space approximately reached when $L/k_\infty \gg l/k$, where $L$ is some length in the outside region at $T_2$ and $l$ is some length of the inside region at $T_1$ (continued) |
| Circular cylinder | 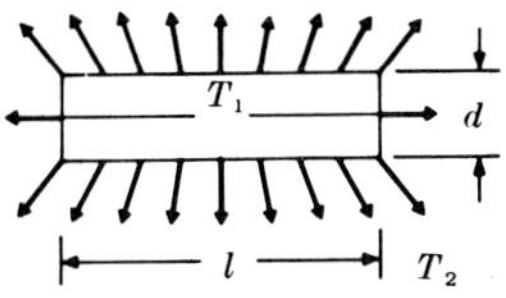 | $\dfrac{1}{2\pi lk_\infty}\ln\dfrac{2l}{d}$ <br><br> $d \ll l$ | |
| Circular cylinder near an insulated surface | 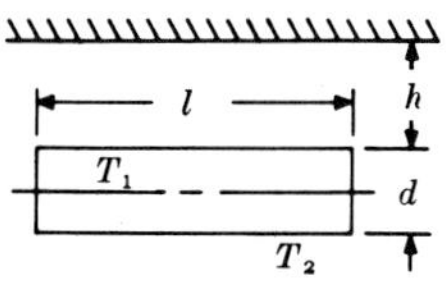 | $\dfrac{1}{2\pi lk_\infty}\ln\dfrac{2l}{d}\left(1+\dfrac{\ln\dfrac{l}{2h}}{\ln\dfrac{2l}{d}}\right)$ <br><br> $d \ll h$ <br> $h \lesssim l$ | |
| Circular cylinder with one end at an insulated surface | 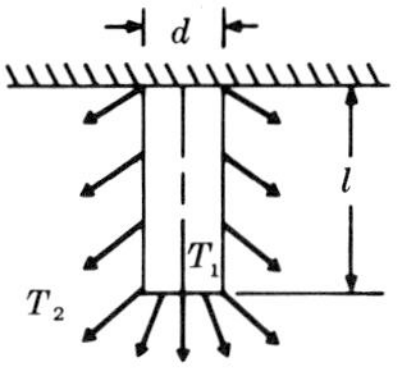 | $\dfrac{1}{2\pi lk_\infty}\ln\dfrac{4l}{d}$ <br><br> $d \ll l$ | |
| Plate | 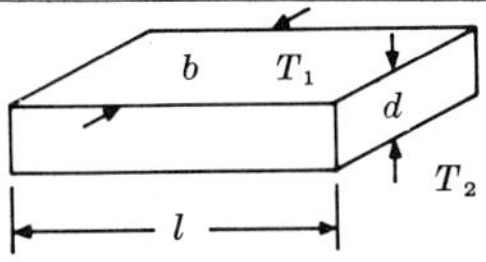 | $\dfrac{1}{2\pi lk_\infty}\ln\dfrac{4l}{b}$ <br><br> $d \ll b$ <br> $b \lesssim l$ | |
| Plate on the surface | 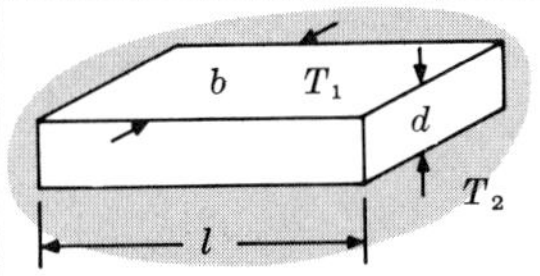 | $\dfrac{1}{\pi lk_\infty}\ln\dfrac{4l}{b}$ <br><br> $d \ll b$ <br> $b \lesssim l$ | |
| Torus | 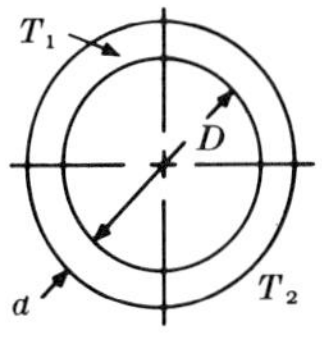 | $\dfrac{1}{2\pi^2 Dk_\infty}\ln\dfrac{8D}{d}$ <br><br> $d \ll D$ | |
| Torus near an insulated surface | 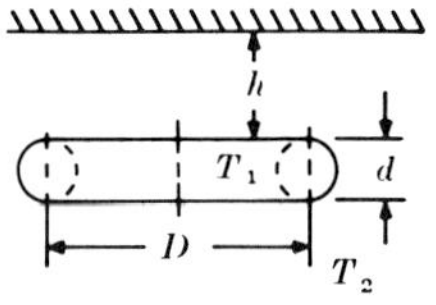 | $\dfrac{1}{2\pi^2 Dk_\infty}\ln\dfrac{8D}{d}\left(1+\dfrac{\ln\dfrac{2D}{h}}{\ln\dfrac{8D}{d}}\right)$ <br><br> $d \ll h$ <br> $h \ll D$ | |

**Fig. 5-10**   Equivalent thermal resistances for various shapes in pure conduction.[4]

**Example 5.5.** In a coaxial cable system, solid-state repeaters are required at periodic intervals. These repeaters, housed in watertight apparatus cases located in manholes, consist of a number of circuits, one of which is an output amplifier. The components of this amplifier are all mounted on an epoxy-glass printed wiring board which is enclosed in a rectangular metallic box for purposes of electrical shielding, Fig. 5-11. The most sensitive elements are three transistors,

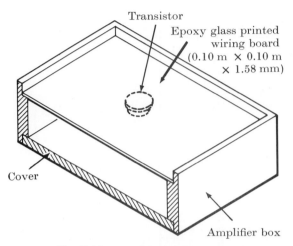

**Fig. 5-11**   Amplifier configuration.

the highest powered one dissipating 2.5 watts. Conditions for long life require that the transistor junction temperature not exceed 125°C. The thermal resistance between junction and case is such that, for 2.5 watts, the case temperature should not exceed 75°C. If the sides of the amplifier box are held at 50°C by conduction through the apparatus case to a manhole temperature of 25°C, determine the required thermal design for a temperature drop of less than 25°C between the transistor case and the sides of the amplifier box.

For simplicity, we will consider only the transistor with the 2.5-watt dissipation and assume that it is located in the center of the board as shown in Fig. 5-11. Consider the transistor as a 12.7-mm-diameter disk on a 1.58-mm-thick epoxy-glass board. If the height of the transistor case (disk) is thermally small (negligible thermal resistance) and the board is thin compared to the radius of the case, then the board's thermal resistance can be approximated as that offered by one-dimensional flow in a concentric cylinder. We are assuming that conduction or convection from the board to the surrounding air is negligible. The outer diameter is effectively somewhere between 0.10 m and 0.14 m. Thus, from Fig. 5-10, with $L = 1.58$ mm and $k = 0.294$ W/m · °C, then

$$\frac{\ln{(0.14/0.0127)}}{2\pi kL} > R_{\text{board}} > \frac{\ln{(0.10/0.0127)}}{2\pi kL}$$

so that

$$\frac{2.416}{2\pi(0.294)(0.00158)} = 828 > R_{\text{board}} > 713 \ ^{\circ}\text{C}/\text{W}$$

and the temperature rise between the box side and the transistor case would be around 2000°C if this were the only conduction path.

If we consider now the conduction through the air, we note that the transistor is mounted on the bottom side of the board so that no convection is possible. (See Chap. 6.) For pure conduction through the air in the amplifier box, the transistor can be treated as the "circular disk on an insulated surface" in Fig. 5-10, so that, for $k_{\text{air}} = 2.5 \times 10^{-2}$ W/m · °C, then

$$R_{\text{air}} = \frac{1}{2kD} = \frac{1}{2(2.5 \times 10^{-2})(0.0117)} = 1710 \ ^{\circ}\text{C}/\text{W}$$

which does not help either.

If we now choose to make the printed wiring board thicker, our simple one-dimensional assumption is no longer valid; so we first consider the best case where the thickness is essentially infinite. The equation above is applicable, now with $k = 0.294$ W/m · °C, so that

$$R_{\text{thick board}} = \frac{1}{2kD} = \frac{1}{2(0.294)(0.0117)} = 145 \ ^{\circ}\text{C}/\text{W}$$

which corresponds to a temperature rise of $(145)(2.5) = 362 \ ^{\circ}\text{C}$.

Lastly, we consider coupling the transistor case to the 6.35-mm-thick aluminum amplifier box cover by bonding a 19-mm-long aluminum stub of $1.27 \times 10^{-4} \ \text{m}^2$ cross-sectional area to the case which is then bolted to the cover. This arrangement is shown in Fig. 5-12. The resistance of the stub, where

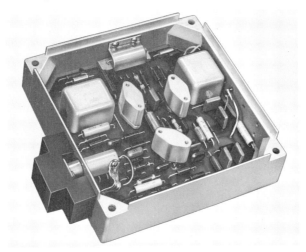

**Fig. 5-12**  Amplifier enclosure with cover removed.

$k$ of aluminum is 204 W/m · °C is

$$R_{\text{stub}} = \frac{L}{kA} = \frac{0.019}{(204)(1.27 \times 10^{-4})} = 0.74 \text{ °C/W}$$

Treating the cover plate as a concentric cylinder,

$$R_{\text{plate}} = \frac{\ln (D_o/D_i)}{2\pi kL} \leqq \frac{2.416}{2\pi(204)(0.00635)} = 0.298 \text{ °C/W}$$

Not forgetting the contact resistance between the plate and the top of the stub, we estimate a contact pressure of $206.7 \times 10^3$ N/m² (30 psi) for the bolted joint; hence, from Fig. 5-4, $h_c = 1.2 \times 10^3$ W/m² · °C and

$$R_{\text{contact}} = \frac{1}{h_c A} = \frac{1}{(1.2 \times 10^3)(1.27 \times 10^{-4})} = 6.6 \text{ °C/W}$$

The total resistance between the transistor case and the box temperature will be the sum of $R_{\text{stub}}$, $R_{\text{plate}}$, and $R_{\text{contact}}$ in parallel with $R_{\text{board}}$:

$$\frac{1}{R_{\text{total}}} = \frac{1}{R_{\text{board}}} + \frac{1}{R_{\text{stub}} + R_{\text{contact}} + R_{\text{plate}}}$$

which reduces to

$$R_{\text{total}} \approx R_{\text{stub}} + R_{\text{contact}} + R_{\text{plate}} = 7.64 \text{ °C/W}$$

At 2.5 W, this resistance causes a temperature rise of 19°C which is within the design requirements. Note the importance of contact resistance which amounts to 86 percent of the temperature rise.

## 5-6. FINITE DIFFERENCE APPROACH TO CONDUCTION PROBLEMS

The principle of conservation of energy has led us to a differential equation in terms of the energy changes in a system. With this equation, solutions to many thermal boundary-value problems are possible, as evidenced by the voluminous collection of Carslaw and Jaeger.[3] However, because of convergence difficulties in the evaluation of some of these solutions and the need for treating complex configurations, the approximate techniques of electrical analogy and finite differences may sometimes offer a more feasible approach.

In the method of finite differences, a body or system is thought to be composed of a number of finite elements on which an energy balance is satisfied. This is equivalent to expressing the differential energy equation as an equation in finite differences.

Consider one-dimensional transient heat conduction in a slab of constant properties and no heat generation. The energy balance within the slab, as given by Eq. (5-3), becomes

$$\frac{\partial T}{\partial t} = \alpha \, \frac{\partial^2 T}{\partial x^2} \tag{5-61}$$

Writing the *difference equation* in terms of a forward difference in time, we have

$$\frac{T(x, t + \delta t) - T(x, t)}{\delta t} = \alpha \left[ \frac{T(x + \delta x, t) - 2T(x, t) + T(x - \delta x, t)}{(\delta x)^2} \right] \tag{5-62}$$

so that

$$T(x, t + \delta t) = \gamma T(x + \delta x, t) + (1 - 2\gamma)T(x, t) + \gamma T(x - \delta x, t) \tag{5-63}$$

where

$$\gamma = \frac{\alpha \delta t}{(\delta x)^2} \tag{5-64}$$

Note that the coefficient $\gamma$ is always positive. However, the coefficient $(1 - 2\gamma)$ could be negative if, for example, $\delta t$ were large. This would produce a physical absurdity since it would say that the warmer the point $x$ is at the time $t$—i.e., $T(x, t)$—the colder it becomes at $t + \delta t$. This requires that we avoid negative coefficients in finite difference equations of the type in Eq. (5-63). In fact, one should also avoid zero coefficients. Consequently,

$$\gamma < \tfrac{1}{2} \tag{5-65}$$

and, hence, $\delta t$ and $\delta x$ cannot be chosen arbitrarily if a stable (meaningful) solution is to be obtained.

To generalize the finite difference equation [Eq. (5-63)] to include three-dimensional variations and boundary conditions, it is helpful to divide the conduction region into several nodes (see Fig. 5-13). If we denote an incremented time by the index $i$ and let $j$, $k$, $m$ denote the incremented space, then

$$T(x, y, z, t) = T(j, k, m, i)$$
$$T(x, y, z, t + \delta t) = T(j, k, m, i + 1), \qquad \text{etc.}$$

To determine the temperature at the new time $t + \delta t$, we form the energy balance at the point $(j, k, m)$ by considering the various modes of input from the neighboring nodes $n = a, b, c, d, e, f$, as shown in Fig. 5-13. The central element handles energy by three methods: (1) heat storage, (2) energy transfer from any node $n$ through a conductance $G_n$, and (3) energy generation within the volume.

The change in the energy storage is given by

$$\rho c \, \delta V \frac{\delta T}{\delta t} (i, j, k, m) = \frac{\rho c \, \delta V}{\delta t} [T(i + 1, j, k, m) - T(i, j, k, m)] \tag{5-66}$$

The energy transfer across the conductances is given by

$$\sum_n G_n(j, k, m)[T_n(i) - T(i, j, k, m)] \qquad (n = a, b, c, d, e, f) \tag{5-67}$$

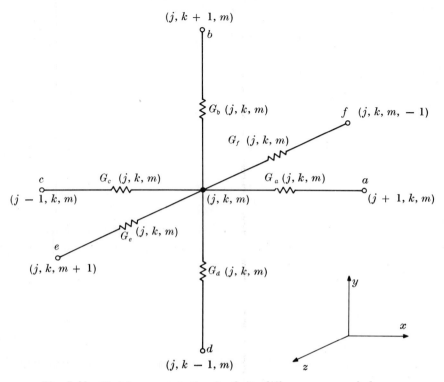

**Fig. 5-13**  Nodal representation for finite difference energy balance.

In three dimensions, the conductances $G_n$ take on six values as a result of conduction from each of the six adjacent nodes. For interior conduction and conduction between two materials in perfect contact,

$$G_n(j, k, m) = \left(\frac{kA}{\delta x}\right)_n (j, k, m) \qquad (5\text{-}68)$$

As indicated in Eq. (5-68), the coefficient $kA/\delta x$ can, in general, depend upon the central node $(j, k, m)$ in question and the particular neighbors, $n$. For the central node on a boundary with convection and/or radiation,[†]

$$G_n(j, k, m) = (hA)_n(j, k, m) \qquad (5\text{-}69)$$

Equating the change in energy storage to that entering from the neighboring nodes plus the internal heat generation, we have

$$\frac{\rho c\, \delta V}{\delta t}\,[T(i + 1, j, k, m) - T(i, j, k, m)] = \sum_n G_n(j, k, m)[T_n(i) - T(i, j, k, m)]$$
$$+ (q''' \, \delta V)(i, j, k, m) \quad (5\text{-}70)$$

---

[†] The case of a predetermined flux on a surface must be treated as a heat generation at the surface nodes.

Solving for the new temperature at $(j, k, m)$, we have

$$T(i + 1, j, k, m) = \sum_n \left[ \frac{G_n(j, k, m) \, \delta t}{\rho c \, \delta V} \right] T_n(i) + \left[ 1 - \sum_n \frac{G_n(j, k, m) \, \delta t}{\rho c \, \delta V} \right] T(i, j, k, m)$$

$$+ \left( q''' \frac{\delta t}{\rho c} \right) (i, j, k, m) \quad (5\text{-}71)$$

Again, all coefficients must be positive, so $\delta t$ is chosen according to

$$\delta t < \frac{\rho c \, \delta V}{\sum_n G_n(j, k, m)} \quad (5\text{-}72)$$

This specifies the maximum value of $\delta t$ but not necessarily the optimum value for a balance between accuracy and computation time. For one-dimensional conduction with negligible heat generation, Eq. (5-71) reduces to Eq. (5-63).

In the case of steady-state conduction, the foregoing discussion must be modified since the time rate of storage is now zero. Equation (5-70) becomes

$$\sum_n G_n(j, k, m)[T_n - T(j, k, m)] + (q''' \, \delta V)(j, k, m) = 0 \quad (5\text{-}73)$$

The temperature field $T(j, k, m)$ can be found by *assuming* a distribution and then, either by iteration or through the relaxation of residuals,[18] modifying the assumed field so that Eq. (5-73) is satisfied at every node. Although the relaxation method is the best for hand calculations, the iteration approach is to be preferred when a digital computer is available. In iteration, one may start at $(1, 1, 1)$ and calculate $T(1, 1, 1)$ so that Eq. (5-73) is satisfied, then move to $T(2, 1, 1)$, etc. After working through the entire array of nodes, the process is repeated by replacing the initially assumed field by the calculated temperature field. One may proceed in this manner until the $(i + 1)$th iteration agrees with the temperatures calculated for the $i$th iteration to within a specified degree of accuracy.

The use of finite differences is illustrated for a one-dimensional transient case in the following example. The approach to steady-state problems would be similar. Certain nomenclature changes will be introduced to aid in the translation of the physical problem to FORTRAN language.

**Example 5.6.** For the problem of periodic heat generation in a diode as discussed in a previous example and as illustrated in Fig. 5-5, it was noted that the analytical solution considered the transients to take place only in the silicon portion of the Kovar-silicon-copper diode structure. To determine the thermal response in a more exact manner, one may write a finite difference description of the diode.

As in Eq. (5-50), the temperature $\theta(x, t)$ can be divided into a fluctuating part $\Phi(x, t)$ and a time-averaged distribution $\psi(x)$, where the reference for these

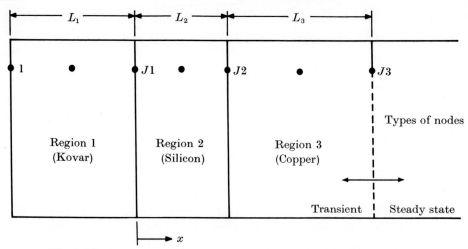

**Fig. 5-14**   Three-material structure—heat generation in silicon region.

temperatures is at a point far enough into the copper that transients are damped out (Node $J3$ in Fig. 5-14). $\psi(x)$ satisfies the differential equations

$$k_i \frac{\partial^2 \psi_i(x)}{\partial x^2} = \begin{cases} 0; & \text{Kovar region;} \quad i = 1 \\[2mm] \dfrac{-q_0 t_1}{t_0}\,; & \text{silicon region;} \quad i = 2 \\[2mm] 0; & \text{copper region;} \quad i = 3 \end{cases}$$

and assuming perfect contact, the boundary conditions are

$$\frac{\partial \psi_1(-L_1)}{\partial x} = 0$$

$$k_1 A_1 \frac{\partial \psi_1(0)}{\partial x} = k_2 A_2 \frac{\partial \psi_2(0)}{\partial x}\,; \qquad \psi_1(0) = \psi_2(0)$$

$$k_2 A_2 \frac{\partial \psi_2(L_2)}{\partial x} = k_3 A_3 \frac{\partial \psi_3(L_2)}{\partial x}\,; \qquad \psi_2(L_2) = \psi_3(L_2)$$

$$\psi_3(L_2 + L_3) = 0$$

where the subscripts identify the regions. Solving for $\psi_1(x)$, we have

$$\psi_1(x) = \frac{q_0 t_1 L_2}{k_2 t_0} \left[ \frac{k_2 A_2 L_3}{k_3 A_3} + \frac{L_2}{2} \right]; \qquad -L_1 \leq x \leq 0$$

$$\psi_2(x) = \frac{q_0 t_1}{k_2 t_0} \left[ \frac{k_2 A_2 L_2 L_3}{k_3 A_3} + \frac{(L_2^2 - x^2)}{2} \right]; \qquad 0 \leq x \leq L_2$$

$$\psi_3(x) = \frac{q_0 t_1 L_2 A_2}{t_0 k_3 A_3} (L_2 + L_3 - x); \qquad L_2 \leq x \leq L_2 + L_3$$

To solve for $\Phi(x, t)$, we write the heat conduction equation for each region illustrated in Fig. 5-14. For matched boundary conditions (assuming perfect contact), we have:

For region 1,  $-L_1 \leq x \leq 0$

$$\frac{\partial \Phi_1}{\partial t} = \alpha_1 \frac{\partial^2 \Phi_1}{\partial x^2}$$

$$\frac{\partial \Phi_1}{\partial x}(-L_1, t) = 0; \qquad \Phi_1(0, t) = \Phi_2(0, t)$$

For region 2,  $0 \leq x \leq L_2$

$$\frac{\partial \Phi_2}{\partial t} = \alpha_2 \frac{\partial^2 \Phi_2}{\partial x^2} + \frac{q_0}{(\rho c)_2}\left[ f(t) - \frac{t_1}{t_0}\right]$$

$$k_1 A_1 \frac{\partial \Phi_1(0, t)}{\partial x} = k_2 A_2 \frac{\partial \Phi_2(0, t)}{\partial x}; \qquad \Phi_2(L_2, t) = \Phi_3(L_2, t)$$

where the heat generation $q'''(t)$ is given by Eq. (5 12) and $f(t)$ is defined such that $q'''(t) = q_0 f(t)$.

For region 3,  $L_2 \leq x \leq L_2 + L_3$

$$\frac{\partial \Phi_3}{\partial t} = \alpha_3 \frac{\partial^2 \Phi_3}{\partial x^2}$$

$$k_2 A_2 \frac{\partial \Phi_2(L_2, t)}{\partial x} = k_3 A_3 \frac{\partial \Phi_3(L_2, t)}{\partial x}; \qquad \Phi_3(L_2 + L_3, t) = 0$$

All regions are subject to the simplest initial condition

$$\Phi_i(x, 0) = 0$$

We wish to cast the three interior equations and the boundary conditions into the form of the generalized finite difference equation for transient problems, Eq. (5-71). The coefficient terms are defined in notation which is compatible with FORTRAN as

$$SNJ = \frac{G_n(j)\,\delta t}{\rho c\,\delta V}; \qquad SJ = 1 - \sum_N SNJ; \qquad QJ(I) = \frac{q'''\,\delta t}{\rho c}$$

For the one-dimensional problem, $N$ takes on two values denoted by $A$ and $C$ which represent the nodes $a$ and $c$, respectively. In FORTRAN notation, $\Phi(x, t)$ becomes

$$\Phi(I + 1, J) = SAJ \cdot \Phi(I, J + 1) + SCJ \cdot \Phi(I, J - 1) + SJ \cdot \Phi(I, J) + QJ(I)$$

As indicated in Fig. 5-14, the diode can be categorized in terms of seven types of nodes, the boundary points $J = 1$, $J1$, $J2$, $J3$, and three nodes corresponding to the interior regions†

$$2 \leq J \leq J1 - 1; \qquad J1 + 1 \leq J \leq J2 - 1; \qquad J2 + 1 \leq J \leq J3 - 1$$

The coefficients $SAJ$, $SCJ$, and $SJ$ are determined in the following manner.

*Node $J = 1$*:

At the insulated boundary, the conductance between $J$ and the hypothetical node $c$ (corresponding to $J = 0$) is zero, so that $SCJ = 0$. Node $a$ (corresponding to $J = 2$) is an interior point; hence, from Eq. (5-68)

$$G_a = \frac{k_1 A_1}{\delta x_1}$$

Now, at the boundary, the volume is given by $\delta V_1 = A_1(\delta x_1/2)$, so that

$$SAJ = \frac{2k_1 \, \delta t}{(\rho c)_1 (\delta x_1)^2} = \frac{2\alpha_1 \, \delta t}{(\delta x_1)^2}$$

and

$$SJ = 1 - (SAJ + SCJ) = 1 - \frac{2\alpha_1 \, \delta t}{(\delta x_1)^2}$$

*Nodes $2 \leq J \leq J1 - 1$*:

All points are interior points; thus,

$$SAJ = SCJ = \frac{k_1 A_1}{\delta x_1} \cdot \frac{\delta t}{(\rho c)_1 A_1 (\delta x_1)} = \frac{\alpha_1 \, \delta t}{(\delta x_1)^2}$$

and

$$SJ = 1 - (SAJ + SCJ) = 1 - \frac{2\alpha_1 \, \delta t}{(\delta x_1)^2}$$

*Node $J1$*:

The boundary condition $\Phi_1(0, t) = \Phi_2(0, t)$ simply means that $x = 0$ can be represented as one node. If a contact resistance were present, then two nodes would be required. For the boundary node between the two materials 1 and 2,

$$\rho c \, \delta V = \frac{(\rho c \, \delta V)_1 + (\rho c \, \delta V)_2}{2}$$

so that

$$SAJ = \frac{k_2 A_2}{\delta x_2} \cdot \frac{2 \, \delta t}{(\rho c \, \delta V)_1 + (\rho c \, \delta V)_2} = \frac{2\alpha_2 \, \delta t}{[1 + (\rho c \, \delta V)_{12}](\delta x_2)^2}$$

where

$$(\rho c \, \delta V)_{12} = (\rho c \, \delta V)_1 / (\rho c \, \delta V)_2 = 1/(\rho c \, \delta V)_{21}$$

The other coefficients become

$$SCJ = \frac{k_1 A_1}{\delta x_1} \cdot \frac{2 \, \delta t}{(\rho c \, \delta V)_1 + (\rho c \, \delta V)_2} = \frac{2\alpha_1 \, \delta t}{[1 + (\rho c \, \delta V)_{21}](\delta x_1)^2}$$

and

$$SJ = 1 - (SAJ + SCJ)$$

---

† Note that $J$ is a parameter that can be set by the user of the program to indicate the number of nodes he desires for his particular problem.

Since the heat generation $q'''$ occurs only in the silicon, then no heat is generated at the boundary in half of the volume element, while the whole volume element absorbs heat in its capacitive nature; therefore

$$QJ(I) = \frac{q''' \, \delta t}{\rho c} = \frac{q''' \, (\delta V_2/2) \, \delta t}{[(\rho c \, \delta V)_1 + (\rho c \, \delta V)_2]/2}$$

$$= \frac{q_0[f(I) - t_1/t_0] \, \delta t}{[1 + (\rho c \, \delta V)_{12}](\rho c)_2}$$

where $f(I)$ simulates the unit step function of Eq. (5-42).

The coefficients for the other nodes are derived in a similar manner, and a complete listing of all of the coefficients is given in Fig. 5-15. The translation of this listing for solution by a digital computer is quite straightforward from this point. Note that $\delta t$ is chosen so that all of the $SJ$ coefficients are positive.

| $J$ | $SAJ$ | $SCJ$ | $QJ(I)$ |
|---|---|---|---|
| $1$ | $\dfrac{2\alpha_1 \, \delta t}{(\delta x_1)^2}$ | $0$ | $0$ |
| $2 \leqq J \leqq J1 - 1$ | $\dfrac{\alpha_1 \, \delta t}{(\delta x_1)^2}$ | $\dfrac{\alpha_1 \, \delta t}{(\delta x_1)^2}$ | $0$ |
| $J1$ | $\dfrac{2\alpha_2 \, \delta t}{[1 + (\rho c \, \delta V)_{12}](\delta x_2)^2}$ | $\dfrac{2\alpha_1 \, \delta t}{[1 + (\rho c \, \delta V)_{21}](\delta x_1)^2}$ | $\dfrac{q_0[f(I) - t_1/t_0] \, \delta t}{[1 + (\rho c \, \delta V)_{12}](\rho c)_2}$ |
| $J1 + 1 \leqq J \leqq J2 - 1$ | $\dfrac{\alpha_2 \, \delta t}{(\delta x_2)^2}$ | $\dfrac{\alpha_2 \, \delta t}{(\delta x_2)^2}$ | $\dfrac{q_0[f(I) - t_1/t_0] \, \delta t}{(\rho c)_2}$ |
| $J2$ | $\dfrac{2\alpha_3 \, \delta t}{[1 + (\rho c \, \delta V)_{23}](\delta x_3)^2}$ | $\dfrac{2\alpha_2 \, \delta t}{[1 + (\rho c \, \delta V)_{32}](\delta x_2)^2}$ | $\dfrac{q_0[f(I) - t_1/t_0] \, \delta t}{[1 + (\rho c \, \delta V)_{32}](\rho c)_2}$ |
| $J2 + 1 \leqq J \leqq J3 - 1$ | $\dfrac{\alpha_3 \, \delta t}{(\delta x_3)^2}$ | $\dfrac{\alpha_3 \, \delta t}{(\delta x_3)^2}$ | $0$ |
| $J3$ | $0$ | $0$ | $0$ |

**Fig. 5-15**   Coefficients for calculating $\Phi(I + 1, J) = SAJ \cdot \Phi(I, J + 1) + SCJ \cdot \Phi(I, J - 1) + SJ \cdot \Phi(I, J) + QJ(I)$, where $SJ = 1 - (SAJ + SCJ)$.

## 5-7. SUMMARY OF AN APPROACH TO CONDUCTION PROBLEMS

The approach to even the most complex conduction heat-transfer problems should begin with a consideration of the applicable form of the governing equation and a specification of the appropriate boundary conditions. Two dimensionless groups are useful in establishing the boundary conditions and in facilitating the subsequent solution of the problem. These are

$$\text{Fourier modulus,} \quad \tau = \frac{\alpha t}{L^2} = \text{natural time}$$

$$\text{Biot number,} \quad N_{\text{Bi}} = \frac{hL}{k} = \frac{\text{internal resistance}}{\text{external resistance}}$$

In the case of periodic heat generation or periodic boundary conditions, the depth to which the associated transients are propagated can be determined from

$$e^{-x\sqrt{\omega/2\alpha}}$$

Should the problem assessed by the above approach still remain too complex for an analytical solution, then the approximate techniques of the electrical analog and/or finite differences can be used.

Although finite differences can nearly always provide a solution, the amount of information and understanding that can be obtained from the analytical formulation and the simultaneous thinking in terms of the electrical analogy make all three approaches necessary tools for thermal design.

## REFERENCES

1. Arpaci, V. S., *Conduction Heat Transfer*, Reading, Mass., Addison-Wesley Publishing Co., 1966. Most complete basic text on conduction. Includes some consideration of approximate techniques.

2. Schneider, P. J., *Conduction Heat Transfer*, Reading, Mass., Addison-Wesley Publishing Co., 1955. A review of the classical separation of variables approach to conduction problems chiefly with constant-temperature boundary conditions. Graphical and other approximate techniques noted.

3. Carslaw, H. S., and J. C. Jaeger, *Conduction of Heat in Solids*, London, Oxford University Press, 1959. A compilation of analytical solutions and the most comprehensive reference book on the mathematical theory of conduction. Not easily read but well worth the effort.

4. Grober, H., S. Erk, and U. Grigull, *Fundamentals of Heat Transfer*, New York, McGraw-Hill Book Co., 1961. An excellent heat transfer text on a level a bit higher than Eckert and Drake. Figure 5-10 by permission.

References 5 through 15 are for the contact resistance presentation.

5. Fenech, H., and W. M. Rohsenow, "Prediction of Thermal Conductance of Metallic Surfaces in Contact," *J. Heat Transfer*, **85**, 15–24, Feb., 1963.

6. Clausing, A. M., and B. T. Chao, "Thermal Contact Resistance in a Vacuum Environment," *J. Heat Transfer*, **87**, 243–251, 1965.

7. Brunot, A. W., and F. F. Buckland, "Thermal Contact Resistance of Laminated and Machined Joints," *Trans. ASME*, **71**, 253–257, 1949.

8. Fried, E., and F. A. Costello, "Interface Thermal Contact Resistance Problem in Space Vehicles," *ARS Journal*, **32**, 237–243, 1962.

9. Fried, E., "Study of Interface Thermal Contact Conductance," *Final Report NASA (M-RP-T)*, Contract NASA-11247, April, 1965.

10. Weills, N. D., and E. A. Ryder, "Thermal Resistance Measures of Joints Formed Between Stationary Metal Surfaces," *Trans. ASME*, **71**, 259–267, 1949.

11. Stubstud, W. R., "Thermal Contact Resistance Between Thin Plates in a Vacuum," *Report 52-0756961-00181M*, Collins Radio Company, Cedar Rapids, Iowa, July, 1964.

12. Fried, E., "Study of Interface Thermal Contact Conductance Summary Report," *NASA (M-RP-T)*, Contract NASA-5207, General Electric Document No. 6450652, May 1, 1964.

13. Bloom, M. F., "Thermal Contact Conductance in a Vacuum Environment," *Douglas Aircraft Report SM 47700*, Dec., 1964. Presented at Fourth Conference on Thermal Conductivity, U. S. Radiological Defense Lab., San Francisco, California, Oct., 1964.

14. Henry, J. J., and H. Fenech, "The Use of Analog Computers for Determining Surface Parameters Required for Prediction of Thermal Contact Conductance," *J. Heat Transfer*, **86**, 543–552, Nov., 1964.

15. Kouwenhoven, W. B., and J. H. Potter, "Thermal Resistance of Metal Contacts," *J. Am. Weld. Soc.*, **27**, Part 2, 515–520, 1948.

16. Moon, J. S., and R. N. Keeler, "A Theoretical Consideration of Asymmetric Heat Flow at the Interface of Two Dissimilar Metals," *Int. J. of Heat and Mass Transfer*, **5**, 967–973, Oct., 1962.

17. Hsu, S. T., *Engineering Heat Transfer*, Princeton, N.J., D. Van Nostrand Co., Inc., 1963.

18. Dusinberre, G. M., *Heat Transfer Calculations by Finite Differences*, Scranton, Pa., International Textbook Co., 1961. An introductory book on numerical techniques emphasizing manual approaches.

*Chapter 6*

# CONVECTIVE HEAT TRANSFER

## L. W. Dickey and C. A. Fritsch

Heat transfer situations can be divided into an internal problem and an external problem. In the first, all the velocities are zero, and pure conduction is the only active mode. In the second, material velocities and radiation may have a significant effect on energy transfer so that, in some cases, all three modes are active. In our study of conduction, the internal and external problems have been coupled by a heat transfer coefficient, $h$. This chapter is concerned with the evaluation of this coefficient in situations where convection is present.

A system of simultaneous, nonlinear, partial differential equations was developed in Chapter 4 to represent the principles of conservation of mass, momentum, and energy. In many cases, these equations have been solved after applying certain restrictions on property variations and flow geometries. Jakob,[1] Schlichting,[2] and Pai[3] cover many of these solutions, while other heat transfer texts[4,5,6,7,8] emphasize the details of certain problems. Here we will review the analytical solutions of only two problems after deriving the pertinent dimensionless groups from the basic equations. Some approximate analytical techniques will then be reviewed, followed by a coverage of experimental results in convection.

## 6-1. DIMENSIONLESS GROUPS IN CONVECTION AND BOUNDARY-LAYER CONCEPTS

The treatment of viscous flow problems can be divided into (1) exact solutions, and (2) boundary-layer flows. In *exact solutions*—such as those for fully developed laminar flow in a pipe, between two parallel plates, and between concentric cylinders—the basic equations simplify to the extent that they can be integrated for the entire velocity field (across the pipe, etc.). In fluids with small viscosities, *boundary-layer flows* exist; therefore, the flow about a body can be divided into two regions: (1) a very thin layer in the neighborhood of the body (boundary layer) where viscous forces play an essential role, and (2) the remaining region outside this layer where friction may be neglected. In both cases, once the velocity profile is determined, this profile is then used in the general energy equation to determine the temperature profile and, subsequently, the heat transfer.

For convenience, consider here† the case of two-dimensional flows with constant properties, as illustrated later in Fig. 6-1. The basic equations become:

Continuity:

$$\frac{\partial u}{\partial x} + \frac{\partial v}{\partial y} = 0 \tag{6-1}$$

Navier–Stokes:

$$\rho \frac{Du}{Dt} = -\frac{\partial p}{\partial x} + F_x + \mu\left(\frac{\partial^2 u}{\partial x^2} + \frac{\partial^2 u}{\partial y^2}\right) \tag{6-2}$$

$$\rho \frac{Dv}{Dt} = -\frac{\partial p}{\partial y} + F_y + \mu\left(\frac{\partial^2 v}{\partial x^2} + \frac{\partial^2 v}{\partial y^2}\right) \tag{6-3}$$

Energy:

$$\rho c_p \frac{DT}{Dt} = \beta T \frac{Dp}{Dt} + \mu \Phi + k\frac{\partial^2 T}{\partial x^2} + k\frac{\partial^2 T}{\partial y^2} + q''' \tag{6-4}$$

We now introduce the dimensionless variables

$$T^* = \frac{T}{T_0} ; \qquad \xi = \frac{x}{L} ; \qquad \eta = \frac{y}{\delta} ; \qquad u^* = \frac{u}{u_0} ; \qquad v^* = \frac{v}{v_0} ; \qquad t^* = \frac{u_0 t}{L} \tag{6-5}$$

and normalized properties

$$\rho^* = \frac{\rho}{\rho_0} ; \qquad p^* = \frac{p}{p_0} ; \qquad \mu^* = \frac{\mu}{\mu_0} ; \qquad k^* = \frac{k}{k_0} ; \qquad c_p^* = \frac{c_p}{c_{p,0}} ; \qquad \beta^* = \beta T_0 \tag{6-6}$$

where the zero subscript signifies a convenient reference state, e.g., the free stream conditions in a boundary-layer flow. Note that $L$ and $\delta$ are characteristic lengths in the $x$ and $y$ directions, respectively.

---

† The more general cases are treated by Pai.[3]

The stipulation of a boundary-layer flow means that $\delta$ is small compared to the length $L$ along the body, i.e., $\delta \ll L$. Thus, as a manner of speaking, we will say that quantities are small when they are of the order of $\delta$ and that, by comparison, quantities such as $L$ are of the order of unity.

If we now consider the continuity equation in terms of the dimensionless variables, Eq. (6-1) becomes

$$\frac{u_0}{L}\frac{\partial u^*}{\partial \xi} + \frac{v_0}{\delta}\frac{\partial v^*}{\partial \eta} = 0 \qquad (6\text{-}7)$$

All dimensionless quantities are of the order of unity, and the two terms of Eq. (6-7) must be of the same order of magnitude. Consequently, $u_0$ must be of order of unity, $v_0$ must be of order $\delta$, and for boundary-layer flows $v_0/u_0 \ll 1$.

Consider next the nondimensional form of the Navier–Stokes equations for the $x$ direction [Eq. (6-2)]. On dividing by the factor $\rho u_0^2/L$, we have

$$\frac{Du^*}{Dt} = \frac{\partial u^*}{\partial t^*} + u^*\frac{\partial u^*}{\partial \xi} + v^*\frac{\partial u^*}{\partial \eta}\cdot\frac{v_0 L}{u_0 \delta} = -\left(\frac{p_0}{\rho_0 u_0^2}\right)\frac{1}{\rho^*}\frac{\partial p^*}{\partial \xi}$$

$$\qquad\qquad 1 \qquad\quad 1 \qquad\qquad\qquad \delta\,\frac{1}{\delta}$$

$$+ \frac{F_x}{\rho^*}\left(\frac{L}{\rho_0 u_0^2}\right) + \left(\frac{\mu}{L\rho_0 u_0}\right)\frac{\mu^*}{\rho^*}\left[\frac{\partial^2 u^*}{\partial \xi^2} + \frac{\partial^2 u^*}{\partial \eta^2}\frac{L^2}{\delta^2}\right] \quad (6\text{-}8)$$

$$\qquad\qquad\qquad\qquad\qquad\qquad\qquad\qquad 1 \qquad\quad \frac{1}{\delta^2}$$

We define the dimensionless ratios as

$$N_{\text{Re}} = \frac{\rho_0 u_0 L}{\mu_0} \qquad\qquad \text{Reynolds number} \qquad\qquad (6\text{-}9)$$

$$N_{\text{Eu}} = \frac{p_0}{\rho_0 u_0^2} \qquad\qquad \text{Euler number} \qquad\qquad (6\text{-}10)$$

$$N_{\text{Fr}} = \frac{u_0 \rho_0^{1/2}}{(LF_x)^{1/2}} \qquad\qquad \text{Froude number} \qquad\qquad (6\text{-}11)$$

Note that, for boundary-layer flows, all the terms on the left side of Eq. (6-8) are of the same order, while the first term in the bracket on the right side is much smaller than the second term. Neglecting the small term, Eq. (6-8) can be written

$$\frac{Du^*}{Dt^*} = -N_{\text{Eu}}\cdot\frac{1}{\rho^*}\frac{\partial p^*}{\partial \xi} + \frac{1}{N_{\text{Fr},x}^2} + \frac{1}{N_{\text{Re}}}\frac{\mu^*}{\rho^*}\left[\frac{\partial^2 u^*}{\partial \eta^2}\cdot\frac{L^2}{\delta^2}\right] \qquad (6\text{-}12)$$

In a similar manner, the second Navier–Stokes equation becomes

$$\frac{v_0}{u_0}\frac{Dv^*}{Dt^*} = \frac{\partial v^*}{\partial t^*}\frac{v_0}{u_0} + u^*\frac{\partial v^*}{\partial \xi}\frac{v_0}{u_0} + v^*\frac{\partial v^*}{\partial \eta}\frac{L}{\delta}\frac{v_0^2}{u_0^2} = -\left(N_{\text{Eu}}\frac{L}{\delta}\right)\frac{1}{\rho^*}\frac{\partial p^*}{\partial \eta}$$

$$\delta \qquad\qquad \delta \qquad\qquad \frac{1}{\delta}\delta^2$$

$$+\frac{1}{N_{\text{Fr},y}^2} + \frac{1}{N_{\text{Re}}}\frac{\mu^*}{\rho^*}\left(\frac{\partial^2 v^*}{\partial \xi^2}\cdot\frac{v_0}{u_0} + \frac{\partial^2 v^*}{\partial \eta^2}\cdot\frac{v_0}{u_0}\frac{L^2}{\delta^2}\right) \qquad (6\text{-}13)$$

$$\delta \qquad\qquad \frac{1}{\delta}$$

It can be readily shown that, for the region outside the boundary layer where the viscous effects are negligible for steady-flow and no body forces, Eq. (6-2) reduces to Bernoulli's equation

$$\tfrac{1}{2}\rho_0 u_0^2 + p_0 = \text{constant} \qquad (6\text{-}14)$$

In any forced flow, therefore, $N_{\text{Eu}}$ is of the order unity. We now consider flows where the Reynolds number is large (as in a low-viscosity fluid). Consequently, $N_{\text{Re}}$ is of the order $1/\delta^2$, and Eq. (6-12) remains the same, while Eq. (6-13) reduces to

$$\frac{N_{\text{Eu}}}{\rho^*}\frac{\partial p^*}{\partial \eta} = \frac{1}{N_{\text{Fr},y}^2}\cdot\frac{\delta}{L} \qquad (6\text{-}15)$$

Under the assumption of $F_y \approx 0$ or, more precisely, if $N_{\text{Fr},y}^2 > 1$, Eq. (6-15) tells us that in two-dimensional boundary-layer flows

$$\frac{\partial p}{\partial y} \approx 0 \qquad (6\text{-}16)$$

Consider now the energy equation in nondimensional form. On dividing by $T_0 u_0 \rho_0 c_{p,0}/L$, we have

$$\rho^* c_p^* \frac{DT^*}{Dt^*} = \rho^* c_p^* \left(\frac{\partial T^*}{\partial t^*} + u^*\frac{\partial T^*}{\partial \xi} + v^*\frac{\partial T^*}{\partial \eta}\frac{v_0 L}{u_0 \delta}\right)$$

$$1 \qquad\qquad 1 \qquad\qquad 1 \qquad\qquad \delta\frac{1}{\delta}$$

$$= \frac{p_0}{\rho_0 u_0^2}\left(\frac{u_0^2}{T_0 c_{p,0}}\right)\beta^* T^* \frac{Dp^*}{Dt^*} + \left(\frac{\mu_0 L}{T_0 u_0 \rho_0 c_{p,0}}\right)\mu^*\Phi + \left(\frac{\mu_0}{L u_0 \rho_0}\right)$$

$$1$$

$$\times \left(\frac{k_0}{\mu_0 c_{p,0}}\right)k^*\left(\frac{\partial^2 T^*}{\partial \xi^2} + \frac{\partial^2 T^*}{\partial \eta^2}\frac{L^2}{\delta^2}\right) + \frac{q'''L}{T_0 u_0 \rho_0 c_{p,0}} \qquad (6\text{-}17)$$

$$1 \qquad\qquad \frac{1}{\delta^2}$$

We define the dimensionless groups:

$$N_{\text{Pr}} = \frac{\mu_0 c_{p,0}}{k_0} \qquad \text{Prandtl number} \qquad (6\text{-}18a)$$

$$N_{\text{E}} = \frac{u_0^2}{c_{p,0} T_0} \qquad \text{Eckert number} \qquad (6\text{-}18b)$$

It can be shown that, for boundary-layer flows, the viscous dissipation function $\Phi$, as defined in Eq. (4-23), reduces to one term of the order $1/\delta^2$, so that

$$\Phi = \left(\frac{\partial u}{\partial y}\right)^2 = \left(\frac{\partial u^*}{\partial \eta}\right)^2 \left(\frac{u_0}{\delta}\right)^2 \qquad (6\text{-}19)$$

Then, on neglecting the lower-order term in the conduction part, Eq. (6-17) with Eq. (6-19) becomes

$$\rho^* c_p^* \frac{DT^*}{Dt^*} = N_{\text{Eu}} N_{\text{E}} \beta^* T^* \frac{Dp^*}{Dt^*} + \frac{1}{N_{\text{Re}} \cdot N_{\text{Pr}}} k^* \frac{\partial^2 T^*}{\partial \eta^2} \cdot \frac{L^2}{\delta^2}$$
$$+ \frac{N_{\text{E}}}{N_{\text{Re}}} \left(\frac{\partial u^*}{\partial \eta}\right)^2 \cdot \frac{L^2}{\delta^2} + \frac{q'''}{T_0 \rho_0 u_0 c_{p,0}} \qquad (6\text{-}20)$$

Under the earlier assumption that $N_{\text{Re}}$ is of the order $1/\delta^2$, all of the terms in the above boundary-layer energy equation remain so long as $N_{\text{Pr}}$ and $N_{\text{E}}$ are both of the order of unity. Note that $\beta^* = \beta T_0$, which is of the order of unity for gases and is identically unity for an ideal gas. For incompressible flows, however, $\beta^*$ is essentially zero. Thus, the pressure term can often be neglected from the energy equation.

The above equations also hold for flow over a curved surface, with one exception. The Navier–Stokes equation for the $y$ direction reduces to

$$\frac{\partial p}{\partial y} = \rho R u^2 \qquad (6\text{-}21)$$

where $R$ is the radius of curvature and is limited to being of the order of unity. This equation states that, for a curved wall, a pressure gradient is necessary to balance the centrifugal force. However, the total change in pressure across the boundary layer is still small, being of order $\delta$, and can be neglected for $R$ of the order one.

From nondimensionalizing the basic equations, we have arrived at a set of dimensionless groups which can be used to characterize particular flows. The restriction for boundary-layer flows is that $N_{\text{Re}}$ be large. Since $N_{\text{Re}}$ can be interpreted as the ratio of the inertia forces to the viscous forces, it is also a measure of whether instabilities in a flow will be damped or propagated. Thus, if $N_{\text{Re}}$ is low enough, these instabilities will be damped, and the flow is called *laminar*. If they are not damped, then the velocity components in the Navier–

Stokes equations are time dependent since they will fluctuate about a mean value in a random manner. Such a flow is called *turbulent*, and the solution for the instantaneous velocity of every particle using the basic equations is not now possible. However, approximate techniques for the description of the mean flow are available,[2] one of which will be discussed later.

## 6-2. ANALYTICAL SOLUTION TO TWO CONVECTION PROBLEMS

The conservation equations are solved here for *forced convection* in a duct and *free convection* over a vertical flat plate. In forced convection, a mechanical means (fan or pump) is used to increase the velocity of the fluid, while the motion of the fluid in free convection is caused by difference in density resulting from temperature gradients. The treatment of both problems assumes laminar two-dimensional flow.

### FORCED CONVECTION IN A DUCT

Forced flow of a fluid in a duct can be considered as consisting of two regimes, as illustrated in Fig. 6-1. In the *entrance region*, a boundary layer

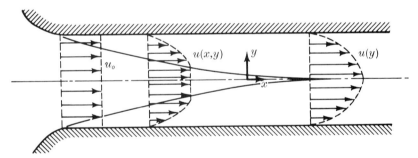

**Fig. 6-1**   Development of velocity profile in forced convection in a duct.

grows on the walls until it covers the entire cross section of the duct. The second regime, which is asymptotically approached, is called *fully developed flow*. In this region there is no change in velocity with distance in the axial direction. In other words, there is no difference in momentum transport at two cross sections of the duct, and the pressure change between two sections may be related simply to the wall shear stress.

Most analytical studies of laminar forced convection in ducts have been concerned with the case of fully developed velocity profiles or have been based on the assumption of a uniform velocity profile (slug flow). For fluids with

Prandtl numbers† near unity, as for air, both the temperature and velocity profiles develop at a similar rate, and neither limiting assumption is satisfactory for many practical duct lengths. Hence, we will first treat the case of fully developed flow between parallel plates with a step change in temperature. Then, we will consider the case where the heating is applied at the entrance of a duct so that the velocity and temperature profiles develop together.

Consider steady, laminar two-dimensional flow of an incompressible fluid between two parallel flat plates as illustrated in Fig. 6-2. If we further assume

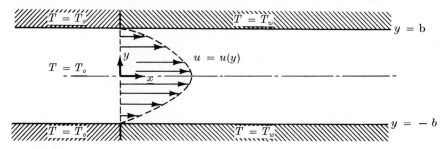

**Fig. 6-2** Fully developed forced convection with a step change in wall temperature.

constant properties and negligible body forces, the basic conservation equations reduce to:

$$\frac{\partial u}{\partial x} + \frac{\partial v}{\partial y} = 0 \tag{6-22}$$

$$u\frac{\partial u}{\partial x} + v\frac{\partial u}{\partial y} = -\frac{1}{\rho}\frac{\partial p}{\partial x} + \frac{\mu}{\rho}\left[\frac{\partial^2 u}{\partial x^2} + \frac{\partial^2 u}{\partial y^2}\right] \tag{6-23}$$

$$u\frac{\partial v}{\partial x} + v\frac{\partial v}{\partial y} = -\frac{1}{\rho}\frac{\partial p}{\partial y} + \frac{\mu}{\rho}\left[\frac{\partial^2 v}{\partial x^2} + \frac{\partial^2 v}{\partial y^2}\right] \tag{6-24}$$

The energy equation (under the stipulation of no sources or sinks) is

$$u\frac{\partial T}{\partial x} + v\frac{\partial T}{\partial y} = \frac{\mu}{\rho c_p}\Phi + \alpha\left[\frac{\partial^2 T}{\partial x^2} + \frac{\partial^2 T}{\partial y^2}\right] \tag{6-25}$$

Note that the flow equations, Eqs. (6-22) through (6-24), are independent of the energy equation, Eq. (6-25). Hence, we can first determine the velocity profile. Then, using that profile in Eq. (6-25), the convective contribution to the heat transfer [the left side of Eq. (6-25)] can be taken into account.

Applying the definition of fully developed flow,‡ i.e., $\partial u/\partial x = 0$, then

--------------

† It will be shown later that the Prandtl number is a measure of the rate at which temperature and velocity disturbances are propagated through a flow field.

‡ Schlichting[2] shows that this is a permissible assumption for duct length greater than $0.04(2b) \cdot N_{\text{Re}}$.

continuity, Eq. (6-22), with the condition $v = 0$ at the impervious walls, requires that $v$ be zero everywhere in the fully developed regime. Consequently, Eq. (6-24) reduces to $\partial p / \partial y = 0$ and Eq. (6-23) becomes

$$\mu \frac{d^2 u}{dy^2} = \frac{dp}{dx} \qquad (6\text{-}26)$$

The boundary conditions of symmetry at the center line and no slip at the wall can be stated as

$$\frac{du}{dy} = 0 \quad \text{at} \quad y = 0, \qquad x \geq 0 \qquad (6\text{-}27\text{a})$$

$$u = 0 \quad \text{at} \quad y = \pm b, \qquad x \geq 0 \qquad (6\text{-}27\text{b})$$

When a function of $y$ is equal to a function of $x$, each must be equal to a constant; therefore, Eq. (6-26) can be integrated, yielding the parabolic velocity profile:

$$u = \frac{b^2}{2\mu} \left( -\frac{dp}{dx} \right) \left[ 1 - \left( \frac{y}{b} \right)^2 \right] \qquad (6\text{-}28)$$

In terms of the mean velocity, $u_m$, we have

$$u = \frac{3}{2} u_m \left[ 1 - \left( \frac{y}{b} \right)^2 \right] \qquad (6\text{-}29)$$

where $u_m$ is related to the pressure drop (friction factor) for the duct configuration of interest.[8]

For fully developed flow, the energy equation, Eq. (6-25), becomes

$$u \frac{\partial T}{\partial x} = \frac{\nu}{c_p} \left( \frac{\partial u}{\partial y} \right)^2 + \alpha \left[ \frac{\partial^2 T}{\partial x^2} + \frac{\partial^2 T}{\partial y^2} \right] \qquad (6\text{-}30)$$

For a step change in wall temperature, the boundary conditions on Eq. (6-30) become

$$T = T_0 \quad \text{at} \quad x = 0, \qquad -b < y < b \qquad (6\text{-}31\text{a})$$

$$T = T_w \quad \text{at} \quad x > 0, \qquad y = \pm b \qquad (6\text{-}31\text{b})$$

$$\frac{\partial T}{\partial y} = 0 \quad \text{at} \quad x > 0, \qquad y = 0 \qquad (6\text{-}31\text{c})$$

We define the dimensionless groups

$$\theta = \frac{T_w - T}{T_w - T_0}, \qquad N_{\text{Re}} = \frac{u_m b}{\nu}, \qquad N_{\text{E}} = \frac{u_m^2}{c_p (T_w - T_0)}$$

$$\zeta = \frac{x}{L}, \qquad \eta = \frac{y}{b} \qquad (6\text{-}32)$$

where $L$ is the heated length of the duct. By substitution of Eq. (6-29) in Eq. (6-30) and use of the above variables, Eq. (6-30) and Eq. (6-31) become:†

$$\frac{3}{2}[1 - \eta^2]\frac{\partial \theta}{\partial \zeta} = -9\frac{N_{\mathrm{E}}}{N_{\mathrm{Re}}}\left(\frac{L}{b}\right)\eta^2 + \frac{1}{N_{\mathrm{Re}}N_{\mathrm{Pr}}}\left(\frac{L}{b}\right)\left[\frac{\partial^2 \theta}{\partial \zeta^2}\left(\frac{b}{L}\right)^2 + \frac{\partial^2 \theta}{\partial \eta^2}\right] \quad (6\text{-}33)$$

$$\theta = 1 \quad \text{at} \quad \zeta = 0, \quad -1 < \eta < 1 \quad\quad (6\text{-}34a)$$

$$\theta = 0 \quad \text{at} \quad \zeta > 0, \quad \eta = \pm 1 \quad\quad (6\text{-}34b)$$

$$\frac{\partial \theta}{\partial \eta} = 0 \quad \text{at} \quad \zeta > 0, \quad \eta = 0 \quad\quad (6\text{-}34c)$$

Some judgment can now be made about the importance of the various terms in the energy equation. Since the normalized variables are of order unity,‡ then the viscous dissipation in duct flow can be neglected as long as $\frac{N_{\mathrm{E}}}{N_{\mathrm{Re}}}\left(\frac{L}{b}\right) \ll 1$. This means that the energy produced due to the total head loss is unimportant, which is frequently the case in electronic equipment cooled by forced convection. Since $\theta$ ranges from zero to unity over $0 \le \eta \le 1$ and $0 \le \zeta \le \infty$, then the normalized derivatives should be of the same order of magnitude for values of $x$ sufficiently removed from the discontinuity at $x = 0$. Hence, as long as the total heated length is much greater than the transverse dimension, the error encountered in neglecting the axial conduction compared to the transverse conduction is probably insignificant. With these two approximations, the energy equation becomes§

$$\frac{3}{2}\left(\frac{b}{L}\right)N_{\mathrm{Re}}N_{\mathrm{Pr}}(1 - \eta^2)\frac{\partial \theta}{\partial \zeta} = \frac{\partial^2 \theta}{\partial \eta^2} \quad\quad (6\text{-}35)$$

The boundary-value problem specified by Eqs. (6-35) and (6-34) has been solved by Prins, et al.[9] They first separated variables by assuming

$$\theta(\zeta, \eta) = Z(\zeta)H(\eta) \quad\quad (6\text{-}36)$$

thus obtaining

$$N_{\mathrm{Re}}N_{\mathrm{Pr}}\frac{dZ}{d\zeta} + \frac{2}{3}\alpha^2 Z = 0 \qu\quad (6\text{-}37)$$

---

† The product $N_{\mathrm{Re}} \cdot N_{\mathrm{Pr}}$ is often called the *Péclet number.*

‡ One has to be careful in assuming that normalized derivatives are of the same order of magnitude. Physical reasoning needs to be brought to bear on such judgments.

§ It is worth noting that under the specification of slug flow the velocity in the convective term of Eq. (6-30) is a constant and the counterpart of Eq. (6-35) becomes analogous to transient one-dimensional conduction problems where the axial coordinate $\zeta(x)$ becomes the analog of time. Solutions of the energy equation are then identical to similar problems in transient conduction.[10]

and

$$\frac{d^2H}{d\eta^2} + \alpha^2(1 - \eta^2)H = 0 \tag{6-38}$$

The solution to Eq. (6-37) is

$$Z = e^{-2\alpha^2 L\zeta / 3N_{Re} \cdot N_{Pr} \cdot b} \tag{6-39}$$

The value of the separation constant $\alpha$ is determined by the boundary condition, Eq. (6-34b):

$$H = 0 \quad \text{at} \quad \eta = \pm 1 \tag{6-40}$$

Hence, Eq. (6-38) with Eq. (6-40) is a Sturm–Liouville system having an infinite set of discrete eigenvalues $\alpha_0, \alpha_1, \alpha_2, \ldots, \alpha_n, \ldots$ and corresponding eigenfunctions $H_0, H_1, H_2, \ldots, H_n, \ldots$ .

To determine the eigenfunction, we first note that the general solution may be written as the sum of two power series.† However, only one of these satisfies the symmetry condition, Eq. (6-34c). Consequently,

$$H_n = \sum_{j=0}^{\infty} a_j \eta^j \tag{6-41}$$

where the $a_j$ are given by the recursion relations:

$$a_0 = 1$$

$$a_1 = 0$$

$$a_2 = -\tfrac{1}{2}\alpha_n^2$$

$$a_3 = 0$$

$$\cdot$$
$$\cdot$$
$$\cdot$$

$$a_j = \frac{\alpha_n^2}{j(j-1)}(a_{j-4} - a_{j-2}) \tag{6-42}$$

The eigenvalues are calculated as the roots of Eq. (6-40), and substitution of each of these values into Eq. (6-41) yields the corresponding eigenfunctions.†

Using the orthogonality properties of these eigenfunctions, the coefficients in the series expansion for $\theta$ have been determined,[9] yielding

$$\theta(\zeta, \eta) = -2 \sum_{0}^{\infty} \frac{H_n e^{-2\alpha_n^2 L\zeta / 3N_{Re}N_{Pr}b}}{\alpha_n(\partial H_n / \partial \alpha_n)_{\eta=1}} \tag{6-43}$$

---

† A similar approach for fully developed flow in a circular tube with a step change in wall temperature, due to L. Graetz, is presented in detail by Jakob.[1] Additionally, it has been shown by Schenk and Dumore[11] that both problems can be solved in terms of confluent hypergeometric functions for a rather general set of boundary conditions.

To find the heat transferred from the wall, we evaluate the derivative in the Fourier–Biot law according to

$$q_w = -k \left.\frac{\partial T}{\partial y}\right|_{y=\pm b} = -k \left.\frac{\partial T}{\partial \eta}\right|_{\eta=\pm 1} \left.\frac{\partial \eta}{\partial y}\right|_{y=\pm b} = \frac{k(T_w - T_0)}{b} \left.\frac{\partial \theta}{\partial \eta}\right|_{\eta=\pm 1} \quad (6\text{-}44)$$

where Eq. (6-43) is used to evaluate $\partial\theta/\partial\eta$. Introducing the concept of a "mixing cup" temperature defined as the *mixed mean temperature* over a cross section, we write

$$T_{\text{mix}} = \frac{\displaystyle\int_{-b}^{+b} T(x, y)\, u(y)\, dy}{\displaystyle\int_{-b}^{+b} u(y)\, dy} \quad (6\text{-}45)$$

so that

$$\theta_{\text{mix}} = \frac{T_w - T_{\text{mix}}}{T_w - T_0} \quad (6\text{-}46)$$

can be evaluated using Eqs. (6-43) and (6-29) in Eq. (6-45). The local heat transfer coefficient $h_x$ can be defined as $q_w(x)/(T_w - T_{\text{mix}})$, and one can define a local Nusselt number as

$$N_{\text{Nu},x} = \frac{h_x b}{k} \quad (6\text{-}47)$$

Both $N_{\text{Nu},x}$ and $\theta_{\text{mix}}$ have been evaluated by Prins et al.[9] as a function of the longitudinal coordinate and $N_{\text{Re}}N_{\text{Pr}}$. The results are listed in Fig. 6-3. Note that $N_{\text{Nu},x}$ reaches an asymptotic value of 1.88 and that $\theta_{\text{mix}}$ tends to zero as $T_{\text{mix}}$ approaches $T_w$.

As stated earlier, the flow in the entrance region at small distances from the inlet section can be characterized as boundary-layer flow over a flat plate.

| $\dfrac{L}{b}\,(\zeta/N_{\text{Re}}N_{\text{Pr}})$ | $\theta_{\text{mix}}$ | $N_{\text{Nu},x}$ |
|---|---|---|
| 0.01 | 0.95 | 3.27 |
| 0.02 | 0.92 | 2.89 |
| 0.05 | 0.85 | 2.35 |
| 0.10 | 0.76 | 2.05 |
| 0.15 | 0.69 | 1.94 |
| 0.20 | 0.63 | 1.90 |
| 0.50 | 0.36 | 1.88 |
| 1.00 | 0.14 | 1.88 |

**Fig. 6-3**  Heat transfer results for fully developed forced convection between parallel plates with a step change in wall temperature.[9]

The heat transfer problem for this configuration has been solved using a similarity transformation—the method applied in the following section to a free convection problem (see Schlichting,[2] pp. 130–134, and Kays,[8] pp. 204–209). In this approach, the boundary-layer approximations are applied to Eqs. (6-22) through (6-25). The $y$-direction momentum equation reduces to Eq. (6-16).

After a sufficient distance along the duct, the decrease in the rate of flow in the thickening boundary layers on the walls must be compensated for by a corresponding increase near the axis. Hence, for flow over a flat plate, the condition of $dp/dx = 0$ is no longer applicable since the flow in the central core will be accelerating. Analytical methods and approximate techniques have been used to study heat transfer in the entrance region of a duct, but the most satisfying is probably the finite difference analysis of Hwang and Fan.[12] These works consider the basic equations, Eqs. (6-22) through (6-25), but assume that the boundary-layer type assumptions apply throughout the entire duct. This is a sort of interpolation between an analysis at the inlet section (true boundary-layer flow) and the fully developed flow region where these approximations can be argued logically.

The numerical solution of the flow problem consists of first writing Eqs. (6-22) and (6-23), subject to the boundary-layer approximations, in dimensionless form, with the mean velocity used as the normalizing parameter. Hence, the additional condition

$$u_m = \frac{1}{b} \int_0^b u \, dy \qquad (6\text{-}48)$$

has to be satisfied. The derivatives are expressed as finite differences in a manner similar to that for the conduction problem of the previous chapter.[12]

Once the two-dimensional velocity components are obtained from the flow equations, the results are used in the energy equation to solve for the temperature profiles. The derivatives of the temperature are expressed as finite differences in terms of the temperatures at each node in the $y$ direction and at $x$ and $x + \Delta x$. The temperatures at $x + \Delta x$ are considered the unknowns. One thus obtains $n$ simultaneous algebraic equations in $n$ unknowns. These linear simultaneous equations can be solved through numerical techniques. One particularly efficient method utilizes the fact that the matrix involved is tridiagonal.[12] Once the temperatures at the axial position $x + \Delta x$ are determined, the process is repeated for the next position at $x + 2\Delta x$. In this manner, the entire temperature field is mapped.

The results of the numerical computation can be used in the Fourier–Biot law to determine the local heat flux. Unfortunately, the workers in this field have given their results only in terms of the average Nusselt number. The heat transfer coefficient is defined as the average heat flux divided by the *log-mean*

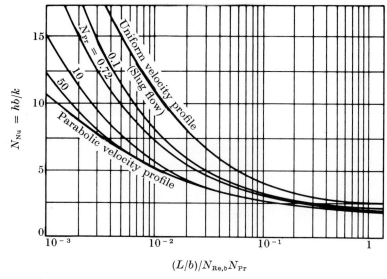

**Fig. 6-4**  Heat transfer results for developing flow between parallel plates of constant wall temperature.[12]

*temperature difference*:

$$\Delta T_{\ln} = \frac{(T_w - T_0) - (T_w - T_{\text{mix}})}{\ln \left[ (T_w - T_0) / (T_w - T_{\text{mix}}) \right]} \tag{6-49}$$

The results in terms of these parameters are given in Fig. 6-4.† The product $N_{\text{Re}} \cdot N_{\text{Pr}} \cdot \left( \dfrac{b}{L} \right)$ is often called the *Graetz number*. The $N_{\text{Re}}$ is defined by Eq. (6-32). Observe that the curve for "parabolic velocity profile" gives the average Nusselt number for the case of fully developed flow. Hence, the accuracy of that assumption can be assessed by comparing the various curves for the duct parameters, $N_{\text{Re}} N_{\text{Pr}} \left( \dfrac{b}{L} \right)$, of interest.

## FREE CONVECTION OVER A VERTICAL FLAT PLATE

Consider an isothermal, vertical, flat plate immersed in a quiescent fluid with a far-field temperature of $T_\infty$, as shown in Fig. 6-5. If we consider only laminar, steady, two-dimensional boundary-layer flow with constant properties (except the density changes necessary for buoyancy forces), then the

---

† Additional results for forced convection are given in Fig. 6-12. The more useful case, for physical design purposes, of uniform wall heat flux is considered in Sec. 6-4.

boundary-layer flow equations reduce to

$$\frac{\partial u}{\partial x} + \frac{\partial v}{\partial y} = 0 \tag{6-50}$$

$$u\frac{\partial u}{\partial x} + v\frac{\partial u}{\partial y} = -\frac{1}{\rho}\frac{\partial p}{\partial x} + \frac{F_x}{\rho} + \frac{\mu}{\rho}\frac{\partial^2 u}{\partial y^2} \tag{6-51}$$

$$\frac{\partial p}{\partial y} = 0 \tag{6-52}$$

Because of the momentum equation for the $y$ direction,

$$p = p(x) \quad \text{and} \quad \frac{\partial p}{\partial x} = \frac{dp}{dx}$$

Thus, the pressure gradient within the boundary layer is that due to the hydrostatic pressure gradient in the bulk fluid. The body force in the $x$ direction is the force due to gravity at the particular value of the $y$ coordinate under consideration. Thus, the "buoyant force" resulting from the combination of the pressure gradient and the body force can be written as

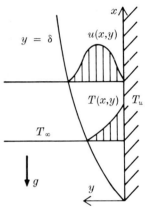

$$\frac{1}{\rho}\left(F_x - \frac{dp}{dx}\right) = \frac{g}{\rho}(\rho_\infty - \rho) \tag{6-53}$$

Note that

$$\beta = \frac{1}{\tilde{v}}\left(\frac{\partial \tilde{v}}{\partial T}\right)_p = -\frac{1}{\rho}\left(\frac{\partial \rho}{\partial T}\right)_p \tag{6-54}$$

and that for small changes in density

$$\beta = -\frac{1}{\rho}\frac{(\rho_\infty - \rho)}{(T_\infty - T)} \tag{6-55}$$

**Fig. 6-5** The isothermal flat plate.

The buoyant force can then be written in terms of $\beta$, and the momentum equations reduce to

$$u\frac{\partial u}{\partial x} + v\frac{\partial u}{\partial y} = \nu\frac{\partial^2 u}{\partial y^2} + g\beta(T - T_\infty) \tag{6-56}$$

Under the above assumptions, and with the additional stipulation of no sources or sinks, the energy equation for boundary-layer flow becomes

$$\rho c_p\left(u\frac{\partial T}{\partial x} + v\frac{\partial T}{\partial y}\right) = \beta T\left(u\frac{\partial p}{\partial x}\right) + \mu\left(\frac{\partial u}{\partial y}\right)^2 + k\frac{\partial^2 T}{\partial y^2} \tag{6-57}$$

Assume further that the viscous dissipation can be neglected and that the temperature gradients are strong enough so that

$$\left|\rho c_p\frac{\partial T}{\partial x}\right| \gg \left|\beta T\frac{\partial p}{\partial x}\right| = |\beta T g \rho_\infty| \tag{6-58}$$

Then, on defining a temperature function

$$\theta = \frac{T(x, y) - T_\infty}{T_w - T_\infty} \tag{6-59}$$

the energy equation reduces from Eq. (6-57) to

$$u \frac{\partial \theta}{\partial x} + v \frac{\partial \theta}{\partial y} = \alpha \frac{\partial^2 \theta}{\partial y^2} \tag{6-60}$$

The boundary conditions for a nonporous, isothermal plate can be stated as

$$\theta = 1 \quad \text{at} \quad y = 0, \qquad x > 0 \tag{6-61a}$$

$$\theta = 0 \quad \text{at} \quad y = \infty, \qquad x = x \tag{6-61b}$$

$$u = 0 \quad \text{at} \quad y = 0, \qquad x > 0 \tag{6-61c}$$

$$u = 0 \quad \text{at} \quad y = \infty, \qquad x = x \tag{6-61d}$$

$$v = 0 \quad \text{at} \quad y = 0, \qquad x > 0 \tag{6-61e}$$

In this case, the flow equations and the energy equation are coupled; hence, they must be solved simultaneously. To facilitate the solution, we introduce a stream function defined as

$$u = \frac{\partial \psi}{\partial y}; \qquad v = -\frac{\partial \psi}{\partial x} \tag{6-62}$$

so that the continuity equation is satisfied exactly. In terms of the stream function, the momentum equation becomes

$$\frac{\partial \psi}{\partial y} \frac{\partial^2 \psi}{\partial x \, \partial y} - \frac{\partial \psi}{\partial x} \frac{\partial^2 \psi}{\partial y^2} = \nu \frac{\partial^3 \psi}{\partial y^3} + g\beta(T_w - T_\infty)\theta \tag{6-63}$$

The equation is now in terms of only one variable, but the order has been increased. Pohlhausen was the first to demonstrate that the above partial differential equation could be reduced to an ordinary differential equation by the following similarity transformation. Let

$$\psi = 4\nu c x^{3/4} \zeta(\eta) \tag{6-64}$$

where

$$\eta = c \frac{y}{x^{1/4}} \tag{6-65}$$

$$c = \sqrt[4]{\frac{g\beta(T_w - T_\infty)}{4\nu^2}} \tag{6-66}$$

The velocity components can be stated as

$$u = 4\nu x^{1/2} c^2 \frac{d\zeta}{d\eta} \tag{6-67}$$

$$v = \nu c x^{-1/4} \left( \eta \frac{d\zeta}{d\eta} - 3\zeta \right) \tag{6-68}$$

The momentum and energy equations become

$$\frac{d^3\zeta}{d\eta^3} + 3\zeta \frac{d^2\zeta}{d\eta^2} - 2\left(\frac{d\zeta}{d\eta}\right)^2 + \theta = 0 \tag{6-69}$$

$$\frac{d^2\theta}{d\eta^2} + 3N_{\mathrm{Pr}}\zeta\theta = 0 \tag{6-70}$$

with boundary conditions

$$\zeta - \frac{d\zeta}{d\eta} = 0 \quad \text{and} \quad \theta = 1 \quad \text{at} \quad \eta = 0 \tag{6-71}$$

$$\frac{d\zeta}{d\eta} = 0 \quad \text{and} \quad \theta = 0 \quad \text{at} \quad \eta = \infty \tag{6-72}$$

Numerical solutions† of this problem were obtained by Pohlhausen with Schmidt and Beckman, and were later extended by Ostrach. (See page 333 of Schlichting.[2]) The analytical results are reproduced in Fig. 6-6.

To evaluate the heat flux at the plate, we write

$$q_w = -k \frac{\partial T}{\partial y}\bigg|_{y=0} = -k \frac{(T_w - T_\infty)}{x^{1/4}} c \frac{d\theta}{d\eta}\bigg|_{\eta=0} \tag{6-73}$$

so that the local heat transfer coefficient is:

$$h_x = \frac{q_w}{T_w - T_\infty} = -\frac{kc}{x^{1/4}} \frac{d\theta}{d\eta}\bigg|_{\eta=0} \tag{6-74}$$

We define a *local Grashof number* (which is the ratio of the buoyant to viscous forces), as:

$$N_{\mathrm{Gr},x} = \frac{g\beta}{\nu^2}(T_w - T_\infty)x^3 \tag{6-75}$$

so that

$$\eta = \frac{y}{x}\left(\frac{N_{\mathrm{Gr},x}}{4}\right)^{1/4} \tag{6-76}$$

---

† One approach to gaining a numerical solution to problems of this type is to use an algorithm such as Runge–Kutta. (See Hildebrand.[13]) The Runge–Kutta method requires the initial values of $\zeta$, $d\zeta/d\eta$, $d^2\zeta/d\eta^2$, $\theta$, and $d\theta/d\eta$. While two of these are not known, they are guessed and the solution is iterated to satisfy the conditions at the other boundary.

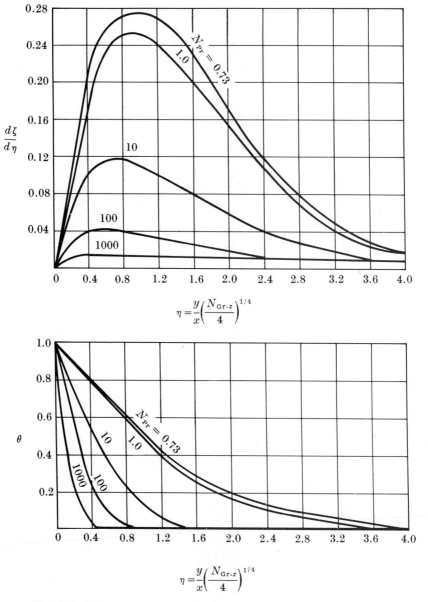

**Fig. 6-6** Velocity and temperature profiles in free convection past an isothermal vertical flat plate.[2]

Then, in terms of a local Nusselt number, Eq. (6-74) becomes

$$N_{\text{Nu},x} = \frac{h_x x}{k} = -\left.\frac{d\theta}{d\eta}\right|_{\eta=0} \left(\frac{N_{\text{Gr}}}{4}\right)^{1/4} \tag{6-77}$$

where $d\theta/d\eta$ evaluated at $\eta = 0$ is related to $N_{\text{Pr}}$ as indicated in Fig. 6-6.

Introducing the average heat transfer coefficient, $h$, we note:

$$h = \frac{1}{L}\int_0^L h_x \, dx = \frac{4}{3}h_{x-L} \tag{6-78}$$

It has been found convenient to relate the mean Nusselt number (characteristic length $L$) to the product $N_{\text{Gr}} \cdot N_{\text{Pr}}$, which is often called the *Rayleigh number*. Thus, the preceding results can be expressed as

$$N_{\text{Nu}} = A(N_{\text{Gr}} \cdot N_{\text{Pr}})^{1/4} \tag{6-79}$$

where the coefficient $A$ lies between $0.517 \leq A \leq 0.670$ for $0.73 \leq N_{\text{Pr}} \leq \infty$.

## 6-3. TECHNIQUES FOR APPROXIMATE SOLUTIONS

The analytical solution of convective heat transfer problems such as those just illustrated is often somewhat cumbersome, time consuming, and necessarily restricted to laminar flow. Consequently, approximate techniques can be employed to advantage as long as we do not require that the basic equations be satisfied for every fluid particle. This fact allows us to also consider turbulent flow.

One such approximate procedure was devised by von Kármán, who considered a momentum balance over a control volume encompassing the boundary layer and the surface of the body in contact with the fluid. (See page 131 of Eckert and Drake.[4])

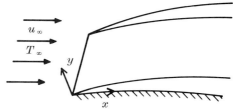

**Fig. 6-7** Two-dimensional boundary-layer flow over a curved surface.

The resulting *momentum integral relation* can also be derived from direct integration of the boundary-layer equations. To this end, we consider the flow of a fluid over a curved surface, as shown in Fig. 6-7. We assume steady, two-dimensional, incompressible boundary-layer flow over a surface whose radius of curvature is much greater than the boundary-layer thickness. Then, for constant properties and negligible body forces, the basic flow equations become

Continuity:

$$\frac{\partial u}{\partial x} + \frac{\partial v}{\partial y} = 0 \tag{6-80}$$

Momentum:

$$u \frac{\partial u}{\partial x} + v \frac{\partial u}{\partial y} = - \frac{1}{\rho} \frac{\partial p}{\partial x} + \frac{\mu}{\rho} \frac{\partial^2 u}{\partial y^2} \tag{6-81}$$

$$\frac{\partial p}{\partial y} = 0 \tag{6-82}$$

To obtain the pressure gradient in Eq. (6-81), we see that Eq. (6-82) tells us that $p = p(x)$. Thus, the pressure at any point in the boundary layer is the same as that in the free stream. Consequently, in the free stream where $\mu(\partial^2 u / \partial y^2)$ can be neglected and $\partial u / \partial y \approx 0$, Eq. (6-81) reduces to

$$u_\infty \frac{du_\infty}{dx} = - \frac{1}{\rho} \frac{dp}{dx} \tag{6-83}$$

Thus, the momentum equation in the boundary layer becomes

$$u \frac{\partial u}{\partial x} + v \frac{\partial u}{\partial y} = u_\infty \frac{du_\infty}{dx} + \frac{\mu}{\rho} \frac{\partial^2 u}{\partial y^2} \tag{6-84}$$

If Eq. (6-84) is integrated over the boundary layer (which amounts to obtaining an average momentum exchange), we have

$$\int_0^{\delta(x)} \left( u \frac{\partial u}{\partial x} + v \frac{\partial u}{\partial y} - u_\infty \frac{du_\infty}{dx} \right) dy = \frac{1}{\rho} \left( \mu \frac{\partial u}{\partial y} \right)_0^{\delta(x)} \tag{6-85}$$

But the definition of the boundary layer is: that region outside of which $\mu(\partial u / \partial y) \approx 0$. Therefore, the right side of Eq. (6-85) reduces to the local shear stress at the wall $\tau_w$.

Considering the continuity equation in an integrated form, we have

$$\int_0^y \frac{\partial u}{\partial x} dy + \int_0^y \frac{\partial v}{\partial y} dy = 0$$

so that

$$v(y) = - \int_0^y \frac{\partial u}{\partial x} dy \tag{6-86}$$

Integrating the left side of Eq. (6-85) by parts and using Eq. (6-86), we find

$$\frac{d}{dx} \int_0^{\delta(x)} (u_\infty - u)u \, dy - \frac{du_\infty}{dx} \int_0^{\delta(x)} (u_\infty - u) \, dy = \frac{\tau_w}{\rho} \tag{6-87}$$

Thus, if we can estimate the form of $u = u(y/\delta)$, we can calculate $\tau_w$ in terms of the boundary-layer thickness $\delta(x)$ and use Eq. (6-87) to find $\delta(x)$.

Consider now the energy equation for our flow. If we specify that the viscous dissipation and the heat generation are negligible, then

$$u \frac{\partial T}{\partial x} + v \frac{\partial T}{\partial y} = \frac{k}{\rho c_p} \frac{\partial^2 T}{\partial y^2} \tag{6-88}$$

Integrating with respect to $y$ from zero to the *thermal boundary-layer thickness* $\delta_\theta$, which is not necessarily equal to $\delta$, we have

$$\int_0^{\delta_\theta(x)} \left( u\,\frac{\partial T}{\partial x} + v\,\frac{\partial T}{\partial y} \right) dy = \frac{1}{\rho c_p}\left( k\,\frac{\partial T}{\partial y} \right)_0^{\delta_\theta(x)} \tag{6-89}$$

The thermal boundary-layer thickness is defined so that $k(\partial T/\partial y) \approx 0$ when $y = \delta$. Thus, the right side of Eq. (6-89) reduces to the local value of the wall heat flux $q_w$. Using Eq. (6-86) and integrating Eq. (6-89) by parts, we have

$$\frac{d}{dx}\int_0^{\delta_\theta(x)} (T_\infty - T)u\,dy = -\frac{q_w}{\rho c_p} \tag{6-90}$$

Again, if the form of the temperature profile $T = T(y/\delta)$ can be estimated, then the wall heat flux $q_w$ can be calculated from the Fourier–Biot law in terms of $\delta_\theta$, and then Eq. (6-90) can be used to solve for $\delta_\theta(x)$.

The two integral relations have been used for a number of different types of flows, several of which are demonstrated by Eckert and Drake.[4] For laminar flow, it is sufficient to assume a polynomial of the form

$$u = a_0(x) + a_1(x)y + a_2(x)y^2 + a_3(x)y^3$$

where the $a_i$ are evaluated to satisfy reasonable conditions at $y = 0$ and $y = \delta$. A similar polynomial can be found for the temperature. In turbulent flow, experimental measurements have been correlated[2] so that velocity profiles representing the time-averaged velocity components can be used in the foregoing integral relations. However, the turbulent eddies produce an additional mechanism of momentum and heat transfer which must be taken into consideration.[8]

If, in addition to the above assumptions, we consider cases where the pressure gradient is zero, then Eqs. (6-85) and (6-89) are analogous in that

$$\theta(x, y, t) = \text{constant} \cdot u(x, y, t)$$

as long as

$$\frac{\nu}{\alpha} = N_{\mathrm{Pr}} = 1$$

If we let $\theta = T - T_w$, then the boundary conditions are the same, and the solution to one of these equations is also the solution for the other. This fact is called the *Reynolds analogy*. It follows from this analogy that the thicknesses of the two boundary layers are the same for $N_{\mathrm{Pr}} = 1$, and that

$$q_w = \frac{c_p(T_w - T_\infty)}{u_\infty}\,\tau_w \tag{6-91a}$$

If we define a *friction factor* $f$ so that

$$\tau_w = \frac{f}{2}\,\rho u_\infty^2 \tag{6-91b}$$

and the *Stanton number* as

$$N_{\mathrm{St}} = \frac{h}{\rho c_p u_\infty} \qquad (6\text{-}91\mathrm{c})$$

then from these three equations we have the Reynolds analogy:

$$N_{\mathrm{St}} = \frac{f}{2} \qquad (6\text{-}91\mathrm{d})$$

This says that the heat transfer coefficient is related to the friction factor, which can often be estimated.

Note that this analogy also gives us an interpretation of the Prandtl number: The velocity (momentum) boundary-layer thickness depends on the diffusivity of momentum $\nu$, and the thermal boundary-layer thickness depends upon the diffusivity of heat $\alpha$. Analyses have shown[4] that, in fact,†

$$\frac{\delta}{\delta_\theta} \approx N_{\mathrm{Pr}}^{1/3} \qquad (6\text{-}92)$$

## 6-4. EXPERIMENTAL RESULTS IN CONVECTION

The principle of what Jakob[1] calls the "differential method of similarity," meaning a consideration of the dimensionless form of the basic equations, demonstrates that the heat transfer coefficient, as it appears in the Nusselt number, is related to some combination of the other basic dimensionless groups. The relationship can be expressed as

$$N_{\mathrm{Nu}} = \phi(N_{\mathrm{Re}}, N_{\mathrm{Gr}}, N_{\mathrm{Pr}}, N_{\mathrm{E}}, N_{\mathrm{Fr}})$$

Assuming negligible viscous dissipation and no body forces (other than buoyant forces), this reduces to

$$N_{\mathrm{Nu}} = \Phi(N_{\mathrm{Re}}, N_{\mathrm{Gr}}, N_{\mathrm{Pr}}) \qquad (6\text{-}93)$$

Once the velocity and temperature fields have been established for one geometrical shape cooled or heated by convection, the results are applicable to another body, provided all of the pertinent dimensionless groups are equal at corresponding points.

If in forced convection the flow rate and corresponding Reynolds number are high enough so that $N_{\mathrm{Re}}^2 \gg N_{\mathrm{Gr}}$, then the effects of free convection are negligible and Eq. (6-93) then becomes

$$N_{\mathrm{Nu}} = \psi(N_{\mathrm{Re}}, N_{\mathrm{Pr}})$$

---

† Additional support for this interpretation can be seen in Fig. 6-4. For a given $N_{\mathrm{Nu}}$ proportional to $\delta_\theta$ the cases for $N_{\mathrm{Pr}}$ becoming small approach the assumption of slug flow, i.e., $\delta \to 0$. On the other hand, as $N_{\mathrm{Pr}}$ becomes large, $\delta$ essentially fills the duct immediately so that the flow is fully developed (parabolic velocity profile) throughout.

If the motion of the fluid is caused primarily by differences in density resulting from temperature gradients so that $N_{Re}^2 \ll N_{Gr}$ (i.e., *natural* or *free convection*), then the influence of Reynolds number is negligible and Eq. (6-93) reduces to $N_{Nu} = \Theta(N_{Gr}, N_{Pr})$. In fact, as suggested by the analytical solution [Eq. (6-79)], considerable experimental free convection data can be correlated by a simplified expression of the form

$$N_{Nu} = C(N_{Gr} \cdot N_{Pr})^n \tag{6-94}$$

where, in some cases, $C$ is a function of $N_{Pr}$.

Just as there exist critical values of the Reynolds numbers where forced flows change from laminar to turbulent flow, the buoyant forces in free convection can become large enough that instabilities propagate and a transition to turbulence takes place. Consequently, the flow in free convection is laminar if $N_{Gr} \cdot N_{Pr} < 10^8$, and the flow is turbulent if $N_{Gr} \cdot N_{Pr} > 10^9$. In the transition range between $10^8$ and $10^9$, the two correlations meet, giving the same values for $N_{Nu}$.

Values of the heat transfer coefficient for the various kinds of convective flows will typically fall in the following approximate ranges.[6]

|  | W/m² · deg |
|---|---|
| Air, free convection | 5–30 |
| Air, forced convection | 30–300 |
| Oil, forced convection | 50–2000 |
| Water, forced convection | 300–10,000 |
| Water, boiling | 3000–50,000 |
| Steam, condensing | 5000–100,000 |

## FREE CONVECTION RESULTS

Values of $C$ and $n$ in Eq. (6-94) are tabulated in Fig. 6-8 for a number of isothermal geometric shapes and boundary conditions. If Eq. (6-94) is rewritten in terms of the definitions of the dimensionless groups, we have

$$\frac{hL}{k} = C\left(\frac{g\beta\theta L^3}{v^2} \cdot \frac{v}{\alpha}\right)^n \tag{6-95}$$

To evaluate the average heat transfer coefficient $h$ from Eq. (6-95) for a given flow ($C$ and $n$), we must specify the length $L$, the temperature difference $\theta$, and the temperature at which the fluid properties are to be determined. For most cases, $\theta$ is $(T_w - T_\infty)$, and the fluid properties are evaluated at the arithmetic mean between the wall temperature $T_w$ and the undisturbed fluid temperature $T_\infty$. It has been suggested that other reference temperatures be used for a slight improvement in accuracy; but the arithmetic mean gives satisfactory

| Geometry | Arrangement and direction of heat flow | $N_{\text{Gr}} \cdot N_{\text{Pr}}$ | | $C$ | $n$ | Characteristic length | Ref. | Remarks |
|---|---|---|---|---|---|---|---|---|
| | | From | To | | | | | |
| Heated vertical plates and cylinders | | $10^4$ | $10^8$ | 0.555 | 0.25 | $l$ | 1 | |
| Heated spheres and blocks | | | | | | $D/2$ for spheres<br>See Eq. (6-96) for blocks | | dia $\geqslant \delta$ |
| Heated horizontal cylinder | | $10^8$ | $10^{12}$ | 0.129 | 0.33 | $2.76D$ | | |

| Configuration | Sketch | $N_{Gr}N_{Pr}$ (from) | $N_{Gr}N_{Pr}$ (to) | $C$ | $m$ | Characteristic length | Fig. | Remarks |
|---|---|---|---|---|---|---|---|---|
| Heated vertical wires | | $10^{-7}$ | $1$ | $1.0$ | $0.10$ | dia | 1 | dia $\leq \delta$ |
| Heated horizontal square plates facing upward and downward | | $10^5$ | $2.0 \times 10^7$ | $0.54$ | $0.25$ | $l$ | 7 | Also describes heat transfer to cooled plates facing downward. |
| | | $2.0 \times 10^7$ | $3.0 \times 10^{10}$ | $0.14$ | $0.33$ | | | |
| | | $3.0 \times 10^5$ | $3.0 \times 10^{10}$ | $0.27$ | $0.25$ | | | Also describes heat transfer to cooled plates facing upward. |
| *Enclosed spaces:* two vertical plates $l > b$ | | $0$ | $10^3$ | $1.00$ | $0$ | $b$ | 14 | For free convection in enclosed spaces, $N_{Gr}$ and $N_{Nu}$ are based on $(T_{w1} - T_{w2})$ rather than some $(T_w - T_\infty)$. Thus, $N_{Nu}$ represents only the heat exchange between the two surfaces forming the enclosed space. The thermal properties are evaluated at $(T_{w1} + T_{w2})/2$. |
| | | $10^3$ | $10^7$ | $0.28\left(\dfrac{b}{l}\right)^{1/4}$ | $0.25$ | | | |
| two horizontal plates with lower one heated | | $1700$ | $3.2 N_{Pr} \times 10^5$ | $0.21$ | $0.25$ | $b$ | 7 | |
| | | $3.2 N_{Pr} \times 10^5$ | $N_{Pr} \times 10^7$ | $0.075$ | $0.33$ | | | |

(a) Tabulation of correlation for different isothermal configurations.

**Fig 6-8** Summary of free convection data.

229

| Geometry | Arrangement and direction of heat flow | $N_{Gr} \cdot N_{Pr}$ From | $N_{Gr} \cdot N_{Pr}$ To | $C$ | $n$ | Characteristic length | Ref. | Remarks |
|---|---|---|---|---|---|---|---|---|
| *Enclosed spaces:* two inclined plates | | $10^5$ | $10^8$ | 0.060 | 0.345 | $b$ | 5 | For free convection in enclosed spaces, $N_{Gr}$ and $N_{Nu}$ are based on $(T_{w1} - T_{w2})$ rather than some $(T_w - T_\infty)$. Thus $N_{Nu}$ represents only the heat exchange between the two surfaces forming the enclosed space. The thermal properties are evaluated at $(T_{w1} + T_{w2})/2$. |
| two inclined plates | | | | 0.043 | 0.33 | | | |
| spherical annular space (inside body heated) | | | | 0.177 | 0.25 | $\frac{1}{2}(D_o - D_i)$ | | |
| cylindrical annular space (inside body heated) | | $6 \times 10^3$ | $10^6$ | 0.11 | 0.29 | | 4 | |
| | | $10^6$ | $10^8$ | 0.40 | 0.20 | | | |

(a) Tabulation of correlation for different isothermal configurations (continued).

**Fig. 6-8** Summary of free convection data (continued).

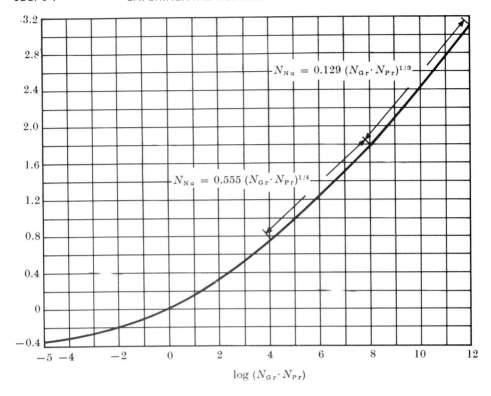

(b) Correlation for isothermal vertical plates and cylinders, spheres, blocks, and horizontal cylinders

**Fig. 6-8**  Summary of free convection data (concluded).[1]

results. The characteristic length $L$ which identifies the configuration is indicated in Fig. 6-8(a).

When the wall temperature is not known, as is the case for a specified heat flux on the wall, a value of $T_w$ must be assumed initially. This value can be used to calculate the heat transfer coefficient to a first approximation. If there is a significant discrepancy between the assumed and calculated values of $T_w$, successive iterations can be made until agreement is reached.

The relations for free convection from isothermal vertical surfaces—as listed in Fig. 6-8(a) for both laminar and turbulent flow—can be extended to other configurations by introducing the proper characteristic length. If the horizontal and vertical dimensions for spheres and blocks are comparable in magnitude, then both dimensions contribute to the characteristic length according to the experimentally determined expression

$$\frac{1}{L} = \frac{1}{\text{vertical dimension}} + \frac{1}{\text{average horizontal dimension}} \qquad (6\text{-}96)$$

For a sphere, this expression reduces to $L = D/2$, where $D$ is the sphere diameter. A vertical cylinder has been found to act like a vertical flat plate so long as the radius $R \gg \delta$, so the correlation applies here also. With a horizontal cylinder, the differential equations for free convection are identical to those for a vertical flat plate under a suitable transformation.[15] Thus, for equal Grashof numbers, the following relation holds in the laminar flow region for cylinder diameters equal to the height of the plate:

$$h_{cyl} = 0.777\, h_{plate}$$

This is equivalent to setting the cylinder characteristic length $L = 2.76D$.

All of the correlations given here are for isothermal surfaces. Other wall conditions have been studied, and one of particular interest is the condition of uniform heat flux.[16] The heat transfer coefficients for constant heat flux were found to be always higher than those for the isothermal plate; however, the coefficients are never more than 8 percent higher, based on the average wall temperature. This helps to explain why experimentally determined Nusselt numbers generally agree with the results for the isothermal plate and why, for design purposes, the isothermal asumption is often adequate.

For laminar flow of air at ordinary temperatures and at atmospheric pressure, the correlation of Fig. 6-8 for vertical plates reduces to

$$h = 1.34 \left( \frac{\theta}{L} \right)^{1/4} \text{W}/\text{m}^2 \cdot \text{deg} \tag{6-97}$$

where $L$ is the characteristic length for blocks, horizontal cylinders, etc. For turbulent flow,

$$h = 1.31(\theta)^{1/3} \text{W}/\text{m}^2 \cdot \text{deg} \tag{6-98}$$

When $R \le \delta$, as for vertical wires, one of the basic assumptions for boundary-layer-type flow is no longer valid, and a different correlation is necessary.

Figure 6-9 illustrates the temperature field in the vicinity of a horizontal square plate in air.[1] The closely spaced isotherms below the plate indicate a greater dependence on pure conduction as compared with the region above the surface, where the fluid velocities (and heat transfer coefficients) are higher. The results for horizontal plates given in Fig. 6-8(a) are consistent with this observation.

Consider next the question of heat transfer by laminar free convection from the interior surfaces of *vertical ducts*† standing in a fluid with a far-field

---

† This heat transfer process is sometimes referred to as the "chimney effect" or "stack effect." However, these are incorrect designations because the fluid buoyancy and resulting velocities in a vertical duct are caused by heat fluxes introduced along the entire height rather than by heat input at only the lower end as is the case for a chimney.

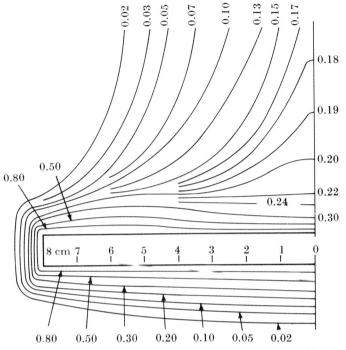

**Fig. 6-9**  Isotherms $(T - T_\infty)/(T_w - T_\infty)$ around one side of a horizontal square plate in air.[1]

temperature $T_\infty$. This case has been investigated by Elenbaas.[17] The results for various cross-sectional geometries of height $H$ are presented in Fig. 6-10, which is a plot of the expression

$$N_{Nu} = \frac{1}{\psi} \frac{L}{H} (N_{Gr} \cdot N_{Pr}) \left\{ 1 - \exp\left[ -\psi \left( \frac{0.5H}{L(N_{Gr} \cdot N_{Pr})} \right)^{0.75} \right] \right\} \qquad (6\text{-}99)$$

The characteristic length is given by

$$L = 2 \frac{\text{cross-sectional flow area}}{\text{wetted perimeter}}$$

which is usually called the hydraulic radius. (For circular sections, $L =$ diameter/2.) The values of $\psi$ for each curve numbered in Fig. 6-10 are listed below.

| Curve number | Duct geometry | $\psi$ |
|:---:|:---|:---|
| 1 | Circle | 16 |
| 2 | Equilateral triangle | 13.33 |
| 3 | Long parallel plates | 24 |
| 4 | Square | 19.05 |
| 5 | Rectangle; $1 \times 2$ | 15.55 |
| 6 | Rectangle; $1 \times 5$ | 14.22 |

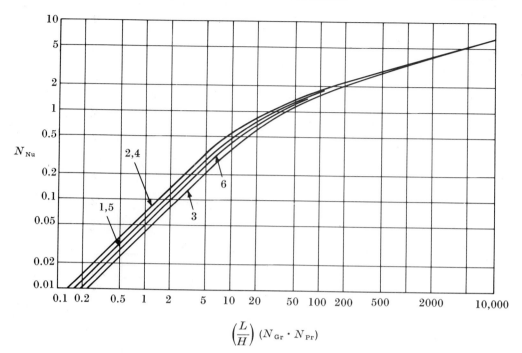

**Fig. 6-10**   Heat transfer from isothermal vertical ducts.[17]

With the exception of $\beta$, which is evaluated at $T_\infty$, all the properties are evaluated at $T_w$. The Grashof number is based on the temperature $T_w - T_\infty$.

Free convection can enhance the energy transfer across enclosed spaces as long as the Grashof number meets certain minimum requirements. For spaces of roughly rectangular cross section and for horizontal transfer, as indicated in Fig. 6-8(a),

$$N_{Gr} \cdot N_{Pr} > 10^3 \tag{6-100}$$

For vertical heat transfer with the hot plate below,

$$N_{Gr} \cdot N_{Pr} > 1700 \tag{6-101}$$

If $N_{Gr}$ should be below these values, then essentially pure conduction exists and $N_{Nu} = 1$ for the rectangular regions.

We now consider the motion of a fluid enclosed between two horizontal surfaces when the lower surface is heated. The warmer fluid particles near the lower surface displace the colder particles above them, giving rise to a cellular flow pattern. This pattern is illustrated in Fig. 6-11. If the heated plate is on top, however, a stable situation exists where no air circulation can take place.

If the enclosed space contains electronic components, a correlation due to Robinson[18,19] may be useful:

$$N_{Nu} = 1.45(N_{Gr} \cdot N_{Pr})^{0.23} \tag{6-102}$$

Here the characteristic length for each component shape is that listed in Fig.

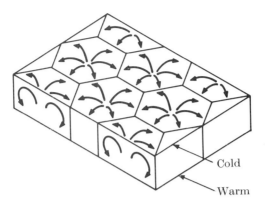

**Fig. 6-11** Cellular motion in an enclosed-plane air layer heated from below.[6]

6-8(a). However, the designer is cautioned to put only limited reliance on this correlation, since the temperature distribution which may exist on the enclosure could seriously affect the results. The $h$ values from Eq. (6-102) are higher than those calculated from Fig. 6-8(a); therefore, an overall convective motion apparently existed in the experiments of Robinson, and the temperature distribution necessary to sustain these motions may not be present for certain outside cooling configurations. Also, the use of Eq. (6-102) requires that the "average" component surface temperature be estimated, which may not be an easy task.

## FORCED CONVECTION RESULTS

Many electrical components are geometrically similar to one of the classical body configurations, such as flat plates, cylinders, etc. For this reason, forced convection heat transfer results are presented in this section for several classical shapes in an otherwise undisturbed flow field. Combinations of some simple shapes are also considered, along with pertinent discussion of thermal aspects of combined configurations found in electronic packages.

Equation (6-93) with $N_{\mathrm{Re}}^2 \gg N_{\mathrm{Gr}}$, rewritten as a power function expression in terms of the defined dimensionless groups, becomes

$$N_{\mathrm{Nu}} = C(N_{\mathrm{Re}})^m (N_{\mathrm{Pr}})^n \qquad (6\text{-}103)$$

With this equation, average heat transfer coefficients can be evaluated for several isothermal geometric forms in different flow ranges. Tabulated numerical values of $C$, $n$, and $m$ appear in Fig. 6-12, along with the proper characteristic length of each shape. When Eq. (6-103) is used with Fig. 6-12, fluid properties should be evaluated at the arithmetic mean of fluid temperature and wall temperature. The velocity is either the upstream fluid velocity $u_\infty$ or the average velocity in a cross section of the flow.

| Geometry | Arrangement and fluid flow direction | $N_{Re}$ From | $N_{Re}$ To | $C$ | $m$ | $n$ | Characteristic length | Ref. |
|---|---|---|---|---|---|---|---|---|
| Flow perpendicular to cylinders | | 0.1 | 50 | 0.91 | 0.385 | 0.31 | $D$ | 1 |
| | | 50 | 10,000 | 0.60 | 0.50 | 0.31 | | |
| | | 4,000 | 40,000 | 0.193 | 0.618 | 0.31 | | |
| | | 40,000 | 250,000 | 0.0265 | 0.805 | 0.31 | | |
| Flow perpendicular to noncircular tubes | | 2,500 | 7,500 | 0.290 | 0.624 | 0.31 | Diameter of circular tube of equal exposed surface | 1 |
| | | 5,000 | 100,000 | 0.246 | 0.588 | 0.31 | | |
| | | 2,500 | 15,000 | 0.249 | 0.612 | 0.31 | | |
| | | 5,000 | 100,000 | 0.153 | 0.638 | 0.31 | | |
| | | 5,000 | 19,500 | 0.160 | 0.638 | 0.31 | | |
| | | 19,500 | 100,000 | 0.039 | 0.782 | 0.31 | | |
| | | 2,500 | 8,000 | 0.178 | 0.699 | 0.31 | | |
| | | 5,000 | 100,000 | 0.102 | 0.675 | 0.31 | | |

Fig. 6-12 Summary of forced convection results.

| Geometry | $N_{Re}$ (lower) | $N_{Re}$ (upper) | $N_{Nu}$ relation | exp. 1 | exp. 2 | Characteristic dimension | Ref. |
|---|---|---|---|---|---|---|---|
| Stagnation of flow on flat plates | 3,000 | 15,000 | 0.094 | 0.804 | 0.31 | half width of plate | 1 |
| Flow over spheres* | 20 | $10^6$ | 0.57 | 0.5 | 0.4 | dia | 8 |
|  |  | 150,000 | 0.37 | 0.60 | 0.333 | dia | 5 |
| Flow parallel to flat plates and cylinders $(R \gg \delta)$ |  | $5 \times 10^5$ | 0.664 | 0.50 | 0.33 | $l$ | 5 |
|  | $5 \times 10^5$ | $10^7$ | 0.037 | 0.80 | 1.00 |  |  |
| Flow through pipes† |  | 2,300 | $1.86 \left(\dfrac{D}{l}\right)^{1/3} \left(\dfrac{\mu_\infty}{\mu_w}\right)^{0.14}$ | 0.333 | 0.333 | dia | 5 |
|  | 3,500 | 11,000 | 0.0067 | 1.00 | 0.37 |  |  |
|  | 10,000 | 90,000 | $0.032 (l/D)^{-0.054}$ | 0.80 | 0.30 |  |  |
| Flow through rectangular and circular annuli (inside surface is heated)† | 2,300 | 10,000 | $0.032 \left(\dfrac{D_{th}}{l}\right)^{0.054}$ | 0.80 | 0.30 | $D_{th}$ | 5 |
|  | 12,000 | 220,000 | $0.023 (D_o/D_i)^{0.53}$ | 0.80 | 0.333 | $D_e$ | 5 |

\* For very low Reynolds numbers, the heat transfer to air flow around a sphere is given by $N_{Nu} = 2 + 0.33 N_{Re}^{1/2}$.

† The reference temperature is the average of the inlet and exit mixed mean temperatures. $N_{Nu}$ is based on the wall temperature minus this reference temperature.

237

Since forced convection heat transfer in all flow regimes depends strongly on surface geometry, caution should be exercised in assuring that the geometry is described by the proper characteristic length. For example, in the calculation of processes taking place in noncircular ducts, it is usual to introduce the *equivalent diameter* $D_e$ as a carry-over from hydrodynamic problems. This term is defined as

$$D_e = 4 \; \frac{\text{cross-sectional area in flow direction}}{\text{wetted perimeter}} \qquad (6\text{-}104)$$

A characteristic length more descriptive of the heat transfer process is the *equivalent thermal diameter* $D_{th}$ (the use of this term is recommended when heat is dissipated over only a portion of the wetted perimeter):

$$D_{th} = 4 \; \frac{\text{cross-sectional area in flow direction}}{\text{heat transfer perimeter}} \qquad (6\text{-}105)$$

To show the difference between these two terms, consider an annulus with outer and inner diameters, $D_o$ and $D_i$, and with the inner surface heated. For this case $D_e = D_o - D_i$ and $D_{th} = (D_o^2 - D_i^2)/D_i$; thus, $D_{th}$ is at least twice $D_e$. This example shows that inappropriate use of $D_e$ instead of $D_{th}$ can cause errors in the prediction of the heat transfer coefficient. In general, the predicted value using $D_e$ is greater than the actual value (15 to 30 percent greater for an annulus), as will be further pointed out in the following discussion of tube fields.

The Nusselt numbers derived from Fig. 6-12 are mean values averaged over the entire body. For heat transfer in the region where either or both the thermal and hydrodynamic conditions are developing, the local Nusselt number varies strongly with position. For developing laminar flow in a circular tube, the variation is illustrated by the analytical results given in Fig. 6-13. Note that $N_{\text{Nu},x}$ approaches a constant value only after $2(x/D) > 0.1 N_{\text{Re}} \cdot N_{\text{Pr}}$. The local heat transfer coefficient for interior flow is based on the wall temperature minus the local mixed mean temperature. For a constant heat flux boundary condition, the local heat transfer coefficient is roughly 20 percent greater than

| $2(x/D)/N_{\text{Re}} \cdot N_{\text{Pr}}$ | $N_{\text{Nu},x}$ | $N_{\text{Nu}}$ |
|---|---|---|
| 0.005 | 11.3 | 17.4 |
| 0.010 | 7.90 | 13.4 |
| 0.020 | 5.82 | 10.0 |
| 0.040 | 4.57 | 7.53 |
| 0.10 | 3.77 | 5.43 |
| 0.20 | 3.67 | 4.56 |
| $\infty$ | 3.66 | 3.66 |

**Fig. 6-13** Combined developing thermal and hydrodynamic conditions for laminar flow in a circular tube at $T_w$ ($N_{\text{Pr}} = 0.7$).[8]

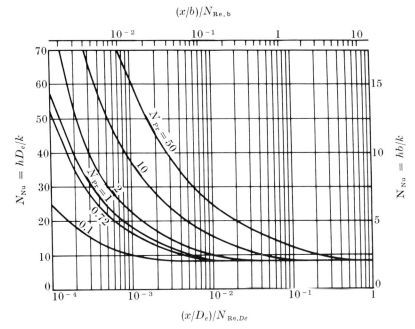

**Fig. 6-14** Combined developing thermal and hydrodynamic conditions for laminar flow between parallel plates with a constant heat flux.[12]

that for a constant wall temperature condition. The results for constant heat flux in a flat duct (parallel plates) are given in Fig. 6-14.

The case of developing hydrodynamic conditions has not been solved for turbulent flow. However, the $N_{Nu}$ for the hydrodynamic entry region in laminar flow is always greater than that for fully developed laminar flow. The same can be assumed for turbulent flow as long as the turbulence exists in the entry region. For fully developed turbulent flow, the Nusselt number for constant heat flux is nearly the same as that for a constant wall temperature. Some typical values of $N_{Nu,x}$ are given in Fig. 6-15 for flow between parallel plates. Kays[8]

| $\dfrac{x}{D_e}$ | $N_{Nu,x}$ | | |
|---|---|---|---|
| | $N_{Re} = 7096$ | $N_{Re} = 73,600$ | $N_{Re} = 495,000$ |
| 1 | 47.3 | 234 | 940 |
| 3 | 37.9 | 203 | 851 |
| 10 | 31.5 | 177 | 761 |
| 30 | 28.0 | 160 | 697 |
| 100 | 27.1 | 152 | 661 |

**Fig. 6-15** Fully developed turbulent flow between parallel plates, one heated at a uniform rate, the other insulated $(N_{Pr} = 1)$.[8]

notes that the parallel-planes results are applicable with only small error to the concentric circular tube annulus for a ratio of inner diameter to outer diameter greater than 0.5. Additionally, if the heat flux is varying along the duct, the $h_x$ from constant heat flux theory can still be used to calculate the local temperature difference as long as the local flux is also used. For additional results for tube and duct flow, see Kays,[8] Chapters 8 and 9.

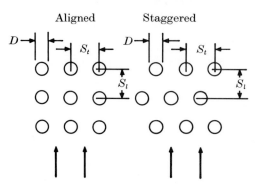

**Fig. 6-16** Aligned and staggered arrangements of tubes in a tube field with spacing $S_t$ and $S_l$ in the direction transverse and longitudinal to flow.

In Fig. 6-12, results are presented for heat transfer from a single cylinder with perpendicular flow. In contrast, as evidence of how the heat transfer is altered by introducing other bodies in the proximity, consider a group of identical cylinders arranged to form a *tube field* with cross flow over the tubes, as shown for two patterns in Fig. 6-16. Tube fields have been studied with application to the design of commercial heat exchangers. The results are applicable to arrangements of electron tubes or transistors on circuit cards in an electronic package.

For heat transfer from tube fields, the power function expression recommended by Eckert and Drake[4] for air can be extended to other fluids by introducing the Prandtl number dependence, which gives

$$N_{\mathrm{Nu}} = C(N_{\mathrm{Re}})^m (N_{\mathrm{Pr}})^{0.31} \qquad (6\text{-}106)$$

This expression can be used to calculate the heat transfer coefficient of tube fields with a Reynolds number range from 2000 to 40,000, where the reference velocity is the average velocity in the narrowest cross section. The characteristic length is the tube diameter $D$. Values of $C$ and $m$ are tabulated in Fig. 6-17 for several ratios of $S_t/D$ and $S_l/D$. For ratios greater than these values the following equation can be used:

$$N_{\mathrm{Nu}} = 0.329(N_{\mathrm{Re}})^{0.602}(N_{\mathrm{Pr}})^{0.31} \qquad (6\text{-}107)$$

Equations (6-106) and (6-107) are based on data of tube fields with ten or more transverse rows. For fewer rows, the heat transfer coefficient is smaller; as an example, the heat transfer coefficient for $N$ aligned rows with $N_{\mathrm{Re}} \geqq 6000$ is given by[4]

$$h_N = 0.68(N)^{0.18} h_{10} \qquad (6\text{-}108)$$

This expression approximates the results of a single cylinder if there is only one row of tubes.

| $S_l/D$ \ $S_t/D$ | 1.25 | | 1.5 | | 2 | | 3 | |
|---|---|---|---|---|---|---|---|---|
| | $C$ | $m$ | $C$ | $m$ | $C$ | $m$ | $C$ | $m$ |
| **ALIGNED TUBES** | | | | | | | | |
| 1.25 | 0.385 | 0.592 | 0.304 | 0.608 | 0.111 | 0.704 | 0.070 | 0.752 |
| 1.5 | 0.406 | 0.586 | 0.276 | 0.620 | 0.112 | 0.702 | 0.075 | 0.744 |
| 2 | 0.463 | 0.570 | 0.331 | 0.602 | 0.253 | 0.632 | 0.219 | 0.648 |
| 3 | 0.321 | 0.601 | 0.395 | 0.584 | 0.414 | 0.581 | 0.316 | 0.608 |
| **STAGGERED TUBES** | | | | | | | | |
| 0.6 | | | | | | | 0.236 | 0.636 |
| 0.9 | | | | | 0.493 | 0.571 | 0.444 | 0.581 |
| 1.0 | | | 0.550 | 0.558 | | | | |
| 1.125 | | | | | 0.529 | 0.565 | 0.573 | 0.560 |
| 1.25 | 0.573 | 0.556 | 0.559 | 0.554 | 0.574 | 0.556 | 0.577 | 0.562 |
| 1.5 | 0.499 | 0.568 | 0.509 | 0.562 | 0.500 | 0.568 | 0.540 | 0.568 |
| 2 | 0.447 | 0.572 | 0.460 | 0.568 | 0.533 | 0.556 | 0.497 | 0.570 |
| 3 | 0.343 | 0.592 | 0.394 | 0.580 | 0.487 | 0.562 | 0.466 | 0.574 |

**Fig. 6-17** Coefficients for calculating the heat transfer from a tube field in cross flow by Eq. (6-106).

Only a limited number of worthwhile studies have been particularly concerned with thermal aspects of electronic packages. One investigation was made by Adelberg and Baker,[20] who attempted to find a generalized expression for forced convection heat transfer from component-filled circuit cards mounted in a card carrier. Although data were obtained on only two component arrangements and one spacing between cards, the result of this study

$$N_{\mathrm{Nu}} = C(N_{\mathrm{Re}})^{0.57}(N_{\mathrm{Pr}})^{1/3} \qquad (6\text{-}109)$$

can serve as a guide to the designer who has this configuration. The value of $C$ was found to be 0.91 for a resistor-filled card with resistor axes parallel to the surface of the card, and 0.95 for the card on which resistors are densely mounted with axes perpendicular to the card. These values were obtained for a Reynolds number range of 200 to 20,000, where the velocity is volumetric fluid flow rate divided by the cross-sectional area.

Adelberg and Baker inappropriately selected the characteristic length as the equivalent diameter [Eq. (6-104)] of the rectangular duct formed between two cards and side walls instead of the equivalent thermal diameter [Eq. (6-105)]; thus, their expression is not general.

Other forced convection measurements have been made on circuit cards mounted in card carriers. Results are reported[18] for heat transfer from cards filled with subminiature electron tubes and for cards filled with prismatic-shaped electronic components (studied by Robinson). In these two investigations, components were positioned on the respective cards to give air flow normal to component axis. The expression

$$N_{Nu} = 0.337(N_{Re})^{0.55} \qquad (700 < N_{Re} < 6000) \qquad (6\text{-}110)$$

was found to describe heat transfer from electron tubes, and the expression

$$N_{Nu} = 0.495 \left[ 1 + 0.639 \left( \frac{S_t}{S_{t(max)}} \right) \left( \frac{L}{S_l} \right)^{0.172} \right] (N_{Re})^{0.57} \qquad (6\text{-}111)$$

$$(2500 < N_{Re} < 8000)$$

was found to represent heat transfer from staggered arrangements of prismatic-shaped components. In both Eqs. (6-110) and (6-111), the reference temperature for evaluating air properties is $T_\infty$, and the velocity is volumetric flow rate divided by the difference of duct area and projected component area. Other terms are defined as:

$$L = \text{characteristic length} = \text{tube diameter in Eq. (6-110)}$$
$$= \text{diameter of cylinder of equal exposed area in Eq. (6-111)}$$
$$S_t = \text{transverse spacing between components}$$
$$S_{t(max)} = \text{maximum transverse spacing when there are different values in the same configuration}$$
$$S_l = \text{longitudinal spacing between components}$$

**Example 6.1.** A chassis filled with electron tubes is arranged in a pattern that can be approximated by the configuration illustrated in Fig. 6-18. These components are cooled by air at 20°C flowing at a rate of 0.015 kg/s through the rectangular space formed by the chassis enclosure.

1. If each component dissipates 1.0 W, what is the component temperature $T_w$?

Based on the component diameter, average velocity, and air properties from Appendix B, Fig. B-1, the Reynolds number is

$$N_{Re} = \frac{\rho u D}{\mu} = \frac{(1.22)(0.01)}{1.82 \times 10^{-5}} \times \frac{0.015/1.22}{(0.15)(0.035) - (4)(0.01)(0.025)]}$$

$$= 1935$$

Free convection is negligible because $N_{Re}^2 \gg N_{Gr}$ where

$$N_{Gr} = \frac{g\beta\rho^2}{\mu^2} D^3(T_w - T_\infty) = 154(T_w - T_\infty)$$

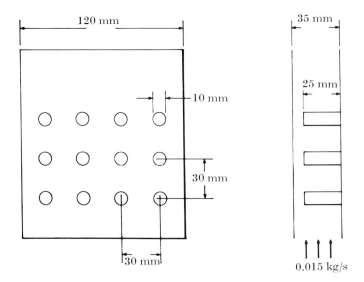

**Fig. 6-18**　Electron tube configuration.

Using Eq. (6-110),

$$N_{\mathrm{Nu}} = \frac{h(0.01)}{0.0256} = 0.337(1935)^{0.55}$$

Thus

$$h = 55.2 \ \mathrm{W/m^2 \cdot {}^{\circ}C}$$

The component temperature $T_w$ from $Q = hA(T_w - T_\infty)$ is

$$T_w = \frac{1.0}{(55.2)[(\pi)(0.01)(0.025)]} + 20 = 43.1^{\circ}\mathrm{C}$$

2. Consider that the height of the rectangular enclosure is reduced to a minimum of 2.5 cm, while the fluid velocity is unchanged. For this geometry, compare relationships given by Eqs. (6-106) and (6-110).

As before, $N_{\mathrm{Re}} = 1935$ since the characteristic length is the component diameter in both these expressions. For ratios of $S_t/D = S_l/D = 3$, the values of $C$ and $m$ are given in Fig. 6-17. Thus, Eq. (6-106) for an aligned tube field becomes

$$N_{\mathrm{Nu}} = \frac{h(0.01)}{0.0256} = 0.316(1935)^{0.608}(0.72)^{0.31}$$

and

$$h = 73 \ \mathrm{W/m^2 \cdot {}^{\circ}C}$$

This value holds true for ten or more rows. We introduce Eq. (6-108) because our arrangement has only three transverse rows,

$$h = (0.68)(3^{0.18})(73) = 60.5 \ \mathrm{W/m^2 \cdot {}^{\circ}C}$$

which is within 10 percent of the value found in part 1. However, as a matter of interest, it can be shown that Eq. (6-109) predicts a considerably higher heat transfer coefficient.

## 6-5. HEAT TRANSFER BY BOILING LIQUIDS

The boiling process may well be the most acceptable method of controlling temperatures of components having inferior thermal paths or surfaces dissipating more than 3000 W/m². Heat transfer coefficients, based on the ratio $q/\theta$, range from a few thousand to over 10,000 W/m²·deg, where $q$ is the surface heat flux and $\theta$ is the surface-to-liquid temperature excess. Heat-generating components can usually be submerged in liquids having a high dielectric strength without altering the electrical function.

Figure 6-19 illustrates the various regimes in the boiling process by de-

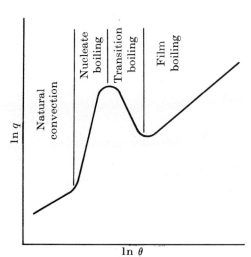

**Fig. 6-19**  Regimes in boiling process depicted by variation of surface heat flux.

picting the variation of surface heat flux. Suppose Fig. 6-19 pertains to a pool of liquid on a horizontal heating surface. Natural convection with heat transfer coefficients in the range of 50 to 2800 W/m²·deg prevails until sufficient heat is added to raise the liquid to its saturation temperature for the existing pressure. The start of the nucleate boiling regime is signified by vapor bubbles forming repeatedly from preferred spots, called nucleation sites, on the surface. A nucleus of finite radius is prerequisite to the formation of a vapor bubble. The driving force, the degree of superheat in the surrounding liquid, must overcome the surface tension acting on the spherical bubble. This opposing force varies as the reciprocal of the radius.

Film boiling is established when the heat input is so large that neighboring vapor bubbles join together to the extent that a vapor film blankets the surface. Everyone has observed film boiling in watching a dancing water droplet on a hot stove. Heat transfer across the vapor film, which exhibits low thermal conductivity, is significant only after the temperature difference is elevated to a point where radiation becomes predominant. This transition from the relatively moderate surface temperatures associated with nucleate boiling to the large temperatures in film boiling is called *burnout*. Burnout is avoided if the peak heat flux, $q_{max}$, is less than the value given by Eq. (6-112).[21]

$$q_{max} = 0.0735\lambda\sqrt{\rho_v g}\,[\sigma(\rho_l - \rho_v)]^{1/4} \qquad (6\text{-}112)$$

where $\rho_l$ and $\rho_v$ are the liquid and vapor densities, respectively, $\lambda$ is the latent heat of vaporization, and $\sigma$ is the surface tension.

The published literature contains many correlations of the relationship between $q$ and $\theta$, but none of them predict boiling behavior for all conditions and all liquids. The simple relation

$$q = C\theta^n \text{ W/m}^2 \qquad (6\text{-}113)$$

approximates this relationship in the nucleate boiling regime. Values of $C$ and $n$ for several liquids are listed in Fig. 6-20. Unless the existing data are directly

| Liquid | C | n |
|---|---|---|
| Freon 113 | 745 | 1.5 |
| water (horizontal tube as heat source) | 1580 | 3.4 |
| water (0.024-in. diameter heated platinum wire) | 0.965 | 4.9 |
| 9.1 percent sodium chloride solution | 930 | 3.4 |
| 26 percent sodium chloride solution | 118 | 3.3 |
| C.P. benzene | 172 | 1.9 |
| kerosene | 41.6 | 3.2 |
| n-heptane | 5.07 | 3.1 |
| 100 percent ethyl alcohol | 0.0315 | 4.7 |

**Fig. 6-20**   Parameters $C$ and $n$ of Eq. (6-113) for several liquids.[21]

applicable, experimental evaluation of the arbitrary constants, $C$ and $n$, is required.

The first step in designing for vaporization cooling is to select a suitable liquid. The following list summarizes desirable properties:

1. low boiling point
2. low surface tension
3. high dielectric strength
4. chemical inertness
5. nonflammable
6. nontoxic

The commercially available fluorochemicals are among the fluids having these properties. Water is definitely unsuitable because leaks could be detrimental to the electrical function. The preferred method of achieving the desired boiling point is to compose a mixture of two or more liquids in proper proportion by weight. Another approach is to vary the pressure; however, it is often desirable to operate near atmospheric pressure to circumvent sealing problems.

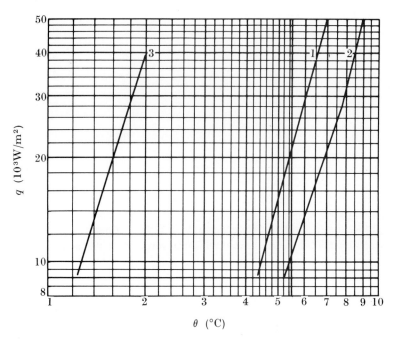

**Fig. 6-21**   Influence of roughness upon temperature difference between horizontal heating surface and boiling water. Curve 1—recently roughened by sandblast; curve 2—same after long use; curve 3—fitted with wire screen.[1]

The geometric shape of the nucleation sites on the heating surface is also a basic factor in predicting the boiling behavior of a given liquid. Artificially roughening the surface improves heat transfer in the nucleate boiling regime since it offers additional nucleation sites. This improvement is shown in Fig. 6-21 along with the effects of aging. Good wetting of the surface has a desirable effect in that the liquid penetrates to the small partially obstructed crevices very near the surface, yielding additional active nucleation sites. Figure 6-22 shows the results of adding a wetting agent.

An enclosed pool of liquid on a horizontal heating surface is an illustration of a simple vaporization cooling device. The rising vapor bubbles condense on the upper surfaces of the enclosure, and the condensate is returned to the

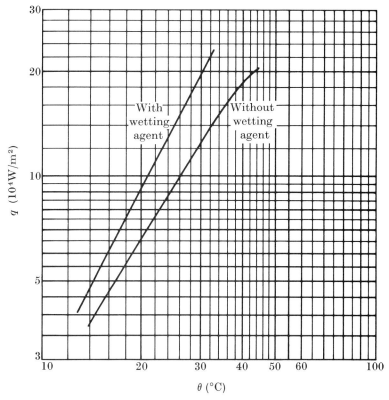

**Fig. 6-22** Effects of a wetting agent on heat transfer from a wire-wound, cylindrical resistor (approximately 0.65 cm diameter by 3.8 cm long) when positioned horizontally in a fluorochemical (Freon 113) bath.[21]

pool by gravity. Heat which is transferred to the condenser can be removed to the eventual sink by natural or forced convection.

This simple device ceases to operate when tilted severely. However, there is another high conductance structure, almost as simple, which operates in any orientation with respect to the gravity field. It is called a *heat pipe*[22] and is illustrated in Fig. 6-23. Refluxing of the condensate to the evaporator is accomplished by capillary action which develops sufficient force to overcome the opposing gravity force. The hot vapor near the evaporator, having a higher vapor pressure, is driven toward the condenser, completing the cycle.

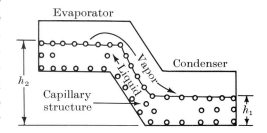

**Fig. 6-23** Heat pipe formed by two concentric cylinders. The capillary action in the annular space was enhanced in the original design by four or five wrappings of woven screen.

## 6-6. EXTENDED AND FINNED SURFACES

The heat flow in convection from an electrical component dissipating heat, or from a package of components, depends upon the flow geometry, the allowable surface temperature, and the amount of area available for convection heat transfer. Flow geometry and surface area are interdependent. Since the heat transfer coefficient depends upon flow geometry, the component temperature rise above the ambient is not necessarily decreased by simply adding more area in the form of fins and extended surfaces.

For a surface of area $A$, the thermal resistance to convection is $1/hA$. The addition of fins increases the area, but the heat transfer coefficient is changed *and* a conductive resistance is added, since some heat must be conducted a greater distance than before the finned area was added. The determination of this conductive resistance consists of solving for the steady-state temperature distribution within a wall with an extended surface, as illustrated in Fig. 6-24. Under the simplest assumption of a constant $h$, it can be shown[4] that the surface heat loss is increased (in spite of the additional conductive resistance) as long as

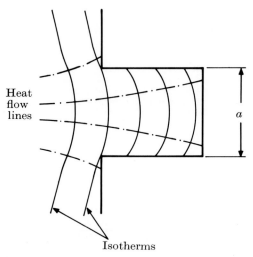

Heat flow lines

$a$

Isotherms

**Fig. 6-24** Temperature distribution and heat flow lines in a short rectangular fin.

$$\frac{2k}{ha} > 1 \qquad (6\text{-}114)$$

where $a$ is the thickness of the fin and $k$ is the fin conductivity.

Since the temperature varies along the fin, its surface does not operate at the same efficiency as a unit area of the original wall. To assess this effect, a fin efficiency can be introduced so that

$$\eta_f = \frac{\text{heat transferred across the fin surface}}{\text{heat transferred if whole fin were at } T_w} \qquad (6\text{-}115)$$

If $T_w$ is the temperature of the wall at the base of the fin, then

$$(hA)_{\text{fin}}\eta_f(T_w - T_\infty) = \text{total heat flow from finned body}$$

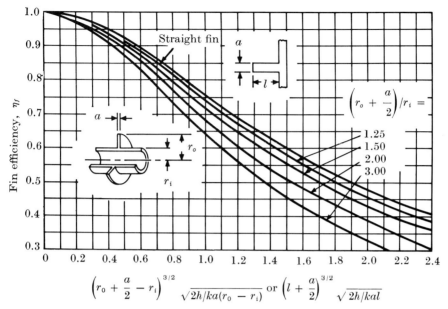

**Fig. 6-25**    Efficiency of circumferential fins of rectangular cross-sectional area.[6]

A plot from Kreith[6] illustrating this efficiency for a straight fin and a circular fin is reproduced in Fig. 6-25. Some improvement in fin efficiency can be gained by using a tapered cross section† instead of a rectangular one; but the saving in weight is not usually worth the effort in ground-based electronic equipment.

The next factor one must consider when using fins is how $h$ changes from that for the original wall to that for the finned wall. The studies by Elenbaas[17] for free convective flow between parallel vertical plates are applicable to a degree (see Fig. 6-26). In Elenbaas' correlation, all of the physical properties are evaluated at the equivalent surface temperature $\eta_f(T_w - T_\infty) + T_\infty$, except $\beta$ which is evaluated at $T_\infty$. In the case of parallel plates, the neighboring fins interfere with the flow if the spacing is close enough. Thus, there is an optimum spacing,‡ found by Elenbaas to be

$$(N_{\mathrm{Gr}}N_{\mathrm{Pr}})\frac{b}{H} \approx 50 \qquad (6\text{-}116)$$

where $b$, the fin spacing, is the characteristic length.

---

† Considering constant $h$, Schneider[23] evaluates the efficiency of various fin cross sections by applying separation of variable techniques.

‡ This spacing is optimum in the sense that it maximizes the heat transferred. Additional work is required to find the spacing which minimizes the wall temperature rise.

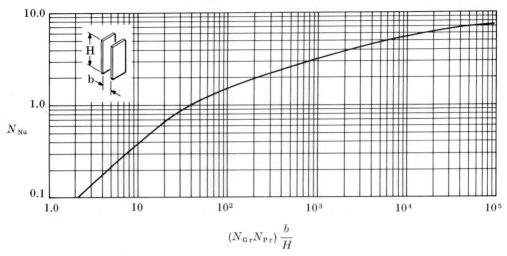

**Fig. 6-26** Free convection heat transfer from two parallel plates of height $H$ separated by a distance $b$.[17]

The fact that actual finned heat exchangers look like three-sided ducts has some bearing on the average heat transfer coefficient $h$. The root wall illustrated in Fig. 6-27 tends to retard the flow in free convection; the degree depends on the orientation of the finned structure with respect to gravity. An experimental study of this type of fin has been performed by Starner and McManus,[24] and the effects of an essentially stagnant region at the fin base were noted in the fact that all the experimental measurements fell somewhat below the parallel plate correlation. The optimum position was the vertical position for all but the shortest fins, i.e., $l/b = 1$. For deep fins (i.e., $l/b = 6$) the horizontal position yielded an $h$ value which was as low as 40 percent of that for the same fin in the vertical position.

Lastly, we make a few observations about heat exchangers which have been dubbed "heat sinks." These finned bodies are actually couplers between the component dissipating heat and the fluid (usually the room air) which ultimately accepts the heat. Approximately 500 different shapes and sizes of heat sinks are commercially available, many of the

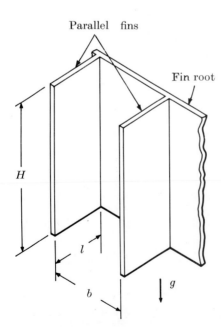

**Fig. 6-27** Finned wall.

shapes being somewhat arbitrary. These devices are tested by placing a heat source at the location for the component and measuring the temperature rise of the source as the power output is increased. The slope of the results is cited as a thermal resistance in terms of °C/W. The designer is cautioned to remember that different orientations can affect this value, and also that the placement of these sinks in the neighborhood of enclosure walls or other dissipating devices can lower the rated value. No generalized description of these devices is currently available.

**Example 6.2.** A finned surface is required to dissipate the heat generated by a high-power transistor. Available mounting space is on a vertical surface 10 cm high and 8 cm wide. The maximum allowable transistor mounting-plate temperature is 40°C and the cooling medium is still air at 25°C (neglect thermal resistance of mounting plate).

1. What fin configuration makes optimum use of the available space?

Assume that the transistor mounting flange has a 3-cm diameter. The optimum spacing is calculated from Eq. (6-116) using properties tabulated in Appendix B, Fig. B-2.

$$b_{\text{opt}} = \left[ \frac{50Hv^2}{g\beta(T_w - T_\infty)N_{\text{Pr}}} \right]^{1/4}$$
$$= \left[ \frac{50(0.1)(1.7 \times 10^{-5})^2}{(9.81)(3.37 \times 10^{-3})(15)(0.72)} \right]^{1/4}$$
$$= 7.98 \times 10^{-3} \text{ m}$$

The available mounting surface will accommodate three 3-mm thick fins on each side of the transistor.

2. If the fin dimensioned in Fig. 6-28 is made of aluminum, how much heat can be dissipated?

From Fig. 6-26 with $(N_{\text{Gr}} \cdot N_{\text{Pr}})b/H = 50$, we find $N_{\text{Nu}} = 1.2$. Thus,

$$h_1 = \frac{1.2k}{b} = \frac{(1.2)(2.7 \times 10^{-2})}{7.98 \times 10^{-3}}$$
$$= 4.06 \text{ W/m}^2 \cdot {}^\circ\text{C}$$

The fin efficiency from Fig. 6-25 for

$$\left( l + \frac{a}{2} \right)^{3/2} \sqrt{\frac{2h_1}{kal}} = \left( 0.03 + \frac{0.003}{2} \right)^{3/2} \sqrt{\frac{2 \, (4.06)}{(138)(0.003)(0.03)}}$$
$$= 0.14$$

is $\eta_f \approx 100$ percent, which means that the entire fin surface is at $T_w = 40$°C. The two fin surfaces adjacent to the transistor and the two outer surfaces have heat transfer coefficients different from $h_1$. Using the fact that the fin temperature

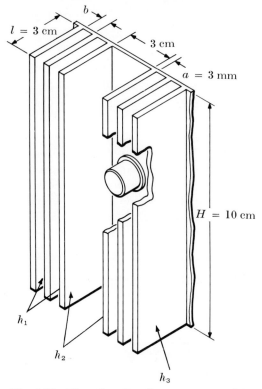

**Fig. 6-28**  Finned surface for a power transistor.

is nearly constant, the first of these, $h_2$, will be evaluated as a fin with spacing 3 cm, and the other, $h_3$, as a vertical flat plate from correlations given in Fig. 6-8.

Considering $h_2$ with $b = 3$ cm, $N_{Gr} \cdot N_{Pr} = 3.34 \times 10^4$, and the corresponding Nusselt number is $N_{Nu} = 5.4$; thus,

$$h_2 = \frac{5.4k}{b} = \frac{(5.4)(2.7 \times 10^{-2})}{3 \times 10^{-2}} = 4.86 \ \text{W/m}^2 \cdot {}^\circ\text{C}$$

The heat transfer from the outer surfaces is

$$N_{Nu} = 0.555 \ (N_{Gr} \cdot N_{Pr})^{1/4}$$

$$\frac{h_3 H}{k} = 0.555 \left\{ \left[ \frac{(9.81)(3.37 \times 10^{-3})(0.1)^3(40 - 25)}{(1.7 \times 10^{-5})^2} \right] \cdot (0.72) \right\}^{1/4}$$

$$= 0.555 \ [(1.71 \times 10^6)(0.72)]^{1/4} = 18.5$$

$$h_3 = \frac{(18.5)(2.7 \times 10^{-2})}{0.1} = 4.99 \ \text{W/m}^2 \cdot {}^\circ\text{C}$$

From these three heat transfer coefficients and the corresponding areas, the total heat dissipated by the fin arrangement is

$$q = [(4.06)(8) + (4.86)(2) + (4.99)(2)][(0.01)(0.03)](40 - 25)$$

$$= 2.35 \ \text{W}$$

Thus, for the stated temperature conditions, this design would accommodate a transistor dissipation of 2.35 W (neglecting a considerable contribution due to radiation). It is interesting to note that $h_2$ and $h_3$ are nearly the same value. This illustrates that the heat transfer from a fin is the same as the heat transfer from a vertical flat plate if the spacing is sufficient to separate the boundary layers. To demonstrate that this is indeed the case, the boundary-layer thickness $\delta$ is calculated here for the vertical surface in question.

From Fig. 6-6 we see that the velocity profile tapers to zero for values greater than 3.8; thus, $\delta = y$ at $\eta = 3.8$.

$$\delta = 3.8x \left( \frac{4}{N_{\mathrm{Gr},x}} \right)^{1/4}$$

or

$$\delta = 3.8(0.1) \left( \frac{4}{1.71 \times 10^6} \right)^{1/4} = 1.48 \times 10^{-2}\,\mathrm{m}$$

at the upper edge of the plate ($x = H = 10$ cm).

3. Compare the configuration in Fig. 6-28 with another arrangement in which only two fins are used, Fig. 6-29. Assume that all dimensions are

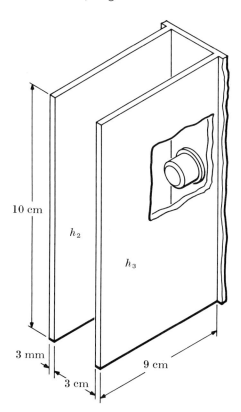

**Fig. 6-29** Alternative fin arrangement for transistor.

unchanged except the fin depth, which is increased to 9 cm to maintain the same total fin surface area. How much heat is now dissipated?

If the two fins are located on either side of the transistor and are spaced 3 cm apart, then $h = h_2 = 4.86$ W/m² · °C. However, the fin efficiency from Fig. 6-25 is now $\eta_f = 93$ percent because

$$\left(0.09 + \frac{0.003}{2}\right)^{3/2} \sqrt{\frac{2\,(4.86)}{(138)(0.003)(0.09)}} = 0.447$$

Since the fin temperature is no longer constant, the heat transfer from the outer surfaces is reduced according to the fin efficiency. The total heat dissipation is

$$q = 0.93[(4.86)(2) + (4.99)(2)](0.1)(0.09)(40 - 25)$$
$$= 2.47 \text{ W}$$

The designer is cautioned not to draw general conclusions from this comparison. Variations in fin dimensions and/or the use of different materials could result in a large decrease in efficiency which could significantly alter the foregoing results. Each individual application should be checked.

## 6-7. FLOW THROUGH CABINETS

In the design of a ventilated cabinet we need to predict the local ambient temperatures, for specific areas and methods of ventilation, as a function of the cabinet size and power dissipated. A paper by Noronha[25] sets out to do this by equating the hydrostatic pressure differential across the cabinet height to the various losses caused by form and frictional drag. Specifically, the pressure head is converted to velocity head at the entrance and this head is dissipated as entrance, orifice, pipe bend, and frictional losses as the air winds its way through the cabinet. Noronha tested this approach experimentally on a cabinet sparsely filled with dissipating components. He compared the observed velocities with his theoretical expressions and derived a factor to account for "unknown losses."

Noronha's work should be considered only as a first step toward development of a rational approach for ventilated cabinet design since most electronic packages are more densely filled than those he considered. In the densely filled cabinets the major losses occur in the vicinity of the components and boards. Additional experimental work is necessary to evaluate these losses. In the absence of such work we must use the published results for flow over tube fields,[4] discrete roughness[2] (spheres, cones, short angles), and flow between parallel plates.[12,17,26]

Bodoia and Osterle[26] analytically described the development of free convection between heated vertical plates. Their heat transfer results were found to agree very closely with the experimental work of Elenbaas[17] as given

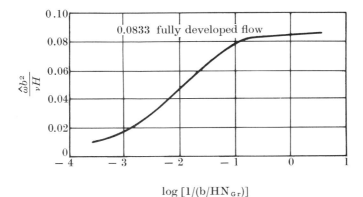

**Fig. 6-30**  Free convection flow in a channel formed by parallel heated plates.

in Fig. 6-26. The flow rate in terms of the average channel velocity $\hat{w}$ is given in Fig. 6-30 as a function of $N_{Gr}$, channel width $b$, and channel height $H$. Using the work cited, the heat transferred to the ventilating air and the flow rate can be determined; then the local air temperature can be calculated.

## 6-8. SUMMARY FOR CONVECTION

The nondimensionalization of the basic conservation equations and their application to a typical forced convection problem and to a typical free convection problem yielded the following relationship for correlating heat transfer results:

$$N_{Nu} = \Phi(N_{Re}, N_{Gr}, N_{Pr}, N_E, N_{Fr})$$

where:

Nusselt number:

$$N_{Nu} = \frac{hL}{k} = \frac{\text{rate of heat transfer by convection}}{\text{heat transferred by pure conduction}}$$

Reynolds number:

$$N_{Re} = \frac{u_{\infty}L}{\nu} = \frac{\text{inertia forces}}{\text{viscous forces}}$$

Grashof number:

$$N_{Gr} = \frac{g\beta}{\nu^2}(T_w - T_{\infty})L^3 = \frac{\text{buoyant forces}}{\text{viscous forces}}$$

Prandtl number:

$$N_{Pr} = \frac{\mu c_p}{k} = \frac{\nu}{\alpha} = \frac{\text{diffusivity of momentum}}{\text{diffusivity of heat}}$$

Eckert number:

$$N_\text{E} = \frac{u_\infty^2}{c_p(T_w - T_\infty)} = \frac{\text{kinetic energy converted to enthalpy by viscous effects}}{\text{enthalpy}}$$

Froude number:

$$N_\text{Fr} = \frac{u_\infty \rho^{1/2}}{(LF_x)^{1/2}} = \frac{\text{inertia forces}}{\text{body forces}}$$

which can also be grouped as:

Stanton number:

$$N_\text{St} = \frac{h}{\rho c_p u_\infty} = \frac{N_\text{Nu}}{N_\text{Re}N_\text{Pr}} = \frac{\text{heat transfer perpendicular to flow}}{\text{heat transfer parallel to flow}}$$

Rayleigh number:

$$N_\text{Ra} = N_\text{Gr} \cdot N_\text{Pr}$$

For most electronic system applications, the effects of $N_\text{E}$ and $N_\text{Fr}$ can be neglected, and relatively simple power functions are successful in predicting the heat transfer coefficient as it appears in $N_\text{Nu}$.

Results for flows through channels and other simple geometries are available for estimating the heat transfer coefficient for many equipment configurations. However, except for the consideration of a tube field, little reliable thermal data for electronic packages exist in the literature. Consequently, the thermal design based on best estimates should be combined with a careful experimental verification.

## REFERENCES

1. Jakob, M., *Heat Transfer*, Vol. I and II, New York, John Wiley & Sons, Inc., 1957. Figures 6-8(b), 6-9, and 6-21 by permission.

2. Schlichting, H., *Boundary Layer Theory*, New York, McGraw-Hill Book Co., 1968. The most comprehensive coverage of flow in viscous fluids.

3. Pai, S., *Viscous Flow Theory*, Vol. I and II, Princeton, N.J., D. Van Nostrand Co., 1957. Very similar to Schlichting with emphasis on analytical approaches.

4. Eckert, E. R. G., and R. M. Drake, *Heat and Mass Transfer*, New York, McGraw-Hill Book Co., 1959.

5. Grober, H., S. Erk, and U. Grigull, *Fundamentals of Heat Transfer*, New York, McGraw-Hill Book Co., 1961.

6. Kreith, F., *Principles of Heat Transfer*, Scranton, Pa., International Textbook Co., 1966. Good introductory text and good source for data on a number of

practical situations not treated in other texts. Figures 6-11 and 6-25 by permission.

7. McAdams, W. H., *Heat Transmission*, New York, McGraw-Hill Book Co., 1954. Leans toward design formulas with adjustment of coefficients to fit author's experience.

8. Kays, W. M., *Convective Heat and Mass Transfer*, New York, McGraw-Hill Book Co., 1966. A comprehensive compilation of analytical and experimental results for the title subject. Emphasis is on design of heat exchangers. Figures 6-13 and 6-15 by permission.

9. Prins, J. A., J. Mulder, and I. Schenk, "Heat Transfer in Laminar Flow Between Parallel Plates," *Applied Science Research*, **A2**, 431–438, 1950. Figure 6-3 by permission.

10. Carslaw, H. S., and J. C. Jaeger, *Conduction of Heat in Solids*, London, Oxford University Press, 1959.

11. Schenk, J., and J. M. Dumore, "Heat Transfer in Laminar Flow Through Cylindrical Tubes," *Applied Science Research*, **A4**, 39–51, 1954.

12. Hwang, C., and L. Fan, "Finite Difference Analysis of Forced-Convection Heat Transfer in Entrance Region of a Flat Rectangular Duct," *Applied Science Research*, **A13**, 401–422, 1964. Figures 6-4 and 6-14 by permission.

13. Hildebrand, F. B., *Introduction to Numerical Analysis*, New York, McGraw-Hill Book Co., 1956. Of particular interest is Chap. 6 on numerical solution of differential equations.

14. Emery, A., and N. C. Chu, "Heat Transfer Across Vertical Layers," *J. Heat Transfer*, **87**, 110–116, Feb., 1965.

15. McFadden, P. W., and R. J. Grosh, "High Flux Heat Transfer Studies—An Analytical Investigation of Laminar Film Boiling," *ANL-6064*, Argonne National Laboratory, Chicago, Oct., 1959.

16. Sparrow, E. M., and J. L. Gregg, "Laminar Free Convection From a Vertical Plate With Uniform Surface Heat Flux," *Trans. ASME*, **80**, 379–386, Feb., 1958.

17. Elenbaas, W., "Dissipation of Heat by Free Convection," Parts I and II, *Philips Research Report*, **3**, 338–360, 450–465, N. V. Philips, Gloeilampenfabrieken, Eindhoven, Netherlands, 1948. Figures 6-10 and 6-26 by permission.

18. "Handbook of Methods of Cooling Air Force Ground Electronic Equipment," Rome Air Development Center, Griffiss Air Force Base, N.Y., *RADC-TR-58-126*, June, 1959, ASTIA 148 907.

19. Kraus, A. D., *Cooling Electronic Equipment*, Englewood Cliffs, N.J., Prentice-Hall, Inc., 1965.

20. Adelberg, M., and E. C. Baker, "Thermal Design of Electronic Packages," *ASME Paper 65-WA/HT-44*.

21. Asch, V., "A Survey of Liquid Boiling Phenomena: Their Prediction and Analysis," *IEEE Transactions*, CP-10, 12–23, March, 1963. Figures 6-20 and 6-22 by permission.

22. Grover, G. M., T. P. Cotter, and G. F. Erickson, "Structures of Very High Thermal Conductance," *J. of Applied Physics*, **35**, 1990–1991, June, 1964.

23. Schneider, P. J., *Conduction Heat Transfer*, Reading, Mass., Addison-Wesley Publishing Co., Inc., 1955.

24. Starner, K. W., and H. N. McManus, "An Experimental Investigation of Free-Convection Heat Transfer From Rectangular-Fin Arrays," *J. Heat Transfer*, **85**, 273–278, Aug., 1963.

25. Noronha, R. I., "Free Convective Cooling of Cabinets Containing Heat Dissipating Components," *Proc. Instn. Mech. Engrs.*, **179**, Pt. I, No. 13, 439–450, 1964–65.

26. Bodoia, J. R., and J. F. Osterle, "The Development of Free Convection Between Heated Vertical Plates," *J. Heat Transfer*, **84**, 40–44, Feb., 1962.

*Chapter 7*

# RADIATIVE HEAT TRANSFER

## C. A. Fritsch

It is a fact of everyday experience that bodies emit thermal radiation in some relation to their temperature. Thermal radiation[1] is electromagnetic in nature, with wavelengths occupying a part of the spectrum from 0.1 $\mu$m to 1000 $\mu$m. The current description of this radiation treats the energy in the form of packets called *photons* which travel in straight lines, generally without mutual interaction. Thus, radiative exchange problems in effect consist of "counting" the number of photons which cross a given control volume. This accounting, however, is done through statistical averaging, using temperature as the labeling factor. For example, the probability that photons incident on a surface will be absorbed, reflected, or transmitted can be determined, theoretically, as a function of their energy and direction of incidence.

Methods for calculating radiative exchanges between surfaces, with certain restrictions, will be developed in this chapter. The interaction of any intervening fluid will be neglected since, for most electronic design problems, the intervening fluid is air which is, practically speaking, transparent.

## 7-I. DEFINITION OF TERMS

We first define a quantity called *intensity*. Let $W_\lambda$ be an amount of radiative energy (the number of photons) in a wavelength interval $\lambda$ to

$(\lambda + d\lambda)$. As shown in Fig. 7-1, this is an amount of energy passing from or to an element of area $dA$ at a point $(x, y, z)$, during a time interval $t$ to $(t + dt)$, within an elemental solid angle $d\omega$ whose apex is on the surface $dA$. Then the *monochromatic intensity* is given by

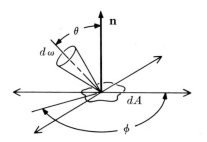

$$I_\lambda = \lim_{dA, d\omega, d\lambda, dt \to 0} \left| \frac{W_\lambda}{\cos \theta \, dA \, d\omega \, d\lambda \, dt} \right| \quad (7\text{-}1)$$

where $\cos \theta \, dA$ is the projected surface area in the direction viewed. The *total intensity*, then, is the sum of $I_\lambda$ over all possible wavelengths, so that

$$I = \int_0^\infty I_\lambda \, d\lambda \quad (7\text{-}2)$$

**Fig. 7-1** Geometry for intensity definition.

which has the units of energy per unit area, time, and solid angle. This is the quantity seen by the eye.

Summing up the contributions of the intensity from all directions $(\theta, \phi)$ on one side of an imaginary plane $dA$, we arrive at the *monochromatic flux*

$$q_\lambda = \int_{\omega=2\pi} I_\lambda \cos \theta \, d\omega \quad (7\text{-}3)$$

Therefore, the radiative flux is given by

$$q = \int_0^\infty q_\lambda \, d\lambda \quad (7\text{-}4)$$

which is a function of the point $(x, y, z)$ and the spatial orientation of the area $dA$. In the case where $q$ is the incident flux, this is sometimes called irradiation. Note that the differential solid angle $d\omega = \sin \theta \, d\theta \, d\phi$, so that

$$q = \int_0^{2\pi} \int_0^{\pi/2} I \cos \theta \sin \theta \, d\theta \, d\phi \quad (7\text{-}5)$$

## 7-2. FUNDAMENTAL CONCEPTS

Consider a completely enclosed cavity whose walls are at a constant temperature. The cavity will be "filled" with radiation which arises from the thermal oscillations of the microscopic charged particles in the walls. These particles act as little antennas, receiving and emitting radiation as they oscillate in the electromagnetic fields of their neighbors. The walls, formed from a collection of such "antennas," thus emit and absorb a chaotic field of super-imposed electromagnetic radiation.

Planck, in his consideration of these oscillations, postulated that the energy was absorbed or emitted in discrete "elements of action" in amounts $hf$, where

$h$ is Planck's constant. This, in essence, limited the energy associated with a given frequency $f$ and a single oscillator to a multiple of $hf$. Furthermore, he proposed a statistical distribution of photons among the possible multiples of $hf$ for a given energy state of a cavity characterized by the energy $kT$, where $k$ is Boltzmann's constant. Thus, by stipulating the population of photons in the possible energy states and by counting all the possible energy states within a cavity, one can then arrive at *Planck's law* for the radiant energy density between $f$ and $f + df$ within an iso-thermal cavity,† expressed as

$$u_f = \frac{8\pi h f^3}{c_0^3} \cdot \frac{1}{\exp\left(hf/kT\right) - 1} \quad (7\text{-}6)$$

Or, in terms of wavelength, $\lambda = c_0/f$, where $c_0$ is the velocity of light in a vacuum, the radiant energy density between $\lambda$ and $d\lambda$ is

$$u_\lambda = \frac{8\pi h c_0}{\lambda^5} \cdot \frac{1}{\exp\left(hc_0/\lambda kT\right) - 1} \quad (7\text{-}7)$$

which is illustrated in Fig. 7-2.

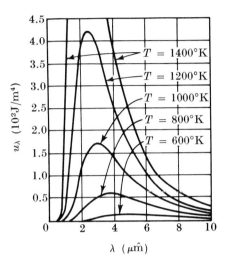

**Fig. 7-2** Radiant energy density versus wavelength for different emitter tempera-tures.

It can be shown[1,2] by arguments from the second law of thermodynamics that the radiant energy density within any isothermal cavity corresponds to that found in a cavity having "black walls," i.e., surfaces which absorb all of the radiation which strikes them. Furthermore, the second law leads one to conclude that the monochromatic intensity of thermal radiation within an isothermal enclosure (in thermodynamic equilibrium) must be homogeneous and isotropic, and this intensity corresponds to that emitted by a blackbody. From a geometric consideration, one can show that the monochromatic intensity inside our isothermal cavity is related to the energy density by

$$I_{b,\lambda} = \frac{c_0 u_\lambda}{4\pi} \quad (7\text{-}8)$$

where the subscript $b$ reminds us that the cavity is a blackbody. From Eq. (7-3), the monochromatic flux for a blackbody becomes

$$q_{b,\lambda} = \int_0^{2\pi} \int_0^{\pi/2} I_{b,\lambda} \cos\theta \sin\theta \, d\theta \, d\phi = \pi I_{b,\lambda}$$

since $I_{b,\lambda}$ is independent of $\theta$ and $\phi$. With this result and Eqs. (7-3) and (7-7),

† See, for example, Chap. 4 of French.[3]

Percent of total energy found below $\lambda$, as a function of $\lambda T$

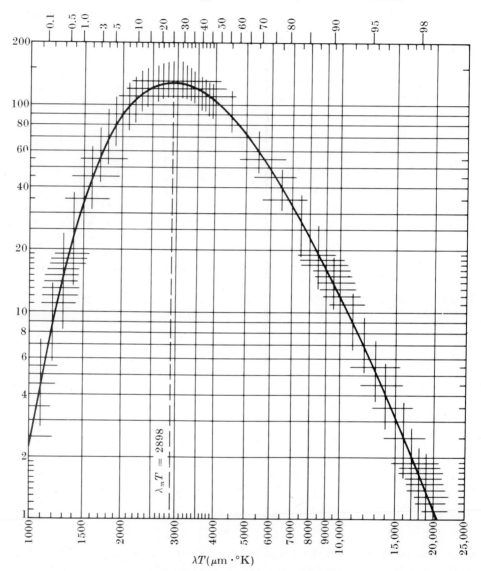

$\lambda T(\mu m \cdot °K)$

**Fig. 7-3**　Energy distribution in a blackbody spectrum as a function of $\lambda T$.[10]

Eq. (7-4) can be integrated,[3] giving

$$q_b = \int_0^\infty q_{b,\lambda}\,d\lambda = \frac{c_0}{4}\int_0^\infty \frac{8\pi hc_0}{\lambda^5}\cdot\frac{1}{\exp{(hc_0/\lambda kT)}-1}\,d\lambda$$

This yields

$$q_b = \frac{12.98\pi k^4 T^4}{h^3 c_0^2} \tag{7-9}$$

From thermodynamic considerations, Boltzmann showed[2] in 1884 that, in agreement with Stefan's measurements, the radiative flux is related to the absolute temperature by the *Stefan–Boltzmann law*

$$q_b = \sigma T^4 \tag{7-10}$$

Comparing Eqs. (7-9) and (7-10), one sees that the Stefan–Boltzmann constant $\sigma$ can be evaluated in terms of the universal constants $h$ and $k$, giving

$$\sigma = 5.67 \times 10^{-8} \text{ W/m}^2 \text{ °K}^4 \tag{7 11}$$

As illustrated in Fig. 7-2, the energy density (monochromatic intensity and flux) as a function of wavelength exhibits a maximum. The value of $\lambda$ for which this occurs can be found by setting $du_\lambda/d\lambda = 0$. From this, Eq. (7-7) yields *Wien's law* for a blackbody emitter temperature $T$:

$$\lambda_m T = 2898 \ \mu\text{m} \cdot \text{°K} \tag{7-12}$$

This relation is useful in predicting the wavelength range which characterizes a given temperature. For example, the effective surface temperature of the sun is about 5600°K, so that wavelengths of the order of 0.5 $\mu$m are present. Figure 7-3 shows the percentage distribution of the emitted energy from a blackbody in relation to $\lambda_m T$ and in terms of the monochromatic flux $q_{b,\lambda}$.

## 7-3. RADIATIVE CHARACTERISTICS OF SURFACES

The interaction of electromagnetic radiation with a surface can be predicted from Maxwell's field equations in terms of Snell's laws and Fresnel's equations[4] as a function of the material properties. For example, the rate at which an electromagnetic wave is attenuated as it passes from free space (air) into a good conductor† is given by

$$E \approx E_0 \exp\left(-\frac{z}{\delta}\right)\exp\left[j\omega\left(t-\frac{z}{\delta\omega}\right)\right] \tag{7-13}$$

---

† Strictly speaking, this requirement is that $\sigma/\omega\epsilon \gg 1$, where $\epsilon$ is the permittivity of the conductor.

Here the penetration depth $\delta$ is defined as the value of $z$ at which $E$ is $1/e$ of $E_0$ and is

$$\delta = \sqrt{\frac{2}{\omega\mu\sigma}} \tag{7-14}$$

The quantity $\mu$ is the permeability of the conductor which, for most nonferrous materials, is approximately the permeability of free space:

$$\mu_0 = 1.257 \times 10^{-6} \, \Omega \cdot s/m \tag{7-15}$$

The quantity $\sigma$ is the electrical conductivity.

If one considers solar radiation characterized by $\lambda = 0.5 \, \mu m$, then the angular frequency is $\omega = 12\pi \times 10^{14}$ rad/s. Thus, for copper [$\sigma = 5.8 \times 10^7$ $1/\Omega \cdot m$], the penetration depth from Eq. (7-14) becomes

$$\delta = \sqrt{\frac{2}{12\pi + 10^{14} (1.257 \times 10^{-6})(5.8 \times 10^7)}} = 2.7 \times 10^{-9} \, m = 0.0027 \, \mu m$$

From this and similar calculations for other wavelengths, it follows that the interaction of thermal radiation with essentially opaque solids can be considered a "surface" phenomenon.†

## DEFINITIONS OF SURFACE PROPERTIES

For opaque surfaces, we now wish to define coefficients for the processes of emission, absorption, and reflection.‡ In the following definitions, as before, the subscript $\lambda$ indicates wavelength dependence, while $(\theta, \phi)$ will mean functional dependence on the outgoing direction and $(\theta', \phi')$ will indicate a dependence on the direction of incidence. (See Fig. 7-4.) Starting first with reflection, we define a *monochromatic reflection function* $\rho_\lambda(\theta, \phi, \theta', \phi')$ as

$$\rho_\lambda(\theta, \phi, \theta', \phi') = \text{fraction of the flux incident in the direction } (\theta', \phi') \text{ which is reflected into the direction } (\theta, \phi)$$

so that

$$dI_{r,\lambda}(\theta, \phi) = \rho_\lambda(\theta, \phi, \theta', \phi') \, I_{i,\lambda}(\theta', \phi') \frac{\cos\theta' \sin\theta' \, d\theta' \, d\phi'}{\pi} \tag{7-16}$$

since from Eq. (7-3) $dq_\lambda = I_\lambda \cos\theta' \, d\omega'$ and the $\pi$ in Eq. (7-16) is a convenient

---

† By comparison, waves at a frequency of $10^3$ Hz have a $\delta$ in copper of about 0.2 cm.
‡ For nonopaque surfaces, transmission must also be included.

normalizing factor. The subscripts $r$ and $i$ refer to reflected and incident radiation, respectively. Consequently, on integrating over all the incoming directions,

$$I_{r,\lambda}(\theta, \phi) = \frac{1}{\pi} \int_0^{2\pi} \int_0^{\pi/2} I_{i,\lambda}(\theta',\phi')$$

$$\times \; \rho_\lambda(\theta, \phi, \theta', \phi')$$

$$\times \; \cos\theta' \sin\theta' \, d\theta' \, d\phi' \quad (7\text{-}17)$$

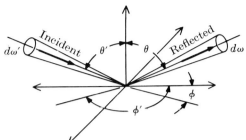

**Fig. 7-4**   Reflection geometry.

A *monochromatic reflectivity* $\rho_\lambda$ can now be defined as the fraction of the incident monochromatic flux which is reflected. It is dependent upon the angular distribution of the incident intensity, as given by Eq. (7-17), so that

$$\rho_\lambda = \frac{\int_0^{2\pi} \int_0^{\pi/2} I_{r,\lambda}(\theta, \phi) \cos\theta \sin\theta \, d\theta \, d\phi}{q_{i,\lambda}} \quad (7\text{-}18)$$

where $q_{i,\lambda}$ is the incident monochromatic flux given by

$$q_{i,\lambda} = \int_0^{2\pi} \int_0^{\pi/2} I_\lambda(\theta', \phi') \cos\theta' \sin\theta' \, d\theta' \, d\phi' \quad (7\text{-}19)$$

The *total (hemispherical) reflectivity* $\rho$ depends upon the wavelength-dependence of the incident flux and is defined as

$$\rho = \frac{\int_0^\infty \rho_\lambda q_{i,\lambda} \, d\lambda}{\int_0^\infty q_{i,\lambda} \, d\lambda} = \frac{\int_0^\infty \rho_\lambda q_{i,\lambda} \, d\lambda}{q_i} \quad (7\text{-}20)$$

Note that $\rho$, $\rho_\lambda$, and $\rho_\lambda(\theta, \phi, \theta', \phi')$ are weighting functions which can be thought of as probabilities that certain photons will be reflected. In particular, the reflection function is analogous to the probability that a photon in the wavelength interval $\lambda$ to $(\lambda + d\lambda)$ and having the incident direction $(\theta', \phi')$ will be reflected into the direction $(\theta, \phi)$.

Turning now to the process of absorption, we define a *monochromatic directional absorptivity* $\alpha_\lambda(\theta', \phi')$ as the fraction of the incident monochromatic intensity which is absorbed. Thus, we can write

$$\alpha_\lambda(\theta', \phi') = \frac{I_{i,\lambda}(\theta', \phi')_{\text{abs}}}{I_{i,\lambda}(\theta', \phi')} \quad (7\text{-}21)$$

Integrating this over all incoming directions, we arrive at the *monochromatic absorptivity* $\alpha_\lambda$. This is the fraction of the incident monochromatic flux which is absorbed. Thus,

$$\alpha_\lambda = \frac{\int_0^{2\pi}\int_0^{\pi/2} I_{i,\lambda}(\theta',\phi')\,\alpha_\lambda(\theta',\phi')\cos\theta'\sin\theta'\,d\theta'\,d\phi'}{q_{i,\lambda}} \qquad (7\text{-}22)$$

so that a *total (hemispherical) absorptivity* becomes

$$\alpha = \frac{\int_0^\infty \alpha_\lambda q_{i,\lambda}\,d\lambda}{\int_0^\infty q_{i,\lambda}\,d\lambda} \qquad (7\text{-}23)$$

Moving now to the process of emission, we first emphasize that absorptivities and reflectivities are defined in terms of the incoming fluxes and intensities, whereas emission is defined in terms of the fluxes and intensities emitted in relation to those of a blackbody. The two types of coefficients are quite independent, but under certain conditions, they can be numerically equated. Starting first with the *monochromatic directional emissivity* $\epsilon_\lambda(\theta,\phi)$, we define this emissivity as the ratio of the intensity emitted in the direction $(\theta,\phi)$ as compared to that emitted by a blackbody. Since blackbody radiation is independent of direction, then

$$\epsilon_\lambda(\theta,\phi) = \frac{I_{e,\lambda}(\theta,\phi)}{I_{b,\lambda}} \qquad (7\text{-}24)$$

The *monochromatic emittance* $\epsilon_\lambda$ is the ratio of the emitted monochromatic flux to that emitted by a blackbody. Hence,

$$\epsilon_\lambda = \frac{q_{e,\lambda}}{q_{e,b,\lambda}} = \frac{\int_0^{2\pi}\int_0^{\pi/2} I_{e,\lambda}(\theta,\phi)\cos\theta\sin\theta\,d\theta\,d\phi}{\pi I_{b,\lambda}} \qquad (7\text{-}25)$$

Thus, using Eq. (7-24) in Eq. (7-25), we have

$$\epsilon_\lambda = \frac{1}{\pi}\int_0^{2\pi}\int_0^{\pi/2}\epsilon_\lambda(\theta,\phi)\cos\theta\sin\theta\,d\theta\,d\phi \qquad (7\text{-}26)$$

The *total (hemispherical) emissivity* $\epsilon$ then is defined as the ratio of the emitted flux to that emitted by a blackbody:

$$\epsilon = \frac{\int_0^\infty q_{e,\lambda}\,d\lambda}{\int_0^\infty q_{e,b,\lambda}\,d\lambda} = \frac{\int_0^\infty \epsilon_\lambda q_{e,b,\lambda}\,d\lambda}{q_{e,b}} \qquad (7\text{-}27)$$

But $q_{e,b} = \sigma T^4$, so that

$$\epsilon = \frac{\int_0^\infty \epsilon_\lambda q_{e,b,\lambda}\, d\lambda}{\sigma T^4} = \frac{\int_0^\infty \left( \int_0^{2\pi} \int_0^{\pi/2} \epsilon_\lambda(\theta, \phi) \cos\theta \sin\theta\, d\theta\, d\phi \right) I_{b,\lambda}\, d\lambda}{\sigma T^4} \qquad (7\text{-}28)$$

## INTERRELATION OF SURFACE PROPERTIES

If we place a small body inside an isothermal cavity, the second law of thermodynamics requires that the incident monochromatic intensity absorbed be equal to the emitted monochromatic intensity. Consequently, when a principle of reciprocity of the reflection function is employed,[1] then when $\theta' = \theta$ and $\phi' = \phi$,

$$\alpha_\lambda(\theta, \phi) I_\lambda(\theta, \phi) = \epsilon_\lambda(\theta, \phi) I_{b,\lambda} \qquad (7\text{-}29)$$

But inside an isothermal cavity, $I_\lambda(\theta, \phi) = I_{b,\lambda}$, so that

$$\alpha_\lambda(\theta, \phi) = \epsilon_\lambda(\theta, \phi) \qquad (7\text{-}30)$$

If one removes the body from the cavity, none of the surface properties has changed. Thus, Eq. (7-30) is still true as long as the process of absorption does not depend upon the magnitude of the intensity. In general, then, the monochromatic directional absorptivity is equal to the monochromatic directional emissivity. This simple fact can be used in a number of special cases.

If we define a *diffuse surface*† as one whose optical properties are independent of direction, then $\alpha_\lambda(\theta', \phi')$ in Eq. (7-22) can be taken out of the integral, so that

$$\alpha_\lambda = \alpha_\lambda(\theta', \phi') = \text{a function of } \lambda \text{ only}$$

Similarly, Eq. (7-26) yields

$$\epsilon_\lambda = \epsilon_\lambda(\theta, \phi) = \text{a function of } \lambda \text{ only}$$

Therefore, from Eq. (7-30) we conclude that, for a diffuse surface, the monochromatic emissivity is equal to the monochromatic absorptivity.

We further define a *gray surface* as one where $\alpha_\lambda$ and $\epsilon_\lambda$ are independent of wavelength. Then from Eqs. (7-23) and (7-27), $\alpha_\lambda$ and $\epsilon_\lambda$ can be taken out of the integrals so that $\alpha = \alpha_\lambda = \epsilon_\lambda = \epsilon$. We can now state that, for a gray diffuse surface, the total emissivity is equal to the total absorptivity.

The last special case to be considered is the most often quoted and most often misused law in the field of radiation properties. It is *Kirchhoff's law*, which states:

> When a system is in thermal equilibrium with its surroundings, the ratio of its total emissive power $q_e$ to its absorptivity is equal to a constant which is the same for all systems at the same temperature.

---

† A diffuse surface should be understood to be one for which incident intensity from any direction is scattered uniformly from the surface, i.e., $\rho_\lambda(\theta, \phi, \theta', \phi') = \text{constant}$.

From this statement one can conclude that $\alpha = \epsilon$, since

$$q_e = \alpha q_b = \epsilon q_b$$

However, this is strictly true only at thermal equilibrium, which means that all of the temperatures (sink and source) are equal. This must not be confused with steady state, which occurs when the temperatures are no longer varying with time. The engineering literature is replete with a confusion of these terms.

Note that, under the various restrictive assumptions, the determination of the absorptivities from emissivity values implies that the various reflectivities can also be determined for an opaque surface, since $\rho$ is equal to $1 - \alpha$.

## DETERMINATION OF SURFACE PROPERTIES

The determination of radiative surface properties is essential to the prediction of radiative transfer. For pure homogeneous materials with optically smooth surfaces, these properties can be predicted from electromagnetic field theory. For engineering materials, however, these conditions are seldom met; as a result, we must rely heavily on experimental measurements. Since $\alpha_\lambda(\theta, \phi) = \epsilon_\lambda(\theta, \phi)$ under rather general circumstances, we can use the defining integrals to calculate the absorptivity for any spectrum and any angular distribution, as long as $\epsilon_\lambda(\theta, \phi)$ measurements are available. Even though such measurements are relatively straightforward, they are only beginning to appear in the literature. We are thus forced to make approximations, and the first one to consider is the assumption of a diffuse surface.

One almost classical set of data are measurements due to Schmidt and Eckert,[5] reproduced in Fig. 7-5. These data are plotted in terms of the elevation angle $\theta$ alone, since most materials are isotropic enough to neglect any azimuthal dependence $\phi$. The measurements were made on the total flux emitted into a given direction, so that

$$\epsilon_\theta = \int_0^\infty \epsilon_\lambda(\theta) I_{b,\lambda} \, d\lambda \tag{7-31}$$

Note that, for both classes of materials, the emissivity is fairly constant over $0 \leq \theta \leq 60°$ where the $\cos \theta$ takes on its largest values. Consequently, the assumption of a diffuse surface is reasonable† except when surfaces are viewed at large values of $\theta$ (i.e., grazing angles). This assumption is further justified if the roughnesses of the surface are large compared to the wavelengths of the flux being considered. For example, most formed surfaces have roughnesses at least

---

† This fact is often referred to as Lambert's cosine law since the flux from a surface will vary according to the cosine of the viewing angle, Eq. (7-3).

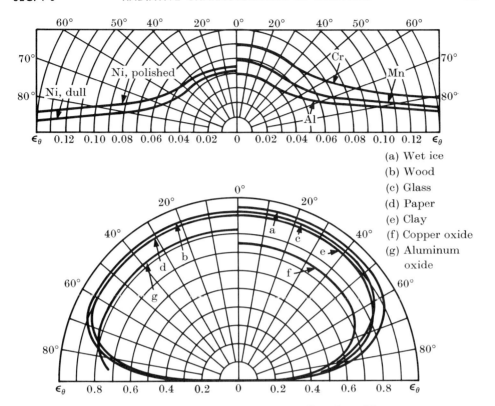

**Fig. 7-5** Emissivity of materials in different directions. The temperature of the radiating metal surfaces was approximately 149°C; that of the nonmetallic surfaces was between 0° and 93°C.[5]

of the order of 3 $\mu$m. Therefore, most surfaces will appear diffuse to thermal radiation shorter than 3 $\mu$m.

Next we wish to consider the assumption of a gray surface. This usually is not as well justified as the diffuse assumption—a fact illustrated by the curves of $\epsilon_\lambda$ for various surfaces in Fig. 7-6. The determination of $\epsilon$ from the data in Fig. 7-6 requires the evaluation of the integral indicated in Eq. (7-27). By comparison, the determination of $\alpha$ under the assumption of a diffuse surface can be carried out using $\epsilon_\lambda$ data in Eq. (7-23), together with the spectral distribution of the incident flux. Numerical techniques for the evaluation of these integrals using Laguerre quadrature are covered in texts on the subject.[1] However, a rough approximation can be quickly gained, if the source temperature is known, by referring to Fig. 7-3 or Wien's law [Eq. (7-12)] to determine the wavelength about which the main portion of the energy is located. This wavelength can be used in Fig. 7-6 to estimate the total absorptivity (or emissivity).

In Fig. 7-7 the total emissivities for several surface temperatures are listed

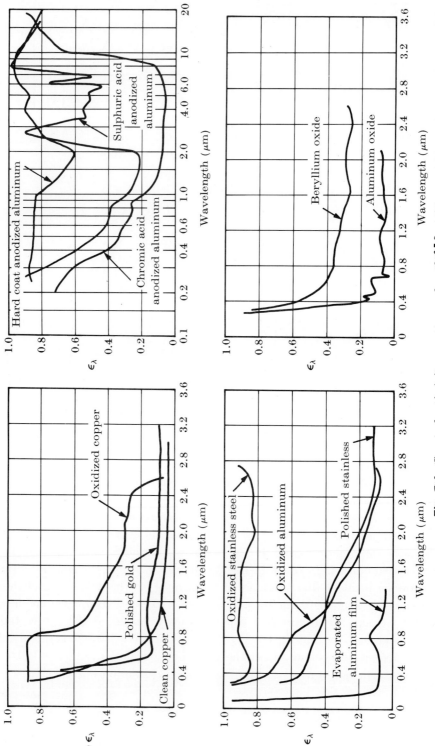

**Fig. 7-6** Spectral emissivity versus wavelength.[6,7,8]

| Material | Total emissivity, $\epsilon$ | | | Solar absorptivity |
| --- | --- | --- | --- | --- |
| | 38°C | 538°C | 1093°C | |
| Aluminum: | | | | |
|   Pure | 0.04 | 0.05 | — | 0.08–0.1 |
|   Alloy (clean) | 0.09 | 0.15–0.22 | — | 0.22 |
| Copper (electrolytic): | | | | |
|   Clean | 0.02–0.05 | 0.02–0.04 | — | 0.13–0.3 |
|   Rough | 0.07 | | — | 0.4–0.76 |
| Germanium | | 0.5 | — | |
| Gold | 0.01–0.022 | 0.018–0.035 | | 0.2 |
| Iron: | | | | |
|   Clean | 0.04 | 0.45 | 0.4 | 0.44–0.52 |
|   Rough | 0.4 | 0.55 | 0.9 | |
| Steel: | | | | |
|   Plain carbon (clean) | 0.1 | 0.20–0.35 | 0.3 | 0.2 |
|   Plain carbon (oxidized) | 0.66 | 0.98 | | |
|   Stainless (clean) | 0.16 | 0.28 | | 0.3–0.5 |
|   Stainless (oxidized) | 0.74 | 0.86 | 0.91 | 0.63 |
| Nickel: | | | | |
|   Clean | 0.04–0.08 | 0.09–0.13 | 0.18 | 0.37 |
|   Oxidized | 0.42 | 0.57 | | 0.79 |
| Platinum | 0.035 | 0.086 | 0.16 | 0.10–0.3 |
| Silver | 0.022 | 0.03 | — | |
| Beryllium oxide (white) | | 0.3 | 0.4 | 0.4–0.5 |
| Aluminum oxide | 0.8 | 0.56–0.66 | 0.35–0.5 | 0.2 |
| Glass | 0.88 | | — | |
| Paper | 0.89 | — | — | 0.28 |
| Plastic laminates | 0.8–0.83 | — | — | 0.44–0.81 |
| Teflon | 0.9 | — | — | |
| *Coatings* | | | | |
| Aluminum paint | | | | |
|   (Varying age and content) | 0.27–0.67 | | | 0.55 |
| Black anodized aluminum | 0.5 | | | |
| Oil paints | | | | |
|   (16 different colors) | 0.92–0.96 | — | — | — |
| White enamel ceramic | 0.156 | | 0.19–0.24 | 0.30 |
| White lacquer | 0.8–0.95 | — | — | 0.4 |
| White paint: | | | | |
|   ($MgCO_3$) | 0.96 | — | — | 0.15 |
|   ($PbCO_3$) | 0.89 | — | — | 0.12 |

**Fig. 7-7**  Emissivity and solar absorptivity for some common materials and coatings.

for the various materials where available.† If the temperature characterizing
the incident flux (the source temperature) is close to one of the emitter temperatures listed, then $\epsilon$ can be used as $\alpha$ by Kirchhoff's law. Obviously, however, the solar absorptivity listed could never be used as an emissivity, since
none of the materials listed could reach anything like 5600°K.

   The influence of the ratio of $\alpha/\epsilon$ on the energy balance for thin sheets of
material exposed to the sun can be seen by comparing the quasi-steady-state
temperatures for a number of surface coatings, as illustrated in Fig. 7-8 from
the data of Dunkle and Gier.[9] Note, particularly, the influence of the layer of
white paint.

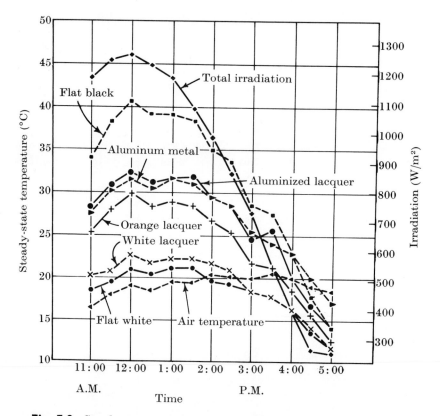

**Fig. 7-8**  Steady-state temperatures for different surfaces exposed to
the sun.

---

   † The difference between emissivity and absorptivity is emphasized when comparing
the room temperature $\epsilon$ to the solar absorptivity. Besides the materials listed in Fig.
7-7, a striking example is frost or snow; these substances have an emissivity of 0.985
(almost a blackbody) but a solar absorptivity of 0.035 (almost a perfect reflector).[2]

Since the optical properties depend on the surface conditions, the designer is cautioned to consider the values in Fig. 7-7 only as approximate for situations other than those under which the values were obtained. Also, dirt, oil films, and weathering can sometimes radically change a value of $\epsilon$ or $\alpha$. For such reasons, tests under laboratory conditions may not represent the situation in service. The final recourse is to good judgment and experience.

## 7-4. RADIATIVE EXCHANGE BETWEEN SURFACES

The net exchange of radiant thermal energy between surfaces having different optical properties and different temperatures can best be determined by considering that these surfaces form an enclosure. A particular type of two-dimensional enclosure is illustrated in Fig. 7-9, where the surfaces in exchange appear as edge views. An imaginary surface stretched across the opening completes the enclosure (control volume). If the flux across the imaginary surface is specified, then the net radiant transfer at any interior point of the enclosure can be determined as shown in the following paragraphs.

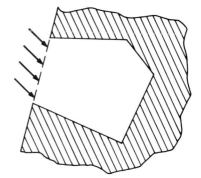

### FORMULATION OF THE GENERAL PROBLEM

Consider a control volume which could consist of surfaces with some temperature distribution $T(x, y)$, and with openings where

**Fig. 7-9** A two-dimensional enclosure.

the monochromatic intensity entering, $I_\lambda(x, y, \theta, \phi)$, is specified across the opening. The intensity at any point $(x, y)$ in the direction $(\theta, \phi)$ on the surface element $dA$ of the enclosure can be written in terms of an integral equation which equates

$$I_{\lambda,\text{leaving}} = I_{\lambda,\text{emitted}} + I_{\lambda,\text{reflected}}$$

Consequently, from Eqs. (7-17) and (7-24),

$$I_\lambda(x, y, \theta, \phi) = \epsilon_\lambda(x, y, \theta, \phi)I_{b,\lambda}[T(x, y)]$$

$$+ \frac{1}{\pi}\int_0^{2\pi}\int_0^{\pi/2} I_\lambda(x, y, \theta', \phi')\,\rho_\lambda(x, y, \theta, \phi, \theta', \phi')\cos\theta'\sin\theta'\,d\theta'\,d\phi' \quad (7\text{-}32)$$

Now, the incident intensity $I_\lambda(x, y, \theta', \phi')$ comes from some other position on the control volume $dA'$, which we can denote by the dummy variables $(\xi, \eta)$. (See Fig. 7-10.) The solid angle $d\omega' = \sin\theta'\,d\theta'\,d\phi'$ can be equated to an area

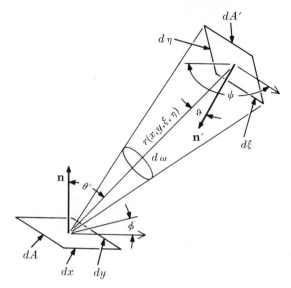

**Fig. 7-10**  Geometry for radiative exchange.

element $dA' = d\xi\, d\eta$ by

$$d\omega' = \frac{\cos\vartheta\, d\xi\, d\eta}{[r(x, y, \xi, \eta)]^2} \tag{7-33}$$

Using this in Eq. (7-32), we have

$$I_\lambda(x, y, \theta, \phi) = \epsilon_\lambda(x, y, \theta, \phi)I_{b,\lambda}[T(x, y)]$$

$$+ \frac{1}{\pi}\iint_{\substack{\text{area seen} \\ \text{from } dA}} \frac{I_\lambda(\xi, \eta, \vartheta, \psi)\, \rho_\lambda(x, y, \theta, \phi, \theta', \phi')\cos\theta'\cos\vartheta}{[r(x, y, \xi, \eta)]^2}\, d\xi\, d\eta \tag{7-34}$$

Here the limits of the integral are such as to include the part of the enclosure which one could see from $dA$ directly, since any blocked area does not contribute to the direct exchange. Assume that the angles $\theta'$ and $\phi'$ are functionally related to $(\xi, \eta)$ and to the angles $\psi$ and $\vartheta$. Then Eq. (7-34) can be solved, at least conceptually, for the intensity at every point $(x, y)$ within the control volume—provided the quantities $\epsilon_\lambda(x, y, \theta, \phi)$, $T(x, y)$, and $\rho_\lambda(x, y, \theta, \phi, \theta', \phi')$ and the shape of the enclosure are specified. Such an equation, called a linear integral equation of the second kind, is too complex to treat in general; therefore, a number of simplifying assumptions will be necessary.

### THE LUMPED SYSTEM OF GRAY DIFFUSE SURFACES

Considerable simplification is gained if we first assume diffuse surfaces. This means that the optical properties are independent of the directions $(\theta, \phi)$. Consequently, the reflection function becomes $\rho_\lambda$. Furthermore, we define the *monochromatic radiosity*, $R_\lambda$, as the monochromatic flux leaving a surface:

$$R_\lambda = \int_{\omega=2\pi} I_\lambda(\theta, \phi) \cos\theta \, d\omega \tag{7-35}$$

Then for a diffuse surface

$$R_\lambda = \pi I_\lambda \tag{7-36}$$

If we now integrate the radiative exchange equation [Eq. (7-34)] over all the outgoing directions—i.e., $\omega = 2\pi$ under the preceding conditions for a diffuse surface—we have

$$R_\lambda(x, y) = \epsilon_\lambda(x, y)\pi I_{b,\lambda}[T(x, y)] + \frac{\rho_\lambda(x, y)}{\pi} \iint_{\substack{\text{area seen} \\ \text{from } dA}} R_\lambda(\xi, \eta) \frac{\cos\theta' \cos\vartheta}{[r(x, y, \xi, \eta)]^2} \, d\xi \, d\eta \tag{7-37}$$

Suppose that the interior surface of our enclosure can be divided into a number of finite areas $A_i$, across which $T_i$, $\rho_{\lambda,i}$, and $R_{\lambda,i}$ do not vary strongly. Then the integral of Eq. (7-37) becomes a summation over the $n$ finite area elements. Furthermore, integrating Eq. (7-37) over the $i$th area element, we have

$$\iint_{A_i} R_{\lambda,i}(x, y) \, dA_i = \iint_{A_i} \epsilon_{\lambda,i}(x, y)\pi I_{b,\lambda}[T_i(x, y)] \, dA_i$$

$$+ \iint_{A_i} \frac{\rho_{\lambda,i}(x, y)}{\pi} \sum_{j=1}^{n} \iint_{A_j} R_{\lambda,j}(x, y) \frac{\cos\theta_i' \cos\vartheta_j}{(r_{ij})^2} \, dA_j \, A_i \tag{7-38}$$

We now interpret $R_{\lambda,i}$, $\epsilon_{\lambda,i}$, $\rho_{\lambda,i}$, and $R_{\lambda,j}$ as the averages defined by the above indicated integrals for the respective area elements. Then on dividing by $A_i$, Eq. (7-38) becomes

$$R_{\lambda,i} = \epsilon_{\lambda,i}\pi I_{b,\lambda}(T_i) + \frac{\rho_{\lambda,i}}{\pi} \sum_{j=1}^{n} R_{\lambda,j} \frac{1}{A_i} \iint_{A_i} \iint_{A_j} \frac{\cos\theta_i' \cos\vartheta_j}{(r_{ij})^2} \, dA_j \, dA_i \tag{7-39}$$

Noting that the last term is simply geometrical, we define the *configuration factor*

$$F_{ij} = \frac{1}{A_i} \iint_{A_i} \iint_{A_j} \frac{\cos\theta_i' \cos\vartheta_j}{\pi(r_{ij})^2} \, dA_j \, dA_i \tag{7-40}$$

This is alternatively called the angle factor, shape factor, or view factor, and it can be defined as

$F_{ij}$ = the fraction of diffuse energy leaving a uniform surface $A_i$ that is directly incident on the surface $A_j$.

Using Eq. (7-40) in Eq. (7-39), we arrive at a set of $n$ simultaneous linear algebraic equations. These equations can be solved by matrix techniques once the $F_{ij}$ are known

$$R_{\lambda,i} = \epsilon_{\lambda,i}\pi I_{b,\lambda}(T_i) + \rho_{\lambda,i} \sum_{j=1}^{n} R_{\lambda,j} F_{ij} \tag{7-41}$$

The number of area elements into which the enclosure is divided can be made large enough so that the uniform assumption is satisfied, and the majority of surfaces encountered in equipment design are, for practical purposes, diffuse. For these reasons, Eq. (7-41) can be a rather accurate description of the radiative transfer. However, the next assumption is strictly valid only for surfaces where $\epsilon_\lambda$ is a constant with wavelength, i.e., the assumption of gray surfaces. But this can be an acceptable approximation if the various temperatures in the enclosure and the temperature characterizing the radiation entering an opening are not too widely different. How much is "widely" depends upon the variation of $\epsilon_\lambda$ with wavelength.

Applying the gray surfaces assumption to Eq. (7-41), we have†

$$R_i = \epsilon_i \sigma T_i^4 + \rho_i \sum_{j=1}^{n} R_j F_{ij} \qquad (7\text{-}42)$$

Equation (7-42) tells us that the flux leaving the surface $A_i$ is equal to the emitted flux plus the reflected portion of the incident flux from all the area $A_j$. The incident flux is, of course,

$$\sum_{j=1}^{n} R_j F_{ij}$$

Consequently, the net heat transfer is

$$q_{\text{net},i} = R_i - \sum_{j=1}^{n} R_j F_{ij} \qquad (7\text{-}43)$$

Thus, using Eq. (7-42) in Eq. (7-43), and using the fact that for a gray diffuse surface $\epsilon_i = \alpha_i = 1 - \rho_i$, we have

$$q_{\text{net},i} = \frac{\epsilon_i}{1 - \epsilon_i} (\sigma T_i^4 - R_i) \qquad (7\text{-}44)$$

## DETERMINATION OF CONFIGURATION FACTORS

We have found from the preceding development that the net radiative heat transfer (flux) at a surface depends upon the geometrical factor $F_{ij}$. This factor, as defined by Eq. (7-40), can be found from direct integration[1,2,5] or by photographic and mechanical integrator techniques.[1,2,5] Published values, some of which are reproduced in Fig. 7-13, are available in most heat transfer

---

† This could also have been written, perhaps more clearly, on an energy basis as

$$A_i R_i = A_i \epsilon_i \sigma T_i^4 + \rho_i \sum_{j=1}^{n} R_j A_j F_{ji}$$

texts, the best source being Jakob,[2] Vol. 2. The use of these published values, however, is greatly facilitated through some algebraic characteristics of $F_{ij}$.

1. Reciprocal relation:
From the definition of Eq. (7-40)

$$A_i F_{ij} = \iint_{A_i} \iint_{A_j} \frac{\cos \theta_i' \cos \vartheta_j}{\pi r_{ij}^2} \, dA_j \, dA_i = A_j F_{ji} \qquad (7\text{-}45)$$

2. Summation rule:
Since $F_{ij}$ is the fraction of the energy leaving $i$ which reaches $j$ directly, then

$$\sum_{j=1}^{n} F_{ij} = 1 \qquad (7\text{-}46)$$

3. Decomposition rule:
Consider an area which can be divided into an area 3 and an area 4. Then,

$$F_{1(3,4)} = F_{13} + F_{14}$$

so that

$$F_{14} = F_{1(3,4)} - F_{13} \qquad (7\text{-}47)$$

Many problems can be treated as two-dimensional problems if the configuration is symmetric with respect to an axis perpendicular to the uniform cross section. The configuration factor can be determined simply from a technique, developed by Hottel,[10] called the method of crossed and uncrossed strings. Consider a cavity, as in Fig. 7-11, in the form of a generalized cylinder having the area 1 exchanging energy with the area 2. To find $F_{12}$, we stretch the "strings" joining the extremities of 1 with 2. These strings will curve around any convexities such as the

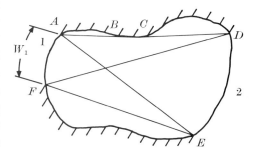

**Fig. 7-11**   Method of crossed and uncrossed strings.

strip $BC$. In this illustration, two of the strings are crossed and two are uncrossed. Hottel has shown[10] that the length of the "strings" can be used to determine $F_{12}$, as

$$W_1 F_{12} = \frac{(FD + AE) - (AD + FE)}{2} \qquad (7\text{-}48)$$

Thus, $F_{ij}$ is equal to the sum of the crossed string lengths minus the sum of the uncrossed string lengths, divided by twice the width of the $i$th region.

One simple but useful result from integrating Eq. (7-40) is the configuration

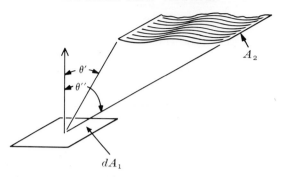

**Fig. 7-12**  Geometry for exchange between element $dA_1$ and a portion of a cylinder.

factor between a small area (differential element) $dA$ and a portion of the aforementioned generalized cylinder, i.e., an area generated by an infinite line moving parallel to itself. The result, stated here without proof[2] for the configuration illustrated in Fig. 7-12 is:

$$F_{(d1)2} = \frac{\sin \theta' - \sin \theta''}{2} \tag{7-49}$$

This result has been used to solve a number of situations without the lumped system assumptions.

Configuration factors for other useful geometries are shown in Fig. 7-13. The use of these is demonstrated in Example 7.1.

### ENCLOSURES CONSISTING OF TWO ZONES

In a large number of physical design problems, the enclosure in which a radiative exchange is taking place can be approximated as two regions: $A_1$ acting as a source (or sink) and $A_2$ acting as the sink (or source), as illustrated in Fig. 7-14. We wish to show that the net flux at the surface 1 in exchange with 2 can be expressed as

$$q_{net,1} = F_{a\epsilon} \sigma (T_1^4 - T_2^4) \tag{7-50}$$

The radiosities for the two-zone system are given by Eq. (7-42) as

$$R_1 = \epsilon_1 \sigma T_1^4 + \rho_1 (R_1 F_{11} + R_2 F_{12}) \tag{7-51a}$$

$$R_2 = \epsilon_2 \sigma T_2^4 + \rho_2 (R_1 F_{21} + R_2 F_{22}) \tag{7-51b}$$

In these equations, we solve for $\sigma T^4$ after eliminating $F_{21}$, $F_{11}$, and $F_{22}$ by the summation and reciprocity rules. We now have

$$\sigma T_1^4 = \frac{(1 - \rho_1)}{\epsilon_1} R_1 + \frac{\rho_1 F_{12}}{\epsilon_1} (R_1 - R_2) \tag{7-52a}$$

$$\sigma T_2^4 = \frac{(1 - \rho_2)}{\epsilon_2} R_2 - \frac{\rho_2 A_1 F_{12}}{\epsilon_2 A_2} (R_1 - R_2) \tag{7-52b}$$

Now from Eq. (7-43), the net flux at 1 is given by

$$q_{\text{net},1} = R_1 - (R_1 F_{11} + R_2 F_{12}) = R_1(1 - F_{11}) - F_{12}R_2$$

But by the summation rule of Eq. (7-46), $1 - F_{11} = F_{12}$, so that

$$q_{\text{net},1} = F_{12}(R_1 - R_2) \tag{7-53}$$

Subtracting Eq. (7-52b) from Eq. (7-52a), we have

$$\sigma(T_1^4 - T_2^4) = \frac{(1 - \rho_1)}{\epsilon_1} R_1 - \frac{(1 - \rho_2)}{\epsilon_2} R_2$$

$$+ \frac{\rho_1 F_{12}}{\epsilon_1} (R_1 - R_2) + \frac{\rho_2 F_{12} A_1}{\epsilon_2 A_2} (R_1 - R_2) \tag{7-54}$$

Comparing Eq. (7-50) with Eq. (7-53) and using Eq. (7-54) for gray diffuse surfaces, where $1 - \rho_1 = \alpha_1 = \epsilon_1$, etc., we have

$$F_{a\epsilon} = \frac{1}{1/F_{12} + \rho_1/\epsilon_1 + \rho_2 A_1/\epsilon_2 A_2} \tag{7-55}$$

Of particular interest is the case of a small body 1 completely enclosed by a large body 2. If body 1 has no negative curvature, then $F_{12} = 1$, and if $\rho_2 A_1/\epsilon_2 A_2 \ll 1$, Eq. (7-55) yields

$$F_{a\epsilon} = \epsilon_1 \qquad \begin{array}{l} \text{small body 1 completely} \\ \text{enclosed by 2} \end{array} \tag{7-56}$$

It can readily be shown that Eq. (7-55) also reduces to

$$F_{a\epsilon} = \frac{1}{(1/\epsilon_1) + (1/\epsilon_2) - 1} \qquad \begin{array}{l} \text{large body 1 completely} \\ \text{enclosed by 2} \end{array} \tag{7-57}$$

$$F_{a\epsilon} = \frac{1}{(1/\epsilon_1) + (1/\epsilon_2) - 1} \qquad \text{infinite parallel planes} \tag{7-58}$$

It must be emphasized that the net heat transfer from a surface 1 is given by Eq. (7-50) only for the case of an enclosure divided into two zones. A number of texts use this form to evaluate the net exchange between 1 and 2 as an approximation, even if other participating areas are present. Since serious errors could result, the designer is cautioned against using Eq. (7-50) for any configuration other than ones which at least approximate two-zone enclosures.

Furthermore, if the two-zone approximation is applicable, then for sufficiently small temperature differences, Eq. (7-50) can be linearized in terms of a heat transfer coefficient. Note that

$$T_1^4 - T_2^4 = (T_1^3 + T_1^2 T_2 + T_1 T_2^2 + T_2^3)(T_1 - T_2)$$

$$\approx (4T_2^3)(T_1 - T_2) \tag{7-59}$$

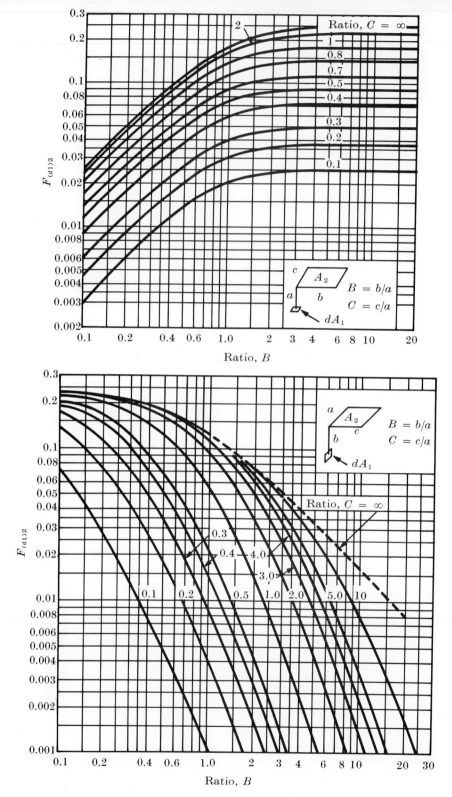

**Fig. 7-13(a)**   Configuration factors for various geometries as indicated.[2]

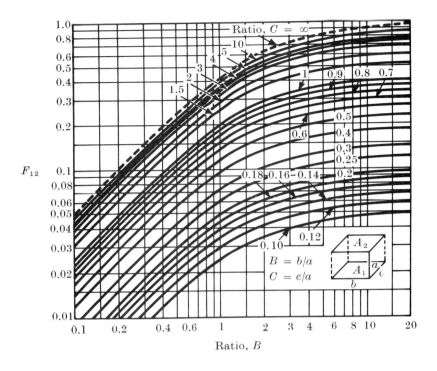

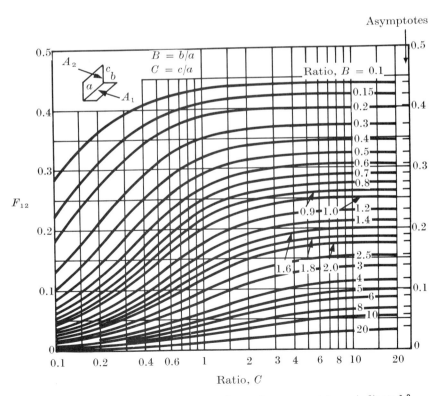

**Fig. 7-13(b)** Configuration factors for various geometries as indicated.[2]

Then Eq. (7-50) yields a radiative heat transfer coefficient

$$h_r = 4F_{a\epsilon}\sigma T_2^3 \qquad (7\text{-}60)$$

which can be used in the same manner as the convective coefficient of Chapter 6. Thus, the two coefficients, treated as conductances, are added.

## ENCLOSURES WITH SPECULARLY REFLECTING SURFACES

Surfaces which appear smooth to the wavelengths of the incident flux are called *specularly†* *reflecting surfaces* in that the angle of incidence is equal to the angle of reflection. At sufficiently low temperatures, for example, what appears to be a diffuse surface for optical radiation may act as a specular surface. For such cases, the preceding discussion of diffuse surfaces is generally not applicable. However, a number of cases applicable to specular surfaces have been solved by considering an accounting of the fractions absorbed as a ray is multireflected.

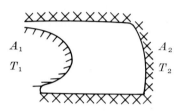

**Fig. 7-14**  A two-zone problem.

For infinite parallel plates, coaxial cylinders, and concentric spheres which reflect diffusely or specularly (except in the latter cases where the outer sphere and outer cylinder reflect diffusely), the relation known as Christiansen's equation[2] can be used to predict $F_{a\epsilon}$ of Eq. (7-50)

$$F_{a\epsilon} = \frac{\epsilon_1}{1 + \epsilon_1(1/\epsilon_2 - 1)(A_1/A_2)} \qquad (7\text{-}61)$$

A number of other specular effects of surfaces have been discussed in the literature. One of the more significant of these, which also considered the wavelength dependence of emissivity, is the evaluation due to Holt, et al.,[11] for parallel plates of high electrical conductivity and temperatures corresponding to the infrared region.‡ All of these specular studies are limited to cases where $T_1$ and $T_2$ are nearly equal, so that Kirchhoff's law allows the equating of emissivity to absorptivity.

> **Example 7.1.** Consider a fin similar to that illustrated in Fig. 6-27 and sketched here in Fig. 7-15. We wish to calculate the net radiant heat transfer from the surfaces of the fin operating at 313°K to the walls of a room at 298°K. We will assume the surfaces are diffuse and, since the temperature differences are small, we will also assume that they are gray.

---

† This is not to be confused with the word *spectral*, a synonym for monochromatic.

‡ As in Eq. (7-13), this really means that $(\sigma/\omega\epsilon)^2 \gg 1$, but for different reasons.[4]

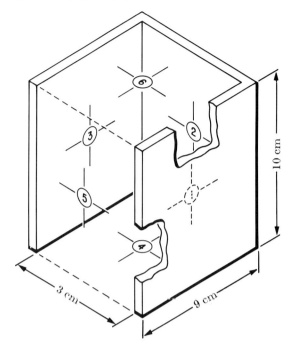

**Fig. 7-15**  Fin notation for radiation.

Consider first the exterior surfaces of the two fins (9 cm × 10 cm). These surfaces act as a small body completely enclosed by the room, i.e., for $\omega = 2\pi$ each surface sees nothing but the room. Consequently, Eq. (7-50) is applicable and $F_{a\epsilon} = \epsilon_f$, so that

$$q_{\text{net},f} = \epsilon_f \sigma (T_f^4 - T_r^4) = \epsilon_f (5.67 \times 10^{-8})(313^4 - 298^4)$$
$$= 97.1 \, \epsilon_f \, \text{W}/\text{m}^2$$

where the subscript $f$ means fin and $r$ means room. Now the total heat flow is

$$q_{\text{net},f} A_f = 97.1 \, \epsilon_f (2)(9 \times 10)$$
$$= 1.75 \, \epsilon_f \, \text{W}$$

Consider now the interior and note that there are six zones as indicated in Fig. 7-15. Zones 1, 2, and 3 are fin surfaces, while 4, 5, and 6 are imaginary surfaces stretched across the openings. Recall Eq. (7-42) for the radiosity of the $i$th surface

$$R_i = \epsilon_i \sigma T_i^4 + \rho_i \sum_{j=1}^{n} R_j F_{ij} \qquad (i = 1, 2, 3, 4, 5, 6)$$

We first reason that, since the room is large compared to the fin, none of the radiation leaving the fin and reaching the room will ever return.† Thus, $\rho_i = 0$ for $i = 4, 5, 6$ even though the flux emitted from the room walls is still limited

---

† Actually, the requirement is roughly $\rho_r A_f / \epsilon_r A_r \ll 1$.

by $\epsilon_r$. For $T_i = T_r$ and $\epsilon_i = \epsilon_r$, Eq. (7-42) then gives

$$R_4 = R_5 = R_6 = \epsilon_r \sigma T_r^4$$

Since the fin surfaces, $i = 1, 2, 3$, are all of the same material and flat, $F_{ij} = 0$, $i = j = 1, 2, 3$, and $\epsilon_i = \epsilon_f$, $\rho_i = \rho_f$, $T_i = T_f$, $i = 1, 2, 3$. Consequently, the remaining three equations become

$$R_1 = \epsilon_f \sigma T_f^4 + \rho_f[R_2 F_{12} + R_3 F_{13} + \epsilon_r \sigma T_r^4(F_{14} + F_{15} + F_{16})]$$

$$R_2 = \epsilon_f \sigma T_f^4 + \rho_f[R_1 F_{21} + R_3 F_{23} + \epsilon_r \sigma T_r^4(F_{24} + F_{25} + F_{26})]$$

$$R_3 = \epsilon_f \sigma T_f^4 + \rho_f[R_1 F_{31} + R_2 F_{32} + \epsilon_r \sigma T_r^4(F_{34} + F_{35} + F_{36})]$$

We need not explicitly determine all fifteen of the $F_{ij}$ in the equations. In fact, we need to evaluate only three of them. First, by symmetry, we see that

$$F_{21} = F_{23}$$

$$F_{24} = F_{26}$$

$$F_{32} = F_{12} = F_{15} = F_{35}$$

$$F_{34} = F_{14} = F_{16} = F_{36}$$

By reciprocity,

$$A_2 F_{21} = A_1 F_{12}; \qquad A_2 F_{23} = A_3 F_{32}; \qquad F_{13} = F_{31}$$

Finally, applying the summation rule and noting that $F_{11} = F_{22} = 0$,

$$F_{12} + F_{13} + F_{14} + F_{15} + F_{16} = 1$$

$$\therefore \quad F_{13} = 1 - 2F_{14} - 2F_{12}$$

$$F_{21} + F_{23} + F_{24} + F_{25} + F_{26} = 1$$

$$\therefore \quad 2F_{24} = 1 - F_{25} - 2F_{21}$$

By inspecting these equations, we see that once $F_{12}$, $F_{14}$, and $F_{25}$ are known, all of the other $F_{ij}$ can be determined.

From Fig. 7-13,

$$F_{12}(B = \tfrac{9}{10}, C = \tfrac{3}{10}) = 0.12$$

$$F_{14}(B = \tfrac{10}{9}, C = \tfrac{3}{9}) = 0.105$$

$$F_{25}(B = \tfrac{3}{9}, C = \tfrac{10}{9}) = 0.09$$

so that a table of $F_{ij}$ becomes

| $i$ \ $j$ | 1 | 2 | 3 | 4 | 5 | 6 |
|---|---|---|---|---|---|---|
| 1 | 0 | 0.12 | 0.55 | 0.105 | 0.12 | 0.105 |
| 2 | 0.36 | 0 | 0.36 | 0.095 | 0.09 | 0.095 |
| 3 | 0.55 | 0.12 | 0 | 0.105 | 0.12 | 0.105 |

Using these values, we have

$$R_1 = \epsilon_f \sigma T_f^4 + \rho_f(0.12 R_2 + 0.55 R_3 + 0.33 \epsilon_r \sigma T_r^4)$$

$$R_2 = \epsilon_f \sigma T_f^4 + \rho_f(0.36 R_1 + 0.36 R_3 + 0.28 \epsilon_r \sigma T_r^4)$$

$$R_3 = \epsilon_f \sigma T_f^4 + \rho_f(0.55 R_1 + 0.12 R_2 + 0.33 \epsilon_r \sigma T_r^4)$$

Note that $R_1 = R_3$ since the first and third equations are identical. Therefore,

$$R_2 = \epsilon_f \sigma T_f^4 + 0.72 \rho_f R_1 + 0.28 \epsilon_r \rho_f \sigma T_r^4$$

Using this expression in the relationship given for $R_1$ above, we have

$$R_1 = \frac{\epsilon_f \sigma T_f^4(1 + 0.12\rho_f) + \epsilon_r \sigma T_r^4(0.33\rho_f + 0.0336\rho_f^2)}{(1 - 0.55\rho_f - 0.0863\rho_f^2)}$$

Recalling Eq. (7-43), the net radiant heat flux for this geometry becomes

$$q_{\text{net},i} = R_i - \sum_{j=1}^{n} R_j F_{ij}$$

$$q_{\text{net},1} = R_1 - [R_2 F_{12} + R_1 F_{13} + R_4(F_{14} + F_{15} + F_{16})]$$

$$q_{\text{net},1} = 0.45 R_1 - 0.12 R_2 - 0.33 R_4 = q_{\text{net},3}$$

$$q_{\text{net},2} = R_2 - 0.72 R_1 - 0.28 R_4$$

If the equations for $R_1$ and $R_2$ are evaluated for various fin and room emissivities and reflectivities, the net radiant heat flow for the fin can be calculated. A case of a bare aluminum fin and a fin painted white are considered below for $\epsilon_r = 0.95$. Note that the radiant heat flow for the white fin is almost the same as the convective heat transfer calculated in Example 6.2.

|  | Bare aluminum | Painted white |
|---|---|---|
| $\epsilon_f$ | 0.09 | 0.9 |
| $\rho_f$ | 0.91 | 0.1 |
| $R_1 = R_3$ | $0.233\sigma T_f^4 + 0.728\sigma T_f^4$ | $0.965\sigma T_f^4 + 0.0335\sigma T_r^4$ |
| $R_2$ | $0.243\sigma T_f^4 + 0.719\sigma T_r^4$ | $0.969\sigma T_f^4 + 0.029\sigma T_r^4$ |
| $R_4 = R_5 = R_6$ | $0.95\sigma T_r^4$ | $0.95\sigma T_r^4$ |
| $q_{\text{net},1} = q_{\text{net},3}$ | $0.0757\sigma T_f^4 - 0.072\sigma T_r^4$ | $0.318\sigma T_f^4 - 0.302\sigma T_r^4$ |
| $q_{\text{net},2}$ | $0.075\sigma T_f^4 - 0.071\sigma T_r^4$ | $0.274\sigma T_f^4 - 0.261\sigma T_r^4$ |
| $(qA)_{\text{interior}}$ | 0.14 W | 0.60 W |
| $(qA)_{\text{total}}$ | 0.30 W | 2.17 W |

## 7-5. SUMMARY OF THERMAL RADIATION

Thermal radiation is electromagnetic in nature and of such short wavelengths that the processes of emission and absorption can be considered, for most materials, as a surface phenomenon. This has allowed us to define a set of optical properties in terms of which the radiative exchange within enclosures can be written [Eq. (7-34)]. Under the simplifying assumption of gray diffuse surfaces, the net radiant heat flux on a given area inside a zoned enclosure can be readily determined through the solution of a set of linear algebraic equations [Eqs. (7-42) and (7-43)].

The net radiant transfer is a strong function of the optical properties which, in turn, are strongly dependent on the surface conditions of a given material and on how that surface appears to the spectral distribution of the incident radiation. However, the assumption of gray diffuse surfaces is applicable for most electronic design problems encountered, except for situations involving exposure to high temperature sources such as the sun, and for situations involving very low temperatures.

## REFERENCES

1. Love, T. J., *Radiative Heat Transfer*, Columbus, Ohio, Charles E. Merrill Books, Inc., 1968. An outstanding text on radiative heat transfer.

2. Jakob, M., *Heat Transfer*, Vol. I and II, New York, John Wiley & Sons, Inc., 1957. Figure 7-13 by permission.

3. French, A. P., *Principles of Modern Physics*, New York, John Wiley & Sons, Inc., 1958. An easy-to-read description of modern physics and the physics of radiation.

4. Stratton, J. A., *Electromagnetic Theory*, New York, McGraw-Hill Book Co., 1941. Of interest here as a comprehensive treatment of electromagnetic waves at interfaces.

5. Eckert, E. R. G., and R. M. Drake, *Heat and Mass Transfer*, New York, McGraw-Hill Book Co., 1959. Figure 7-5 by permission.

6. Goldsmith, A., H. J. Hirschhorn, and T. E. Waterman, "Thermophysical Properties of Solid Materials," Vol. I–V, Armour Research Foundation, *WADC TR 58-476*, Nov., 1960.

7. Richmond, J. C., editor, "Measurement of Thermal Radiation Properties of Solids," *NASA SP-31*, Washington, D. C., 1963.

8. Katzoff, S., editor, "Symposium on Thermal Radiation of Solids," *NASA SP-55*, Washington, D. C., 1965.

9. Kreith, F., *Principles of Heat Transfer*, Scranton, Pa., International Textbook Co., 1958.

10. McAdams, W. H., *Heat Transmission*, New York, McGraw-Hill Book Co., 1954. Figure 7-3 by permission.

11. Holt, V. E., R. J. Grosh, and R. Geynet, "Evaluation of Net Radiant Heat Transfer Between Specularly Reflecting Plates," *Bell System Technical Journal*, **41**, Nov., 1962.

*Chapter 8*

# THERMAL DESIGN AND EVALUATION

L. W. Dickey and C. A. Fritsch

Heat transfer considerations must proceed in parallel with the other aspects of design. For this reason, the first treatment of the thermal characteristics of preliminary circuit and package configurations need not be as precise as later descriptions. In fact, expedient assumptions may be necessary to gain an answer (with a certain degree of confidence) that will serve as a useful input in circuit and physical design modifications on the time scale required for the development.

The thermal design of a system, based on thermal analysis and data gathered from experimental measurements on parts of the system, will usually be confirmed by an experimental evaluation of the completed system. It must be emphasized, however, that experimental evaluation by itself is not recommended because it usually cannot be made until the design is final, and it is then too late to make changes other than those necessary to avert a catastrophe.

The approach to thermal design of electronic systems presented here is based on the fundamental concepts of heat transfer developed in the previous chapters. An analysis of a typical electronic unit is illustrated, followed by a survey of techniques in temperature measurement and thermal evaluation.

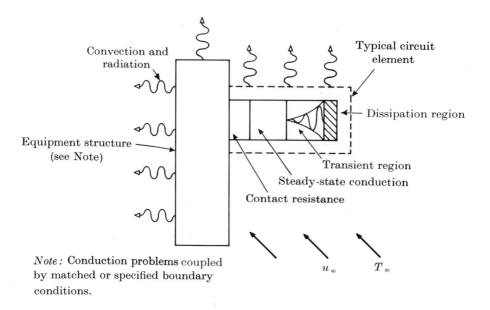

*Note:* Conduction problems coupled by matched or specified boundary conditions.

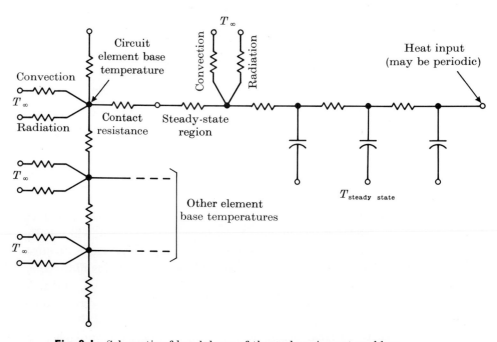

**Fig. 8-1**  Schematic of breakdown of thermal equipment problem.

## 8-1. PROBLEM DEFINITION

The thermal aspects of a typical equipment design problem can best be understood (at least in the initial stages) by dividing the problem into regions where specialized but generally different assumptions can be made. These regions then are coupled and interconnected through specified or matched boundary conditions. Such a division is illustrated in Fig. 8-1 in the form of a block diagram of the regions and an overall electrical analog.

In conjunction with the separation of a complex system into smaller regions where simpler subsystems can be considered, the division of the heat transfer into three modes separates these regions into two classes. These two classes, as previously noted, are the internal and the external problems. The internal problem deals with regions in pure conduction having boundary conditions which couple it to the external problem. In the external problem, convection and radiation may also occur. Sources of internal heat must lose that heat through conduction paths having various thermal resistances. The heat is lost to such sinks as room air, air or other fluids mechanically circulated, a heat exchanger or refrigeration system (including what is often referred to as a "cold plate"), and environment boundaries (e.g., room walls) which can accept radiation.

Defining the problem in this manner requires a flow of information. The information starts with certain prescribed input conditions and estimated temperatures for evaluating boundary conditions of the internal problem, and it leads to predictions of the various temperatures throughout the system. This flow of information requires feedback for an iterative estimate of the coefficients

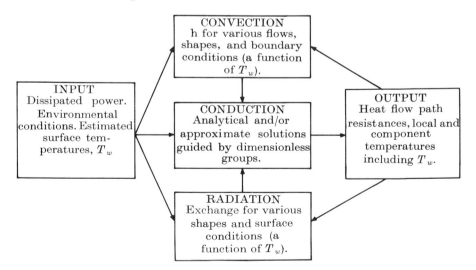

**Fig. 8-2**   Flow of information for solution of complex thermal problems.

that couple the two classes of problems. Such a process is illustrated in the block diagram, Fig. 8-2. This approach is demonstrated in the thermal analysis presented next.

## 8-2. THERMAL ANALYSIS APPLIED TO THE DESIGN OF A TYPICAL UNIT

The thermal design problem formulated here is intended to illustrate the method of approach just outlined. The analysis is based on information available to the physical designer in the initial stages of design. This includes an estimate of the circuits required, an estimate of the component heat dissipation, and a tentative description of the overall configuration. This treatment demonstrates the type of analysis one might perform. Detailed computations have been avoided where they are repetitive or where they do not contribute to an understanding of the problem.

### GENERAL DESCRIPTION

An electronic switching system will be considered. This system shows typical complex geometries and interspersed thermal paths that are often found in electronic equipment. The system has the following characteristics:

1. The switching functions required of a typical customer-premise telephone business installation will be performed. Each unit of the system, as shown in Fig. 8-3, is capable of handling up to 60 station lines or extensions for light traffic, or 45 lines for heavy traffic.
2. Thin-film circuits and discrete circuit elements or components will be mounted on approximately 100 printed wire boards. The boards will be inserted side-by-side into five horizontal rows of card carriers. The card carriers are individually hinged to the cabinet frame.
3. The unit should be attractive in external design and have overall dimensions† identical to those of a commercial office filing cabinet so that installation in a customer's office space is possible.

The thermal specifications are:

1. Ambient temperature may be 24°C but not more than 49°C.
2. Total heat dissipation will be 500 W or about 5 W per board.
3. Component case temperatures must not exceed 65°C.
4. Preferred method of cooling is by free (natural) convection since maintenance requirements and noise limitations make the use of a fan or blower undesirable.

---

† See Fig. 8-3. Other dimensions are introduced throughout the section as they are needed.

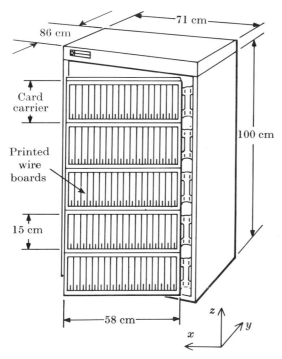

**Fig. 8-3** Equipment cabinet (front cover removed).

This unit of electronic equipment can be considered on three different geometric scales corresponding to the physical dimensions of the problem. On the largest scale, we have heat transfer from the cabinet to the ambient cooling air. On smaller scales, we have the thermal aspects of the card carrier and the printed wire board. Finally, we have the components whose thermal behavior will be the true measure of the effectiveness of the proposed cooling method.

We first evaluate the maximum heat transfer for a given temperature difference from the equipment cabinet, which we assume to be isothermal. To determine the convective transfer from the vertical cabinet surfaces, we must compute $N_{Gr} \cdot N_{Pr}$ to establish the type of flow (laminar or turbulent). For an estimated temperature difference $(T_w - T_\infty)$ of 14°C, $N_{Gr} = 4 \times 10^9$ and $N_{Pr} = 0.72$, so that $N_{Gr} \cdot N_{Pr} > 10^9$. Consequently, the flow is turbulent and $h$ is calculated from Eq. (6-98), so that

$$h = 1.31(T_w - T_\infty)^{1/3} = 3.16 \text{ W/m}^2 \cdot °\text{C} \qquad (8\text{-}1)$$

For this small temperature difference, the radiative transfer can be estimated from Eq. (7-60) where $F_{a\epsilon} = \epsilon$ since the cabinet acts as a small body inside a large room at, say, $T_\infty = 38°\text{C} + 273 = 311°\text{K}$. Thus, if $\epsilon = 0.96$, which is a typical value for a painted surface,

$$h_r = 4\epsilon\sigma T_\infty^3 = 6.53 \text{ W/m}^2 \cdot {}^\circ\text{C} \tag{8-2}$$

Therefore, the total effective heat transfer coefficient is $6.53 + 3.16 = 9.69$.

Note that the back of the cabinet will not contribute to the heat losses since, in most situations, it will be against a wall which will restrict convection heat transfer. Building walls are frequently constructed of low conductivity materials so that the wall temperature at the rear of the cabinet would approximate the cabinet temperature, and, consequently, radiation or conduction to the wall would not be significant. We will also neglect heat transfer from the top surface of the cabinet, since it may be covered with office materials that could impede heat flow substantially. Thus, the rise of the cabinet temperature above the room air temperature is given by

$$T_w - T_\infty = \frac{Q}{hA} = \frac{500}{(9.69)(2)(0.86)(1) + (0.71)(1)}$$

$$= 21^\circ\text{C}$$

Consequently, even if the internal thermal resistance between the transistors and the cabinet walls were zero, the operating temperature in a 49°C room would be above the 65°C maximum specified. Thus, if the component temperatures are to be maintained within the prescribed limits by means of natural convection, air must flow *through* the cabinet so that a direct exchange between the smaller scale surfaces and the cooling air will take place.

We will therefore assume that ambient air is permitted to enter at the bottom of the cabinet and flow vertically between the printed wiring boards and between the card carriers and front cover to eventually exit at the top of the cabinet. The nature of this problem requires the simultaneous evaluation

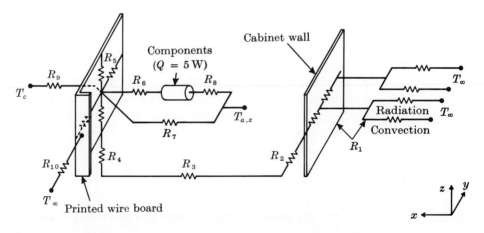

**Fig. 8-4**  Electrical network analogous to the thermal system.

of the entire system of multiple series and parallel thermal paths which connect the heat dissipating components to the ultimate sink (the cooling air and the room walls at temperature $T_\infty$). An electrical network that is analogous to the thermal system is shown in Fig. 8-4. The thermal resistances of this network are

$R_1$ = resistance of side panel of enclosing cabinet (includes convection and radiation resistance to the room)

$R_2$ = conduction resistance of hinge

$R_3$ = conduction resistance of card carrier

$R_4$ = contact resistance between card carrier and printed wire board

$R_5$ = conduction resistances of printed wire board

$R_6$ = conduction resistances of lead wires and other mountings connecting the components to the printed wire board

$R_7$ = convection from noncomponent side of printed wire board to air in vertical ducts formed by the printed wire boards at temperature $T_{a,z}$

$R_8$ = convection from side of board with components to air at temperature $T_{a,z}$

$R_9$ = radiation and convection exchange from components on one board to adjacent printed wire board

$R_{10}$ = radiation and convection exchange from printed wire board front surface to sink air at essentially $T_\infty$

The task at hand is to evaluate these internal and external resistances and to use them in solving the resulting network. As in all free convection problems, this task is complicated because the heat transfer coefficients depend upon the temperature excess in the Grashof number. Thus, the equation set characterizing the network is nonlinear and can be solved only by a process of successive iterations.

## CONDUCTION

Consider first the thermal resistance as seen by the heat flowing from the hinge through the cabinet wall to the room air, $R_1$. Since the air on the inside of the cabinet is somewhat heated, we will assume that this inside surface is insulated. The cabinet wall can then be treated as a fin having some temperature profile in proportion to the heat lost from its outer surface, and the thermal resistance can be computed from Fig. 6-23 if we replace $a/2$ by the wall thickness. This modification is necessary because Fig. 6-23 was computed for fins with convection from both sides, and the symmetry at the plane $a/2$ is equivalent to that plane being insulated.

Computing the convective contribution of $h$ from Eq. (6-98) for an assumed temperature difference of 5.6°C, we have $1.31(5.6)^{1/3} = 2.34 \text{ W}/\text{m}^2 \cdot {}^\circ\text{C}$. The radiation coefficient is given by Eq. (8-2) as 6.53 W/m² · °C so that the total heat transfer coefficient becomes 8.87 W/m² · °C. Using this to calculate the abscissa of Fig. 6-23, we have

$$\left(l + \frac{a}{2}\right)^{3/2} \sqrt{\frac{2h}{kal}} = (0.86 + 0.0015)^{3/2} \sqrt{\frac{8.87}{(43)(0.0015)(0.864)}}$$

$$= 9.8 \qquad\qquad (8\text{-}3)$$

where the cabinet wall has been taken as a 1.5-mm steel sheet having $k = 43$ W/m · °C. Referring to Fig. 6-23, we can conclude that this is a very inefficient fin. Since the curve shown there indicates an efficiency of 42 percent for Eq. (8-3) equal to 2.4, and since this corresponds to about $2.4/9.8 \approx 1/4$ of the cabinet wall, we might then estimate that the total efficiency for the entire wall is, say, 15 percent. The value of $R_1$ can be calculated in terms of $(T_w - T_\infty)$ using Eqs. (6-98) and (8-2) so that, for the portion of the wall adjacent to each card carrier (0.152 m), we have

$$R_1 = \frac{1}{(hA)_{\mathrm{fin}}\eta_f} = \frac{1}{[(1.31)(T_w - T_\infty)^{1/3} + 6.53](0.152)(0.864)(0.15)}$$

$$= \frac{38.8}{(T_w - T_\infty)^{1/3} + 4.98} \ \text{°C/W} \qquad\qquad (8\text{-}4)$$

The major resistance in the path through the hinge is the contact resistance at the hinge joint. The contact resistance depends on the contact pressure which, in this case, is related to the weight of the card carrier and contact areas involved. The contact resistance or $R_2$ was found to be

$$R_2 = 0.46 \ \text{°C/W} \qquad\qquad (8\text{-}5)$$

Turning now to the thermal resistance of the card carrier, $R_3$, we note that this resistance is not simply the length divided by the product of conductivity and cross-sectional area, as would be the case if the card carrier were insulated along its length. Instead, heat is transferred to the carrier from each of the twenty printed wire boards distributed along the carrier (Fig. 8-5). Assuming that this heat transfer $q_1$ is the same for all boards, then the card carrier can be approximated thermally by a uniform heat flux input of $20\ q_1/x_1$. This input will appear as a heat generation $q''' = 20\ q_1/x_1 A$ for the cross-sectional area $A$ of the card carrier. Equation (5-4), describing steady one-dimensional conduction, becomes

$$\frac{d^2\theta(x)}{dx^2} = \frac{-20\ q_1/x_1}{kA} \qquad\qquad (8\text{-}6)$$

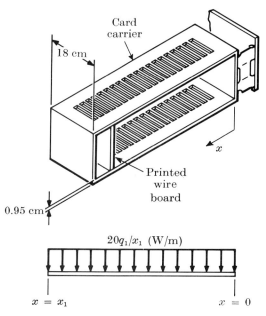

**Fig. 8-5** Heat inputs to card carrier.

where $\theta(x)$ is the temperature excess above the hinge temperature at $x = 0$. The boundary conditions are

$$\theta(0) = 0$$

$$\frac{d\theta}{dx}\bigg|_{x=x_1} = 0$$

The second boundary condition, $(d\theta/dx)\big|_{x=x_1} = 0$, results from the assumption that convective transfer from the left end of the card carrier is negligible compared to the heat conducted through the hinge. The solution becomes

$$\theta(x) = \frac{-20q_1}{kAx_1}\left(\frac{x^2}{2} - x_1 x\right) \tag{8-7}$$

The thermal resistance for the printed wire board farthest from the hinge (worst case) can be defined in terms of $\theta$ at $x = \frac{19}{20}x_1$, so that for our geometry:

$$R_3 = \frac{\theta(19/20x_1)}{q_1} \approx \frac{10x_1}{kA} = 12.4 \ °C/W \tag{8-8}$$

Note that this is a factor of ten above the one-dimensional (insulated) relation.

For an estimate of the contact resistance between the boards and the card carrier, $R_4$, we assume that the carrier grooves can be manufactured so that a force of about three pounds is necessary to insert the cards.† This corresponds to a contact pressure of roughly $1 \times 10^5 \, \text{N}/\text{m}^2$ (15 psi), which, for aluminum (Fig. 5-4), gives $h_c = 700 \, \text{W}/\text{m}^2 \cdot °\text{C}$. Thus,

$$R_4 = \frac{1}{h_c A} = \frac{1}{700(7.6 \times 10^{-4})(9 \times 10^{-2})} = 20.8 \, °\text{C}/\text{W} \qquad (8\text{-}9)$$

where contact is made over only one-half of the board length because of the cooling air holes provided in the card carrier. The board thickness is 0.76 mm. The contact resistances at the top and bottom of the board have been assumed the same since the board weight is negligible.

Evaluation of the conduction resistance of the printed wire board, denoted in general as $R_5$, requires the consideration of a two-dimensional analog representation. Before the nodal points are selected in this type of problem, insight and improved accuracy can be gained if the temperature field is sketched. Since component layouts are not known in the early stages of design, we assume that the various heat-producing elements are distributed randomly about the board. This permits us to further assume uniform heat generation over the board for the purpose of sketching the isotherms. The isotherms for a typical printed wire board are as shown in Fig. 8-6(a), while a rough, "first-cut" selection‡ of nodal points is illustrated in Fig. 8-6(b). These resistances represent the orthogonal temperature gradients. For example, the resistance between nodes 3 and 4, which we will arbitrarily call $R_5$, is

$$R_5 = \frac{L}{kA} = \frac{8.75 \times 10^{-2}}{(43)(7.5 \times 10^{-2})(0.8 \times 10^{-3})} = 34 \, °\text{C}/\text{W} \qquad (8\text{-}10)$$

Finally, we wish to consider the conduction resistances between the components and the printed wire board. The surface temperature of each component will depend on the thermal resistance of the conduction path to the board and the thermal resistance due to the flow of air over the component in free convection.§ If each component were to be considered separately, the

---

† The contact resistance of the board to the card carrier depends largely on the construction details of the card carrier itself. For example, one possibility which differs from the assumption made above would be to provide a free fit for the board. The contact resistance of the lower edge of the board would then be a function of the board weight. The major conduction heat transfer path from the board to the card carrier would undoubtedly be through the lower edge of the card.

‡ Note the shift in the nodal points toward the front of the board where the isotherms are closer together.

§ At this stage in the design, we shall neglect direct heat exchange between components. However, in the final stage of design, this may be a factor of considerable importance.

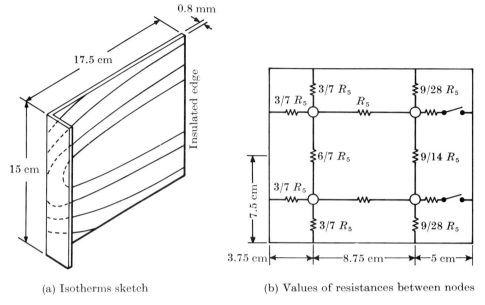

(a) Isotherms sketch          (b) Values of resistances between nodes

**Fig. 8-6**  Resistance representation of printed wire board, $R_5$.

resulting problem would be too complex to solve. A more reasonable approach, and the one chosen here, is to determine an average or weighted component temperature, $T_c$, for calculating both the conduction resistance to the board, $R_6$, and the convection resistance to the air. This temperature must be weighted in terms of the convective heat transfer surface area of the components since two devices dissipating the same power but with different surface areas would not contribute in the same manner. The success of this approach will depend on the variation of component temperatures.

If the modular package at hand is typical, then each circuit card is filled with three types of components or circuits which dissipate heat: resistors, logic circuits, and individual transistors. See Fig. 8-7. It is necessary to define a number of symbols relating to the three types of components which will be

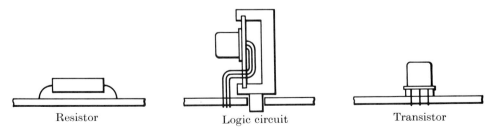

Resistor          Logic circuit          Transistor

**Fig. 8-7**  Geometry of components mounted on printed wire boards.

denoted by the superscripts $r$, $l$, $t$. The symbols defined for the resistors are as follows:

$R^r \equiv$ conduction resistance of the average resistor to the board

$\theta^r \equiv$ temperature excess of average resistor relative to the board

$N^r \equiv$ number of resistors on the board

$\alpha^r \equiv$ ratio of heat conducted from average resistor to total heat conducted from all components to the board

$\gamma^r \equiv$ ratio of average resistor convective heat transfer area to the total heat transfer area of all the components

From these definitions, it follows that $N^r\alpha^r + N^l\alpha^l + N^t\alpha^t = 1$ and $N^r\gamma^r + N^l\gamma^l + N^t\gamma^t = 1$. The temperature excess (above the board temperature) of a single component is the product of heat flow and thermal resistance. For example, the temperature excess of the "average" resistor† is $\theta^r = (R^r)(\alpha^r Q)$, where $Q$ is the total heat conducted from all components to the board. The temperature excess of the logic circuits and transistors is $\theta^l = (R^l)(\alpha^l Q)$ and $\theta^t = (R^t)(\alpha^t Q)$. From this, the temperature profile of a component heat transfer surface area can be plotted (Fig. 8-8). The average temperature excess on the surface $(T_c - T_b)$ is then the shaded area divided by the unity base:

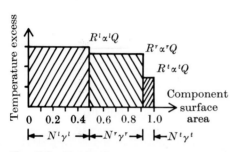

**Fig. 8-8** Temperature profile of components on a typical printed wire board.

$$T_c - T_b = (R^r\alpha^r Q)(N^r\gamma^r) + (R^t\alpha^t Q)(N^t\gamma^t) + (R^l\alpha^l Q)(N^l\gamma^l)$$

The equivalent conduction resistance between all the components and the board is $R_6 = (T_c - T_b)/Q$ or

$$R_6 = N^r R^r \alpha^r \gamma^r + N^l R^l \alpha^l \gamma^l + N^t R^t \alpha^t \gamma^t \tag{8-11}$$

which essentially expresses the weighting‡ of the individual resistances to account for their contribution to the total heat dissipation and to the total heat transfer surface area.

---

† We will assume that all resistors are identical, which means that they all have the same $\theta^r$.

‡ An additional weighting factor could be introduced in each of the products on the right-hand side to account for differences in component shapes as it affects the convection heat transfer. This adjustment should not be significant since, as will be argued later, most of the components are essentially buried in the boundary layer. In a later, more precise analysis, the designer might take this into account.

Even though only limited information is available in the early design stages, a reasonable anticipation of the final design can help the designer arrive at approximate values for component densities and dissipations. For this example, we have the following values† (the component thermal resistances were computed on the basis of conduction through the component leads).

|  | $N$ | $R$ | $\alpha$ | $\gamma$ | Temperature excess $R\alpha Q$ | Heat generated $N\alpha$ | Surface area $N\gamma$ | Resistance $NR\alpha\gamma$ |
|---|---|---|---|---|---|---|---|---|
| Resistors | 14 | 284 | 0.02 | 0.035 | 5.69 $Q$ | 0.28 | 0.492 | 2.79 |
| Logic circuits | 6 | 56.9 | 0.10 | 0.07 | 5.69 $Q$ | 0.60 | 0.420 | 2.39 |
| Transistors | 4 | 41 | 0.03 | 0.022 | 2.73 $Q$ | 0.12 | 0.088 | 0.25 |
| Total |  |  |  |  |  | 100% | 100% | 5.43 |

Using these values in Eq. (8-11), we obtain

$$R_6 = 5.43°\text{C/W} \qquad (8\text{-}12)$$

and the surface temperature distribution shown in Fig. 8-8 can be specified. From this profile we are justified in assuming a uniform component surface temperature, since $\theta^r \approx \theta^l$ and $N^r\gamma^r + N^l\gamma^l \approx 100$ percent.

Since all of the components will be pulsed on and off, transients will exist in the region close to these components. Once the frequency of these transients is known, the depth to which they must be considered can be calculated, as in Example 5.4. For this analysis, we will assume that these depths are small and essentially inside the components themselves.

## CONVECTION AND RADIATION

Commencing our discussion of the external problem, we will assume that printed wire boards are positioned to have vertical air passages between them,

---

† Recall that the quantity $\alpha$ is defined in terms of the heat conducted to the board, but this cannot be evaluated exactly until the temperatures $T_c$, $T_b$, $T_{a,z}$ are known. In determining $R_6$ here, we have taken as a first approximation $\alpha$ = (total heat generated by one component)/(total heat generated by all components) which can be specified. This, in essence, assumes that the heat generated by an individual component so divides that the ratio of heat conducted to heat radiated and heat convected does not depend on the class of component considered. The approximation made for $\alpha$ must be checked; if the approximation is incorrect, iteration is required until an adequate choice of $\alpha$ is reached. The choice of $\alpha$ used here was found to be reasonable since the values of temperature determined from the solution of Eq. (8-21), when taken with the appropriate geometrical terms in the above table, gave $R_6 = 5.12$. This result is in reasonable agreement with Eq. (8-12).

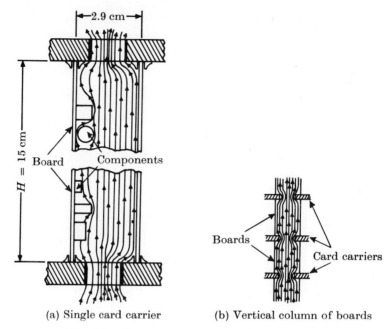

(a) Single card carrier     (b) Vertical column of boards

**Fig. 8-9**  Air flow between printed wire boards.

as illustrated in Fig. 8-9(a). In these passages, the upward air buoyancy and resulting heat transfer are somewhat equivalent to heat transfer from a series of heated vertical ducts having a height equivalent to five card carriers. See Fig. 8-9(b). The heat transfer coefficients from the components and printed wire boards are assumed identical and all equal to the heat transfer coefficient of this duct.†

For such a heated duct, in the Grashof number range of interest here, the characteristic length $L$ is a major factor in the thermal process. For our configuration, if

$l$ = board length
$H$ = board height
$A_b$ = area of noncomponent side of board = $lH$
$A_c$ = equivalent area of component side
$b$ = spacing between boards

then

$$L = 2\,\frac{\text{cross-sectional flow area}}{\text{wetted perimeter}}$$

$$= \frac{2lb}{(A_c + A_b)/H} = \frac{2b}{1 + A_c/A_b} \tag{8-13}$$

† This is something of a conservative assumption since $h$ for the small components will actually be a little larger.

The typical center-to-center board spacing on a card carrier is 2.9 cm. However, the card thickness and the projecting components reduce this space by an estimated 1.3 cm. Furthermore, the effective spacing for fluid flow is still smaller, since one must take into account the pressure drops caused by constrictions at the card carrier. It will be assumed that the holes in the card carrier provide an open area of 20 percent of the total area, so that the equivalent spacing at the constriction is 0.58 cm. The spacing that is hydrodynamically equivalent to the actual configuration would best be determined by experiments but for now we will simply take the arithmetic average of the two values:

$$b = \frac{(2.9 - 1.3) + 0.58}{2} = 1.1 \text{ cm}$$

Thus, $b = 1.1$ cm will be taken as the spacing controlling the fluid flow in the vertical ducts, while $b' = 2.9 - 1.3 = 1.6$ cm will be used for any heat exchange between adjacent cards.

As indicated in Eq. (8-13), the surface areas $A_b$ and $A_c$ must also be known before the characteristic length is completely described. Of course, the surface area $A_b$ is board height times length. On the component side ($A_c$), the surface irregularities increase the effective heat transfer area to varying extents, depending on how many of the various components project through the boundary layer formed on the board. To gain an estimate of this boundary-layer thickness, we refer to the solution for free convection on a vertical flat plate. As shown in Fig. 6-6, the velocity is essentially zero for values of $\eta$ greater than 3.8. From this, for a plate of height $H = 15$ cm and an estimated temperature difference of 17°C, we have

$$\delta = 3.8H\left(\frac{4}{N_{\text{Gr}}}\right)^{1/4} = 3.8(0.15)\left(\frac{4}{6.6 \times 10^6}\right)^{1/4}$$

$$= 1.6 \text{ cm} \tag{8-14}$$

Obviously, the flow over a component-filled board with restrictions at both ends, as illustrated in Fig. 8-9, is not the same as for the simple free flat plate, but the maximum boundary-layer thickness in the actual case should be around 1.3 cm. Consequently, the components in the upper half of the board are almost completely immersed in the boundary layer, and their total surface area does not contribute equally to the convective heat transfer.† Again, the effective area could best be determined experimentally, but for now we will estimate that the projecting components increase $A_c$ by 30 percent. Thus, $A_c = 1.3A_b$. Using

---

† Parts of the various components as shown in Fig. 8-7 act like horizontal plates so that the isotherms are similar to those in Fig. 6-9.

this and $b = 1.1$ cm, the characteristic length of Eq. (8-13) becomes

$$L = \frac{2(1.1)}{1 + 1.3} = 0.96 \text{ cm} \tag{8-15}$$

The heat transfer coefficient for this duct will be essentially that for parallel plates, as given by the correlation of Eq. (6-99). Referring to Fig. 6-10, we see that this equation can be simplified if the abscissa is less than 10, which is satisfied, to give

$$N_{\text{Nu}} = \frac{1}{24}\left[\frac{L}{5H}(N_{\text{Gr}} \cdot N_{\text{Pr}})\right]$$

where the term $5H$ is introduced because the total duct height is five times that of one board. Thus,

$$h = \frac{k}{L} N_{\text{Nu}} = \frac{k}{24L}\left[\frac{L}{5H}(N_{\text{Gr}} \cdot N_{\text{Pr}})\right]$$

$$= 0.116[0.931(T_b - T_\infty)] = 0.108(T_b - T_\infty) \text{ W/m}^2 \cdot {}^\circ\text{C}$$

where the fluid properties† are evaluated at an estimated board temperature $T_b = 49{}^\circ$C, $H = 15$ cm, and the Grashof number is based on $L = 0.96$ cm. This heat transfer coefficient is the average of the local heat transfer coefficient $h_z$ and gives the average wall heat flux $q_w = h(T_d - T_\infty)$ for the duct. The local heat flux, $q_{w,z} = h_z(T_d - T_{a,z})$, is less than $q_w$ for values of $z$ near the top of the duct (we are concerned with the uppermost printed wire board since it represents the worst case). This is because both $h_z$ [Eq. (6-74) gives $h_z \approx 1/z^{1/4}$ for a vertical isothermal plate] and $T_d - T_{a,z}$ decrease with increasing $z$. Even though $h_z$ is not known and we are restricted to using $h$, we can make a closer approximation to the local heat flux on the upper walls of the duct by using $h(T_w - T_{a,z})$ rather than $h(T_w - T_\infty)$. From this, the convection resistance between the noncomponent side of the board and the cooling air at $T_{a,z}$ is

$$R_7 = \frac{1}{hA_b} = \frac{1}{[0.108(T_b - T_\infty)](0.175)(0.152)}$$

$$= \frac{353}{T_b - T_\infty} {}^\circ\text{C/W} \tag{8-16}$$

In a similar manner, if we neglect the slight variation of property values with wall temperature, the convection resistances between the components at temperature $T_c$ and the cooling air is

$$R_8 = \frac{1}{hA_c} = \frac{1}{[0.108(T_c - T_\infty)](1.3)(0.175)(0.152)}$$

$$= \frac{272}{T_c - T_\infty} {}^\circ\text{C/W} \tag{8-17}$$

† Actually $\beta$ should be evaluated at the ambient air temperature $T_\infty$.

We will now determine how much heat is transferred to the component-free side of the board from the components on its neighbor, $R_9$. This heat transfer process will be analyzed as if these two boards formed a vertical space, limited at the top and bottom by the corresponding card carriers,† as shown in Fig. 8-10. To determine whether interior free convection exists, we must satisfy Eq. (6-100):

$$N_{Gr} \cdot N_{Pr} > 10^3$$

while the Grashof number is

$$N_{Gr} = \frac{g\beta\rho^2 L^3 \theta}{\mu^2} = (11.2 \times 10^7)(1.6 \times 10^{-2})^3 (T_c - T_b) = 460(T_c - T_b)$$

Thus,

$$N_{Gr} \cdot N_{Pr} = 330(T_c - T_b) > 10^3$$

Thus, for $(T_c - T_b) < 8°C$ (which will later be demonstrated), a free convection due to $T_c \neq T_b$ does not exist. However, there is a radiation exchange between the two surfaces. If the two parallel plates have a surface emissivity of approximately 1, then the thermal resistance evaluated from Eq. (7-60) with Eq. (7-56) is

$$R_9 = \frac{1}{h_r A_b} = \frac{1}{(4\sigma T_b^3)A_b} \approx \frac{1}{(6.83)(0.175)(0.152)}$$
$$= 5.55 °C/W \tag{8-18}$$

Consider now the heat transfer from the front of the board to the cabinet front cover and to the air between the cabinet front and the card carriers. The fact that the expected heat transfer to this air is small leads us to assume that the air temperature is at $T_\infty$. Assume that the front of each board is shaped as shown in Fig. 8-11 to form a continuous vertical surface parallel to the cabinet door. The heat transfer coefficient for turbulent flow [Eq. (6-98)] from this vertical plate is $1.31(T_b - T_\infty)^{1/3}$. The radiative heat transfer coefficient [Eq. (7-60) and Eq. (7-56)], again for surface emissivities of approximately 1, is $h_r = 4\sigma T_b^3 \approx 6.83$. The corresponding thermal resistance is controlled by $h = 1.31(T_b - T_\infty)^{1/3} + 6.83$, so that

$$R_{10} = \frac{1}{hA} = \frac{1}{h(0.58/20)(0.152)}$$
$$= \frac{230}{1.31(T_b - T_\infty)^{1/3} + 6.83} °C/W \tag{8-19}$$

Lastly, we wish to calculate the air temperature at the top of the cabinet $T_0$ in order to evaluate the worst-case condition. The air temperature increases

---

† This interpretation is not completely representative of the actual convection heat exchange because the fluid flow patterns that would normally be established by cellular fluid motion in a vertically *enclosed* space is displaced upward in our case here by the more predominant velocities in the heated duct.

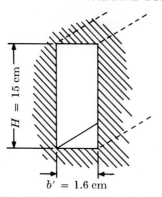

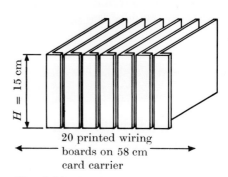

**Fig. 8-10**  Vertically enclosed space formed by two adjacent boards.

**Fig. 8-11**  Vertically front surface formed by the array of boards.

in direct proportion to the heat it absorbs from the walls of the heated duct and as the reciprocal of the product of air mass flow rate and specific heat, so that

$$T_0 - T_\infty = \frac{\text{heat absorbed by air from first four rows}}{\hat{w}bl\rho c_p}$$

where $\hat{w}$ is the average velocity of air flowing inside the duct. Investigations have been made[1] of free convection in ducts formed by two heated vertical plates. The flow rate results are reproduced in Fig. 6-30. Assuming a duct temperature of 39°C, from Fig. 6-30

$$\hat{w} = 0.07\,\frac{\mu N_{\mathrm{Gr}}}{b}$$

where the coefficient 0.07 applies only to a range close to the assumed values. The heat absorbed by the air is equal to the average wall heat flux as noted in the discussion preceding Eq. (8-16). Thus,

$$Q_{\mathrm{air}} \approx h(4H)(2l)(T_d - T_\infty)$$

or

$$Q_{\mathrm{air}} = \frac{2kl}{24}\,N_{\mathrm{Gr}} \cdot N_{\mathrm{Pr}}(T_d - T_\infty)$$

On combining these expressions, the outlet air temperature is

$$T_0 - T_\infty = \frac{1.6(T_d - T_\infty)}{0.07(24)}$$

The duct temperature, $T_d$, is not constant but varies with duct height. An estimate of $T_0$ is obtained by basing $T_d$ on the average temperature of the first four rows recognizing that the air enters at $T_\infty$. Thus

$$T_0 = 0.19(T_c + T_b) + 0.62T_\infty\,°\text{C} \tag{8-20}$$

## ANALYSIS OF THE NETWORK CHARACTERIZING
## THE THERMAL SYSTEM

Once all the thermal resistances have been determined, the remaining tasks are to solve the thermal resistance network (Fig. 8-12) for the temperature at points of interest and to determine the manner in which the heat flow is apportioned between the various parallel and series paths. Two methods of solution are available. One method is to assemble an analogous electrical network with the current sources and probe the voltage at selected nodal points. The second method is to solve the set of simultaneous nodal equations to find the temperature profile.

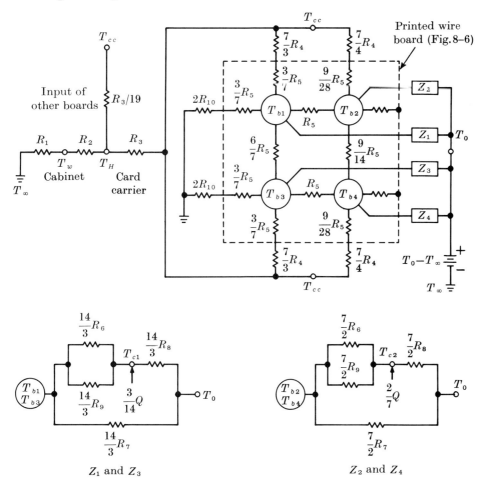

**Fig. 8-12** Resistive network characterizing the thermal paths between the cooling environment and the printed wire board at the far end of the card carrier.

Even though an equivalent electrical network could be readily constructed and changes in the resistance values could be easily made, we will solve the nodal equations for the purpose of presentation here. These equations can be written as

$$T_w\left(\frac{1}{R_1} + \frac{1}{R_2}\right) - T_H\left(\frac{1}{R_2}\right) = T_\infty\left(\frac{1}{R_1}\right) \tag{8-21a}$$

$$-T_w\left(\frac{1}{R_2}\right) + T_H\left(\frac{1}{R_2} + \frac{20}{R_3}\right) - T_{cc}\left(\frac{20}{R_3}\right) = 0 \tag{8-21b}$$

$$-T_H\left(\frac{1}{R_3}\right) + T_{cc}\left(\frac{1}{R_3} + \frac{2}{\frac{7}{3}R_4 + \frac{3}{7}R_5} + \frac{2}{\frac{7}{4}R_4 + \frac{9}{28}R_5}\right)$$
$$- T_{b1}\left(\frac{2}{\frac{7}{3}R_4 + \frac{3}{7}R_5}\right) - T_{b2}\left(\frac{2}{\frac{7}{4}R_4 + \frac{9}{28}R_5}\right) = 0 \tag{8-21c}$$

$$-T_{cc}\left(\frac{1}{\frac{3}{7}R_5 + \frac{7}{3}R_4}\right) + T_{b1}\left(\frac{1}{2R_{10} + \frac{3}{7}R_5} + \frac{1}{\frac{3}{7}R_5 + \frac{7}{3}R_4}\right.$$
$$\left. + \frac{1}{R_5} + \frac{3}{14R_6} + \frac{3}{14R_7} + \frac{3}{14R_9}\right) - T_{b2}\left(\frac{1}{R_5}\right) - T_{c1}\left(\frac{3}{14R_6} + \frac{3}{14R_9}\right)$$
$$= T_\infty\left(\frac{1}{2R_{10} + \frac{3}{7}R_5}\right) + T_0\left(\frac{3}{14R_7}\right) \tag{8-21d}$$

$$-T_{cc}\left(\frac{1}{\frac{7}{4}R_4 + \frac{9}{28}R_5}\right) - T_{b1}\left(\frac{1}{R_5}\right)$$
$$+ T_{b2}\left(\frac{1}{R_5} + \frac{1}{\frac{7}{4}R_4 + \frac{9}{28}R_5} + \frac{2}{7R_6} + \frac{2}{7R_9} + \frac{2}{7R_7}\right)$$
$$- T_{c2}\left(\frac{2}{7R_6} + \frac{2}{7R_9}\right) = T_0\left(\frac{2}{7R_7}\right) \tag{8-21e}$$

$$-T_{b1}\left(\frac{1}{R_6 + R_9}\right) + T_{c1}\left(\frac{1}{R_6 + R_9} + \frac{1}{R_8}\right) = Q + T_0\left(\frac{1}{R_8}\right) \tag{8-21f}$$

$$-T_{b2}\left(\frac{1}{R_6 + R_9}\right) + T_{c2}\left(\frac{1}{R_6 + R_9} + \frac{1}{R_8}\right) = Q + T_0\left(\frac{1}{R_8}\right) \tag{8-21g}$$

Of course $R_1$, $R_7$, $R_8$, and $R_{10}$ are temperature-dependent. After three iterations, the following temperatures were obtained for $T_\infty = 24°C$ and $Q = 5$ watts per board. The board and component temperatures correspond to a worst-case condition—namely, a board at the left end of the uppermost card carrier.

$$\left.\begin{array}{l} T_{c1} = T_{c3} = 55°C \\ T_{c2} = T_{c4} = 58°C \end{array}\right\} \quad T_c = \tfrac{4}{7}T_{c2} + \tfrac{3}{7}T_{c1} = 57°C$$

$$\left.\begin{array}{l} T_{b1} = T_{b3} = 48.3°C \\ T_{b2} = T_{b4} = 52°C \end{array}\right\} \quad T_b = \tfrac{4}{7}T_{b2} + \tfrac{3}{7}T_{b1} = 51°C$$

$$T_w = \text{temperature of cabinet wall} = 43°C$$

$$T_H = \text{temperature of card carrier hinge} = 45.6°C$$

$$T_{cc} = \text{temperature of card carrier} = 48°C$$

$$T_0 = \text{outlet air temperature} = 35.4°C$$

The heat flow apportionment in watts is shown in Fig. 8-13.

From the preceding list of nodal temperatures, we see that the maximum weighted component temperature is $T_{c2} = 58°C$ for a room air temperature $T_\infty - 24°C$. This is quite close to the thermal requirements stated at the beginning of this section. However, for higher ambient temperatures and certainly for $T_\infty = 49°C$, the maximum component temperature will appreciably exceed the requirements because all the temperatures will be higher by approximately $49 - 24 = 25°C$.

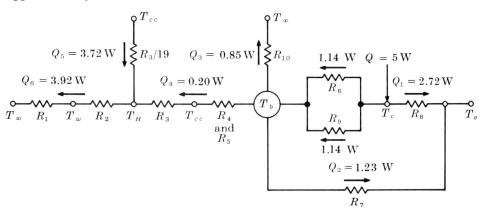

| Symbol | Value (W) | From | To |
|---|---|---|---|
| | | Heat Flow | |
| $Q_1 + Q_2$ | 3.95 | Components and board | Cooling air |
| $Q_3$ | 0.85 | Front of board | Room air |
| $Q_4$ | 0.20 | Board | Card carrier |
| Total | 5.00 | | |
| $Q_5$ | 3.72 | Other boards | Card carrier |
| $Q_6$ | 3.92 | Card carrier | Room air |

**Fig. 8-13** Apportionment of heat flux.

Realizing that a problem exists and understanding the cause are, in essence, the purpose of making an initial thermal analysis. The situation should now be viewed in terms of improving the thermal behavior to attain the requirements. In doing this, the designer might pursue a compromise of the ambient conditions, the thermal requirements, and the packaging configuration. Usually the first two possibilities are not amenable to compromise.† However, certain alterations will probably be acceptable in the packaging configuration. The recommendations offered by the designer might therefore include:

1. Increasing the open area in the card carriers. For example, if 50 percent of the area is open instead of 20 percent, then the duct characteristic length of Eq. (8-13) increases to about 1.3 cm. This reduces $R_7$ and $R_8$, so that a greater quantity of heat could be transferred directly to the cooling air. It can be shown that the maximum component temperature is 48°C in this case.
2. Locating temperature sensitive boards on the bottom card carriers where $T_{a,z}$ is lower. Locating these boards closer to the card carrier hinge yields only a slight improvement.
3. Orienting cylindrical- and prismatic-shaped components with the longitudinal axis vertical to minimize flow restrictions. This also implies that large unheated components do not block the air flow over smaller heated ones that are on the same board or a board above.

The relative advantages of these recommendations can be evaluated either by introducing the corresponding changed parameters in the preceding analytical process or by performing experiments. For example, the merits of increasing the open area in the card carriers might be easily determined by assembling a test fixture with this provision or by calculating the component temperature for various values of characteristic length, Eq. (8-13).

Other experiments might be programmed at this point to verify the assumptions that were necessary in the initial analysis:

1. Contact resistance of printed wire board and card carrier hinge.
2. Fluid flow and thermal aspects of component-filled board.
   (a) pressure drops caused by projecting components and constrictions at the card carrier.
   (b) effective heat transfer area of component side.

---

† This is true particularly if the temperature limits are specified for standard components, as is the case here. The necessity of less severe ambient conditions should be recommended only after pursuits of other possibilities have proved fruitless, including cooling the unit with a fan or blower.

(c) heat conduction from components to the board.

(d) heat transfer coefficient of board and of irregular surface on component side.

At a later time, experimental evaluation should be made of the final equipment configuration in its entirety. A realistic evaluation is assured if the procedures presented in the following sections are followed.

## 8-3. TEMPERATURE MEASURING INSTRUMENTS

The concept of hotness and coldness arises from our senses, particularly the sense of touch. This concept is more concretely formulated, however, through the thermodynamic variable, temperature, which is defined in terms of the operation of a Carnot cycle. The Thermodynamic Temperature Scale so defined is related to the International Practical Scale through definition at the triple point of water, $0.01°C$, and through thermodynamic relations (mainly gas thermometry) at six other fixed points.[2] In between these fixed points, various instruments are used as rather precise interpolation standards—for example, the platinum resistance thermometer in the range $-183°$ to $630.5°C$ and the platinum-platinum rhodium thermocouple in the range $630.5°$ to $1063°C$.

In general, any property having an appreciable and consistent temperature variation could serve to indicate temperature. In contrast, the sense of touch is inconsistent in that cold materials with a high $\sqrt{k\rho c}$ will appear colder than other bodies at the same temperature but having a lower $\sqrt{k\rho c}$. This has been demonstrated analytically.[3]

A thermometer is an instrument devised to indicate its own temperature. The utility of such an instrument requires a knowledge of the difference between the undisturbed body temperature and the reading of the thermometer. In the following discussion, we will review the various instruments of interest to the equipment engineer and will suggest some precautions and practices which should lead to more meaningful thermal evaluations of proposed designs.†

Devices utilized for temperature measurements can be grouped into three classes: (1) a solid thermometer element which makes contact with or is inserted into a body; (2) a pyrometer operating at a distance which responds to the radiation emitted from the body, indicating an apparent temperature; and (3) the body itself, which acts as its own thermometer. Some very broad advantages and disadvantages for these groups are noted in Fig. 8-14. For the physical designer, the thermocouple and the thermistor are of primary importance, while the electronic circuit element can also be used to advantage if

---

† For a more complete coverage, refer to books by Baker, Ryder, and Baker.[4] If more detail is desired, Ref. 2 may be helpful.

| Instrument | Utility | Limitations |
|---|---|---|
| GROUP 1 | | |
| Liquid-in-glass | $-110$ to $1200°C$. Direct reading. | Must be immersed to same depth and in same attitude as calibrated. Drift in calibration when held at high temperatures. Size limitations. |
| Bimetallic strips | Up to $260°C$. Direct reading and control. | $\pm 5\%$ accuracy. Size limitations. |
| Thermocouples | Near absolute zero to $3000°C$. Element arbitrarily small, easily attached, cheap. Accurate when used with good practice. | Calibration subject to spurious temperature changes. Output sensitive to induced emfs. |
| Resistance thermometers (including thermistors) | Near absolute zero to $650°C$. Greatest sensitivity. Do not require reference temperature. | Precision elements possess size and shape limitations. Thermistors subject to drifts and inaccuracies. |
| GROUP 2 | | |
| Radiation pyrometer | $>150°C$. Capable of indicating and controlling. Sensing element does not reach temperature of body viewed. | Measurement depends on emissivity or that $\epsilon_\lambda(\lambda_1) = \epsilon_\lambda(\lambda_2)$ when using "two-color principle." Subject to radiation from other bodies in vicinity. |
| Optical pyrometer | $>730°C$. Otherwise same as for radiation pyrometer. | Same as for radiation pyrometer. |
| GROUP 3 | | |
| Resistance of circuit elements | Any range in which element operates. No corrections required as long as operating conditions are not disturbed. | Require calibration (in mode of operation if resistance depends on mode, e.g., diodes). |

**Fig. 8-14**  Comparison of temperature-indicating instruments.

calibrated to indicate temperature. Infrared photography and the use of certain luminescent phosphors, although sensitive, have not yet been developed to the extent where they can be considered as engineering tools. However, infrared radiometric microscopes are becoming commonplace.

## THERMOCOUPLE THERMOMETRY

The mechanism of thermoelectricity is not fully understood, even though the field is well over 100 years old. However, three separate effects have been discussed† and these can be described as follows:

1. *Seebeck effect.* If a circuit is formed from two dissimilar metals $A$ and $B$, and if one of the junctions of $A$ and $B$ is at $T_1$ while the other is at $T_2$, a current will flow in the circuit.
2. *Peltier effect.* When a current flows in a circuit formed from two metals, it gives rise to an absorption of heat at one junction and a liberation at the other.
3. *Thomson effect.* In a homogeneous conductor in which there is a temperature gradient, heat is absorbed by the conductor when a current flows in the direction opposite to the flow of heat, and heat is liberated if the current is reversed.

All of these effects are reversible; however, they do produce an irreversible joulean heating effect (i.e., $i^2 R$ loss usually of the order of $10^{-10}$ W). It can be shown from thermodynamics that the thermoelectric effects are interrelated in that the algebraic sum of the Peltier and the Thomson effects gives the Seebeck effect.

In a thermocouple circuit constructed from metals $A$ and $B$, the emf due to the Seebeck effect can be used to deduce the temperature $T_2$ at one junction if (1) $T_1$ at the other junction is some known reference temperature, and if (2) the relationship between the measured emf and temperature difference has been established for the combination $A$ and $B$. The Seebeck effect is illustrated in Fig. 8-15; here the emf per degree temperature difference—usually called the *thermoelectric power*—is shown for some common thermocouple materials with platinum as the reference material in each case. The thermoelectric power for a combination of any two materials shown would be the algebraic sum of the values shown. For example, at room temperature (25°C), the output of a chromel-alumel thermocouple would be about 40 $\mu$V$/$°C junction temperature difference. Picking a suitable reference temperature (e.g., the ice point), the functions

---

† For a more complete discussion of this subject, refer to Paper No. 1 of part 2 of Ref. 2.

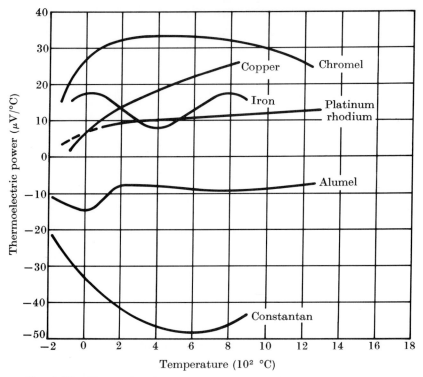

**Fig. 8-15** Thermoelectric powers of common thermocouple materials against platinum.[2]

indicated in Fig. 8-15 can be integrated for various material combinations, yielding plots of thermocouple emf versus temperature, as shown in Fig. 8-16.†
For a reference junction $T_1$ other than $0°C$, the output can still be read from Fig. 8-16 as the emf at $T_2$ minus the emf at $T_1$ above $0°C$.

The experimentally observed action of thermocouples allows us to state that the emf resulting from the junction of two homogeneous dissimilar metals is related to the temperature difference of the two junctions, regardless of the temperature variation along the wires. However, if an inhomogeneity exists in the circuit due to a change in chemical or metallurgical composition,‡ errors can be encountered depending on the local temperature variation. In the thermocouple wires themselves, these effects can generally be neglected if they are purchased from a reliable manufacturer and handled with reasonable care.

---

† The output signal can be increased by connecting several couples in series to form a *thermopile*. The average temperature of a number of points can be obtained directly by connecting several couples in parallel. Neither practice is recommended in equipment evaluation, however, since special care must be taken to electrically isolate the various junctions.

‡ This includes effects due to cold working.

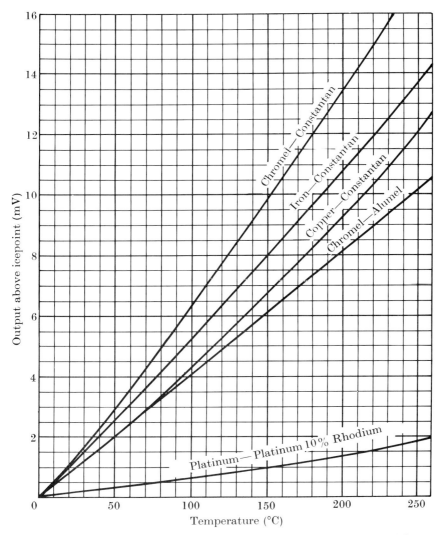

**Fig. 8-16**   Thermocouple output versus temperature for various material combinations.[2]

One extreme case of inhomogeneity would be the introduction of a third metal into a thermocouple circuit. It is often desirable where long lead lengths are required, for example, to use copper wire leads. This reduces the total resistance so that the time response of the system will not be degraded. The effects of this third metal can be eliminated if the junctions of the third metal with the thermocouple wires are maintained at the same temperature. Physically, this requires the fabrication of an "isothermal box" as illustrated in Fig. 8-17. Once the copper leads are introduced in the isothermal region,

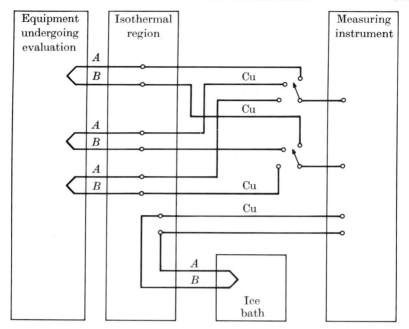

**Fig. 8-17**  A typical thermocouple circuit.

switches and indicating instruments can be included. Generally, one need not be concerned about the temperature variations through the instruments since they are usually constructed from materials having low thermoelectric powers with respect to each other, e.g., brass, lead-tin solder, silver, copper, and manganin. The lead joints should be soldered, fused, or brazed to eliminate possible parasitic emfs and erratic behavior. The thermocouple junctions should always be fused, but soldering will often suffice.

Another source of error that can appear, due to inhomogeneities, is voltaic emfs resulting from the electrical connection of dissimilar metals through some form of electrolyte such as condensed moisture. Since these emfs can sometimes be as large as the total output of the thermocouple, good practice demands that electrical insulation be kept impervious and undamaged, particularly around soldered joints.†

Of the five common thermocouples considered in Fig. 8-16, platinum-platinum rhodium has the highest precision and stability; hence, it is used both as a standard for part of the international practical temperature scale and as a secondary standard for laboratory calibration. However, the low thermoelectric output limits it to these functions and to very high temperature usage.

Iron-constantan enjoys the highest popularity, mainly because of its low

---

† For the same reason, one should never use acid flux for soldering these joints.

cost and relatively high thermoelectric power despite the errors due to inhomogeneities in both materials and the loss of calibration due to corrosion on unprotected wires. Copper-constantan is basically a more accurate couple, but its usefulness is somewhat limited by the high thermal conductivity of copper, as will be discussed later. The upper limit is about $350°C$ since copper oxidizes rapidly above this temperature. The constantan for copper-constantan couples, called "Adams" constantan, is a different alloy from that used with iron, while the copper may be any wire, as long as it conforms to ASTM Spec. B3-45 for soft or annealed copper wire.

Chromel-alumel thermocouples have oxidation resistance characteristics superior to the iron-constantan and copper-constantan couples. The thermoelectric power is adequately high, and the material composition is controlled within narrow limits.† The one disadvantage of this couple is the brittle nature of alumel, especially at low temperatures. Consequently, the chromel-constantan thermocouple is coming into use. This couple has the highest output of the commonly used couples and has a very good emf stability over the range $-18°$ to $870°C$.

The manufacture of thermocouple wires is currently controlled to the extent that calibrations are generally not required for equipment work. Expected errors are listed below. When both a percentage of temperature change and a number of degrees are indicated, the larger of the two quantities is the error to be expected.

| | | | |
|---|---|---|---|
| Platinum-platinum rhodium | $\pm 0.25\%$ | | |
| Iron-constantan | $\pm 0.75\%$ | or | $\pm 2.2°C$ |
| Copper-constantan | $\pm 0.5\%$ | or | $\pm 0.83°C$ |
| Chromel-alumel | $\pm 0.75\%$ | or | $\pm 2.2°C$ |
| Chromel-constantan | $\pm 0.5\%$ | or | $\pm 1.7°C$ |

The errors quoted for the last three types can be halved if matched wires are furnished by the manufacturer. If the foregoing accuracies are not adequate, a simple check can be made against a platinum-platinum rhodium couple by inserting both couples inside a heavy copper block heated by a furnace. Under no circumstances should a calibration be attempted using a pot of boiling water since serious errors can easily be encountered. Special instruments are available for the steam-point calibration as well as for calibrations at other fixed points.[2]

As mentioned earlier, the reference junction can be inserted into an ice bath or can be held at any other known temperature. If the ice point is chosen, it should be prepared by filling a Dewar flask with finely crushed ice, then adding cold water to cover the ice. Distilled (or deionized) water should be used,

---

† Especially since these wires are produced only by the Hoskins Manufacturing Company, Detroit, Michigan.

mainly to eliminate voltaic emfs, since pure water is a good dielectric. Once a significant amount of water without ice gathers at the bottom,† it should be drawn off, since water has its maximum density at 4°C which could cause a significant error. For precision work, the recommendations found on page 60 of Ref. 4, Vol. 1, should be followed.

## THERMISTORS AND RESISTANCE THERMOMETRY

Resistance thermometry is based on the fact that the electrical resistance of materials changes with temperature, increasing in metals‡ and decreasing in nonmetals with increasing temperatures. Platinum is the standard material for precision work, although other metallic resistance thermometers are commercially available.[2,4] However, metallic resistance thermometry is usually of interest in equipment design only in that the resistance of various components such as wire-wound resistors and strip-lines can be used as a measure of the temperature of the components.

More important are thermistors, which means "thermally sensitive resistor." The temperature coefficients of these semiconductors are a factor of ten higher than that of metal, and the resistivity is substantially higher, so that small units can be manufactured which still have high resistance.§ Lead and electrical contact resistance difficulties are virtually eliminated in these units. Some typical commercial thermistor shapes and resistances are shown in Fig. 8-18.

Thermistors combine the best features of thermocouples and resistance thermometry, but they are not without disadvantages. One inconvenient feature is the nonlinear variation of resistance with temperature, a good approximation being

$$R \propto e^{a/T}$$

A bridge has been designed[2] to give a nearly linear output over a sequence of temperature ranges; it is based on a series expansion of ln $R$. Such a bridge is available from the General Electric Co.

Stability, particularly in the tiny coated units and in the larger uncoated units, can be a problem under extreme conditions of long exposure (10 to 100 days) at 100° to 200°C. Drift errors as large as 10°C have been noted under these conditions.[2] However, the fair-size coated thermistors exhibit a stability

---

† This separation can also be prevented by stirring, but this is usually inconvenient.

‡ The temperature coefficient for metals is usually around $3.6 \times 10^{-3}$ to $5.4 \times 10^{-3}$ $\Omega/\Omega \cdot °C$.

§ In going from room temperature to $-198°C$, a resistance increase of a typical thermistor could be approximately $10^{13}$.

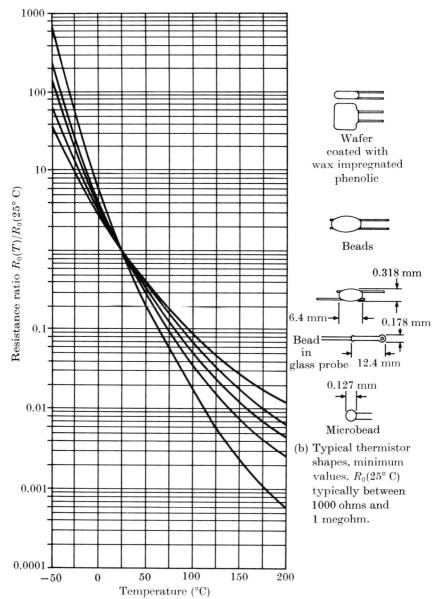

(a) Typical temperature versus resistance ratio for various thermistors

**Fig. 8-18**  Typical characteristics of commercial thermistors.

to better than 0.25°C, and, under less adverse conditions, retain their calibrations for months with less than 0.01°C variation. Calibrations (and recalibrations) require a check at only one point, after which the stock thermistor will conform to standard calibration curves to within 0.55°C.

Thermistors and simple carbon resistors are excellent sensing elements near absolute zero. As noted earlier, the negative temperature coefficient provides considerable sensitivity and adequate resistance, even in the minute sizes needed for fast response.

Carbon elements can be made by stripping the paper off radio resistors and by applying a coat of baked-on Glyptal. Resistance curves for such "home-made" elements are reproducible in the range of $1°$ to $20°K$ to within 0.2 percent. In the range of $20°K$ to $55°K$ and below $1°K$, accuracies to within 1 percent can be readily obtained. When cycled, however, these elements tend to lose their calibration, and below $4°K$, stray rf fields reduce their dc resistance, which can cause errors as high as 50 percent at $0.3°K$.

## 8-4. TEMPERATURE MEASUREMENTS†

In general, the temperature-measuring instrument will experience a temperature somewhat different from the undisturbed value of the temperature desired, due to the effects of all three modes of heat transfer. Heat is conducted across a contact resistance at the point of attachment and along the leads. Convection comes into the picture in cases where the wires and leads are suspended in a fluid or when the temperature of the fluid is desired. The effects of radiation are felt whenever the surroundings are at a temperature different from the temperature of the point to be measured. Whenever any or all of these modes are operative, a temperature difference, and hence a thermometer error, will exist.

### SURFACE TEMPERATURE MEASUREMENTS

Two conditions are of primary importance in surface temperature measurements: (1) minimization of the contact resistance between the temperature-sensing element and body surface, and (2) minimization of the heat conducted along the leads or thermocouple wires away from the measurement point. The contact resistance, as seen in Sec. 5-2, depends upon the pressure at the point of contact, and it is easy to demonstrate that thermocouples held on by tape will usually not give a correct temperature reading. Consequently, thermistors and thermocouples should be cemented, soldered, peened, or welded in place. On frames and surfaces that can be slightly marred, thermocouples can be readily attached with a capacitance welder. It should be kept in mind, however, that discharge welding may have adverse effects on circuit components if performed in the immediate vicinity of the components. Many suitable cements are available.‡ The only precaution is that the bead must be

† See Chapter 33 of Jakob[5] for more detail.

‡ One good cement which is easily removed from hard surfaces after the measurements are finished is Sauereisen cement.

close to the surface point of interest to avoid any sizable temperature drop across the cement.

The minimization of heat conduction along the wires is generally a simple problem to solve if the isotherms on the surface can be estimated. Since conduction requires a temperature gradient, a simple rule is to lay the wires along an isothermal line before traversing a temperature field of considerable gradient. The length necessary depends on the conductivity of the wire and on the conductivity of the body; the higher the first and the lower the second, the longer this length should be.† Of course, the thermal conductivity of the wires should be as low as possible, and usually the diameter of the wires should be as small as practical. An estimate of this type of error can be gained by considering a thermocouple fastened to a wall and protruding normal to the wall into an environment with a heat transfer coefficient $h$. The analytical solution of this problem can be gained by considering the conduction along the wire and, on neglecting the radial gradients, by treating the heat transfer at the surface as a heat generation.[3,5]

The thermometer error $T_w - T_0$ in relation to the temperature of the wall $T_w$ above the environment temperature $T_\infty$ is given as

$$\frac{T_w - T_0}{T_w - T_\infty} = \frac{\pi \sqrt{k_{\text{wire}} h r / 8}}{k_w + \pi \sqrt{k_{\text{wire}} h r / 8}} \tag{8-22}$$

where $T_0$ is the thermometer temperature, $r$ is the wire radius, and $k_w$ is the conductivity of the wall. In the case of essentially bare wires, the heat transfer coefficient can be evaluated from Fig. 6-8(b) for the wire radius $r$. If the wires are insulated, a thermal resistance‡ due to the insulation must be added in series with the thermal resistance due to convection, the total giving $1/h$. The thermal conductivities for some typical thermocouple materials and insulations are listed in Appendix B.

Lastly, the effects of radiation can be minimized by simply coating the sensor to match the optical properties of the wall surface of interest. If this is not possible, the use of radiation shields mentioned later may be necessary.

**Example 8.1.** An essentially bare 18-gauge copper-constantan thermocouple is to be used to measure the temperature of a steel wall at 93°C and an epoxy-glass printed wire board at 93°C. The thermocouple wires are allowed to protrude normal to the surface into a room at 38°C. Calculate the temperature errors encountered.

---

† For a copper-constantan thermocouple on cork, a length of 75 mm gives a 10 percent error in $(T_w - T_\infty)$, while a length of 50 mm gives a 1 percent error on iron.

‡ The wire-insulation composite can be treated as coaxial cylinders (see Fig. 5-10).

1. An 18-gauge wire has a diameter of 1 mm, and from Appendix B, $k_{\text{steel}} \approx 43$, $k_{\text{copper}} \approx 407$, $k_{\text{constantan}} \approx 23$ W/m · °C. To evaluate $h$, we take $N_{\text{Pr}} = 0.72$ for air and calculate $N_{\text{Gr}}$ using the properties in Appendix B:

$$N_{\text{Gr}} = \frac{g\beta}{\nu^2}(T_w - T_\infty)D^3 = \frac{(1.3 \times 10^6)(55)(0.001)^3}{1728} = 4.8$$

Consequently, $\log(N_{\text{Pr}} \cdot N_{\text{Gr}}) = \log[(0.72)(4.8)] = 0.538$, and from Fig. 6-8(b), $N_{\text{Nu}} \approx 1.3$, so that

$$h = \frac{1.3 k_{\text{air}}}{D} = \frac{1.3(0.027)}{0.001} = 35 \text{ W/m}^2 \cdot \text{°C}$$

Using these numbers in Eq. (8-22) and noting that $k_{\text{copper}} \gg k_{\text{constantan}}$, we have

$$\frac{T_w - T_0}{T_w - T_\infty} = \frac{\pi\sqrt{(407)(35)(5.1 \times 10^{-4})/8}}{43 + \pi\sqrt{0.638}} = 5.5 \text{ percent error}$$

or, for $T_w - T_\infty = 38$°C, the error is 2.1°C.

2. Using the above values, only now considering the epoxy-glass printed wire board for which $k_w = 0.29$ W/m · °C, we have:

$$\frac{T_w - T_0}{T_w - T_\infty} = \frac{\pi\sqrt{0.638}}{0.29 + \pi\sqrt{0.638}} = 91 \text{ percent error}$$

This means that the thermocouple will read 58.4°C when it should read 93°C. If one chooses lower-conductivity wires, then both wires will have to be included, using an effective radius for the combined areas in Eq. (8-22). Actually, the two wires conduct in parallel and Eq. (8-22) should be modified to account for this. In any case, the importance of the foregoing recommendations has been clearly demonstrated.

## GAS TEMPERATURE MEASUREMENTS

For accurate temperature measurements in either still air or flowing gases, two conditions are important: (1) the heat transfer coefficient between the gas and the sensor should be as high as possible, and (2) the radiative exchange between the sensing element and the environment should be as small as possible.

In both free and forced convection, the correlations shown in Figs. 6-8 and 6-12 indicate that $h$ varies inversely as some power of the wire size. Hence, for minimum error, the smallest wire practical should be used and, in this case, all but a varnish or similar insulation should be stripped off. Not only will the wire temperature be closer to the gas temperature under these conditions, but also the thermal time constant for transient and fluctuating measurements will be improved.

Consider steady-state temperature measurements of a gas where the heat conduction along the measuring instrument can be neglected by placing the instrument along an isotherm. In this case, the convection heat flow to the element can be equated to the radiative heat flow.† This results in a thermometer error that depends directly upon the emissivity of the thermometer and upon the gas and wall temperatures, and inversely upon the convection coefficient. It is good practice, then, to plate the sensing element with aluminum or gold. When this is not practical or sufficient, an aluminum or gold foil surrounding the sensor will serve as a radiation shield and will therefore lessen the thermometer error‡ as long as the convection coefficient is not substantially decreased.

For measurements in flowing fluids, the kinetic energy of the fluid is converted to enthalpy once the fluid is stopped by the surfaces of the sensing element. This conversion results in a temperature of the fluid at the sensing element that is higher than the temperature of the moving fluid. In fact, in viscous fluids the recovery factor[6] must also be used to account for the viscous dissipation due to the fluid being stopped by the sensor. These considerations are not important, however, for most equipment work where the velocities are sufficiently low and the fluid is usually air.§

## APPLICATIONS

In making temperature measurements for equipment evaluation, a careful layout of the sensing elements along with good mounting practices will make the measurements more meaningful. Since heat-flow paths as well as temperatures are important in design, one should mount a line of sensors normal to isotherms (which have been predicted or estimated from the thermal resistance concepts). In this manner, the heat flow can be determined from knowledge of the thermal resistance and from the measured temperature difference across that resistance, and alternate designs can then be logically compared.

If temperature sensors are strategically placed, then a reasonable estimate of the effectiveness of all the heat-flow paths can be used to compare the total heat flow to the total power dissipated in a circuit, cabinet, room, or whatever the unit might be. This comparison should be made as a check on the understanding of a thermal design so that significant heat-flow paths have not been forgotten or errors overlooked.

If possible, when using thermocouples, temperature *difference* measurements should be made, since systematic errors will often be canceled by this technique. This, of course, requires that some base temperature be approximately known

---

† See page 160 of Vol. 2 of Jakob.[5]

‡ A mercury-in-glass thermometer suspended without shielding in room air at 20°C will read 14.4°C if the walls of the room are at 0°C (see Ref. 5).

§ A velocity of 30.48 m/s amounts to a change of 0.78°C in air.

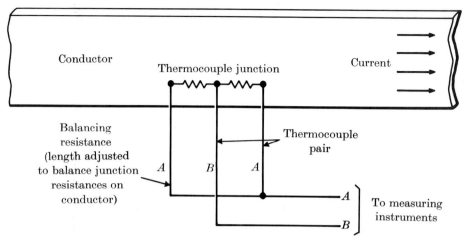

**Fig. 8-19** Thermocouple circuit for bodies having a voltage drop.

since the thermoelectric power is not exactly a constant over temperature ranges that may be encountered.

Instrumentation for the use of thermocouples and thermistors cannot be adequately covered here, but it is worth noting that thermocouple emfs can be measured either directly through electronic amplification and recording or by the potentiometric method of null balancing, i.e., comparison of the emf to a known voltage through use of a voltage divider. Thermistors can be used in bridge circuits; one specialized bridge was mentioned earlier. The most common bridge is the Wheatstone bridge, which utilizes a null-balance as a resistance indication. The Mueller bridge is useful in precision work where lead and electrical contact resistances may be important.

Lastly, it is necessary to say a few words about the use of thermocouples to measure the temperature of metals through which a current is flowing. In such cases, the voltage drop across the thermocouple junction may be of the same order as the emf due to the thermoelectric effect. This spurious voltage drop can be eliminated by the Wheatstone bridge arrangement illustrated in Fig. 8-19. Any remaining unbalance (as well as any parasitic voltages in a bridge circuit) can be accounted for if a reversing switch in the current circuit can be employed and the thermocouple readings are averaged.

## 8-5. SUMMARY OF THERMAL DESIGN AND EVALUATION

Thermal considerations must be included in the early stages in the development of an electronic system. Heat transfer paths for proposed system configurations are identified and subdivided into simpler subsystems. This usually results in a separation of the internal or pure conduction problem from the external or convection and radiation problem. The subsystems are coupled through matched or specified boundary conditions which may be conveniently visualized in terms of an electrical analog network. The parameters of the network are established by means of the heat transfer techniques presented in the previous chapters.

Starting with input conditions of dissipated power and environmental temperatures, an analysis of the network gives temperature predictions at various points of interest in the system. As illustrated in this chapter, this requires an iterative estimate of the coefficients that couple the two classes of problems.

As the development progresses, more precise analytical descriptions are obtained in conjunction with experimental evaluation of parts of the system. These results are ultimately confirmed by an experimental evaluation of the completed system. Thus, the complementary use of analytical and experimental techniques is necessary to achieve a good thermal design. This approach should result in: (1) higher system reliability, (2) a more compact system through integration of the cooling elements in the overall design, and (3) possible improvement in system performance.

## REFERENCES

1. Bodoia, J. R., and J. F. Osterle, "The Development of Free Convection Between Heated Vertical Plates," *J. Heat Transfer*, **84**, 40–44, Feb., 1962.

2. Herzfeld, C. M., F. G. Brickwedde, and A. I. Dahl, editors, *Temperature—Its Measurement and Control in Science and Industry*, **3**, parts 1 and 2, New York, Reinhold Publishing Corp., 1962. Figure 8-15 by permission.

3. Grober, H., S. Erk, and U. Grigull, *Fundamentals of Heat Transfer*, New York, McGraw-Hill Book Co., 1961.

4. Baker, H. D., E. A. Ryder, and N. H. Baker, *Temperature Measurement in Engineering*, New York, John Wiley & Sons, Inc., Vol. I, 1953; Vol. II, 1961. A good introductory text to the field.

5. Jakob, M., *Heat Transfer*, Vol. I and II, New York, John Wiley & Sons, Inc., 1949.

6. Eckert, E. R. G., and R. M. Drake, *Heat and Mass Transfer*, New York, McGraw-Hill Book Co., 1959.

# ELECTRICAL INTERACTIONS

*Chapter 9*

# SIGNAL TRANSMISSION

## R. G. Buus

The successful design of an electronic system depends on the satisfactory performance of its intended electrical function. This requires not only a high degree of skill in the design of the circuits, but also an accurate translation of the circuits into practical equipment. The importance of this translation or physical design results from the close relationship between circuit performance and the physical nature of the components or elements that comprise the system. Electrical interactions in the form of parasitics and interference depend on the type of materials employed, the geometry and construction of the components and interconnections, and their proximity and orientation relative to each other. The intent of the two chapters comprising Part III of this volume is to provide the designer with an understanding of the nature of electrical interactions and to equip him with both analytical and experimental tools to handle design problems in a logical manner.

This chapter begins with a brief review of some fundamentals of electromagnetic field theory. These fundamentals are then used to develop the transmission characteristics of various types of interconnections and to discuss the parasitic parameters associated with circuit elements. The following chapter deals with sources and methods of interference coupling and with various means of reducing interference.

## 9-I. FUNDAMENTALS OF ELECTROMAGNETIC FIELDS

The fundamental quantity of electricity is the charge, although a more familiar quantity is electric current, which is simply moving charge. Charges can interact with other charges even when they are separated by a vacuum. This "action at a distance" phenomenon is due to a field being set up around a charge. In fact, it is this phenomenon that is responsible for much of the interference and coupling between portions of equipment. The effects of coupling become more pronounced when the charge is moving as it is when current flows. Additional coupling effects arise when the current flow varies with time or when current-carrying conductors are moving. Moving charges and time-varying currents are both common conditions encountered in electronic systems and thus are of interest to us.

### THE ELECTRIC FIELD

Some of the properties of a stationary point charge, which may be an electron or a proton, will be investigated first. If a point test charge is placed in the field of the charge under investigation, a force will be found to act on the test charge. This was investigated by Coulomb in the 17th century, and he noted the following properties:

1. The force is of such a direction that like charges of the same polarity repel and opposite-polarity charges attract each other.
2. The magnitude of the force is directly proportional to the product of the magnitudes of the two charges.
3. The magnitude of the force is inversely proportional to the square of the distance separating the two charges.
4. The magnitude of the force is inversely proportional to a property of the material surrounding the charges called the *permittivity*. Permittivity will be discussed in more detail later.

If we use the SI system of units, the unit of charge is the coulomb, the unit of force is the newton, and the unit of distance is the meter. A common way to describe the field surrounding a charge is in terms of the force acting on a unit positive test charge. This is called the *electric field intensity* and is measured in newtons per coulomb (force per unit charge). We shall later define a new quantity called the *volt* which, dimensionally, is newton-meter per coulomb. From this, it can be seen that the electric field intensity can be expressed (as it usually is) in volts per meter. This electric field intensity is denoted by **E** and is a vector quantity. Figure 9-1 illustrates the direction of this **E** vector for a positive point charge in one plane of the spherical field. The magnitude of this vector increases as $1/r^2$ as we approach the point charge. If the point charge were a negative charge, all of the streamlines, which indicate the direction of the field, would change direction, and the arrows would all point to the charge. These electric streamlines originate and terminate at electric charges which can be thought of as sources and sinks for the field lines.

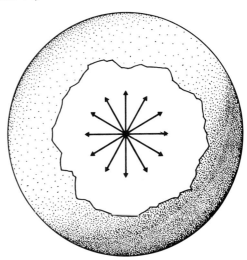

It was mentioned that Coulomb had observed that the force (consequently the electric field intensity, **E**) was inversely proportional to the permittivity of the material surrounding the charge. It is often convenient to consider the properties of charges without bringing in the characteristics of the material surrounding them. This can indeed be done if we define a new vector quantity called *electric flux density*,

**Fig. 9-1**  Direction of **E** vector around a positive point charge.

**D**, which is measured in coulombs per square meter. This brings us to the first of four fundamental laws of fields known as Maxwell's equations:

$$\oint_{\text{surface}} \mathbf{D} \cdot d\mathbf{A} = \int_{\text{volume}} \rho_V \, dV \qquad (9\text{-}1)$$

The vector area, **A**, is perpendicular to the differential area and points out from the closed surface of integration. The volume, $V$, referred to on the right side is the volume enclosed by this surface, and $\rho_V$ is the charge density in the volume. This equation then relates a surface integral to a volume integral and is often a means of determining **D** from a knowledge of the charges enclosed in any arbitrary surface.

For example, consider a single point charge, $Q$. Then the volume integral for any closed surface enclosing the charge equals $Q$. With the direction of **D** the same as that of **E**, it can be assumed from the previous discussion that **D** will be normal to the surface of a concentric sphere surrounding the charge. Since all points on the surface of the sphere are the same distance from the point charge, the magnitude of **D** is a constant. Then

$$\oint_{\text{surface}} \mathbf{D} \cdot d\mathbf{A} = D \oint_{\text{surface}} dA \qquad (9\text{-}2)$$

Integrating over the surface of a sphere of radius $r$ gives the familiar $4\pi r^2$ for the surface area. Thus we have

$$D4\pi r^2 = Q \quad \text{or} \quad D = \frac{Q}{4\pi r^2} \tag{9-3}$$

We can see that the magnitude of **D** is directly proportional to the charge $Q$ and inversely proportional to the square of the distance from the charge. This makes it very similar to the electric field intensity, **E**, except that **E** is also inversely proportional to the permittivity of the material. Indeed, **D** and **E** are related to each other by the *permittivity*, $\epsilon$, of the surrounding material by

$$\mathbf{D} = \epsilon\mathbf{E} \tag{9-4}$$

For most practical materials, this permittivity is constant ($\epsilon$ not a function of $E$) and isotropic ($\epsilon$ not a function of the direction of **E**). It is thus a scalar quantity, and **D** and **E** are parallel vectors. If this were not the case, $\epsilon$ would have to be treated as a tensor, and the direction of the **E** vector would not necessarily be parallel to that of the **D** vector. We will not consider such cases here since they are rather specialized. The units for $\epsilon$ are coulomb²/newton-meter². A more convenient unit is the farad (to be discussed later) having the dimensions of coulomb²/newton-meter, so that the units for $\epsilon$ become simply farad/meter.

The permittivity of free space, or a vacuum, has the magnitude

$$\epsilon_0 = 8.854 \times 10^{-12} \approx \frac{10^{-9}}{36\pi} \text{ F/m} \tag{9-5}$$

The permittivity of materials is often expressed relative to the permittivity of a vacuum by defining the relative permittivity as

$$\epsilon_r = \frac{\epsilon}{\epsilon_0} \tag{9-6}$$

The relative permittivity (commonly called dielectric constant) is given in Fig. 9-2 for several common materials.[1]

We may derive the **D** field about an infinite line charge of a charge per meter, $\rho_L$, if a cylinder is used as the surface of integration, as shown in Fig. 9-3. If we consider the line of charge to consist of many point charges, the resulting **D** field will equal the vector sum of the individual fields produced by each charge. However, the components of these contributions along the line of the charge cancel, so that the resultant field is perpendicular to the line of charge. Thus, the **D** field will be normal to the curved surface of the cylinder and parallel to the ends of the cylinder. Therefore,

$$\int_{\text{ends}} \mathbf{D} \cdot d\mathbf{A} = 0 \quad \text{and} \quad \int_{\substack{\text{curved} \\ \text{surface}}} \mathbf{D} \cdot d\mathbf{A} = D\int_{\substack{\text{curved} \\ \text{surface}}} dA \tag{9-7}$$

| Material | Dielectric constant or relative permittivity $(\epsilon_r)$ |
|---|---|
| Magnesium silicate (ceramic) | 5.0 to 6.0 |
| Porcelain | 5.7 |
| Glass | 5.0 to 9.0 |
| Bakelite | 4.0 to 6.0 |
| Epoxy resin | 3.0 to 5.0 |
| Nylon | 3.0 to 4.0 |
| Polyethylene | 2.25 to 2.35 |
| Teflon | 2.1 |
| Polystyrene | 2.56 |
| Rubber | 2.3 to 4.0 |
| Wood | 1.3 to 8.0 |
| Mica | 5.6 to 9.0 |
| Paper | 2.0 to 3.3 |

**Fig. 9-2**  Relative permittivity (dielectric constant) for some common materials.

We then integrate over the curved surface of the cylinder to obtain the surface area, $2\pi rl$. Since the volume integral is the total charge enclosed by the cylinder, this integral becomes simply $\rho_L l$. On substitution into Eq. (9-1), we obtain

$$D(2\pi rl) = \rho_L l \qquad (9\text{-}8)$$

or

$$D = \frac{\rho_L}{2\pi r} \qquad (9\text{-}9)$$

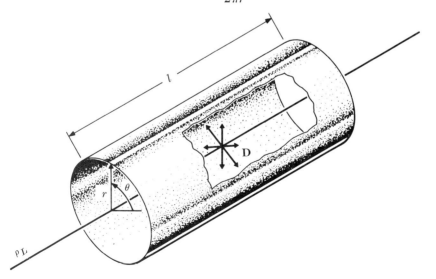

**Fig. 9-3**  Cylinder about an infinite line charge.

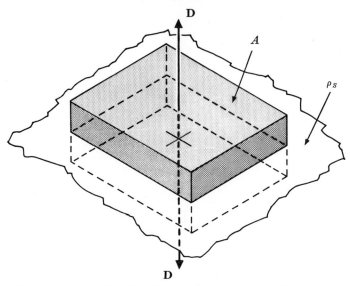

**Fig. 9-4** A closed surface intersecting an infinite sheet charge.

Note that in this case the electric flux density is still directly proportional to the charge $\rho_L$ but is inversely proportional to the radial distance $r$ rather than to the square of the distance, as it is for a point charge.

One last application of Eq. (9-1) is to consider an infinite sheet with charge per square meter, $\rho_S$. For the closed surface, we can choose a rectangular box as shown in Fig. 9-4. By an argument similar to that given for the line charge, it can be seen that the direction of the **D** vector will always be normal to the plane. The surface integral is zero for the sides of the box, and it is necessary to consider only the top and bottom where the **D** vector is normal to the surface area, $A$. The enclosed charge is simply $\rho_S A$. Therefore, proceeding as before, $2AD = \rho_S A$, or

$$D = \frac{\rho_S}{2} \qquad (9\text{-}10)$$

Thus, in the case of an infinite plane of $\rho_S$ coulombs per square meter, the magnitude of **D** is $\rho_S/2$ regardless of the distance from the plane. The direction of **D** is normal to the plane. The **E** field can be obtained in the preceding examples by dividing **D** by $\epsilon$.

We are now in a position to define *potential difference*, $V$, as the work done in moving a unit positive charge from one point to another in an electric field. In the SI system of units, work is measured in newton-meters, and the unit of charge is the coulomb; hence, the potential difference usually measured in volts is dimensionally newton-meters per coulomb, as previously mentioned. This work, or potential difference, can be expressed in terms of the electric field intensity as

$$V = -\int_{\text{initial point}}^{\text{final point}} \mathbf{E} \cdot d\mathbf{l} \tag{9-11}$$

or the voltage between two arbitrary points (i.e., from $B$ to $A$) is given by

$$V_{AB} = \int_{A}^{B} \mathbf{E} \cdot d\mathbf{l} \tag{9-12}$$

## CAPACITANCE

Any two conductors separated by an insulator can be considered a capacitor. If there is a total charge of $+Q$ on one conductor and $-Q$ on the other conductor, the electric field in the insulator can be described as

$$\mathbf{E} = Q\mathbf{F}(x, y, z) \tag{9-13}$$

where $\mathbf{F}$ is a vector function of space and depends upon the configuration or geometry and the properties of the insulator material. Then, integrating from one conductor to the other

$$\int \mathbf{E} \cdot d\mathbf{l} = Q\int \mathbf{F} \cdot d\mathbf{l} \tag{9-14}$$

where $\int \mathbf{F} \cdot d\mathbf{l}$ is a constant for any fixed geometry and is not dependent upon time or the voltage between the conductors. By definition,

$$\int \mathbf{F} \cdot d\mathbf{l} = \frac{1}{C} \tag{9-15}$$

where $C$ is the *capacitance* of the structure and is measured in farads. The integral $\int \mathbf{E} \cdot d\mathbf{l}$ may be taken along any convenient line from the positive conductor to the negative one, and it gives the voltage, $V$, between the conductors. Substituting back into Eq. (9-14) gives the familiar equation

$$V = \frac{Q}{C} \quad \text{or} \quad C = \frac{Q}{V} \tag{9-16}$$

Consider two parallel plates with charge density $-\rho_S$ on one and $+\rho_S$ on the other. If their separation, $d$, is small compared to their linear dimensions, we can assume that the interior $\mathbf{D}$ field will be normal to the plates. The presence of the second charged plate will double the $\mathbf{D}$ field between the plates (as compared to the $\mathbf{D}$ field of a single plate) and will cause the field external to the plate to vanish. Obviously, the magnitude of the $\mathbf{E}$ field will be given by

$$E = \frac{D}{\epsilon} = \frac{\rho_S}{\epsilon} \tag{9-17}$$

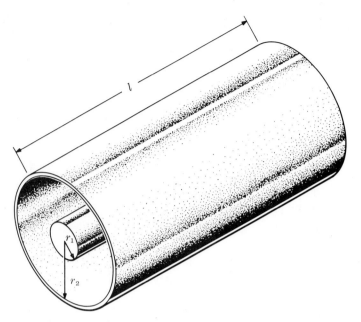

**Fig. 9-5** A coaxial structure with inner conductor radius $r_1$ and outer conductor radius $r_2$.

The charge on either plate is given by $Q = \rho_S A$, where $A$ is the total area of the plate. We can now find $C$ for this capacitor by

$$C = \frac{Q}{\int \mathbf{E} \cdot d\mathbf{l}} = \frac{\rho_S A}{\int_0^d (\rho_S / \epsilon) dx} = \frac{\rho_S A}{(\rho_S / \epsilon) d} = \frac{\epsilon A}{d} \qquad (9\text{-}18)$$

As a final exercise in determining capacitance, consider a coaxial structure as shown in Fig. 9-5. This has practical application since coaxial structures are often used as transmission lines in electronic equipment. Since the capacitance of such structures is directly proportional to length, it is convenient to consider the capacitance per meter (farads/meter). The **D** field in the region between the inner and outer conductors is the same as that produced by a line of charge located at the center of the structure with the same charge per meter as the inner conductor. We can then make good use of our previous investigation of the **D** field around a line charge of $\rho_L$ coulombs per meter; hence,

$$D = \frac{\rho_L}{2\pi r} \qquad (9\text{-}19)$$

or

$$E = \frac{\rho_L}{2\pi \epsilon r} \qquad (9\text{-}20)$$

The total charge on the inner conductor is $Q = \rho_L l$, so that the capacitance per meter becomes

$$C' = \frac{Q/l}{\int \mathbf{E} \cdot d\mathbf{l}} = \frac{\rho_L}{(\rho_L/2\pi\epsilon) \int_{r_1}^{r_2} (1/r)\, dr} = \frac{2\pi\epsilon}{\ln r_2 - \ln r_1} \qquad (9\text{-}21)$$

or

$$C' = \frac{2\pi\epsilon}{\ln (r_2/r_1)} \qquad (9\text{-}22)$$

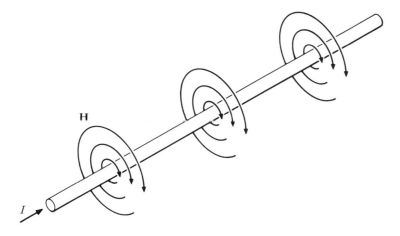

**Fig. 9-6**  Magnetic field around a wire carrying a current $I$.

## THE MAGNETIC FIELD

If the charges previously considered are not stationary but are moving (e.g., a current flowing through a wire), a magnetic field is also produced. This field is characterized in one of Maxwell's equations by

$$\oint_{\text{line}} \mathbf{H} \cdot d\mathbf{l} = I \qquad (9\text{-}23)$$

where $\mathbf{H}$ is the *magnetic field intensity* and is orthogonal to both the current flow and the electric field. Note that $\mathbf{H}$ is independent of the electrical characteristics of the surrounding material. The line integral is to be taken around a closed path that encircles the current, $I$.† If the current is in amperes (coulombs per second), then the magnetic field intensity, $\mathbf{H}$, is in amperes per meter. Figure 9-6 illustrates the $\mathbf{H}$ field around a conductor carrying a total current, $I$. Due to the symmetry of the $\mathbf{H}$ field, we can assume that $\mathbf{H}$ is a constant at a constant

---

† The current, $I$, consists of the sum of conduction and displacement currents, as explained later in this section.

radius from a wire carrying a current, $I$. The easiest way to evaluate this **H** field is to choose a set of cylindrical coordinates coincident with the axis of the wire. Then, the only nonzero **H** component is that which is in the $\theta$ direction. If we choose as our closed path a circle of radius $r$ enclosing the wire, Eq. (9-23) gives

$$\int_{\theta=0}^{2\pi} Hr\, d\theta = 2\pi r H = I \tag{9-24}$$

or

$$H = \frac{I}{2\pi r} \tag{9-25}$$

Just as we previously considered the existence of both an electric flux density, **D** (independent of surrounding material), and an electric field intensity, **E**, we can also consider a *magnetic flux density*, **B**. The magnetic flux density, **B**, is related to **H** by

$$\mathbf{B} = \mu \mathbf{H} \tag{9-26}$$

where $\mu$ is a property of the surrounding material and is called *permeability*. In the SI system, **B** is expressed in webers per square meter; so the units for $\mu$ become webers per ampere-meter. We will later discuss in detail a unit called the henry which is one weber per ampere. Then the units for $\mu$ become henry/meter. For free space,

$$\mu_0 = 4\pi \times 10^{-7} \text{ H/m} \tag{9-27}$$

Permeability is often given for many materials relative to the free space value, $\mu_0$. Thus

$$\mu_r = \frac{\mu}{\mu_0} \tag{9-28}$$

All nonferrous materials, with the exception of certain alloys of cobalt and nickel, have relative permeabilities very close to unity. The relative permeability of magnetic materials is a function of the physical and magnetic state of the material and also depends on the frequency of excitation. It can vary from near unity to values of several thousand.

Another of Maxwell's basic equations is

$$\oint_{\text{surface}} \mathbf{B} \cdot d\mathbf{A} = 0 \tag{9-29}$$

Note the similarity between Eq. (9-29) and Eq. (9-1). Equation (9-29) implies that a magnetic field has no point sources or, stated differently, that magnetic field lines must close upon themselves and cannot terminate or originate at any points in contrast to the electric field lines.

The fourth (and last) of Maxwell's equations is

$$\oint_{\text{line}} \mathbf{E} \cdot d\mathbf{l} = -\frac{\partial}{\partial t} \int_{\text{area}} \mathbf{B} \cdot d\mathbf{A} \tag{9-30}$$

The closed line integral bounds the surface area over which $\mathbf{B} \cdot d\mathbf{A}$ is integrated. This is the first appearance of time in Maxwell's equations. Obviously, time has been a factor previously because a current implies time-varying charge. Since we already know that $\int \mathbf{E} \cdot d\mathbf{l}$ defines a voltage, this equation tells us that a voltage can be generated by a time-varying magnetic $\mathbf{B}$ field. Furthermore, the magnitude of this generated (or induced) voltage is directly dependent upon the time rate of change of the $\mathbf{B}$ field. It is also one of the most common means of obtaining undesired interaction between circuits operating at high frequencies or with fast rising pulses. Much of this and the following chapter will dwell upon means of minimizing the effects described by this basic equation.

## INDUCTANCE

A current flowing in a conductor produces a magnetic field intensity $\mathbf{H}$ in the space surrounding the conductor which is directly proportional to the current. Since $\mathbf{B}$ and $\mathbf{H}$ are linearly related by $\mu$, we have

$$\mathbf{B} = I\mathbf{G}(x, y, z) \tag{9-31}$$

where $\mathbf{G}$ is a vector function of the configuration and permeability of the surrounding space and is a constant (time invariant) for any particular configuration. Substituting into Eq. (9-30) gives

$$\oint_{\text{line}} \mathbf{E} \cdot d\mathbf{l} = -\frac{\partial}{\partial t} \int_{\text{area}} I\mathbf{G} \cdot d\mathbf{A} = -\frac{dI}{dt} \int_{\text{area}} \mathbf{G} \cdot d\mathbf{A} \tag{9-32}$$

External inductance, $L$, is defined as

$$L = \int_{\text{area}} \mathbf{G} \cdot d\mathbf{A} \tag{9-33}$$

therefore

$$\oint \mathbf{E} \cdot d\mathbf{l} = -L \frac{dI}{dt} \tag{9-34}$$

Dimensionally, $L$ is in webers per meter. A more commonly used (and equivalent) unit is the henry which was previously mentioned.

Comparing the right sides of Eqs. (9-30) and (9-34) gives

$$L \frac{dI}{dt} = \frac{\partial}{\partial t} \int_{\text{area}} \mathbf{B} \cdot d\mathbf{A} \tag{9-35}$$

or

$$L = \frac{1}{I} \int_{\text{area}} \mathbf{B} \cdot d\mathbf{A} \tag{9-36}$$

where $\int_{\text{area}} \mathbf{B} \cdot d\mathbf{A}$ is the magnetic flux linking the current $I$.

We will again consider the coaxial structure of Fig. 9-5 and derive an expression for the inductance of the cable. The **H** field between the two conductors is given by Eq. (9-25). There is no **B** or **H** field outside the coaxial structure if we assume that all of the current flowing in the center conductor returns by the outer conductor. This may be established from Eq. (9-23) since the net current enclosed by a closed path around the outside conductor is zero. If the surface of integration of Eq. (9-36) is chosen so that all of the flux, **B**, lying between the conductors per unit length of coaxial is intersected, the area will lie in the $r, l$ plane. The equation for inductance $L'$ per meter then becomes:

$$L' = \int_0^1 \int_{r_1}^{r_2} \frac{\mu}{2\pi r} \, dr \, dl = \frac{\mu}{2\pi} \ln \frac{r_2}{r_1} \tag{9-37}$$

This is the external inductance since it does not include the effects of magnetic flux within the conductors. Actually, the total inductance is equal to the sum of the internal and external inductances. The internal inductance per meter, for example, of a round straight wire carrying direct current uniformly distributed throughout the cross section can be derived from energy considerations[2] as

$$L' = \frac{\mu}{8\pi} \tag{9-38}$$

In time-varying fields, however, a phenomenon called the *skin effect* causes high-frequency currents to be concentrated near the surface of conductors. As a consequence, there will be little magnetic flux present within the conductors, and the external inductance will be the only inductance of significance.

The idea of internal and external inductance can give one at least a qualitative idea of what skin effect is. The impedance of a unit length of wire is given by

$$Z' = R' + j\omega L' \tag{9-39}$$

where $R'$ is the resistance per meter, $\omega = 2\pi$ times the frequency in hertz, and $L'$ is the total inductance per meter of the wire. One may intuitively expect that, as the frequency increases, the current flow through the wire will distribute itself such that the magnitude of the impedance is minimized. When the frequency becomes high enough, the $j\omega L'$ term will always become predominant, and the current will distribute itself to minimize $L'$ by flowing on the outside surface of the wire, causing the internal inductance to become negligible. This results in an increased $R'$ component since the effective cross section of the wire has been substantially reduced. The two opposing effects always adjust themselves to minimize the magnitude of $Z'$. The frequency at which the skin effect becomes significant is dependent upon the conductivity of the conductor and upon its permeability. A more quantitative treatment of skin effect will be presented later in this chapter.

From the preceding discussion, the following general rules can be justified at least in principle:

1. Capacitance and inductance are independent of the magnitude of the applied voltage and current.
2. Capacitance is directly proportional to the permittivity of the material separating the conductors, while inductance is directly proportional to the permeability of the material surrounding the conductors.
3. Capacitance tends to increase as the size of the conductors increases or the spacing between them decreases.
4. Inductance generally tends to increase as the area enclosed by conductors increases or as the size of the conductor decreases.
5. The capacitance and external inductance of a coaxial structure are functions of the ratio of the radii.

## 9-2. FIELD MAPPING TECHNIQUES

The examples thus far have involved simple symmetrical configurations. While such configurations are not uncommon, we are frequently concerned with more complex geometries as encountered, for example, in the design of circuit interconnections. In general, a common problem is to determine the electric field configuration in a dielectric medium resulting from potentials applied to conductors embedded in that dielectric.

Consider an elemental volume ($\Delta V = \Delta x \, \Delta y \, \Delta z$) in a dielectric medium as shown in Fig. 9-7. The electric flux vector $\mathbf{D}$ is resolved into $x$, $y$, and $z$ components in the rectangular coordinate system as shown. Application of Eq. (9-1) gives

$$\oint_{\text{surface}} \mathbf{D} \cdot d\mathbf{A} = \frac{\partial D_x}{dx} \Delta V + \frac{\partial D_y}{dy} \Delta V + \frac{\partial D_z}{dz} \Delta V = \rho_V \, \Delta V$$

and, in the limit as $\Delta V$ approaches zero,

$$\frac{\partial D_x}{\partial x} + \frac{\partial D_y}{\partial y} + \frac{\partial D_z}{\partial z} = \rho_V$$

For a constant, isotropic dielectric, Eq. (9-4) applies and, when substituted in the above expression, gives

$$\frac{\partial E_x}{\partial x} + \frac{\partial E_y}{\partial y} + \frac{\partial E_z}{\partial z} = \frac{\rho_V}{\epsilon}$$

Since the partial derivative of voltage with respect to any coordinate is equal to the negative of the corresponding electric field component [as may be inferred from Eq. (9-11)], we write

$$\frac{\partial^2 V}{\partial x^2} + \frac{\partial^2 V}{\partial y^2} + \frac{\partial^2 V}{\partial z^2} = -\frac{\rho_V}{\epsilon} \tag{9-40}$$

which is Poisson's equation.

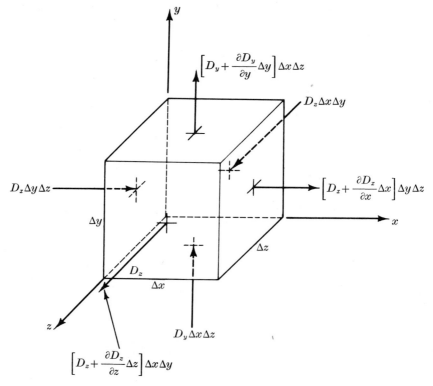

**Fig. 9-7**  A Gaussian surface within a dielectric medium.

When there is no charge in the dielectric between conductors ($\rho_V = 0$), Poisson's equation reduces to Laplace's equation:

$$\frac{\partial^2 V}{\partial x^2} + \frac{\partial^2 V}{\partial y^2} + \frac{\partial^2 V}{\partial z^2} = 0 \qquad (9\text{-}41)$$

By similar reasoning, Laplace's equation in cylindrical $(r, \varphi, z)$ coordinates is

$$\frac{1}{r}\frac{\partial}{\partial r}\left(r\,\frac{\partial V}{\partial r}\right) + \frac{1}{r^2}\left(\frac{\partial^2 V}{\partial \varphi^2}\right) + \frac{\partial^2 V}{\partial z^2} = 0 \qquad (9\text{-}42)$$

and in spherical $(r, \theta, \varphi)$ coordinates

$$\frac{1}{r^2}\frac{\partial}{\partial r}\left(r^2\,\frac{\partial V}{\partial r}\right) + \frac{1}{r^2 \sin \theta}\frac{\partial}{\partial \theta}\left(\sin \theta\,\frac{\partial V}{\partial \theta}\right) + \frac{1}{r^2 \sin^2 \theta}\frac{\partial^2 V}{\partial \varphi^2} = 0 \qquad (9\text{-}43)$$

The potential in a dielectric between conductors must satisfy Laplace's equation. Given the potential on all conductors as boundary conditions, the problem is one of finding a solution to the differential equation. Most solutions[3] to nontrivial configurations involve summations of many harmonics.

In many practical cases, more than one dielectric material may be present, and boundary conditions at the interface between dielectrics must also be satisfied. It can be shown that electric fields are refracted as they cross a dielectric interface in such a way that the tangential component of the E field and the normal component of the D field are continuous across the boundary.[2] The two discontinuous field components can be determined from Eq. (9-4). This permits a determination of the field on one side of a conductor if the field on the other side is known. The presence of more than one dielectric, however, usually adds to the complexity of the problem.

Many practical problems can be considered two-dimensional since there are many cases where the lengths of the conductors are large compared to the cross-sectional dimensions. In such cases, Laplace's equation is reduced to two dimensions, and the solutions are called circular harmonics.

Conformal transformations[4,5] are also useful in providing solutions to complex two-dimensional problems. The geometry of the problem is transformed by a conjugate function that preserves the orthogonality of the electric streamlines and potential lines to produce a simpler geometry for which solutions are available. The solution in the transformed geometry is then transformed backward to obtain the solution to the original problem. The Schwartz-Christoffel transformation is one of the most useful. It transforms the upper half of the complex plane into the interior of a polygon in the complex plane.

There are also several techniques for obtaining approximate solutions to two-dimensional field problems. Some of these procedures will be briefly described.

## METHOD OF CURVILINEAR SQUARES

The method of curvilinear squares is a graphical technique for mapping two-dimensional field problems. The electric field and potential lines are drawn by hand according to the following rules:

1. Conductor boundaries are at constant potential.
2. Electric field and flux density are perpendicular to the equipotential surfaces.
3. Lines of flux begin and terminate on charge and in a charge-free, homogenous dielectric, begin and terminate on conductor boundaries.

Figure 9-8 illustrates the streamlines which are everywhere tangent to the E field between the two rectangular conductors. The lines are drawn so that each flux path formed by adjacent streamlines carries an equal amount of flux from one conductor to the other. Also shown are the equipotential lines drawn with a constant potential difference between lines and orthogonal to the

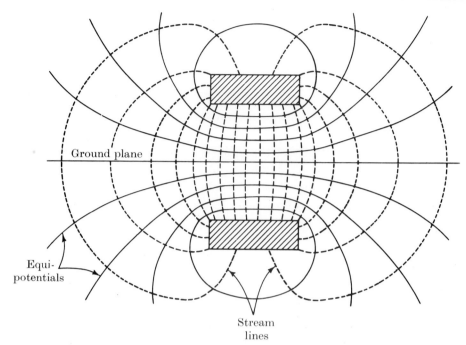

Ground plane

Equi-
potentials

Stream
lines

**Fig. 9-8**   A field plot for two parallel rectangular conductors.

streamlines. These requirements are satisfied at any point if the distance
between streamlines equals the distance between equipotentials.[2] This divides
the region between the conductors into curvilinear squares which have slightly
curved but approximately equal sides as shown, and which can be rapidly
sketched.

The resulting capacitance is equal to the ratio of charge on one conductor
to the potential difference between conductors. Since charge is proportional
to the number of flux paths, $n_f$, and voltage is proportional to the number of
potential increments, $n_v$, the capacitance per meter can be shown to be

$$C' = \epsilon F \qquad (9\text{-}44)$$

where the form factor, $F$, is equal to the ratio $n_f/n_v$. The form factor is a
function only of the geometry of the configuration. Note that an infinite
conducting ground plane can be introduced midway between the two conductors. It is obvious from Eq. (9-44) that the capacitance from any one
conductor to the ground plane is twice the capacitance between conductors.

A more typical configuration involves multiple dielectrics as shown in Fig.
9-9 for a conductor over a ground plane on a printed wire board. For clarity
in the figure, the relative permittivity of the board is assumed to be only 2.
Larger values of $\epsilon_r$ (4 to 6) are more typical, but a field map for such values

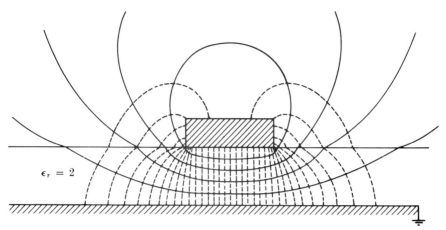

**Fig. 9-9** Conductor on printed board with ground plane.

would result in either undue crowding of the flux lines in the dielectric or a very sparse set of lines in the air. Note that Fig. 9-9 has been drawn so as to maintain curvilinear rectangles in the dielectric. The ratio of distance between potential lines and streamlines at any point in the dielectric is $\epsilon_r$.

Once the field map is established, the capacitance of the structure is easily determined by counting squares and rectangles. In this case, $n_f = 33$ and $n_v = 5$ so that $C' = 6.6\epsilon_0$. Note that $\epsilon_0$ is used in calculating the capacitance because the effects of the higher permittivity of the dielectric are automatically considered in the curvilinear rectangles. If one had chosen to plot curvilinear squares in the dielectric, rectangles with $1/\epsilon_r$ voltage to flux ratio would appear in the air, and the permittivity of the dielectric would be used in Eq. (9-44).

It should be evident that field plotting of multiple dielectric problems is not an easy task. However, since the dielectric attracts flux lines (see Fig. 9-9), sufficient accuracy can often be obtained by ignoring the flux paths in the air. A method of achieving improved accuracy[6] is to assume that the field lines are not altered by the presence of the dielectric and to weight the curvilinear squares in the dielectric material relative to those in the air path. In a homogeneous dielectric material, the curvilinear squares represent equal capacitance. In this case, each curvilinear square in the board material is multiplied by its relative permittivity. The capacitance values of all the curvilinear squares are then combined to give the total capacitance of the structure. Another approach is to alter the effective thickness of the dielectric material making it inversely proportional to relative permittivity, and solving as a single dielectric problem. Both methods require that the field lines be nearly normal to the dielectric interface for high accuracy.

SEMI-ANALYTIC METHOD

This technique[7] is closely related to the method of curvilinear squares and is useful in determining capacitance or inductance rather than for determining an exact field configuration. To illustrate the method, consider the problem of determining the capacitance of a wiring strip of rectangular cross section above a ground plane, as shown in Fig. 9-10. Because of the symmetry of the problem,

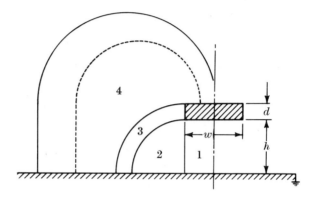

**Fig. 9-10**   Conductor above a ground plane.

it is necessary to consider only the left half of the cross section. The resulting capacitance is doubled to obtain the total capacitance of the structure.

The first step is to subdivide the area into geometrically simple shapes, as shown in Fig. 9-10, for the purpose of computing form factors for each area. Each area represents a grouping of flux paths, so the sides of these areas should approximately coincide with flux flow lines. If we plotted the field in detail, the form factor would be equal to the ratio of the number of flux paths to the number of potential increments between conductors. By this method, an equivalent form factor, $F_i$, for any cross-sectional area is given by

$$F_i = \frac{A_i}{l_m^2} \tag{9-45}$$

where $l_m$ is the length of the mean flux path in the area $A_i$, and the ratio $A_i/l_m$ is the number of paths. Area 1 is the simplest to calculate and can be written by inspection as

$$F_1 = \frac{(w/2)(h)}{h^2} = \frac{w}{2h}$$

For area 2, the mean path length is a line midway between the vertical radius and the arc which is equal to $1.22h$ for this geometry. Since the area is $\pi h^2/4$, then

$$F_2 = \frac{\pi h^2/4}{(1.22h)^2} = 0.52$$

which is independent of the size of the quadrant. In similar fashion, for area 3,

$$F_3 = \frac{(\pi d/4)(2h + d)}{(\pi^2/16)(2h + d)^2} = \frac{4}{\pi(2h/d + 1)}$$

Area 4 is the most difficult to compute because it does not have a simple analytical shape and is not easily defined. An estimate can be obtained by roughly bounding the area and estimating a mean path length. The form factor is not sensitive to the precise manner in which this is done, and it may represent only a small contribution to the total capacitance.

The total capacitance is obtained by summing the individual form factors to obtain the form factor for the entire configuration and then multiplying by the permittivity [Eq. (9-44)]. This technique can be extended to other shapes, to multiple dielectric problems, and even to three-dimensional configurations.[7]

Thus far the discussion has centered around the electric field and capacitance determination. The similarity between Eq. (9-1) for electric fields and Eq. (9-29) for magnetic fields suggests that the same techniques can be applied to magnetic fields. The basic difference is that the current flow is producing magnetic flux which is represented by flux lines encircling the conductor. Inductance is determined by the ratio of the number of magnetic flux paths encircling the current to the corresponding number of magnetic equipotential lines. (A flux line encircling two conductors carrying equal but opposite currents does not contribute to the inductance.) This ratio is equal to the inverse of the form factor $F$; thus, external inductance per meter is given by

$$L' = \frac{\mu}{F} \tag{9-46}$$

where $\mu$ is the permeability of the surrounding medium containing the field. The form factor, $F$, must not include any effects of dielectric constant resulting from scaled dimensions or curvilinear rectangles. The dielectric has no effect on inductance if its relative permeability is unity.

It can be deduced from Eq. (9-46) that the external inductance per meter of a single conductor over a ground plane is exactly half that of the pair of conductors. This is confirmed by Eq. (9-36) since the area of integration is halved by the insertion of the ground plane.

## ITERATION AND RELAXATION METHODS

Numerical techniques are also available for solving Laplace's equation.[2] Except for relatively simple problems, the computation is too tedious to accomplish manually. However, the techniques are easily applicable to machine computation. The method of solution by iteration and relaxation was outlined in Chapter 5 in relation to the solution of steady-state thermal conduction problems and will not be treated here.

EXPERIMENTAL METHODS

There are several experimental methods of field mapping available. Actual measurement of the field potential is difficult because the insertion of a measuring instrument in the field can significantly modify the field. In mapping fields, it is common to use a current analogy for electric flux. By applying conductors to appropriate parts of resistance paper and measuring voltages on the resistance sheet with a probe, the equipotential lines can be established. Similar information can be obtained from electrolytic tanks which have the added flexibility of being able to simulate different dielectrics by variations in the depth of the electrolytic solution.[5]

**Example 9.1.** Systems that handle high voltage usually require that high-voltage conductors be carried through a grounded metal case (e.g., a capacitor

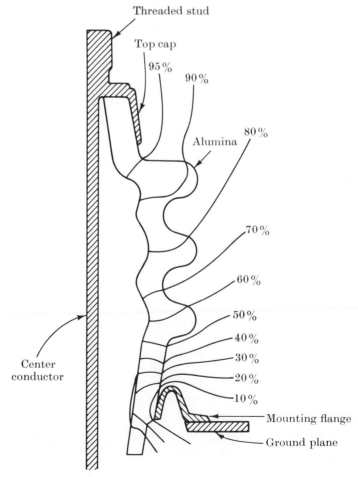

**Fig. 9-11**   Equipotential plot of a high-voltage terminal.[8]

or transformer housing). This requires the use of a high-voltage terminal usually making use of an alumina (ceramic) insulating material. A typical terminal[8] is shown in cross section in Fig. 9-11. The high voltage is carried through the ground plane by the center conductor, while the alumina structure with its undulations provides a long leakage path between the top cap and ground.

Figure 9-11 also shows several equipotential lines obtained by building a resistance analog of the insulator and plotting the equipotentials. The benefit derived by determining the field configuration is immediately obvious from the figure. Note how closely the equipotentials are spaced in the air near the mounting-flange–alumina interface. The electric field in this area may easily be high enough to locally ionize the air. While not causing insulator breakdown, the ionization does result in corona which introduces noise and interference in the system, as will be discussed in the next chapter. Thus, it is necessary to determine how the terminal may be redesigned to reduce its susceptibility to corona.

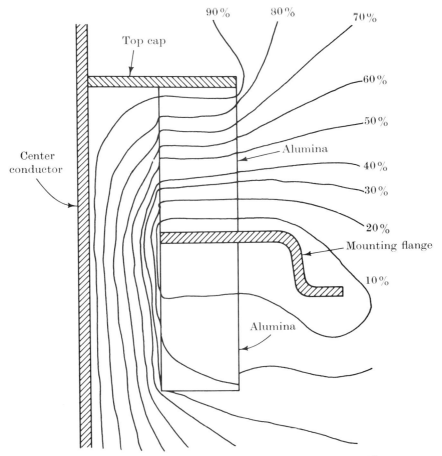

**Fig. 9-12**  Equipotential plot of proposed corona-free terminal.[8]

To see the effects of changing the mounting-flange–alumina interface, the model shown in Fig. 9-12 was constructed with resistance paper and equi-potentials plotted as shown. This is a much better terminal, and one can easily surmise from the figure that the high-voltage performance of this terminal should be better than that of the previous one. It should be noted that a high electric field in the alumina is not so serious since alumina has a much higher dielectric strength than that of air. Also, the space between the center conductor and the alumina is usually filled with oil or a high-breakdown gas such as sulfur hexafluoride to avoid breakdown in this region.

It is also evident from Fig. 9-12 that the remaining weak point in the terminal model is the field concentration resulting from sharp edge of the top cap. This can be alleviated by making all corners of the top cap of large radii.

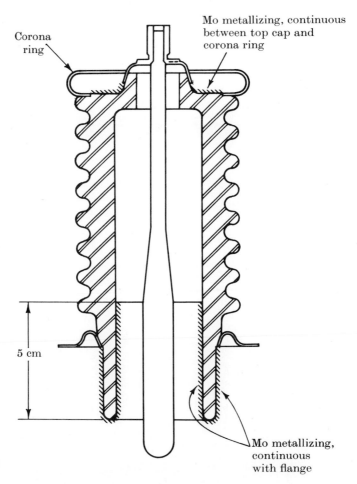

**Fig. 9-13**   Redesigned alumina terminal with internal metallizing and corona shield.[8]

A practical embodiment of the model in Fig. 9-12 is shown in Fig. 9-13. The corona ring avoids the field concentrations around the top cap. The nickel-plated molybdenum metalizing on the lower end of the insulator "shields" the critical flange-alumina interface and eliminates the resulting field enhancement. Tests made with this terminal have shown it to be corona free to nearly its breakdown voltage.

## 9-3. CIRCUIT THEORY FROM FIELD CONCEPTS

The common expressions of circuit analysis are directly derivable from Maxwell's equations with the following constraints:

1. The conducting path or circuit is defined by a filamentary conductor of negligible cross section.
2. The physical dimensions of the circuit are small as compared with a wavelength.
3. No part of the circuit is within a time-varying field due to external causes nor is any part of the circuit moving in a magnetic field.
4. All electric flux is confined to capacitors.
5. All magnetic flux is confined to inductors.
6. Nonzero resistivity is confined to resistors.

The third constraint avoids consideration of any spurious coupling from a separate circuit. This is usually desired but not always obtained in practice. The last three constraints can often be circumvented by simply adding additional capacitors, inductors, or resistors (generally called strays) until these constraints are satisfied. This, of course, complicates the representation of the circuit considerably.

Consider the simple configuration shown in Fig. 9-14. An external electric field is applied between the points 0 and 1 and is independent of the current that may flow (an ideal voltage source). Between points 2 and 3 there is a resistor; the voltage across the resistor is directly proportional to the current through it (Ohm's law is satisfied). Points 4 and 5 are plates of a capacitor of area $A$, spacing $d$, and material of permittivity $\epsilon$ between the plates. Between points 6 and 7, the conductor is wound into a coil or helix of very fine pitch.

Beginning with Eq. (9-30):

$$\oint_{\text{line}} \mathbf{E} \cdot d\mathbf{l} = -\frac{\partial}{\partial t} \int_{\text{area}} \mathbf{B} \cdot d\mathbf{A}$$

we will consider the surface integral on the right. The conductor between points 6 and 7, being wound in a helix, produces a much larger magnetic field within the helix than in any other region along the filament. It can then be

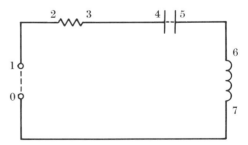

**Fig. 9-14**   A series $RLC$ circuit.

assumed that the inductance given by

$$L = \frac{1}{I} \int_{\text{area}} \mathbf{B} \cdot d\mathbf{A}$$

is the inductance of the helix, or

$$\oint \mathbf{E} \cdot d\mathbf{l} = -L \frac{dI}{dt}$$

where $I$ is the current in the filamentary conductor.

The closed line integral is taken along the filament, directly between the capacitor plates and points 0 and 1, as indicated by the dashed line in Fig.9-14. The contribution from the perfectly conducting filament is obviously zero. Therefore,

$$\oint \mathbf{E} \cdot d\mathbf{l} = \int_0^1 \mathbf{E} \cdot d\mathbf{l} + \int_2^3 \mathbf{E} \cdot d\mathbf{l} + \int_4^5 \mathbf{E} \cdot d\mathbf{l} \tag{9-47}$$

The first intergal on the right is the negative of the voltage between points 1 and 0:

$$\int_0^1 \mathbf{E} \cdot d\mathbf{l} = -V_{10}$$

This integral is a function only of the external source, and since the external source is usually considered as a voltage instead of an electric field intensity, the result is called the applied voltage, $V_0$.

$$\int_0^1 \mathbf{E} \cdot d\mathbf{l} = -V_0 \tag{9-48}$$

The second integral of Eq. (9-47) is taken across the resistor of total resistance, $R$, so that

$$\int_2^3 \mathbf{E} \cdot d\mathbf{l} = IR \tag{9-49}$$

The third integral of Eq. (9-47) is across the region between the capacitor plates. From Eq. (9-14) and the definition of $C$,

$$\int_4^5 \mathbf{E} \cdot d\mathbf{l} = Q \int_4^5 \mathbf{F} \cdot d\mathbf{l} = \frac{Q}{C} = \frac{1}{C} \int I\, dt \tag{9-50}$$

Combining these results gives

$$-V_0 + IR + \frac{1}{C} \int I\, dt = -L \frac{dI}{dt} \tag{9-51}$$

or

$$V_0 = IR + L \frac{dI}{dt} + \frac{1}{C} \int I\, dt \tag{9-52}$$

which is the equation of circuit theory for the $RLC$ series circuit.

## 9-4. PROPAGATION OF ELECTROMAGNETIC WAVES

Electrical energy can be propagated either by conduction along wires or by radiation through the "action at a distance" phenomenon of fields. The type of propagation most familiar (and most widely understood) is that via conducting wires or transmission lines. Any current flowing through a wire in one direction must have a return path which allows the same current to flow in the reverse direction. This return path may be via a similar wire, a combination of several wires, or a common ground plane. As a consequence, any wire can be treated as a transmission line, provided the return path is considered.

### TRANSMISSION LINES

A section of a transmission line is shown in Fig. 9-15. We will consider the response of the line to a sinusoidal excitation. For a differential length, $dx$, of the line, there is a differential voltage change $dV$ resulting from the line current $I$ flowing through the impedance $(R' + j\omega L')\, dx$, where $R'$ is the resistance of the line per meter, $L'$ is the inductance per meter, and $\omega$ is $2\pi$ times the frequency in hertz. The differential current change, $dI$, results as a flow of current between the wires through the admittance $(G' + j\omega C')\, dx$, where $G'$ is the shunt conductance per meter and $C'$ is the capacitance per meter. These can be written in the form of equations:

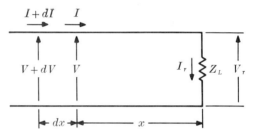

**Fig. 9-15** A section of terminated transmission line.

$$dV = I(R' + j\omega L')\, dx \qquad (9\text{-}53)$$

$$dI = V(G' + j\omega C')\, dx \qquad (9\text{-}54)$$

Letting $R' + j\omega L' = Z'$, the impedance per meter and $G' + j\omega C' = Y'$, the admittance per meter, and rearranging, we obtain

$$\frac{dV}{dx} = (R' + j\omega L')I = Z'I \qquad (9\text{-}55)$$

$$\frac{dI}{dx} = (G' + j\omega C')V = Y'V \qquad (9\text{-}56)$$

An equation in terms of only voltage can be obtained by differentiating Eq. (9-55) with respect to $x$, and substituting Eq. (9-56) to eliminate the resulting

$dI/dx$. This gives

$$\frac{d^2 V}{dx^2} = Z'Y'V \tag{9-57}$$

Similarly, the differential equation in terms of current $I$ is

$$\frac{d^2 I}{dx^2} = Z'Y'I \tag{9-58}$$

Equations (9-57) and (9-58) are not independent of each other, since they are related through Eq. (9-55) or (9-56).

Equations (9-57) and (9-58) have solutions of the form

$$V = V_1 e^{\sqrt{Z'Y'}\,x} + V_2 e^{-\sqrt{Z'Y'}\,x} \tag{9-59}$$

$$I = I_1 e^{-\sqrt{Z'Y'}\,x} + I_2 e^{-\sqrt{Z'Y'}\,x} \tag{9-60}$$

where $V_1$, $V_2$, $I_1$, and $I_2$ are constants of integration whose values are determined by the boundary conditions. Although four constants appear in these equations, only two of them are independent. This can be shown by substituting Eq. (9-60) into Eq. (9-56) and comparing the result with Eq. (9-59). As a result,

$$I_1 = \frac{V_1}{\sqrt{Z'/Y'}} \tag{9-61}$$

$$I_2 = -\frac{V_2}{\sqrt{Z'/Y'}} \tag{9-62}$$

Thus, Eqs. (9-59) and (9-60) can then be written as

$$V = V_1 e^{\sqrt{Z'Y'}\,x} + V_2 e^{-\sqrt{Z'Y'}\,x} \tag{9-63}$$

$$I = \frac{V_1}{Z_0} e^{\sqrt{Z'Y'}\,x} - \frac{V_2}{Z_0} e^{-\sqrt{Z'Y'}\,x} \tag{9-64}$$

where $Z_0 = \sqrt{Z'/Y'}$ is called the characteristic impedance of the line.

Equations (9-63) and (9-64) contain two arbitrary constants, $V_1$ and $V_2$, which can be evaluated at the load impedance where $x = 0$, the voltage is $V_r$, the current is $I_r$, and the load impedance is $Z_L = V_r/I_r$. Substituting these relations leads to

$$V_1 = \frac{V_r}{2}\left(1 + \frac{Z_0}{Z_L}\right) = \frac{V_r + I_r Z_0}{2} \tag{9-65}$$

$$V_2 = \frac{V_r}{2}\left(1 - \frac{Z_0}{Z_L}\right) = \frac{V_r - I_r Z_0}{2} \tag{9-66}$$

The relations expressed by Eqs. (9-63) and (9-64) are capable of simple physical interpretation. It will be noted that the voltage and current that exist on the transmission line consist of two components. The first of these is a voltage $V_1 e^{\sqrt{Z'Y'}x}$, where $V_1$ is given by Eq. (9-65) with an associated current that is equal to this voltage divided by the characteristic impedance $Z_0$. This combination of voltage and current can be interpreted as a wave traveling toward the receiver. The second component of the voltage and current distribution consists of the voltage $V_2 e^{-\sqrt{Z'Y'}x}$, where $V_2$ is given by Eq. (9-66), accompanied everywhere by a current equal to this voltage divided by $-Z_0$ (the minus sign means the current travels toward the generator). This second voltage and current distribution can be considered as a wave train traveling from the receiver toward the generator. This second wave train can be thought of as resulting from the reflection of the first wave by the load impedance at the receiving end of the line. For this reason, the wave traveling to the receiver is often designated as the incident wave, while the second wave is termed the reflected wave.

The term $\sqrt{Z'Y'}$, called the propagation constant, is a complex quantity and can be written as the sum of a real part $\alpha$ and an imaginary part $\beta$:

$$\sqrt{Z'Y'} = \alpha + j\beta \qquad (9\text{-}67)$$

We then have

$$e^{\sqrt{Z'Y'}x} = e^{\alpha x - j\beta x} = e^{\alpha x}e^{j\beta x} \qquad (9\text{-}68)$$

$$e^{-\sqrt{Z'Y'}x} = e^{-\alpha x - j\beta x} = e^{-\alpha x}e^{-j\beta x} \qquad (9\text{-}69)$$

Since $e^{j\beta}$ can be interpreted as a unit phasor at an angle of $\beta$, it is seen that the incident wave becomes larger at increasing distance from the receiver in accordance with the exponential $e^{\alpha x}$ and that the phase of this wave advances $\beta$ radians per meter, as one approaches the generator end. If, instead of measuring the length from the receiver to the generator, we considered the length to increase toward the receiver, then this incident wave would decrease in magnitude by the factor $e^{-\alpha x}$ as it approached the receiver and would drop back $\beta$ radians in phase per meter as it approached the receiver. By a similar reasoning, the reflected wave can be considered as traveling toward the generator and decaying in magnitude and phase as it travels.

It can be seen that this quantity, $\alpha$, is the loss per meter of a transmission line terminated by its characteristic impedance, and it gives the loss directly in nepers per meter. The transmission line loss is more often expressed as a power loss per meter, with the loss expressed in decibels. The decibel is defined as 10 log of a power ratio. Thus, in this case, the loss could be given by

$$10 \log (e^x)^2 = 20 \log e^x = 20\alpha \log e = 8.686\alpha \quad \text{dB/meter}$$

The wavelength is defined as the length of transmission line in which the traveling wave phase changes $2\pi$ radians. This length can be seen to be

$$\lambda = \frac{2\pi}{\beta} \qquad (9\text{-}70)$$

In this chapter, lines of length less than $\lambda/2\pi$ will be considered electrically short lines where phase shift can be ignored to a first approximation. Lines of greater length will have significant phase shift which must be considered.

It can be shown that $\beta$ is not independent of frequency. In fact, for most transmission lines, a less frequency-dependent parameter is the velocity of propagation, given by:

$$c = f\lambda = \frac{2\pi f}{\beta} = \frac{\omega}{\beta} \tag{9-71}$$

The velocity of propagation for a lossless coaxial cable ($R = G = 0$) is dependent only upon the permeability and permittivity of the material in the space between the two conductors. In general,

$$c = \frac{c_0}{\sqrt{\epsilon_r \mu_r}} \tag{9-72}$$

where $c_0$ is the velocity of propagation of light in free space, or

$$c_0 \approx 3 \times 10^8 \text{ m/s} \tag{9-73}$$

Equation (9-73) shows that conductors surrounded by materials of higher permittivity than air (e.g., conductors of a printed circuit board) will have a velocity of propagation less than that of free space.

In a similar manner, the wavelength is given by

$$\lambda = \frac{\lambda_0}{\sqrt{\epsilon_r \mu_r}} \tag{9-74}$$

where $\lambda_0$ is the free space wavelength which is plotted as a function of frequency in Fig. 9-16.

The incident and reflected waves existing on a transmission line must be so related that at the receiving end they add to give the receiving voltage and current. The vector ratio $V_2/V_1$ of the reflected voltage to the incident voltage is called the reflection coefficient and is found from Eqs. (9-65) and (9-66) to be

$$\text{Reflection coefficient} = \rho = \frac{(Z_L/Z_0) - 1}{(Z_L/Z_0) + 1} = \frac{Z_L - Z_0}{Z_L + Z_0} \tag{9-75}$$

It will be noted that the reflection coefficient depends only upon the vector ratio $Z_L/Z_0$ (ratio of load impedance to characteristic impedance). The reflection coefficient is often expressed as return loss, which is defined as

$$\text{Return loss} = 20 \log \left| \frac{1}{\rho} \right| = 20 \log \left| \frac{Z_L + Z_0}{Z_L - Z_0} \right| \tag{9-76}$$

This is equal to the power ratio between the incident and reflected waves at the receiver.

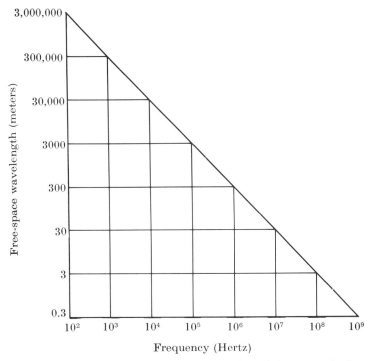

**Fig. 9-16**  The relation between wavelength and frequency in free space.

Another common way of expressing reflection characteristics is by means of the voltage standing wave ratio (VSWR). This is defined as the ratio of the voltage of the incident and reflected waves when they are in phase (the sum of $V_1$ and $V_2$) to the voltage of the two waves when they are in phase opposition (the difference between $V_1$ and $V_2$). Thus,

$$\text{VSWR} = S = \frac{V_1 + V_2}{V_1 - V_2} \tag{9-77}$$

It can be shown that, when the VSWR is known, then the reflection coefficient can be found from

$$\rho = \frac{S - 1}{S + 1} \tag{9-78}$$

The normal operation of a transmission line, in which equal and opposite currents flow in each of the two conductors, is characterized by the fact that the electric and magnetic fields are transverse to the direction of propagation. This mode of propagation is called TEM (Transverse Electric and Magnetic). Other modes of propagation are possible, for example, when the currents in the conductors are not equal or do not flow in opposite directions. An unbalanced component of current (longitudinal current) results in a longitudinal electric field component which gives rise to a longitudinal or TM wave. As frequencies become sufficiently high so that transmission line cross-sectional dimensions are large compared to a wavelength, many different TE and TM modes of propagation are possible. Generally, such modes are not significant until frequencies in the gigahertz range or pulses having rise times of a fraction of a nanosecond are used.

### RADIATION

Before proceeding with a discussion of radiation, it is necessary to re-examine one of Maxwell's equations which was previously given as Eq. (9-23):

$$\oint_{\text{line}} \mathbf{H} \cdot d\mathbf{l} = I$$

This equation defined the current $I$ as the current flow that pierces a surface containing the closed path of integration. An apparent paradox results when one considers a closed path such that the surface associated with it lies entirely between the plates of an ideal capacitor. Since no current flows between the capacitor plates by conduction and zero current flow in Eq. (9-23) implies no magnetic field $\mathbf{H}$, the first impression is that the magnetic field is zero. There is a magnetic field around the conductors on each side of the capacitor, and it has been observed that the field is continuous even through the capacitor. Equation (9-23) can be modified to be consistent with fact if we define the current $I$ as being made up of the sum of two components: a *conduction current*, $I_c$, and a *displacement current*, $I_d$. The displacement current results from the time-varying $\mathbf{D}$ field and is given by

$$I_d = \int_{\text{area}} \frac{\partial \mathbf{D}}{\partial t} \cdot d\mathbf{A} \tag{9-79}$$

Therefore, Eq. (9-23) can be rewritten as

$$\oint_{\text{line}} \mathbf{H} \cdot d\mathbf{l} = I_c + \int_{\text{area}} \frac{\partial \mathbf{D}}{\partial t} \cdot d\mathbf{A} \tag{9-80}$$

Equation (9-80) indicates that a time-varying $\mathbf{D}$ (or $\mathbf{E}$) field will produce a magnetic $\mathbf{H}$ (or $\mathbf{B}$) field. Equation (9-30) also relates a time-varying $\mathbf{B}$ (or $\mathbf{H}$) field to an $\mathbf{E}$ (or $\mathbf{D}$) field. Thus, it is not possible to isolate either the electric or magnetic field when they are time varying; this suggests the possibility of wave propagation in space where conduction current is nonexistent.

A radiating antenna consists of a length of wire connected to a source in such a way that a time-varying current and charge distribution is set up in the wire. We will not concern ourselves with exactly how this antenna is excited, but we can follow the charging and discharging process in some detail by referring to Fig. 9-17. Part (a) of the figure shows the position of the charges (shown just as a positive and negative charge pair) shortly after the excitation

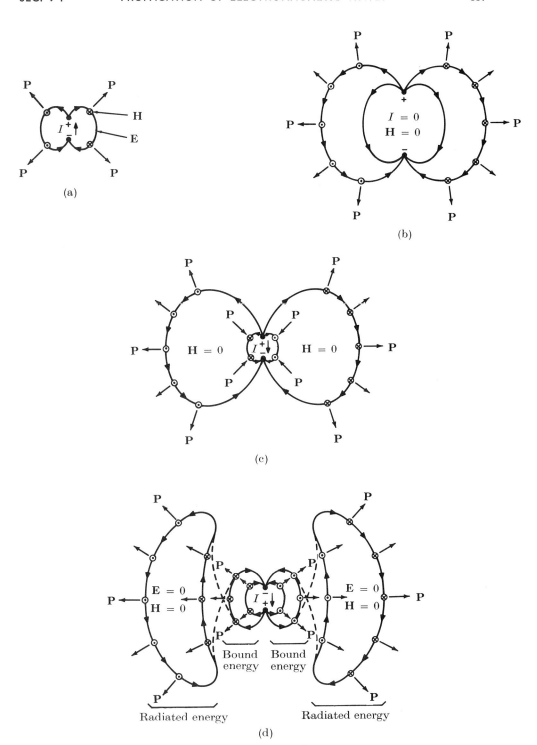

**Fig. 9-17**   The fields near a radiating source.

is applied, which causes the charges to move away from each other. The resulting current and associated magnetic and electric field are as shown. These
fields are difficult to show; but in this diagram, the electric field is shown by the
electric flux lines with arrows, and the magnetic field is shown by the presence
of small circles with dots for one polarity and crosses for the other polarity.
The fields shown in Fig. 9-17(a) will propagate outward at the velocity of light.
At a somewhat later time (a quarter of a cycle later), the field configuration will
be as shown in Fig. 9-17(b). Here the charges have moved as far apart as they
can before the source excitation causes them to change direction. At this
instant, the electric field is maximum, and one would expect the magnetic field
to disappear since the charges are no longer moving (the instantaneous current
is zero). However, the magnetic field does not collapse at all points instantaneously because of the limitation of the velocity of light. As a result, a
magnetic field still exists at a distance from the charges as shown in (b). The
situation nearly a quarter of a cycle later is shown in Fig. 9-17(c). Here, the
current has reversed sign (the charges are moving toward each other), and an
opposite polarity magnetic field has been generated. As the two charges pass
each other, the electric field changes polarity, and a new set of flux lines is
produced as shown in Fig. 9-17(d). Note that, in this part of the figure, the
electric field lines have broken into two sets. If the lines had not broken, they
would have crossed each other as shown by the dotted lines. Since this cannot
happen, the electric flux lines form a closed loop which moves away from the
radiator. The associated energy of this "broken away" field is the radiated
energy of the system. The expanding and collapsing field near the radiator,
containing bound energy, is called the induction field. Our discussion of fields
up to this point has been concerned with the induction field (sometimes called
the near field). The relative magnitudes of the electric and magnetic components
of the induction field are dependent upon the impedance of the source. High
currents at low voltages produce a field predominantly magnetic, whereas low
currents at high voltages produce a predominantly electric field. For moving
point charges, the induction field diminishes with distance from the charges as
$1/r^2$ or $1/r^3$. The radiation field (also called far field) diminishes with distance
as $1/r$ so that, at great distances from the source, the radiation field will
predominate. At a distance $r = \lambda/2\pi$, or at a distance from the origin of
approximately $\frac{1}{6}$ wavelength, the induction and radiation fields are equal in
magnitude. This then becomes the dividing line between treating a problem as
an induction field using the techniques previously discussed, or considering the
problem as a radiation field.

The magnitude of the electric (**E**) and magnetic (**H**) components of the
radiation field are related by the permeability and permittivity of the material
they are being propagated in by

$$\frac{E}{H} = \sqrt{\frac{\mu}{\epsilon}}$$

(9-81)

Note the similarity to the characteristic impedance of a transmission line. In fact, this ratio has the dimensions of ohms and is called the intrinsic impedance of the medium. For free space,

$$\frac{E}{H} = \sqrt{\frac{\mu_0}{\epsilon_0}} = 376.7 \ \Omega \tag{9-82}$$

The velocity of propagation of the radiated field is given by

$$c = \frac{1}{\sqrt{\epsilon\mu}} \tag{9-83}$$

Again, note the similarity to the velocity of propagation of a wave along a transmission line. For free space,

$$c_0 = \frac{1}{\sqrt{\epsilon_0\mu_0}} \approx 3 \times 10^8 \ \text{m/s} \tag{9-84}$$

This apparent analogy between transmission lines and radiation will prove very useful when we consider the effects of shields on radiated energy; it will be treated in more detail later in the chapter.

The **E** and **H** components of a radiated wave are orthogonal and perpendicular to the direction of propagation of the wave. The instantaneous power density of the radiated wave is given by the cross product of the **E** and **H** vectors and is known as the Poynting vector **P**. Thus,

$$\mathbf{P} = \mathbf{E} \times \mathbf{H} \tag{9-85}$$

It can be shown[4] that the integration of the Poynting vector over a closed surface yields the total power crossing the surface.

## SKIN EFFECT

The skin effect, as mentioned previously in Sec. 9-1, results in a concentration of current near the surface of a conductor when excited by a time-varying field. Consider a high-frequency **E** field in the vicinity of the conductor shown in Fig. 9-18. The **E** field will cause current flow in the conductor, producing a magnetic field at right angles to **E**. This changing magnetic field will produce an induced electric field **E**′ which will oppose **E**. If we apply Eq. (9-30) to this problem and investigate the two closed line integrals 1-2-3-4-1 and 1-2′-3′-4-1, we will find that more magnetic flux is enclosed in the latter case, so that the induced opposing

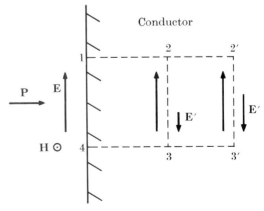

**Fig. 9-18**  Boundary between a conductor and an **E** field in space.

voltage is greater in this case. The result is that there is less net field present to produce current flow as one progresses farther into the conductor.

A quantitative analysis of this effect,[2,4,9] which is similar to the transmission line analysis, uses Maxwell's equations in differential form to obtain a solution for the current density, $J$, along the axis of a conductor and at a depth $x$ from the surface of the form

$$J = C_1 e^{-\tau x} + C_2 e^{\tau x} \tag{9-86}$$

where $\tau$ is a complex number given by

$$\tau = (1 + j)\sqrt{\pi f \mu \sigma} \tag{9-87}$$

and $\sigma$ is the conductivity of the metal conductor. The constant $C_2$ must be zero to keep the current from becoming infinite at infinite depths into the conductor. $C_1$ is evaluated at $x = 0$ and found to be the current density at the surface of the conductor. If a quantity $\delta$ is defined as

$$\delta = \frac{1}{\sqrt{\pi f \mu \sigma}} \tag{9-88}$$

the current density at any depth $x$ in a conductor can be expressed in terms of the current density at the surface $J_0$ by

$$J = J_0 e^{-x/\delta} e^{-j(x/\delta)} \tag{9-89}$$

In this form it is apparent that the magnitude of the current decreases exponentially with distance into the conductor, and $\delta$ is the depth at which the current density has decreased to $1/e$ of its value at the surface. This quantity $\delta$ is called the skin depth. It is a useful parameter for evaluating the skin effect since it can be shown (by integrating $e^{-x/\delta}$ from zero to infinity) that the effective resistance of a conductor is obtained exactly by assuming that all of the current is uniformly distributed from the surface of the conductor to a depth $\delta$. As an example, consider a round cross-sectional conductor of radius $a$. The dc resistance of this conductor is inversely proportional to the cross-sectional area or $\pi a^2$. The resistance at high frequencies at which $\delta$ is much less than $a$ is inversely proportional to the product of the skin depth and the circumference of the conductor or $2\pi a \delta$. The ratio between the ac resistance and the dc resistance becomes:

$$\frac{R_{ac}}{R_{dc}} = \frac{a}{2\delta} = \frac{a\sqrt{\pi f \mu \sigma}}{2} \tag{9-90}$$

Since $a$, $\mu$, and $\sigma$ are all constants for a given conductor, it can be seen that the resistance of a conductor will generally increase with the square root of frequency.

In review, we note that:

1. The depth of penetration is decreased as the conductivity, permeability, and/or frequency increase since skin depth is inversely proportional to the square root of each of these.
2. Current actually penetrates beyond the skin depth, decaying exponentially. The rate of decay is determined by the skin depth.

## 9-5. SIGNAL TRANSMISSION MEDIA

In electronic systems, signals are transmitted between circuit elements and equipment units by various means, ranging from deposited conductors of a few tenths of a millimeter in length to coaxial cable runs of several hundred meters. In each case, the characteristics of the conducting media are chosen so that the performance of the system will not be significantly impaired.

Closely related with interconnections are the contacts and connections between signal paths. Because of their importance and special nature, however, they will be treated in depth in other chapters. Similarly, transmission of signals by radiation, while of considerable practical importance, will not be discussed here because of its special nature. The physical designer is more concerned about the interference aspects of radiation, and this will be discussed in the next chapter.

The circuit elements or components themselves may also be thought of as transmission media, but they are intended to modify signals in a desired way. They are never ideal, however; they deviate from the desired characteristics because of the presence of unwanted or parasitic electromagnetic coupling. The choice of components and interconnecting media for any particular application will depend upon many factors, of which signal characteristics, circuit requirements, and cost are important.

## TRANSMISSION LINES

Interconnections may be treated as transmission lines; hence, the general transmission line theory developed in the previous section is applicable. Figure 9-19 shows simple comparisons of a number of commonly used interconnections.

Coaxial lines are extensively used, particularly at high frequencies, largely because of their excellent shielding qualities. The range of impedances conveniently obtainable with coaxial lines is from 50 to 100 ohms. In printed circuits, strip line is often used in place of coaxial line because of its simpler

| Transmission line | Configuration | Conditions of application* | Characteristic impedance (ohms) |
|---|---|---|---|
| Coaxial | 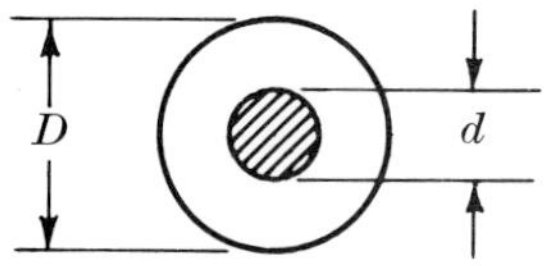 | | $\dfrac{\sqrt{\mu/\epsilon}}{2\pi}\ln\dfrac{D}{d}$ |
| Strip line | 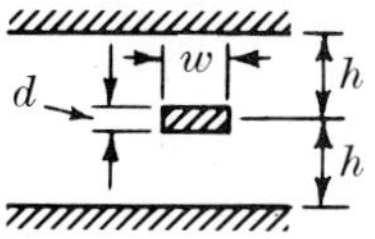 | $h \ll w$ <br> $d \ll h$ | $\sqrt{\dfrac{\mu}{\epsilon}}\,\dfrac{h}{2w}$ |
| Parallel wire | 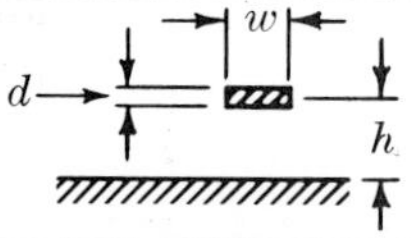 | | $\dfrac{\sqrt{\mu/\epsilon}}{\pi}\cosh^{-1}\dfrac{2h}{d}$ |
| Parallel strip | 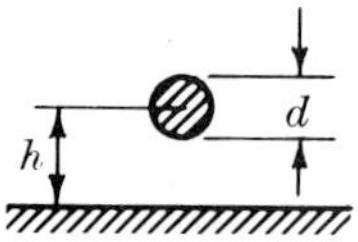 | $2h \ll w$ <br> $d \ll 2h$ | $\sqrt{\dfrac{\mu}{\epsilon}}\,\dfrac{2h}{w}$ |
| | | $2h \gg w$ | $\dfrac{\sqrt{\mu/\epsilon}}{\pi}\ln\left[\dfrac{2\pi h}{w+d}\right]$ |
| Wire over ground | 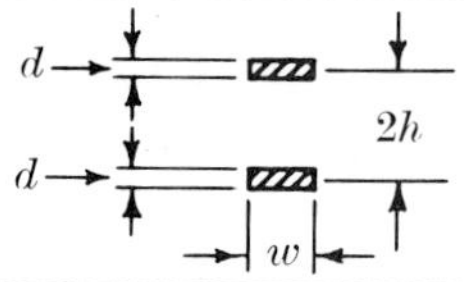 | | $\dfrac{\sqrt{\mu/\epsilon}}{2\pi}\cosh^{-1}\dfrac{2h}{d}$ |
| Microstrip | 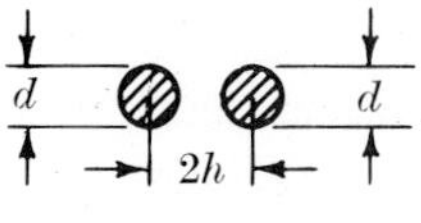 | $2h \ll w$ <br> $d \ll h$ | $\sqrt{\dfrac{\mu}{\epsilon}}\,\dfrac{h}{w}$ |
| | | $2h \gg w$ | $\dfrac{\sqrt{\mu/\epsilon}}{2\pi}\ln\left[\dfrac{2\pi h}{w+d}\right]$ |

\* In all cases: line length $\ggg h$; homogeneous dielectric surrounding conductors; zero

Note: $\sqrt{\mu/\epsilon} = 376.7$ ohms for free space; $\cosh^{-1} x \approx \ln (2x)$ for large $x$; $R_s = 2.61 \times 10^{-4}$

**Fig. 9-19** Parameters of common

| Capacitance (farad/meter) | Inductance (henry/meter) | Resistance (ohm/meter) |
|---|---|---|
| $\dfrac{2\pi\epsilon}{\ln(D/d)}$ | $\dfrac{\mu}{2\pi}\ln\dfrac{D}{d}$ | $\dfrac{R_s}{\pi}\left(\dfrac{1}{D}+\dfrac{1}{d}\right)$ |
| $\dfrac{2\epsilon w}{h}$ | $\dfrac{\mu h}{2w}$ | $\dfrac{R_s}{2w}$ |
| $\dfrac{\pi\epsilon}{\cosh^{-1}(2h/d)}$ | $\dfrac{\mu}{\pi}\cosh^{-1}\dfrac{2h}{d}$ | $\dfrac{2R_s}{\pi d}\left[\dfrac{2h/d}{\sqrt{(2h/d)^2-1}}\right]$ |
| $\dfrac{\epsilon w}{2h}$ | $\dfrac{2\mu h}{w}$ | $\dfrac{2R_s}{w}$ |
| $\dfrac{\pi\epsilon}{\ln\left[\dfrac{2\pi h}{w+d}\right]}$ | $\dfrac{\mu}{\pi}\ln\left[\dfrac{2\pi h}{w+d}\right]$ | $\dfrac{R_s}{w+d}\left[\dfrac{\pi h/(w+d)}{\sqrt{[\pi h/(w+d)]^2-1}}\right]$ |
| $\dfrac{2\pi\epsilon}{\cosh^{-1}(2h/d)}$ | $\dfrac{\mu}{2\pi}\cosh^{-1}\dfrac{2h}{d}$ | $\dfrac{R_s}{\pi d}\left[\dfrac{2h/d}{\sqrt{(2h/d)^2-1}}\right]$ |
| $\dfrac{\epsilon w}{h}$ | $\dfrac{\mu h}{w}$ | $\dfrac{R_s}{w}$ |
| $\dfrac{2\pi\epsilon}{\ln\left[\dfrac{2\pi h}{w+d}\right]}$ | $\dfrac{\mu}{2\pi}\ln\left[\dfrac{2\pi h}{w+d}\right]$ | $\dfrac{R_s}{2(w+d)}\left[\dfrac{\pi h/(w+d)}{\sqrt{[\pi h/(w+d)]^2-1}}\right]$ |

resistivity ground planes.

ohms for copper at 1.0 megahertz.

transmission line configurations.

mechanical construction. The characteristics of strip line are very similar to those of the coaxial except that the degree of shielding is not quite as great.

Somewhat higher impedances may be obtained conveniently with parallel-wire lines. These find wide application, although susceptibility to electrical interference makes them undesirable in many high-frequency applications. To avoid this problem, twisted-pair interconnections are extensively used. The analogous line in printed circuits is the parallel strip, which has similar characteristics although the impedances are generally lower than for the parallel-wire line.

The single wire over a ground plane has characteristics very similar to those of the parallel wire. Although not often thought of as a transmission line, this configuration is often used in circuit wirings for short interconnections. The microstrip used on printed circuits is very similar to the single wire over a ground plane and is often used because of its relative ease of fabrication.

Note that for the parallel strip and microstrip configurations two sets of formulas are given. For $2h \ll w$ all fringing is neglected, and for $2h \gg w$ fringing is included. In the latter case, the formulas are derived from the analogous round-wire solution by equating the round wire and strip conductor circumferences. At $2h = w$, both solutions are inaccurate.

Capacitance and inductance of the transmission lines shown in Fig. 9-19 can be derived using the techniques described in the previous section. When the capacitance and inductance per unit length are known, the characteristic impedance for a lossless line is given by

$$Z_0 \approx \sqrt{\frac{L'}{C'}} \qquad (9\text{-}91)$$

Since most transmission lines are designed and intended for use in applications where the loss of the line is kept to a practical minimum, the characteristic impedance is almost entirely real and is given quite accurately by the above expression. The characteristic impedances listed in Fig. 9-19 are derived using Eq. (9-91).

Comparing Eqs. (9-44) and (9-46) leads one to conclude that the capacitance and inductance per meter of a transmission line are not independent. By applying Eq. (9-67) to a lossless line ($\alpha = 0$), we obtain:

$$\beta = \omega \sqrt{L'C'}$$

Equations (9-71) and (9-72) combine to give:

$$\beta = \frac{\omega \sqrt{\epsilon_r \mu_r}}{c_0}$$

Equating the two expressions yields:

$$\sqrt{L'C'} = \frac{\sqrt{\epsilon_r \mu_r}}{c_0}$$

This result, when combined with Eq. (9-91), gives the following useful relationships:

$$L' = \frac{Z_0 \sqrt{\epsilon_r \mu_r}}{c_0} \tag{9-92}$$

$$C' = \frac{\sqrt{\epsilon_r \mu_r}}{Z_0 c_0} \tag{9-93}$$

These simple relationships are valid only for lossless lines in which the field is completely contained in a homogeneous medium. However, many practical problems involving short interconnections satisfy these conditions.

The last parameter of Fig. 9-19 to be discussed is the resistance per meter. This is given in terms of the parameter $R_s$ which is the dc resistance of a square meter of the conductor material one skin depth, $\delta$, thick. It can be shown that

$$R_s = \frac{1}{\sigma} \cdot \frac{1}{\delta} = \frac{\sqrt{\pi f \mu \sigma}}{\sigma} = \sqrt{\frac{\pi f \mu}{\sigma}} \tag{9-94}$$

where $\sigma$ is the conductivity in mhos per meter, and the skin depth is as defined in Eq. (9-88). The result is that $R_s$ is directly proportional to the square root of frequency. To aid in numerical calculations, the value of $R_s$ is given for copper at 1 MHz at the bottom of Fig. 9-19.

It can be shown[10] that the attenuation of cable, $\alpha$, is approximately given by

$$\alpha = \frac{R'}{2Z_0} + \frac{G' Z_0}{2} \quad \text{neper/m} \tag{9-95}$$

where $G'$ is the conductance per meter due to the dielectric. For most good dielectrics, the conductance is negligible until the frequency becomes very high (tens or hundreds of megahertz), and the second term of Eq. (9-95) can often be ignored. The loss in decibels per meter is simply 8.69 times the loss in nepers. If we ignore conductance and assume the presence of skin effect, doubling the dimensions of the conductors of a transmission line will halve the resistance, $R'$, and consequently will halve the loss in dB. As a calibration point, the loss per meter of 2 cm O.D., 50-ohm coaxial cable at 1 MHz is about $1.85 \times 10^{-3}$ dB. By the above discussion, the loss of 1.0 cm O.D., 50-ohm cable at 1 MHz is about $3.7 \times 10^{-3}$ dB/m.

It should be noted that the relationships shown in Fig. 9-19 are valid only when the configuration satisfies the listed requirements (i.e., perfectly conducting ground planes and small spacings of the various flat strips compared to the width of the strips). For configurations not meeting these requirements, the accuracies of the given relationships become questionable. However, we can generally bracket the problem by using two of the listed configurations to get at least a general idea of the magnitude of the parameter under investigation. (For more accurate results, it would be necessary to analyze the actual configuration by the methods outlined previously or to measure the quantities experimentally.)

**Example 9.2.** Impedance discontinuities in transmission lines result in signal reflections that degrade the rise time of transmitted pulses and increase the effective signal propagation delay. This requires that transmission line connectors in high-speed pulse systems be matched to the characteristic impedance of the line. A 50-ohm coaxial connector described by Blonder and Evans[11] illustrates the design techniques required to realize a matched impedance connector.

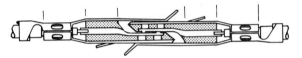

**Fig. 9-20**  Coaxial connector.[11]

The connector, shown in Fig. 9-20, consists of two identical mating sections. Each section consists of a rectangular copper-alloy inner conductor surrounded by a Teflon dielectric ($\epsilon_r = 2.1$) within a phosphor bronze rectangular outer conductor. To be compatible with earlier connectors, it was required that the new connector have a rectangular outside cross section of 2.64 mm by 2.03 mm. Since the conductor was to be formed from standard sheet stock of 0.254-mm thickness, the maximum inside dimensions are 2.13 mm by 1.52 mm, as shown in Fig. 9-21. We wish to investigate the feasibility of realizing a 50-ohm characteristic impedance rectangular-within-rectangular configuration with the stated constraint.

An approximate calculation for the characteristic impedance can be made using the semi-analytical method previously described. The characteristic impedance from Eq. (9-91) is:

$$Z_0 = \sqrt{\frac{L'}{C'}}$$

Substituting Eqs. (9-44) and (9-46) into Eq. (9-91) gives

$$Z_0 = \sqrt{\frac{\mu}{\epsilon}}\frac{1}{F}$$

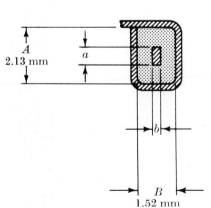

**Fig. 9-21**  Design section for impedance calculation.

where $F$ is the form factor for the configuration as defined by Eq. (9-45). In Fig.
9-22, the conductor cross section is divided
into sub-areas for the purpose of computing the form factor. From symmetry,
the form factor for the entire cross section
is equal to four times the sum of the form
factors for areas 1 and 2, where

$$F_1 = \frac{A_1}{l_{m1}^2} = \frac{\frac{1}{2}(A-a)(b+B)}{\frac{1}{4}(B-b)^2 + (A-a)^2}$$

and

$$F_2 = \frac{A_2}{l_{m2}^2} = \frac{\frac{1}{2}(B-b)(a+A)}{\frac{1}{4}(A-a)^2 + (B-b)^2}$$

The results of the impedance calculation
are shown in Fig. 9-23 for two different
thicknesses of center conductor. Note that
various combinations of conductor thickness and width will give the desired
50-ohm impedance.

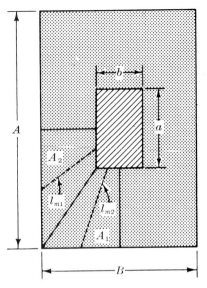

**Fig. 9-22** Idealized connector design section.

Blonder and Evans[11] obtained a more accurate evaluation of $Z_0$ by
numerically solving Laplace's equation for the potential at points within the
dielectric. This analysis was able to handle the conditions of off-center conductors and round conductor corners and thus establish the effects of mechanical
tolerances and deviations from the ideal configuration.

Once a connector has been designed, its performance must be measured.
A standard method of doing this is to terminate one end of the connector into
its nominal characteristic impedance (in this case, 50 ohms) and measure the
impedance seen on the other side of the connector as a function of frequency.
As one would expect, the effect of the connector on the impedance is not very
significant until frequencies are reached where the length of the connector is a
significant fraction of a wavelength (generally the GHz region). At high
frequencies, the measurement of VSWR is more straightforward and is usually
the preferred approach. In either case, the reflection coefficient of the connector
can then be determined from Eq. (9-77) or (9-78) as a function of frequency. In
pulse circuits, however, frequency response is not of as much direct interest as is
time response. Although related by the Fourier integral and transform, a more
direct time response characterization is often desirable.

The time response is obtainable by a technique called time domain reflectometry which has recently come into practical use. A zero rise-time pulse
applied to a terminated connector is partially reflected at each impedance discontinuity. The amount of energy reflected back toward the source from a

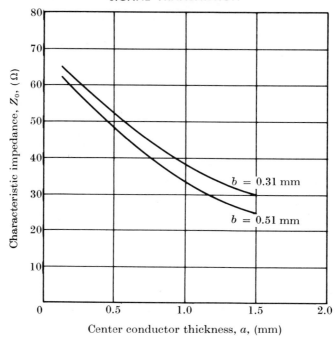

**Fig. 9-23**  Characteristic impedance of connector design section.

discontinuity is determined by the reflection coefficient at that point as given by Eq. (9-75), where $Z_0$ is the impedance before the discontinuity and $Z_L$ is the impedance after the discontinuity. By sensing the reflected energy appearing at the source, one can determine the distance to the discontinuity (directly proportional to the time delay) and the reflection coefficient at the discontinuity (directly proportional to the reflected energy at that time). Zero rise-time pulses are not practical and, as a result, the reflections are somewhat smeared and merged due to the finite rise time of even the fastest pulse. In general, the resolving power is limited to distances approximately equal to the propagation distance of a pulse during its rise time (i.e., about 0.6 cm for 28-ps pulses in Teflon).

Time domain reflectometry not only gives time domain results but, because time and distance are directly proportional, it also relates performance to specific physical areas of a connector and is thus a powerful design diagnostic tool.

The application of this technique to the coaxial connector is shown in Fig. 9-24. Note that the three different transmission line sections can be resolved with the 28-ps rise-time pulse. The coaxial cable termination section has the highest reflection coefficient. This is primarily a result of the inhomogeneity of the dielectric near the center conductor splice which would require special splicing techniques to be improved significantly. The excellent performance

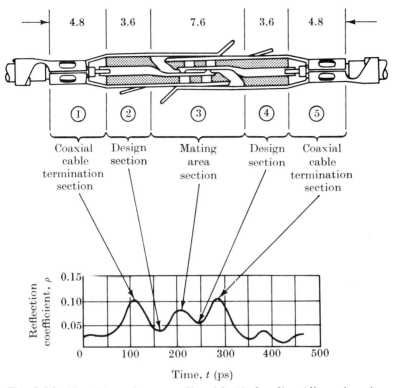

**Fig. 9-24** Mated impedance profile with 50-ohm line (dimensions in millimeters).[11]

of the design section is relatively easy to achieve. Additional improvements in this section would not necessarily be warranted due to the poorer performance of the other sections. Reflections in the mating area section result from discontinuities in the dielectric and the off-center position of the mating center conductors.

As a result of this effort, an economical connector was designed to transmit pulses with rise times as short as 150 ps with negligible distortion. Time domain reflectometry readily identifies the physical areas of the connector that contribute to pulse reflections and thus is a valuable aid in connector design.

We would now like to consider the characteristics of a short length of interconnecting wire. As previously indicated, even a short piece of wire can be treated as a transmission line. If the line is terminated with a load impedance equal to the characteristic impedance of the line, the effect of the line is simply that it causes the signal waveform at the receiving end load to be delayed in time from that transmitted, and to be attenuated by the loss of the line. For typical electrically short lines (length less than $\frac{1}{6}$ wavelength for frequencies of interest), both these effects can usually be ignored, and the line can be considered to have no effect upon the signal passing through it. This result holds only if the line is terminated by its characteristic impedance so that the series inductance and shunt capacitance of the line exactly compensate for each other.

Consider now an open-circuited line of electrically short length. In this case, no significant current flows through the line so that the series inductance of the line can be ignored. As a result, such a line in a circuit would "look like" a lumped capacitor whose value is equal to the capacitance of that length of line, as obtained from Fig. 9-19.

If the foregoing line is terminated with a resistance $R_L$ that is greater than the characteristic impedance $Z_0$, the line will still look like a capacitor, but the effective capacitance will be less than the total capacitance of the line. For electrically short misterminated lines, the actual excess capacitance is more closely approximated by

$$C_{\text{effective}} \approx C_{\text{cable}}\left(1 - \frac{Z_0^2}{R_L^2}\right) \tag{9-96}$$

In an analogous manner, an electrically short line terminated by a short circuit will look like a lumped inductor of value equal to the total inductance of that length of line, as obtained from Fig. 9-19. If this short-circuited line is terminated instead by a resistance $R_L$ that is less than the characteristic impedance $Z_0$, the line will still look like an inductor. However, the effective series inductance will be less than the total inductance of the line and will be given by

$$L_{\text{effective}} \approx L_{\text{cable}}\left(1 - \frac{R_L^2}{Z_0^2}\right) \tag{9-97}$$

As a result, it is important in high-impedance circuits to keep the wiring away from the ground plane in order to minimize shunt capacitance. In low-impedance circuits, it is important to keep the wiring very close to the ground plane to minimize series inductance.

If electrically long lines are misterminated, frequency resonance conditions will be observed. For instance, lines whose lengths are odd multiples of a quarter wavelength will look like open circuits when the far end is shorted; they will look like short circuits when the far end is open-circuited. Methods of analyzing such lines are treated in some detail in Ref. 12, but in most equipment design, resonance phenomena are generally avoided by properly terminating all electrically long lines with their characteristic impedances.

Misterminated electrically long lines are also troublesome in digital circuits.[13] In this case, the relative length of the line is determined by the rise time of the pulses on the line. In fact, any line whose propagation delay is longer than the rise time of the pulses carried may be considered electrically long. When electrically long lines are misterminated on both ends, the resulting multiple reflections cause severe pulse distortion and significantly lengthen the effective rise and fall times of any pulses carried on the line. For instance, if both ends of the line are terminated with very high impedances, the rise time (and consequently, the delay) of the pulse will be considerably increased (perhaps several times the propagation delay of the cable) by the capacitance of the line. If low impedances are on each end, the effective rise time will be stretched by the inductance of the line. If the impedance at one end is low and that at the other end is high, an oscillatory or "ringing" condition will prevail. While not specifically degrading the rise time, the "ringing" can cause spurious operations of logic circuits so that the effective delay (until the ringing has damped to a small value) may be increased considerably. Whenever possible, electrically long lines carrying pulses should be properly terminated on at least one end. If such is not possible or practical, the degradation in pulse shape must be considered.

Even when properly terminated, electrically long lines can seriously affect circuit or equipment performance. This results from the phase shift or delay of long lines due to the finite propagation time through the cable. In analog or linear equipment, phase shift must often be closely controlled, especially in feedback loops. In digital or pulse equipment, the timing is often very important, as is distortion of the waveforms as they pass through a long cable.

**Example 9.3.** Consider pulse circuits for a high-speed digital system as shown in Fig. 9-25. The circuits have the following requirements:

1. The driver has an output impedance of 200 Ω and is designed to deliver pulses into a resistive load of 1000 Ω.

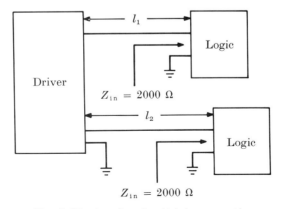

**Fig. 9-25** A pulse circuit interconnection.

2. Each logic circuit must be driven within 10 ns after the driving circuit supplies the pulse.

3. Both logic circuits must be driven within 5 ns of each other.

4. The input impedance of each logic circuit is 2000 Ω resistive.

The problem is to find the best means of interconnecting these circuits, along with some maximum allowable spacings between them.

It would be desirable to make the characteristic impedance of the lines between the driver and each logic circuit 2000 Ω. In this way, the load on the driver would be 1000 Ω resistive, and lead length restrictions would be due only to propagation delay time. Examination of the results presented in Fig. 9-19 will show that it is somewhat impractical to achieve a line impedance of 2000 Ω without going to extremes like placing a single wire several million wire diameters above a conducting ground plane. A much more practical choice for the connecting line impedance is 200 Ω. This is an easily achievable value for a wire placed above a ground plane and has the further advantage of matching the line impedance to the output impedance of the driver. This avoids any possible problems with multiple reflections on an electrically long line, and one can assume that the pulse delay time through the line is exactly the same as the propagation delay.

Assuming that the connecting wires are not surrounded by any significant dielectric other than air, the speed of propagation along the lines is that of light in free space or about 0.3 m/ns. To meet the timing requirements, the logic circuits must be no farther than about 3 m from the driver, and each must be within 1.5 m of the same distance from the driver.

To appreciate the effects of a misterminated line, let us see what would happen if we used a commercial 50-Ω coaxial cable for the interconnections. Now we are misterminated on both ends of the line, and we must consider the effects of multiple reflections. When the pulse is first transmitted by the driver, the line looks infinitely long to the pulse until it reaches the far end. Thus, the load on the driver will be just 50 Ω. When the pulse reaches the far end at time $T$, part of it will be reflected, given by the reflection coefficient from Eq. (9-75) as

$$\rho_r = \frac{Z_L - Z_0}{Z_L + Z_0} = \frac{2000 - 50}{2000 + 50} = 0.95 \approx 1$$

Since this is a positive number, the reflected wave will be in phase with the incident wave and will add directly to it at this end. Similarly, at the driver end, the reflection coefficient is 0.6; consequently, 0.6 of the reflected wave will again be reflected at time $2T$ and travel toward the load. Plotting the voltage across the 2000-Ω load as a function of time will result in a stepwise approximation to an exponential that approaches a final steady-state value. It can be shown that, after a time period of $7T$, the voltage across the load will be about 87 percent of the final value. If this is assumed to be the threshold of the logic circuits, then this voltage must be attained within 10 ns to meet requirement 2. This implies that the maximum delay through the coaxial cable must be less than $\frac{10}{7}$ ns.

Assuming a polyethylene insulated cable ($\epsilon_r = 2.3$), the speed of propagation through the cable is about 0.2 m/ns, so that $\frac{10}{7}$ ns corresponds to a maximum total cable length of about 0.3 m. This is considerable reduction from that considered earlier.

Another way of looking at the same problem is to consider the transmission line as a lumped capacitor and determine the maximum capacitance that can load the driver and still meet requirement 2. To be consistent with the previous assumptions, we will assume that the 2000-$\Omega$ load impedance is an open circuit (this corresponds to assuming that the reflection coefficient at the receiving end is unity) and that the threshold of the logic circuits is reached at 2 time constants (corresponds to the 87 percent value quoted previously). In this case, we must set the time constant $RC = 5$ ns. With $R = 200 \ \Omega$ (the output impedance of the driver—the high load resistances can be ignored), we find that the maximum capacitance allowable is 25 pF. For a 50-$\Omega$ polyethylene insulated cable, Eq. (9-93) tells us that this corresponds to a length of about 0.25 m. Within the limitations of the approximations made, this agrees with the previous result.

The advantage of the open connecting wire matching the impedance at one end is obvious. The only disadvantage of the open wire, as we shall see later, is the fact that the susceptibility to interference is rather high as is the generation of a significant time-varying field around the wire.

If the two logic circuits can be placed in proximity to each other, a better solution would be to connect the two logic circuits in parallel and run a single lead from the driver to the inputs. In such a case, all of the capacitance can be allocated to the single cable, thus allowing twice the distance from the driver to the logic circuits.

## CIRCUIT ELEMENTS

In many cases, passive circuit elements such as resistors, capacitors, and inductors are considered ideal, and the rules of circuit theory are applicable. Unfortunately, though, these elements are never ideal, and if they are treated as such, the result is only an approximation. In the frequency range of most equipment design (up to a few hundred megahertz), a better approximation can be obtained by considering an equivalent circuit for each of these components, consisting of a network of several ideal components. The degree of complication of this equivalent circuit depends upon the required degree of accuracy and upon the frequency range of interest.

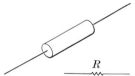

**Fig. 9-26** A resistor and its common schematic representation.

**Resistors.** Consider a resistor shown physically and schematically in Fig. 9-26. There are several possible physical designs for a resistor (composition, wire-wound, thin-film, etc.), but for the purposes of this discussion, assume a cylinder of resistive material with a connecting lead attached on each end. One imperfection of such a resistor is that, because of the phenomenon of skin effect, its resistance will increase with increasing frequency. If the resistivity of the material is very high, this may not be a very significant effect; but it should be investigated in each particular case. To reduce skin effect, high-frequency resistors are usually made with thin resistive films deposited on an insulator.

A series inductance is also associated with this resistor because of the magnetic field produced by the current flowing through it. The value of the inductance depends upon the geometry of the resistor and its surroundings. For example, a wire-wound resistor consisting of a helix of resistance wire will have considerable series inductance, making it impractical for use at any but very low frequencies (below a few hundred kilohertz). To reduce this inductance, some wire-wound resistors are made bifilar. That is, the length of resistance wire is first doubled back on itself, and the resulting pair of wires are wound as a single strand. The result is a resistor with the proper resistance between the original two ends of the wire but with much lower inductance since the resistor "looks like" a closely spaced parallel-wire transmission line shorted at the far end (it could also be considered the equivalent of two closely coupled inductors whose mutual inductance cancels most of the self-inductance).

The inductance of a simple cylindrical resistor can be calculated if we assume that it is a conductor of the same dimensions and use the formulas given in numerous references.[14,15] To a first approximation, for resistors whose length-to-width ratio is considerably greater than 1, this inductance is of the order of 6 or 8 nanohenrys per centimeter of length. In the equivalent circuit, this inductance should be placed in series with the resistor. Note that, for high-resistance values, the reactance of the series inductance is very possibly negligible compared to the resistance value, even at rather high frequencies.

There is an electric field both in the resistor itself and in the space surrounding the resistor because of the voltage drop across it and the potential difference to ground. These effects can be approximated in an equivalent circuit by the addition of capacitors. Below several hundred megahertz, this effect can be characterized by a single capacitor across the terminals of the resistor and by additional capacitors at each end of the resistor going to ground. For resistors with low resistance values and near ground potential, these capacitors can be ignored at all frequencies at which their reactive values are much greater than the resistance itself. The resulting equivalent circuit for the resistor is shown in Fig. 9-27, along with some approximate values for a typical resistor about 1 cm long and $\frac{1}{3}$ cm in diameter, placed about 2 cm above a ground plane.

If a model is desired that would be good at higher frequencies (where resistor size becomes an appreciable part of a wavelength), or if high precision is required in the model (small fractions of a percent), the equivalent

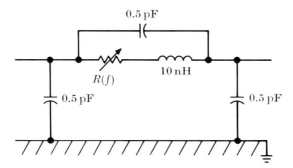

**Fig. 9-27** A typical equivalent circuit for a small resistor.

circuit would have to be developed in much more detail. For example, it would be necessary to remove the one shunt capacitor across the resistor and replace it with many capacitors, each shunted across a small part of the total resistance. Also, small capacitors would be placed to ground at each resistance increment. The limit is reached when the capacitance, inductance, and resistance are all considered uniformly distributed throughout the resistor. In this case, transmission line theory would apply, or the problem could be handled using Maxwell's equations directly. However, unless extreme accuracy is required or the frequencies become very high, such procedures are unnecessary.

**Inductors.** In a manner analogous to that used for the resistor, the equivalent circuit for the inductor can also be derived. This is shown in Fig. 9-28, along with some typical values for a small, air-core solenoid about 1 cm in diameter and 2 cm long, and about 2.5 cm from a ground plane.

Note that the circuit has the same form as the resistor equivalent circuit. Now, however, the resistance becomes a "stray," and the inductance is the desirable parameter. In most inductors, the resistance of the wire is the most important parameter degrading performance. Because of skin effect, this

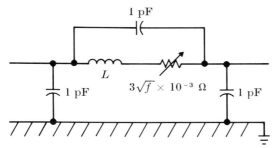

**Fig. 9-28** A typical equivalent circuit for an inductor.

resistance will vary as the square root of frequency. The effect of this resistance is usually characterized by the $Q$ of the coil,

$$Q = \frac{\omega L}{R} \qquad (9\text{-}98)$$

where $\omega = 2\pi f$, and $R$ is the wire resistance at the frequency $f$. Since $R$ is proportional to the square root of frequency, it follows that $Q$ is proportional to the square root of frequency.

This relation is true, however, only for a limited frequency range. From the equivalent circuit, we see that the inductor will eventually resonate with its shunt capacitance at some high frequency. At this point, the impedance of the structure will be all real and will be extremely high, so that the $Q$ will become zero. Above this frequency, the inductor will not behave like an inductor at all, but will instead resemble a capacitor that is equivalent to the shunt capacitor of the equivalent circuit. A more complex equivalent circuit can be formulated in a fashion similar to that described for the resistor.

**Capacitors.** The equivalent circuit for a capacitor can be derived in a similar manner. The most significant difference is that the series resistance of most capacitors is negligible. Also, the leakage of most dielectrics used in capacitors is very small; therefore, the shunt conductance across the capacitor plates is also negligible. The equivalent circuit for a small, low-voltage mica capacitor is shown in Fig. 9-29 with typical values.

It is common practice to convert the shunt conductance to an equivalent series resistance and to add it to the series resistance already present. If the series resistance is much less than the capacitive reactance, and if the shunt conductance is much less than $\omega C$, this transformation becomes

$$R_e \approx X_c^2 G \qquad (9\text{-}99)$$

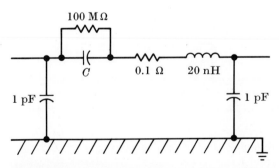

**Fig. 9-29**   A typical equivalent circuit for a small mica capacitor.

where $X_c = 1/\omega C$, $G$ is the shunt conductance, and $R_e$ is the equivalent series resistance.

**Example 9.4.** Consider an inductor connected between two coaxial connectors as shown in Fig. 9-30. The inductor is to be connected into nominal 50-$\Omega$ impedance circuitry by means of coaxial cable. It is required that the circuit "look like" a 50 $\mu$H $\pm$ 10 percent inductor with a minimum $Q$ of 60 at 5 MHz.

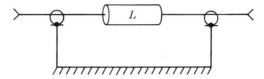

**Fig. 9-30**   Inductor configuration.

The inductor to be used is a single-layer solenoid with a diameter of 4 cm. This coil has been measured at 100 kHz (where all strays can be neglected) and found to be 50.0 $\mu$H, with a $Q$ of 10. We want to estimate the performance of such a component at 5 MHz.

We first draw the equivalent circuit with all significant parasitic elements as shown in Fig. 9-31. The values for $C_2$ and $C_3$ must be estimated from the physical

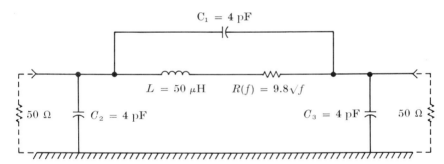

**Fig. 9-31**   Inductor equivalent circuit.

configuration of the circuit. They are considerably larger than the estimates shown in Fig. 9-28 because of the larger physical size of the inductor. The capacitance, $C_1$, for a single-layer solenoid of fixed length-to-width ratio can be related to its diameter. It is found that the capacitance in picofarads is approximately equal to the diameter of the solenoid in centimeters; thus $C_1 \approx 4$ pF. The value for $R$ at 100 kHz can be obtained from Eq. (9-98), so that $R = \omega L/Q$. Remembering that $R$ will be proportional to the square root of frequency (due to skin effect), we obtain the expression for $R$ as $R = 9.8\sqrt{f}$, with $R$ in ohms and $f$ in megahertz.

We neglect $C_2$ and $C_3$ because the reactances of these capacitors $(1/\omega C)$ at 5 MHz is much greater (by a factor of 150) than the 50-$\Omega$ terminations. The only significant part of the circuit, then, is the impedance between the two jacks. It can be shown that this impedance is given by

$$Z = \frac{R + j\omega[L(1 - \omega^2 LC_1) - C_1 R^2]}{(1 - \omega^2 LC_1)^2 + \omega^2 C_1^2 R^2} \ \Omega$$

To evaluate this at 5 MHz, it is easier to convert to reactances where $X_L = \omega L$ and $X_C = 1/\omega C_1$, thus obtaining

$$Z = \frac{R + j\left[X_L\left(1 - \frac{X_L}{X_C}\right) - \frac{R^2}{X_C}\right]}{\left(1 - \frac{X_L}{X_C}\right)^2 + \frac{R^2}{X_C^2}}$$

At 5 MHz, $X_L = 1500 \ \Omega$, $X_C = 7500 \ \Omega$, and $R = 22.2 \ \Omega$. Evaluating, we obtain

$$Z = \frac{R}{0.64} + \frac{j\omega L}{0.8} \ \Omega$$

The result is that, at 5 MHz, the apparent $R$ is increased over the "real" value by some 55 percent, while the apparent $L$ is increased over its low-frequency value by about 25 percent. At 5 MHz, this circuit will look like an inductor of 62.5 $\mu$H with a $Q$ of 54, which does not satisfy our requirements. The resulting performance is due to the capacitance $C_1$ across the inductor. To meet the stated requirements, it is necessary to reduce the value of capacitance $C_1$ to approximately 1 pF. This can often be accomplished by winding the inductor in sections or "pies," which is comparable to using several smaller inductors in series ($n$ similar capacitors of capacitance $C$ in series produces a total capacitance of $C/n$).

**Active Devices.** To accurately characterize the performance of active devices, it is necessary to develop equivalent circuits for these elements in the same manner as described before. All leads carrying current have inductance associated with them, and all points at different potentials have capacitance between them. For active devices, the equivalent circuit is further complicated by the fact that the effects of certain parasitic capacitances or inductances are enhanced by the gain characteristics of the device. Equivalent circuits have been developed for most common active devices. However, because of the large number of different types of devices in existence, no attempt will be made to consider their equivalent circuits here.

## REFERENCES

1. *Reference Data for Radio Engineers*, 4th ed., New York, International Telephone and Telegraph Corp., 1956. Electrical properties of many materials are given, and the chapter on transmission lines is quite informative.

2. Hayt, W. H., *Engineering Electromagnetics*, New York, McGraw-Hill Book Co., 1958. A very clearly written book on field theory. Highly recommended as a first book on fields.

3. Javid, M., and P. M. Brown, *Field Analysis and Electromagnetics*, New York, McGraw-Hill Book Co., 1963. A good presentation of solutions of Laplace's equation as applied to electric field problems.

4. Ramo, S., and J. R. Whinnery, *Fields and Waves in Communication Electronics*, New York, John Wiley & Sons, Inc., 1965. A very readable treatment of field theory. Chapter 3 describes many techniques for determining the electric field between various conductor geometries. Chapter 4 contains a good discussion of skin effect.

5. Weber, E., *Electromagnetic Fields*, Vol. I, New York, John Wiley & Sons, Inc., 1950. A good treatment of analytical and experimental solutions to electric field problems.

6. Cordi, V. A., S. C. Kingsley, and A. M. Shah, "Predicting Transmission-Line Properties of Printed-Circuit Conductor Geometry." *National Electronic Packaging and Production Conference Proceedings*, June, 1965. A review of several techniques for accurately calculating the impedance of common printed circuit transmission lines. Includes a comparison between calculated and measured data for several configurations.

7. Roters, H. C., *Electromagnetic Devices*, New York, John Wiley & Sons, Inc., 1941. Chapter 5 includes methods for estimating magnetic permeances that are directly convertible to dielectric acceptances.

8. Bonnesen, J. S., "A Corona Free High Voltage Feedthrough Terminal Design for Electronic Applications," *Proc. 1965 Electronic Components Conference*, 584–594, Institute of Electrical and Electronic Engineers. Reference for high voltage terminal design. Figures 9-11, 9-12, and 9-13 by permission.

9. Schelkunoff, S. A., *Electromagnetic Fields*, New York, Blaisdell Publishing Co., 1963. A different approach to fields that is quite readable. Almost 100 pages are devoted to problems with solutions which often illustrate points not easily grasped by reading the text.

10. Jordan, E. C., *Electromagnetic Waves and Radiating Systems*, Englewood Cliffs, N.J., Prentice-Hall, Inc., 1950. Chapter 8 is an extension of the treatment of transmission lines given in this chapter.

11. Blonder, H. H., and R. T. Evans, "Electromechanical Design of a Matched Impedance Connector," *8th International Electronic Circuit Packaging Symposium*, 1967. Reference for matched impedance connector design. Figures 9-20 and 9-24 by permission.

12. Kimbark, E. W., *Electrical Transmission of Power and Signals*, New York, John Wiley & Sons, Inc., 1949. A fairly clear treatment of transmission lines, although oriented strongly toward power transmission.

13. Jarvis, D. B., "The Effects of Interconnections on High-Speed Logic Circuits," *IEEE Trans. on Electronic Computers*, Oct., 1963. A clear explanation (with a light analytical treatment) of the necessity of properly terminating long transmission lines carrying pulses.

14. Terman, F. E., *Radio Engineers' Handbook*, New York, McGraw-Hill Book Co., 1943. Section 2 is a reasonably complete empirical treatment of circuit components, coupling, and shielding.

15. *Handbook of Chemistry and Physics*, Cleveland, Ohio, Chemical Rubber Publishing Co., 1954. Includes a section of mathematical tables that is available separately. Several formulas are given for inductance and capacitance of various configurations of conductors.

*Chapter 10*

# ELECTRICAL INTERFERENCE

## R. G. Buus

Two aspects of interference must be considered in the design of electronic systems: first, a tolerably low level of interference within the system to permit reliable operation, and second, compatibility with surrounding equipment to avoid interference between one system and another. To achieve these objectives requires careful design of signal characteristics, impedance levels, transmission media and routing arrangements, placement of components and subsystems, and grounding. The importance of these is accentuated when dealing with circuits involving high speed, high power, or high sensitivity.

This chapter begins by examining sources of interference and methods of interference coupling. Consideration is then given to methods of interference reduction which include equipment layout, shielding, and grounding. The chapter concludes with a review of typical means of characterizing and measuring interference.

### 10-1. SOURCES OF INTERFERENCE

Some common sources of interference are listed in Fig. 10-1, along with general descriptions of the characteristics and nature of the disturbances. The list is by no means all-inclusive, nor are the classifications clear-cut.

| Source | Frequency spectrum | Interfering effect | Examples |
|--------|-------------------|--------------------|----------|
| Switching transients | Broadband. Top frequency determined by circuit parameters in switched line which affect the rate of change of current. Can be as high as hundreds of MHz. | Pulses are produced in inadequately shielded equipment near the switched line. | Switch contacts, relay contacts, some logic circuits. |
| Commutating devices | Similar to switching transients with additional energy at multiples of the commutating frequency. | Long trains of random pulses are induced. Energy concentrated in certain frequency bands. | Motors, generators, inverters, vibrators, bells, buzzers. |
| Gaseous discharges | Narrow bands of energy at all multiples of the energizing frequency (usually 60 Hz). | Generally very similar to that for commutating devices. | Neon lamps, fluorescent lamps, gaseous rectifiers, spark plugs. |
| Corona | Random bursts of wideband (dc to several MHz) low-level energy. | Randomly spaced noise pulses which can cause false operation of logic circuits. | Application of high voltage to dielectrics. Usually not serious below a few kV. Almost always serious above 5–10 kV. |
| Contact potential | Dc voltage. | Shift in operating points and signal bias. | Unbonded or poorly bonded dissimilar metal contacts. |
| Sinusoidal generators | Fundamental oscillator frequency and all harmonics. | Induced sinusoids at the fundamental and harmonics. | High-power oscillators, parasitic oscillation in amplifiers. |
| Nonsinusoidal generators | Frequency equal to the repetition rate plus harmonics. | Same as sinusoidal generators except that the harmonics are generally stronger. | Multivibrators and logic gates; pulse systems. |
| Electromagnetic pulse (EMP) | Low kHz to tens of MHz. | Equipment damage due to excessive currents and voltages. | Nuclear blast near hardened equipment. Distant high-altitude nuclear explosions. |
| Lightning | Random bursts of wideband high-level energy concentrated below 100 kHz. | Noise bursts at a considered distance. Hits or near hits can cause equipment damage due to excessive currents and voltages. | Lightning hitting building housing equipment, hitting exposed parts of equipment or interconnecting power or signal cables. |

**Fig. 10-1**  Some common sources of interference.

Most of the listed sources of interference are familiar. Switching transients result any time a current is suddenly interrupted with a resulting large rate of change of current $(dI/dt)$. Commutating devices which switch currents at higher rates are even more likely to produce interference than are simple switches. In many cases, it is arcing of the switch contacts (gaseous discharge) that causes most of the interference. In addition to unintentional arcs, many gaseous discharges are controlled for a specific purpose such as in fluorescent lamps or automobile spark plugs.

Corona is a special type of gaseous discharge which is important in high-voltage applications. One usually thinks of corona as a glow discharge around a high-voltage terminal at points of geometric field enhancement. A very serious case of corona also takes place in many solid dielectrics where inhomogeneities such as gas-filled voids are present. The enhancement of the field in the void partially ionizes the gas, giving rise to impulse-type noise. Prolonged exposure at high energy levels may also cause chemical degradation and ultimate failure of the dielectric. It is not uncommon to experience corona in dielectrics when the applied voltage is as low as 1000 V, and it is almost always a serious problem when applied voltages exceed 5000 V.

Contact potential between conducting members, as a result of unbonded or poorly bonded connections, is frequently of concern. A bond between dissimilar metals in the presence of moisture forms a chemical cell which can produce dc potentials of up to several hundred millivolts. In addition to dc voltage shifts, serious corrosion can occur, resulting in open circuits.

Sinusoidal sources, not being perfect, contain not only the desired output frequency, but also many multiples or harmonics of the fundamental frequency. In addition, nonlinear devices (such as bonds between dissimilar metals) remote from the source can "pick up" energy from the source and modulate it with other sinusoidal generators that may be present to produce signals at various sum and difference frequencies. The harmonics of pulse generators are much larger and generally increase as the rise and fall times of the pulses decrease.

The explosion of a nuclear weapon is accompanied by the generation of a strong electromagnetic field, commonly called electromagnetic pulse (EMP). The pulse results from the interaction of the outwardly moving nuclear radiation with the atmosphere. It is a large area phenomenon and is a major threat to electronic equipment even at great distances from a blast center where all other effects are negligible. Since the transient is coupled into the total system, protection must be based on system concepts.

Lightning represents a hazard to both equipment and personnel. Special grounding and protection schemes are employed to protect susceptible equipment against lightning. These techniques often result in higher noise environments within a system, which will be discussed in a later section.

The interfering effect of a disturbing signal on an electronic circuit depends on the magnitude and type of interfering signal, the attenuation of the signal between source and receiver, and the susceptibility of the receiver. Analog or linear equipment, for example, may be highly susceptible to interference at its operating frequencies and may be practically immune to interference at other frequencies. The interfering effect would depend on the interfering signal power present at the operating frequencies. In pulse or digital circuits, the interfering signal must exceed a certain magnitude in order to cause a logic error before it degrades the performance of the circuit. The interfering effect in some digital circuits depends on the number of errors produced per unit time or the number of errors for a given number of signal pulses. The susceptibility of a circuit to different types of interference also depends on the impedance level of the circuit. Low-impedance circuits are very susceptible to time-varying magnetic fields, while high-impedance circuits are most susceptible to time-varying electric fields.

The ratio between the power at the interfering source and the power induced in the interfered-with equipment is generally called *crosstalk*. Because the possible values of crosstalk can vary over a very wide range, it is often more desirable to express the crosstalk on a logarithmic basis or in decibels (dB). The decibel was defined earlier as 10 log of the ratio of two powers. Since power is proportional to the square of the voltage in a given impedance, the decibel can also be defined as 20 log of a voltage ratio (or current ratio), provided the impedances associated with the two voltages (or currents) are the same.

The decibel can be modified in many ways to facilitate its use. For instance, it is common to characterize absolute powers on this logarithmic scale. This is done in terms of dBm which is defined as 10 log of the power expressed in milliwatts. In a similar manner, voltage can be characterized by the unit dBv which is 20 log of the voltage in volts (rms value unless otherwise specified). Another dB unit sometimes used in crosstalk measurements to avoid using negative numbers is the dBx. This is defined as 10 log of the ratio of $10^9$ times the induced power to the disturbing power, or

$$\mathrm{dBx} = 10 \log \frac{10^9 P_i}{P_s} \tag{10-1}$$

where $P_i$ is the power in the disturbed circuit, and $P_s$ is the power in the disturbing circuit.

## 10-2. METHODS OF INTERFERENCE COUPLING

Interference is introduced or coupled into electronic equipment by conduction, by near-field induction, and by radiation.

## CONDUCTION

The simplest type of coupling to understand is that due to conduction through a common impedance located between the interfering source and the interfered-with equipment. Conducted interference can occur through any common impedance ($R$, $L$, $C$, or any combination of these) and, in general, is frequency dependent.

One may question why conducting paths exist between two circuits that require electrical isolation. For reasons of economy or space, it is often necessary to share a common power supply and common ground path with many equipment units. Consequently, supposedly isolated circuits are coupled by the resulting common impedance.

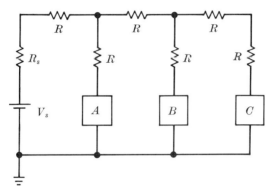

**Fig. 10-2** Powering several circuits from a common supply.

Consider the voltage supply shown in Fig. 10-2, which supplies a voltage to circuits $A$, $B$, and $C$. If circuit $C$ draws high peaks of power (e.g., a moderately powered pulse driver), the resistance, $R$, of the wiring will cause a small voltage swing at the power terminals of the $A$ and $B$ circuits. If one of these circuits is a very low-level device such as a preamplifier or low-level logic circuit, it is possible that the variation in voltage will interfere with its operation. This situation is not unusual, since it is very common to cascade several stages of amplification, with a power amplifier at the output and with very low-level power at the input. In this case, the presence of coupling between the output and the input acts as an undesirable feedback path.

This arrangement could be improved by a number of methods. Three possibilities are:

1. Rearrange the circuits on the power line to minimize the coupling effect.
2. Use separate leads from the supply to each circuit.

3. Add $RC$ low-pass filters in the power leads to block the high-frequency components of interference.

We will discuss these techniques in greater detail in a later section.

Another example of a conduction problem is shown in Fig. 10-3. Assume that the piece of equipment of interest is a high-loss attenuator which attenuates an input signal by 80 dB. Both the source driving the attenuator and the load being driven by the attenuator are unbalanced structures, with one side of the

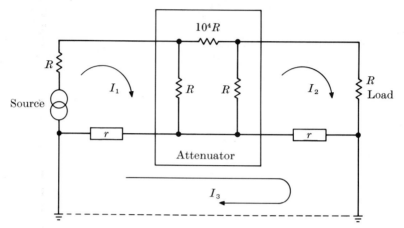

**Fig. 10-3** Common impedance or conduction coupling around a high-loss attenuator.

signal transmission lead connected to ground. The resistance $r$ represents a small but finite lead resistance. Coupling takes place because the input current $I_1$ causes a voltage to be developed across the resistance (or impedance) $r$; this voltage will appear across the output of the attenuator. It can be shown that the loss through the common ground path is given by

$$\text{Loss, dB} = 20 \log \frac{I_1}{I_2} = 20 \log \frac{4R + r}{r} \approx 20 \log \frac{4R}{r}$$

where $I_2$ is the current at the load, resulting from the common ground path.

If the attenuator just discussed has an input resistance of 50 ohms, it can be seen that a ground resistance $r$ of only 0.02 ohm will result in a loss around the spurious path equal to that through the attenuator (80 dB).

## NEAR-FIELD INDUCTION

In the following discussion, we will consider inductive and capacitive coupling between circuits. Inductive coupling will be treated as a mutual impedance, and capacitive coupling will be considered as a mutual admittance.

The mutual impedance between two circuits is defined as the voltage in one circuit produced by a current flow in the other circuit,† or

$$\text{Mutual impedance, } Z_{21} = \left.\frac{V_2}{I_1}\right|_{I_2=0} \tag{10-2}$$

In a similar manner, mutual inductance is defined as the voltage developed in one circuit by a time-varying current in the other circuit, or

$$\text{Mutual inductance, } L_m = \left.\frac{V_2}{dI_1/dt}\right|_{I_2=0} \tag{10-3}$$

Thus the mutual impedance between two circuits with mutual inductance $L_m$ at the sinusoidal frequency $\omega$ radians per second is given by

$$Z_{21} = j\omega L_m \tag{10-4}$$

In general, the value of mutual inductance is difficult to determine analytically for all but simple configurations. References 1, 2, and 3 give relations for the mutual inductance of several common configurations. These relations are usually adequate for obtaining rough approximations. Quite often, a measurement of the mutual inductance offers the easiest solution in cases where unusual geometries are encountered or where a more precise answer is required.

The mutual inductance per meter between two long parallel filamentary wires spaced $s$ units apart and located $h$ units above a ground plane is given by Gray[4] as

$$L'_m \approx \frac{\mu}{2\pi} \ln \frac{\sqrt{s^2 + 4h^2}}{s} \quad \text{H/m} \tag{10-5}$$

If the conductors are not ideal filaments (i.e., nonzero radius), a more precise expression may be obtained by replacing $s$ by the geometric mean distance.[5] Equation (10-5) does illustrate, however, that mutual inductance is minimized by separating the wires and keeping them close to the ground plane.

In general, inductive coupling can be minimized by:

1. Minimizing the circuit area.
2. Using the greatest possible circuit separation.
3. Orienting circuits properly (i.e., avoid parallel leads).
4. Limiting frequencies and rise times of currents.

The use of shielding and field cancellation techniques is also an effective means of reducing coupling and will be treated in a following section.

---

† Common impedance could also be treated as a mutual impedance, as defined by Eq. (10-2).

The dual to the mutual inductance problem is that due to the mutual admittance, usually in the form of capacitive coupling between circuits. The mutual admittance is defined as the current flow in one circuit due to a voltage in the other circuit, or

$$\text{Mutual admittance, } Y_{21} = \frac{I_2}{V_1}\bigg|_{V_2=0} \qquad (10\text{-}6)$$

The mutual admittance between two circuits with a coupling capacitance $C_m$ and at the sinusoidal frequency $\omega$ radians per second is given by

$$Y_{21} = j\omega C_m \qquad (10\text{-}7)$$

The mutual capacitances for an $n$ conductor system can be derived from the solution of $n$ simultaneous equations with elastance coefficients obtained from Green's reciprocation theorem.[6] For example, the mutual capacitance per meter between two parallel, round wires of diameter $d$, a distance $s$ apart, and at a height $h$ from the ground plane is[4]

$$C'_m = \frac{2\pi\epsilon \ln \dfrac{\sqrt{s^2 + 4h^2}}{s}}{\left[\ln \dfrac{4h}{d}\right]^2 - \left[\ln \dfrac{\sqrt{s^2 + 4h^2}}{s}\right]^2} \quad \text{F/m} \qquad (10\text{-}8)$$

for $h \gg d$ and $s \gg d$.

This shows that the mutual capacitance is minimized by separating the wires and keeping them close to the ground plane. Thus, both mutual capacitance and inductance may be minimized in the same way. Consequently, it is good practice to keep all wiring as close to a good ground plane as possible, unless the resulting shunt capacitance becomes more of a problem than the coupling.

One way of reducing the amount of capacitance between two points is to place a good metal ground between the points or at least keep the points close to ground. This increases the capacitance to ground of each point, but it causes a decrease in the direct capacitance between the points. It can be shown that the placement of an ungrounded conductor between the two points serves to increase the direct capacitance between the points. For this reason, it is important that any conducting shields around conductors be adequately grounded.

The amount and type of interaction between two circuits also depend on the impedance levels of the circuits. Consider two circuits over a ground plane, as shown in Fig. 10-4, in which both mutual capacitance and mutual inductance are present. The interfering voltage and current are $V_s$ and $I_s$, respectively. The induced signal on the interfered-with line at the end near the voltage generator (near end) is denoted by the voltage $V_{ne}$ and the current $I_{ne}$. At the other end (far end), the induced signal is $V_{fe}$ and $I_{fe}$. It will be assumed that

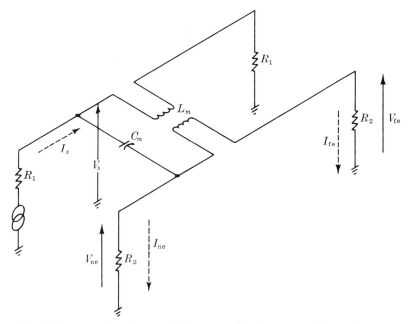

**Fig. 10-4**  Two circuits coupled by mutual inductance and capacitance.

the lengths of the two wires are short compared to a wavelength or pulse rise time. Then the mutual capacitance, $C_m$, and mutual inductance, $L_m$, can be considered lumped elements as given by Eqs. (10-5) and (10-8).

The interaction between the two circuits can be determined by solving the appropriate mesh or nodal equations of the resulting network. For most coupling problems, however, the circuit impedances ($R_1$ and $R_2$) are large compared to the mutual impedance (due to mutual inductance) and are small compared to the capacitive reactance between the circuits. This permits the effects of $L_m$ and $C_m$ to be considered separately and then combined to give the total interfering effect. By ignoring $C_m$, we have (sinusoidal excitation):

$$V_{ne} - V_{fe} = I_s(j\omega L_m) \tag{10-9}$$

Similarly, by ignoring $L_m$, we have:

$$I_{ne} + I_{fe} = V_s(j\omega C_m) \tag{10-10}$$

Since $V_s \approx I_s R_1$, Eq. (10-9) can be written as

$$V_{ne} - V_{fe} = V_s\left(\frac{j\omega L_m}{R_1}\right) \tag{10-11}$$

Also, since $V_{ne} = I_{ne}R_2$ and $V_{fe} = I_{fe}R_2$, Eq. (10-10) becomes

$$V_{ne} + V_{fe} = V_s(j\omega C_m R_2) \tag{10-12}$$

The combined effect is obtained by adding Eqs. (10-10) and (10-11) to obtain $V_{ne}$, and by subtracting Eq. (10-10) from Eq. (10-11) to obtain $V_{fe}$ as:

$$V_{ne} = \frac{V_s}{2}(j\omega C_m R_2) + \frac{V_s}{2}\left(\frac{j\omega L_m}{R_1}\right) \tag{10-13}$$

$$V_{fe} = \frac{V_s}{2}(j\omega C_m R_2) - \frac{V_s}{2}\left(\frac{j\omega L_m}{R_1}\right) \tag{10-14}$$

A more convenient form for pulse circuits is obtained by replacing $j\omega V_s$ by $dV_s/dt$ in the preceding equations, or

$$V_{ne} = \frac{C_m R_2}{2}\frac{dV_s}{dt} + \frac{L_m}{2R_1}\frac{dV_s}{dt} \tag{10-15}$$

$$V_{fe} = \frac{C_m R_2}{2}\frac{dV_s}{dt} - \frac{L_m}{2R_1}\frac{dV_s}{dt} \tag{10-16}$$

Each of these equations has two terms: one is proportional to $C_m$ and is called capacitive crosstalk, and the other is proportional to $L_m$ and is called inductive crosstalk. Since both inductance and capacitance are proportional to the length of the line, both components of crosstalk are also proportional to length for electrically short lines. Note that for high-impedance circuits (large $R_1$, $R_2$), capacitive coupling is the most significant mode of interference, whereas for low-impedance circuits, capacitive effects are minimized and inductive coupling is most significant. Note also that the far-end inductive and capacitive effects are 180° out of phase and tend to cancel each other.

Obviously, the foregoing procedure will not be applicable if the length of a transmission line becomes long compared to a wavelength or pulse rise time. In this case, the solution can be obtained by examining the crosstalk coupled to an elemental length of line and then summing contributions over the entire length of the line, taking into account attenuation and phase shift. For example, consider parallel transmission lines of length $L$, terminated in the same characteristic impedance, $Z_0$. The voltage and current at a distance $x$ from the source, as derived from Eqs. (9-59) and (9-60), are

$$V_s(x) = V_{s0}e^{-\sqrt{ZY}x}$$

$$I_s(x) = \frac{V_{s0}}{Z_0}e^{-\sqrt{ZY}x}$$

This produces crosstalk signals on a differential length of interfered-with line; to obtain the signals, we write Eqs. (10-9) and (10-10) in differential form as

$$dI(x) = j\omega C'_m V_s(x)\,dx \tag{10-17}$$

$$dV(x) = j\omega L'_m I_s(x)\,dx \tag{10-18}$$

where $C'_m$ and $L'_m$ are mutual capacitance and inductance per meter, respectively.

These differential crosstalk signals propagate in both directions on the interfered-with line without reflection. In traveling a distance $x$ back to the near end, the waves undergo further phase shift and attenuation. The differential crosstalk voltage at the near end due to crosstalk at $x$ is obtained by writing Eq. (10-13) in differential form as:

$$dV_{ne}(x) = \frac{1}{2} dV(x) \, e^{-\sqrt{Z'Y'}x} + \frac{Z_0}{2} dI(x) \, e^{-\sqrt{Z'Y'}x} \tag{10-19}$$

The total near-end crosstalk voltage is obtained by integrating Eq. (10-19) over the entire length of the line $l$ to give

$$V_{ne} = \frac{j\omega V_{s0}}{4\sqrt{Z'Y'}}\left(\frac{L'_m}{Z_0} + Z_0 C'_m\right)(1 - e^{-2\sqrt{Z'Y'}l}) \tag{10-20}$$

An understanding of Eq. (10-20) can be gained by recalling that $\sqrt{Z'Y'}$ can be written as $\alpha + j\beta$. Thus, for short lines, the near-end crosstalk will be nearly proportional to length since $(1 - e^{-2(\alpha+j\beta)l}) \approx 2(\alpha + j\beta)l$. If loss is negligible, the crosstalk will show resonant conditions at a given frequency as $l$ is increased, and it will go through a maximum and minimum for every half wavelength of $l$. If loss is present, the fluctuations with increasing $l$ will be damped by the $e^{-2\alpha l}$ term. Thus, for high-loss lines, the near-end crosstalk becomes independent of the length of the lines. A similar analysis shows that far-end crosstalk is proportional to length regardless of the lengths of the cables.[4]

The same technique can be applied to cover pulse transmission and other cases including lines that are not terminated in their characteristic impedances. To be exact, crosstalk to a line from a number of parallel interacting lines would have to include not only direct terms but also higher-order terms due to the crosstalk causing additional crosstalk. Higher-order terms can usually be ignored, and the total crosstalk into a particular line can be determined by superposition of all of the direct crosstalk components from the active lines.

**Example 10.1.** Microstrip signal paths are frequently used in high-speed pulse circuits. For the particular case of fiber-glass epoxy boards with lines terminated in their characteristic impedances, determine the relationship between crosstalk voltage, signal rise time, conductor geometry, conductor separation, and parallel line length.

The crosstalk equations for identical parallel lossless lines of length $l$ terminated in their characteristic impedance $Z_0$ (Fig. 10-5), as derived in Ref. 4, are

$$V_{ne} = K_{ne}\left[V_{s0}(t) - V_{s0}\left(t - \frac{2l}{c}\right)\right]$$

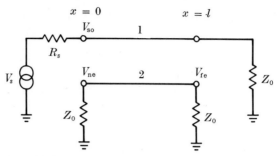

**Fig. 10-5** Schematic diagram for computing crosstalk between lines of characteristic impedance $Z_0$ with coupled length $l$.

where

$$K_{ne} = \frac{c}{4}\left(Z_0 C_m' + \frac{L_m'}{Z_0}\right)$$

and

$$V_{fe} = K_{fe}l\frac{d}{dt}V_{s0}\left(t - \frac{l}{c}\right)$$

where

$$K_{fe} = \frac{1}{2}\left(Z_0 C_m' - \frac{L_m'}{Z_0}\right)$$

and $V_{ne}$ is the near-end noise voltage, $V_{fe}$ is the far-end noise voltage, $V_{s0}$ is the interfering signal voltage, $c$ is the velocity of propagation, and $K_{ne}$ and $K_{fe}$ are near-end and far-end crosstalk constants. Note that $V_{s0}(t - 2l/c) = 0$ for $t < 2l/c$ and $V_{s0}(t - l/c) = 0$ for $t < l/c$. These equations are valid for parallel pairs, a single wire over a ground plane, and strip-line and microstrip

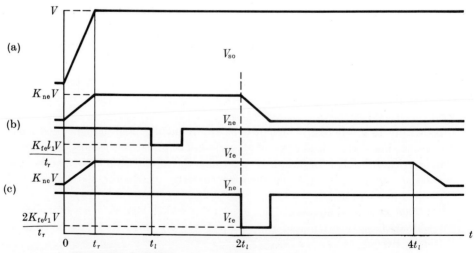

**Fig. 10-6** Variation in crosstalk waveforms with coupled length: (a) disturbing signal, (b) crosstalk waveforms for lines of length $l$, and (c) crosstalk waveforms for lines of length $2l$.

transmission lines. The constants $K_{ne}$ and $K_{fe}$ depend only on the geometry of the lines and are independent of length, time, and voltage. Note that if $Z_0 = \sqrt{L'_m/C'_m}$, $K_{fe} = 0$ and all of the energy is coupled in the backward direction to produce near-end crosstalk. This can occur when the surrounding dielectric is homogeneous. For a two-dielectric medium, as in the case of microstrip, $K_{ne}$ is negative, and the far-end crosstalk signal will always be opposite in polarity to the driving signal with $K_{ne}$ always positive. Typical crosstalk waveforms for a strip-line configuration are shown in Fig. 10-6.

The constants $K_{ne}$ and $K_{fe}$ are most readily obtained experimentally because the predominance of fringe fields and the usual existence of more than one dielectric medium make analysis difficult. Typical crosstalk constants are given in Figs. 10-7 and 10-8[8] for fiber-glass epoxy dielectric strip-lines as a

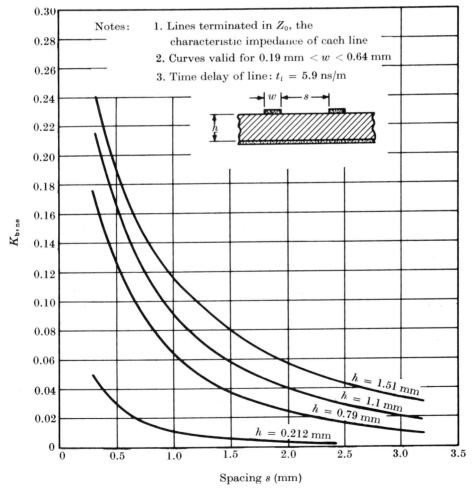

**Fig. 10-7**  Back crosstalk constant as a function of spacing.[8]

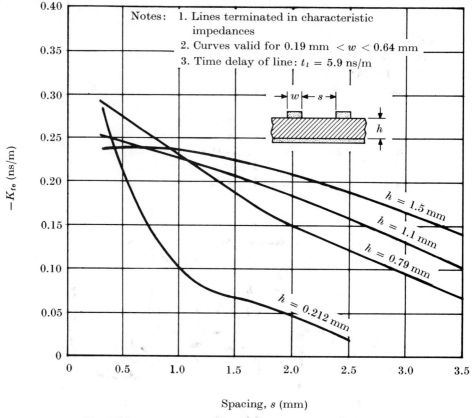

**Fig. 10-8** Forward crosstalk constant as a function of spacing.[8]

function of line spacing $s$ and substrate thickness $h$. The constants, and hence the noise coupling, decrease as spacing increases, and substrate thickness decreases as would be expected.

From the previously presented equations and the crosstalk constants given in Figs. 10-7 and 10-8, relationships among the various parameters can be established. Figure 10-9 gives crosstalk voltage versus coupled line length for a 0.79-mm-thick board with a line separation of 0.64 mm for several rise times. Note that under these conditions, near-end crosstalk is controlling for short line lengths, and far-end crosstalk is predominant for long lengths. Figure 10-10 gives crosstalk voltage versus line spacing for a 3-ns rise time for several values of coupled length. As an example of the use of Fig. 10-10, if the maximum crosstalk voltage must not exceed 6 percent of the drive voltage, the following restrictions on spacing and lead length would be required.

| Limiting noise | Maximum length | Minimum spacing |
|---|---|---|
| Near-end | 0.6 m | 1.02 mm |
| Far-end | 0.9 m | 1.52 mm |

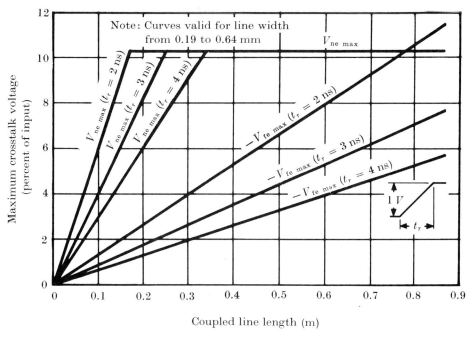

**Fig. 10-9**  Crosstalk between lines on a 0.79 mm board separated by 0.64 mm as a function line length for several rise times.[8]

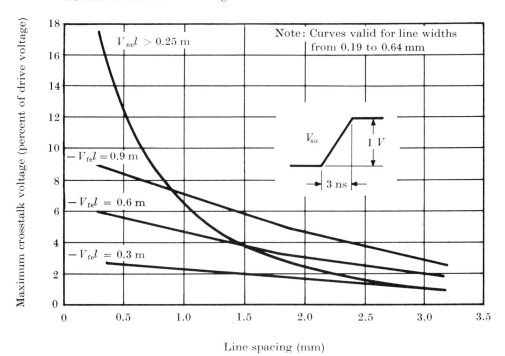

**Fig. 10-10**  Crosstalk between microstrip lines on 0.79 mm board as a function of line spacing for three coupling lengths and 3-ns transition time.[8]

By such techniques, the noise susceptibilities of various transmission line formats can be compared in terms of circuit and physical design alternatives in order to establish a system transmission plan and to establish rules and constraints for designing the system.

## RADIATION

The modes of interference coupling that have been discussed thus far are conduction through common impedances and near-field induction resulting from mutual inductance and capacitance. Near-field effects are reduced by physical separation by $1/r^2$ or $1/r^3$ as discussed in Sec. 9-4. On the other hand, the radiation field falls off as $1/r$ and, consequently, is the only field of interest at points distant from the source. It was previously stated in Sec. 9-4 that the distinction between near and far fields is in terms of wavelength where the dividing point is at a distance of $\lambda/2\pi$, or about $\frac{1}{6}$ wavelength from the radiation source.

Thus, the significant mode of interference (i.e., near-field induction versus radiation) depends upon the distance between the source and receiver and upon the frequency of the source. From Eq. (9-71) or Fig. 9-16, we can see that, at low audio frequencies, all conceivable coupling is due to the near (or induction) field. At the higher frequency of 3 MHz, the wavelength has decreased and the induction field is predominant out to distances of about 15 meters. The radiation of interest at these frequencies is usually only that due to sources outside of the equipment of interest. These sources may be broadcast or other radio transmitters that cause interference because of their high-power output, even though they may be at considerable distances from the receiver. At still higher frequencies such as 30 MHz, the wavelength is becoming short enough so that effects due to radiation become significant at distances of less than 2 meters. Obviously, the effects of radiation within a system become more significant at these frequencies.

In the case of pulse circuits, it is necessary to have an approximate idea of the frequency spectrum of the pulses in order to establish the principal mode of interference. This can be accomplished by converting the time-varying pulse into the frequency domain by the Fourier transform, using techniques described in Papoulis.[7] There are often times when we do not want to carry out this somewhat longer analysis, and the result of the following simple analysis is often adequate.

The time rate of change of a sinusoidally varying signal is given by its derivative with respect to time. The maximum time rate of change is $2\pi f$ times the peak amplitude of the signal. The maximum time rate of change of a pulse of rise time $t_r$ can usually be approximated by $1/t_r$ times its peak amplitude. On equating the two expressions, the rise time can be related to maximum frequency by

$$f = \frac{1}{2\pi t_r} \tag{10-21}$$

Note that this relation is not exact, since the frequency spectrum of a pulse depends upon the shape of the entire pulse. For nonrepetitive pulses, all frequencies from dc on up are present. Repetitive pulses have no frequencies below their repetition frequency.

The susceptibility of equipment to radiated interference depends to a considerable extent on its size and configuration. Receivers and transmitters of radiation are designed purposely with large antenna systems which, in general, have a length equal to $\frac{1}{2}$ the signal wavelength (or multiples of $\lambda/2$) in order to achieve maximum efficiency. Thus, any long leads in equipment can serve as efficient transmitting or receiving antennas. Lead lengths of less than $\frac{1}{6}$ of a wavelength are generally poor transmitters or receivers of radiated energy.

In cases where long wires are unavoidable, it is usually possible to either shield the wire or break it into smaller effective sections by the judicious use of bypass capacitors or series inductors.

## 10-3. ELECTROMAGNETIC SHIELDING

Shielding is an effective technique for suppressing interference. It is well known that a conducting sheet placed between two points will decrease the coupling of electrical energy between them. This simple shield works well in some applications but very poorly in others. In some cases, grounding the shield improves the shielding effect, while in other cases it makes very little difference. Hence, we must know something of the theory of shielding if we are to design adequate shields.

Shields are required to attenuate near fields (**E** and **H**) as well as the radiation or far field. Generally, shields designed to contain energy, because of their nearness to the source, are designed to contain the **E** and **H** near fields. However, shields for protecting susceptible equipment from outside interference may be designed with regard to either the near or far field, depending on the proximity of the source to the shield.

The simplest type of shield is that designed to contain an electric field. The surface of a metallic conductor is nearly equipotential, and there is no significant **E** field within the conductor. Thus, if the shield is grounded or connected to a reference potential, any effects of changing potentials or charges on one side of the shield will not appear on the other side. The perfect shield for electric fields would be an ideal (zero resistance) conductor connected through a zero impedance to a reference potential or ground. Since many

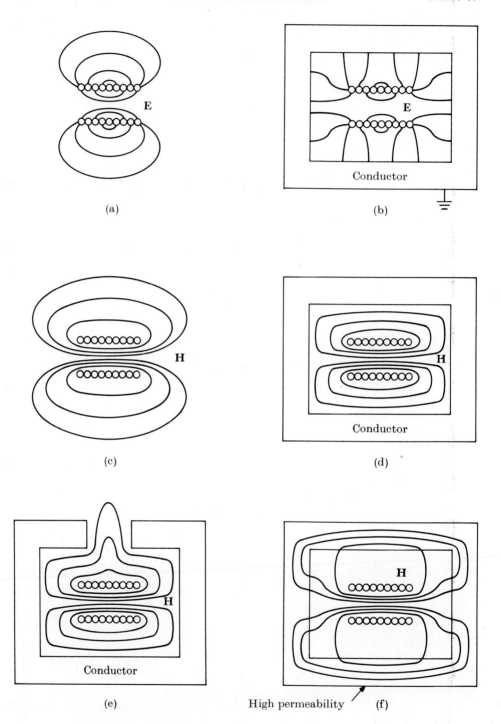

(a)

(b)

(c)

(d)

(e)

High permeability     (f)

**Fig. 10-11**  The effect of various shields around an inductor.

metals are good conductors, it is relatively easy to obtain very good shielding of electric fields.

A much more difficult problem is the shielding of a low-frequency magnetic **H** field. The reason for the difficulty is that there is no near-ideal material (like the metal conductor for the **E** field) that will "short out" the magnetic field. What is needed is a material with a very high relative permeability. As pointed out in the discussion of permeability, such materials are very limited and have permeabilities that are a function of the previous history of the material and of the magnetic flux density within the material.

Surprisingly, high-frequency magnetic fields are easier to shield than are the low-frequency fields. A time-varying magnetic field will induce a potential in any conductor through which the field passes. This induced voltage will cause a current to flow in the conductor which, in turn, produces a magnetic field which will oppose the incident field. In fact, for a perfect conductor, the opposing field would exactly cancel the incident field. However, for materials of finite conductivity, the field is only attenuated by the conductor. The degree of attenuation is directly related to the skin depth phenomena discussed earlier and, consequently, increases with increasing frequency. Thus, a good conducting material will attenuate high-frequency magnetic fields quite well. Furthermore, since the magnetic field decays exponentially as it penetrates into the shield, the attenuation (in dB) furnished by the shield is directly proportional to the thickness of the shield.

As an aid in visualizing the effects of conducting and magnetic shields on electric and magnetic fields, Fig. 10-11 shows the electric and magnetic flux lines around an inductor carrying a time-varying current and surrounded by various types of shields. Figure 10-11(a) shows the electric flux lines around the inductor in free space, and part (b) of the figure shows the flux lines when the inductor is surrounded by a conducting shield. Note how the electric flux lines appear to be attracted to the shield. The magnetic flux lines around the inductor in free space are shown in Fig. 10-11(c), and the same magnetic flux lines are shown in (d) with the inductor surrounded by a conducting, nonmagnetic shield. Note in Fig. 10-11(d) that the flux lines tend to be "pushed away" from the shield. This is due to the opposite-polarity field being set up around the conducting shield due to the induced currents in the shield.

If a hole is placed in the conducting shield, as shown in Fig. 10-11(e), some of the effectiveness of the shield is lost, depending upon the size of the hole. We can think of the conducting shield as containing magnetic flux that is trying to get out. Any holes in the shield will allow some of the flux to leak out, making the shield less effective. For this reason, conducting shields designed to retain magnetic fields must completely enclose the magnetic field, and all joints must make good electrical contact so as not to restrict the induced currents in any way. For example, the leakage resulting from the placement of

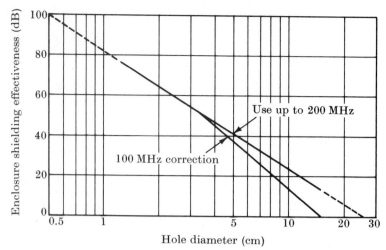

**Fig. 10-12** Shielding effectiveness as a result of placing various-sized holes in an enclosure (plane wave).[9]

holes in an otherwise ideal enclosure is illustrated in Fig. 10-12. Leakage through unavoidable holes, however, can be reduced by the use of screens, gaskets, and waveguides.[9]

Suppose now that the inductor is surrounded by a high-permeability shield material, as shown in Fig. 10-11(f). The magnetic flux lines will be attracted to the shield material (to seek a minimum-reluctance path), and almost all of the flux will be concentrated in the shield material. Small holes in this shield will not seriously affect the shielding properties because the flux lines are more attracted to the shield material than they are to a hole or gap. If the flux lines do not leave the shield enclosure, there can be no unwanted coupling.

Obviously, the ideal shield is a material with both high permeability and high conductivity. Such properties do not usually go together, however, as is shown in Fig. 10-13. This is a list of the relative permeability and conductivity of various common shield materials. For reasons previously discussed, high permeability is very difficult to obtain reliability in a shield material. Any working or heating of most magnetic materials results in marked changes in the relative permeability of the material. Also, the permeability and losses of permeable materials depend on frequency and generally are drastically degraded at higher frequencies. For example, the relative permeability of iron at 10 MHz is only 50 percent of its static value; at 100 MHz, it is 10 percent of its static value; and at 1000 MHz, it is only 1 percent of its static value.

At low frequencies (below a few hundred kilohertz), conducting shields become impractical because of the large shield thickness required to attenuate the field. At these frequencies, materials of high permeability, which provide a

| Material | Relative conductivity with respect to copper | Relative static permeability |
|---|---|---|
| Copper | 1.00 | 1 |
| Aluminum | 0.61 | 1 |
| Magnesium | 0.38 | 1 |
| Brass | 0.26 | 1 |
| Phosphor-bronze | 0.18 | 1 |
| Iron | 0.17 | 1,000 |
| Steel, SAE 1045 | 0.10 | 1,000 |
| Beryllium | 0.10 | 1 |
| Hypernick | 0.06 | 80,000 |
| Monel | 0.04 | 1 |
| Mu-metal | 0.03 | 80,000 |
| Permalloy | 0.03 | 80,000 |
| Steel, stainless | 0.02 | 1,000 |

**Fig. 10-13** Relative permeability and conductivity of various shielding materials.

low-reluctance path for the field, provide the best defense against magnetic interference. At higher frequencies, the properties of many magnetic materials are degraded, and we can usually obtain a more efficient shield by using a tightly enclosed conductor.

The attenuation of electromagnetic fields as they pass through a conductor is directly related to the skin effect. As a matter of fact, the attenuation of the field is exactly the same as the attenuation of current as it penetrates a conductor. Thus, the rate of attenuation is given by

$$\alpha = \frac{1}{\delta} = \sqrt{\pi f \mu \sigma} \text{ neper/m} = 8.68\sqrt{\pi f \mu \sigma} \text{ dB/m} \qquad (10\text{-}22)$$

where the notation is the same as that used in Sec. 9.4. This attenuation is caused by transformation of electric energy into heat and is proportional to the square root of the product of frequency, permeability, and conductivity. Figure 10-14 gives this absorption loss in decibels per millimeter at several frequencies for copper and iron. Values for other materials listed in Fig. 10-13 can be deduced from these results, although care should be taken with the high-permeability materials because permeability is frequency-dependent.

Another source of attenuation from shield materials is that due to reflection. It was noted in the discussion on transmission lines that a mis-terminated line does not deliver all of its energy to the load—some is reflected. The proportion reflected is given by the reflection coefficient, which is related to the ratio of load impedance to line impedance by Eq. (9-75). In an analogous manner, we can characterize reflection of a radiated electromagnetic wave as it passes from one medium to the next. The impedance of any medium to an

|           | *Absorption loss* (dB/mm) | |
| *Frequency* | *Copper* | *Iron* |
| --- | --- | --- |
| 10 kHz  | 13.4   | 173   |
| 100 kHz | 41     | 600   |
| 1 MHz   | 134    | 1,430 |
| 10 MHz  | 410    | 3,540 |
| 100 MHz | 1,340  | 5,400 |
| 1 GHz   | 3,540  | 6,500 |
| 10 GHz  | 10,800 | 5,700 |

**Fig. 10-14**  Absorption loss of copper and iron at several frequencies.

electromagnetic wave is given by the ratio of the magnitudes of the electric **E** field and the magnetic **H** field.  Equation (9-82) shows that this impedance for free space is about 377 ohms.  In metals, this impedance is related to frequency, permeability, and conductivity by the relation

$$Z_s = \sqrt{\frac{j\omega\mu}{\sigma}} = \sqrt{\frac{\pi f \mu}{\sigma}} + j\sqrt{\frac{\pi f \mu}{\sigma}} = R_s(1 + j) \qquad (10\text{-}23)$$

Since $R_s$ is small ($2.61 \times 10^{-4}$ Ω for copper at 1 MHz according to Fig. 9-19) and since the impedance of free space is 377 ohms, the ratio of the two impedances becomes very small, and the reflection coefficient is close to $-1$.  This means that most of the incident radiated energy will be reflected at the junction between free space (or air) and a good conductor.

The ratio of the **E** field to the **H** field is obviously not 377 ohms near an electric or magnetic field source.  For distances $r$ less than $\lambda/2\pi$ from an *electric* field source, the impedance of free space is given approximately by

$$Z_0 \approx -\frac{j}{\omega\epsilon_0 r} \qquad (10\text{-}24)$$

Since the magnitude of this impedance is greater than 377 ohms, we can expect a higher reflection loss at a conducting shield than is obtained for a radiated wave (far field).

Similarly, for distances $r$ much less than $\lambda/2\pi$ from a *magnetic* field source, the impedance of free space is given approximately by

$$Z_0 \approx j\omega\mu_0 r \qquad (10\text{-}25)$$

Since the magnitude of this impedance is less than 377 ohms, we can expect a lower reflection loss at a conducting shield than is obtained for a radiated wave.

| Frequency | Copper | | | Commercial iron | | | Purified iron | | | Co-netic | | | 4-percent silicon-iron | | |
|---|---|---|---|---|---|---|---|---|---|---|---|---|---|---|---|
| | $R$ (dB) | $\alpha t$ (dB) | $t$ (mm) | $R$ (dB) | $\alpha t$ (dB) | $t$ (mm) | $R$ (dB) | $\alpha t$ (dB) | $t$ (mm) | $R$ (dB) | $\alpha t$ (dB) | $t$ (mm) | $R$ (dB) | $\alpha t$ (dB) | $t$ (mm) |
| 1 kHz | 13 | 67 | >25 | 0 | 80 | 7.6 | 10 | 70 | 0.56 | 22 | 58 | 0.53 | 11 | 69 | 2.3 |
| 10 kHz | 22 | 58 | 4.1 | −1 | 81 | 3.1 | 3 | 7 | 0.22 | 13 | 67 | 0.19 | 4 | 76 | 0.81 |
| 100 kHz | 32 | 48 | 1.1 | 4 | 76 | <3.1 | −1.4 | 82 | 0.076 | 5.5 | 74.5 | 0.065 | −1 | 81 | 0.28 |
| 1 MHz | 42 | 38 | 0.31 | 12 | 68 | <3.1 | 2 | 78 | 0.076 | −1 | 81 | <0.025 | 1 | 79 | <0.28 |
| 100 MHz | 62 | 18 | 0.025 | 32 | 48 | <3.1 | 18 | 62 | <0.076 | 6 | 74 | <0.025 | 17 | 63 | <0.28 |
| 10 GHz | 82 | 10 | 0.025 | 52 | 28 | <3.1 | 38 | 42 | <0.076 | 24 | 56 | <0.025 | 36 | 44 | <0.28 |

**Fig. 10-15** Shielding effectiveness of materials located 2.5 cm from a magnetic field source.[10]

In all cases, the reflection loss in dB is given by

$$R = 10 \log \left| \frac{(Z_s + Z_0)^2}{4 Z_s Z_0} \right| \text{ dB} \qquad (10\text{-}26)$$

where $Z_s$ is the shield impedance and $Z_0$ is the impedance of free space adjacent to the shield. The reflection loss is the ratio of the incident to the transmitted energy expressed in decibels.

The total shielding effectiveness of a particular shield, in terms of the insertion loss of the shield, $S$, in dB is given as

$$S = \alpha t + R \text{ dB} \qquad (10\text{-}27)$$

where $\alpha$ is the absorption loss given by Eq. (10-22), $t$ is the material thickness, and $R$ is the reflection loss given by Eq. (10-26). In general, the reflection loss is predominant at frequencies below about 10 MHz and the absorption loss is predominant above a few hundred MHz.

The relative effectiveness of several possible shield materials located 2.5 cm from a magnetic field source is shown in Fig. 10-15 for a frequency range of 1 kHz to 10 GHz. In each case, the shield thickness has been adjusted to give a total shielding effectiveness due to reflection and absorption of 80 dB. Note that, at audio frequencies, the required thickness of copper (and typically all nonferrous metals) is impractical, whereas for a ferrous material, the required thickness at these frequencies is much more reasonable.

**Example 10.2.** An attractive construction technique is to encapsulate components in a plastic foam material. This technique was used for many circuits in the Telstar satellite. Generally, a given circuit is foamed into a block. In subsequent operations, several of these circuit blocks may be foamed into a larger block. Since the foam is a plastic with a high percentage of gas bubbles, there is substantially no practical shielding obtained from the foam itself. In fact, effects of capacitive coupling are slightly enhanced since the effective dielectric constant of the foam is about 1.1 to 1.2. The obvious way to obtain shielding between circuits is to enclose the foamed circuit block in a metal container. This either becomes quite expensive or severely limits the available number of possible shapes for circuit assemblies. A more flexible solution (and one that is more economical of space and weight) is to spray a metal coating on the foamed plastic block.

We wish to establish the feasibility of providing such a shield for the foamed block shown in Fig. 10-16. The magnetic field source contained within the block must be attenuated by 50 dB at a frequency of 1 MHz. Due to

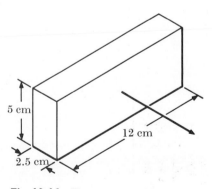

5 cm

12 cm

2.5 cm

**Fig. 10-16**   Foam-encapsulated circuit.

mechanical bonding problems, a coating of solder must first be applied to the foam. Then a coating of copper is sprayed over the solder. What thickness of copper is required to achieve a shielding loss of 50 dB? How could the shield best be designed to increase the shielding loss by a factor of two?

Incident energy will be absorbed in both the solder and copper and reflected at each of the three interfaces. However, reflections at the solder-foam interface will not contribute to the loss of the shield because reflections inside the shield are not absorbed but simply impinge upon other parts of the shield. However, reflections at the copper-solder and copper-air interface will be attenuated in the solder and copper, respectively.

To find the reflection losses, we must determine the impedances of the copper and solder and of the space surrounding the metals. Using Eq. (10-23) for copper, with $R_s = 0.00026 \ \Omega$ at 1.0 MHz, we obtain:

$$Z_{\text{copper}} = 2.6 \times 10^{-4}(1 + j) \ \Omega$$

$R_s$ is inversely proportional to the square root of the conductivity. Since the conductivity of solder is $\frac{1}{9}$ that of copper, the impedance of solder is three times that of copper or

$$Z_{\text{solder}} = 7.8 \times 10^{-4}(1 + j) \ \Omega$$

The impedance of the space on each side of the shield is *not* 377 $\Omega$ because the magnetic field source is so close to the shield (about 1 cm if the source is in the middle of the block shown in the figure). Thus, Eq. (10-25) must be used to find the impedance of the air around the shield. For $\omega = 2\pi \times 10^6$ rad/s, $\mu_0 = 4\pi \times 10^{-7}$ H/m, and $r = 0.01$ m, we obtain

$$Z_{\text{air}} = j\omega\mu_0 r = j(0.079) \ \Omega$$

The reflection losses can then be obtained from Eq. (10-26). At the copper-air interface:

$$R_{\text{copper-air}} = 10 \log \left| \frac{(Z_{\text{copper}} + Z_{\text{air}})^2}{4 Z_{\text{copper}} Z_{\text{air}}} \right|$$
$$= 10 \log 53.8 = 17.3 \text{ dB}$$

At the copper-solder interface:

$$R_{\text{copper-solder}} = 10 \log \left| \frac{(Z_{\text{copper}} + Z_{\text{solder}})^2}{4 Z_{\text{copper}} Z_{\text{solder}}} \right|$$
$$= 10 \log 1.33 = 1.2 \text{ dB}$$

From Fig. 10-14, we find that the absorption loss of copper at 1.0 MHz is 134 dB/mm. Equation (10-22) indicates that the absorption loss at a given frequency is directly proportional to the square root of the conductivity for a nonmagnetic material. Thus, solder has an absorption loss that is $\frac{1}{3}$ that of copper. This results in an absorption loss of 45 dB/mm, or 11.2 dB for the 0.25 mm thickness of solder.

The total shielding effectiveness, $S$, from Eq. (10-27) is

$$S = \alpha t_{\text{copper}} + \alpha t_{\text{solder}} + R_{\text{copper-air}} + R_{\text{copper-solder}}$$

The last three terms account for 29.7 dB of attenuation. Thus, the copper must attenuate the magnetic field by 20.3 dB to achieve the 50 dB required shielding loss. Since the attenuation of copper at 1 MHz is 134 dB/mm, the copper coating must have a thickness of approximately 0.15 mm.

An efficient way to improve the shielding is through the use of a double shield. This could be accomplished by encapsulating the coated block in a slightly larger foam block and recoating this larger block with the copper-solder combination used previously. This will double (in dB) both the absorption loss and the reflection loss and thus double the shielding effectiveness in dB. There is also an additional reflection loss at the solder-foam interface of the outside shield. Energy entering the foam layer between the metals will be reflected at the solder interface, go back to the copper interface, be reflected again, etc., until all of the energy is dissipated in the absorption losses of the copper and solder. This loss can be shown to be approximately:

$$R \approx 10 \log \frac{Z_{copper} + Z_{solder}}{Z_{solder}} = 1.2 \text{ dB}$$

The shield need not be grounded in order to attenuate magnetic interference. However, if we wish to shield against electric fields as well, at least one of the shields must be grounded. If grounding is required, the paths of all ground currents should be carefully considered. For instance, if the circuit grounds are connected to the inner shield, this shield should be connected to equipment ground near the signal input and output leads as shown in Fig. 10-17. Both correct and incorrect methods are shown. The incorrect method

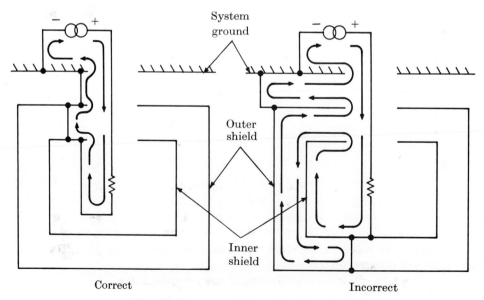

**Fig. 10-17**   Grounding of a double shield.

can cause spurious coupling paths with any other currents that may be circulating in the shield and will severely reduce the effectiveness of the shield.

## 10-4. COMPONENT INTERFERENCE REDUCTION

Many interference problems result from a single component producing an interfering field that is picked up by a susceptible component. This is a near-field effect resulting from a mutual impedance or admittance. An understanding of the nature of the components and circuitry will often permit the designer to predict possible interference problems of this type and avoid them early in the design.

It is generally important to isolate components which are carrying signals at widely different levels. One of the simplest and most economical means of electrical isolation is physical separation, since all fields are attenuated with distance from the source. Unfortunately, space is often a very important factor, and critical components must be so close together that the shielding advantages of physical separation cannot be realized. Even with close spacings, the mutual coupling between components can be reduced considerably by proper orientation of the components. For instance, inductors wound as solenoids should be kept with their axes at right angles to minimize the mutual inductance between them (the mutual inductance is eliminated when the magnetic field lines of the two inductors are orthogonal). Mutual capacitances are minimized by maintaining as much spacing as possible between points of high potential difference or by providing a metallic shield between the points.

Consider the circuit shown in Fig. 10-18, which is to be wired in cordwood fashion between two printed circuit boards. This circuit is intended to serve as a low-pass filter and should attenuate all energy above a certain frequency as it passes from the input to the output. In the passband, the filter should offer little or no attenuation. For low-frequency signals, the physical arrangement of the circuit is not critical. Since the level differences through the filter are small, coupling effects can be ignored at the low frequencies. At the higher frequencies, where the filter should have considerable loss, we can find many sources of trouble that will limit its performance.

Recall from the discussion of equivalent circuits for lumped elements that all inductors have associated with them a shunt capacitance, and that all capacitors have an associated series inductance. At sufficiently high frequencies, the inductors shown in Fig. 10-18 will resonate with their shunt capacitances, and above this frequency, all inductors will look like capacitors. Similarly, at high frequencies, the capacitors will series-resonate with their series inductance, and above these frequencies, the capacitors will look like inductors. Thus, the low-pass filter is transformed into its dual by converting all inductors to capacitors and all capacitors to inductors. This results in a high-pass filter.

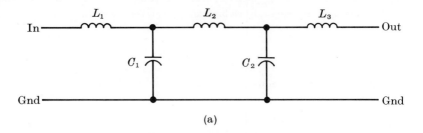

(a)

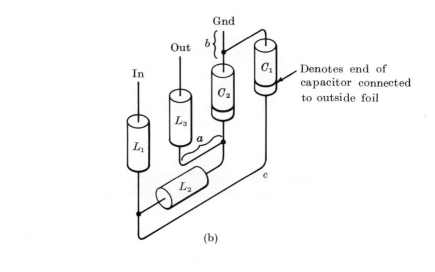

Denotes end of capacitor connected to outside foil

(b)

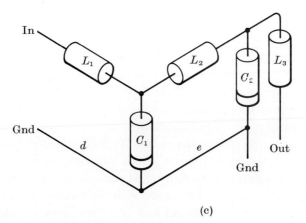

(c)

**Fig. 10-18**  A filter circuit with two possible component layouts.

In general, therefore, unless special precautions are taken, a low-pass filter is actually a band-elimination filter that passes both low frequencies, as designed, and high frequencies due to stray inductance and capacitance. The goal is to minimize these stray effects through control of component design, component orientation, and wiring layout.

Consider the layout shown in part (b) of Fig. 10-18. For clarity, the components are shown without a printed wire board. This layout has many disadvantages. Perhaps the most obvious is the presence of the mutual inductance between inductors $L_1$ and $L_3$. These inductors, assumed to be wound as solenoids, have maximum mutual inductance when they are placed together and have their axes parallel as shown. The mutual inductance between them is particularly bad because $L_1$ at the input will carry a relatively high current, resulting in a large magnetic field. This field will induce a relatively large voltage across $L_3$ which is in the low-level output of the circuit. At high frequencies, therefore, there will be considerable undesired transmission between the input and output of the filter through this path.

Considering further the input and output of the arrangement shown in Fig. 10-18(b), we can see another undesirable coupling path at high frequencies. This is due to the capacitance between the input and output leads of the filter. Again, this results from the nearness of these points and could be eliminated by a grounded conducting shield placed between the two leads.

With this layout, the stray capacitances across the inductors are increased because of several factors. For instance, the capacitance across $L_2$ is increased by the parallel wiring denoted by "a" in the figure. Also, the presence of the "outside foil" notation on the capacitors shows that $C_2$ is wired in such a way as to increase the capacitance across $L_3$. If this capacitor were turned the other way, the additional capacitance due to the outside foil would not be so serious. The reason is that the outside foil would then be connected to ground, and the stray capacitance would appear between the output and ground (not necessarily very serious) and in parallel with $C_2$ (this can be compensated by trimming the value of $C_2$ slightly).

The last significant source of coupling in the circuit of Fig. 10-18(b) is due to the way $C_1$ is wired. First, the ground lead marked "b" in the layout is common to both the input and output of the filter. As pointed out previously, the impedance of this ground lead can cause considerable coupling between input and output if the loss through the filter is high—as it should be at high frequencies. The other flaw in the wiring of $C_1$ is the long length of lead marked "c" in the figure. This lead not only contributes to additional stray capacitance across $L_2$ but also increases the stray inductance in series with $C_1$, thus lowering the maximum frequency at which $C_1$ behaves as a capacitor.

These "flaws" degrade performance and make it difficult to approach the theoretical performance suggested by the schematic diagram. In fact, such a filter would probably be unusable if it were built to the layout shown in Fig. 10-18(b).

All of the problems of this layout can be minimized or eliminated by changing the layout to the one shown in Fig. 10-18(c). Note that this new layout does not include any shields but does occupy slightly more space.

Layout (c) has the axes of all three inductors mutually perpendicular to minimize mutual inductance. Furthermore, the inductors are physically separated to further reduce the mutual inductance. Note that the input and output ports of the filter are fairly widely separated to reduce the capacitance between them. Also, the capacitors have very short leads, which minimizes the associated series inductance. The ground leads marked "d" and "e" do not count as capacitor lead lengths but can instead be considered in series with $L_1$ and $L_2$, respectively. By making the filter a four-terminal network with separate ground leads on the input and output, the problems associated with a common impedance in the ground path between input and output are avoided. Last but not least, the outside foils of the capacitors are connected to ground so that stray capacitances across the inductors are minimized. The resulting layout is thus much better than the one in (b). If better isolation were required, we would have to resort to different techniques, such as individually shielding the sections of the filter.

Shielding is often required to reduce spurious coupling. In most such cases, it is desirable to pinpoint the coupling as accurately as possible and design the shield accordingly. Obviously, the indiscriminate use of shielding is not good because it adds unnecessary shielding and also does not protect against internal coupling within each shield. Shielding an interfering source is often advantageous since all coupling paths from that source are thereby eliminated. However, this is not always the best decision since (1) shields designed to protect susceptible components are usually more efficient than shields which contain interference because they are able to reflect a greater amount of the incident energy; and (2) the susceptible component may occupy a smaller volume than the source and, thus, may be more easily shielded.

A common interference problem in large systems is the arcing of switch or relay contacts. Arcing is caused by the transient that occurs during switching of reactive loads due to energy that is either supplied to, or stored in, the electrical circuit. The primary effect of this arcing is that it generates energy with an extremely broad frequency spectrum. The secondary effect is that it causes deterioration, and eventually destruction, of the arc contact surfaces.

Although not always totally effective, the simple placement of a small capacitor (0.01 $\mu$F) across arcing electrical contacts can often reduce the arcing considerably. Such a capacitor should be placed as close to the switch contacts as possible so that the inductance between the arc electrodes (the switch contacts) and the capacitor is very low. If this is not done, the resonant circuit formed by the stray inductance and the added capacitor acts as a radio transmitter when excited by the arc and can cause undesirable interference.

Special networks are available for arc suppression. These networks avoid arcing by providing an alternate path for the stored energy in the inductors. For inductive loads such as relays, there are four commonly used arc-suppression networks (also called contact-protection networks). These are shown in Fig. 10-19.

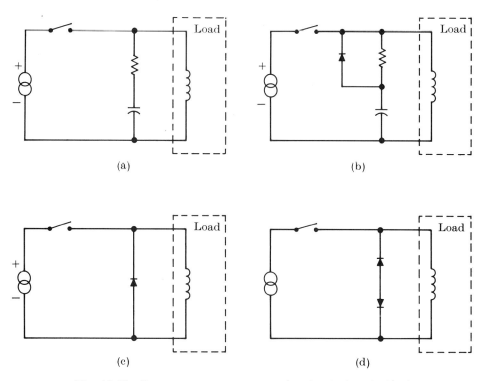

**Fig. 10-19**   Some common arc-suppression (contact-protection) networks.

The resistor-capacitor network in Fig. 10-19(a) is a commonly used type. When the switch contacts are opened, disconnecting the voltage source, the current flowing through the inductor cannot change instantaneously and flows through the capacitor and resistor until the capacitor becomes discharged. Available commercial networks are designed to be used over a certain range of relay coil characteristics.

The diode-capacitor-resistor network in Fig. 10-19(b) is an improvement over the network in part (a). The diode allows the use of a larger value of $R$, thus decreasing the current when contact is made, but maintaining a low voltage across the contacts when the circuit is broken. The simple circuit in Fig. 10-19(c) uses only a diode to achieve the same effect. Although simple, this circuit is not often used because it causes the magnetic field produced by the inductance to decay very slowly and thus causes relays using this scheme to be "sticky" or slow to release.

The two diodes wired back-to-back, as shown in Fig. 10-19(d), are often used in switching inductive loads in ac power circuits. This scheme relies upon the reverse voltage characteristic of the diodes so that one diode is a short circuit and the other acts like a nonlinear resistor. Because of the symmetry of this network, the polarity of the supply voltage at the time of breaking contact will not affect its arc-suppression properties.

In all of the configurations shown in Fig. 10-19, the suppression networks are shown wired in parallel with the inductive load (relay coil). Actually, they can sometimes be more effective when wired across the contacts. Generally, if one set of contacts controls several different loads, it may be more economical to place one suppression network across the contacts. Conversely, in circuits where several contacts can control a single load, it is more economical to place the protection across the load, as shown, rather than across each contact.

Interference problems often arise in transistors and logic circuits as a result of their high speed of operation. Recent advances in semiconductor technology often make it economical and practical to use high-speed transistors or logic circuits in applications where the speed is unnecessary. The high switching speeds produce fields with very high time rates of change which can, for example, cause adjacent logic circuits to change state.

Obviously, the solution is to slow down the circuits by adding series inductance and shunt capacitance at the transistor leads or to use slower transistors in the circuit. Such measures not only reduce the high-frequency energy in the transients produced but also make the circuit less susceptible to high-frequency fields in the vicinity.

In analog or linear circuits, the same problem exists. In this case, we achieve circuits having much higher frequency response than is necessary. Besides being susceptible to interference over a wider frequency spectrum, such conditions also increase the possibility of spurious or parasitic oscillations.

## 10-5. INTERFERENCE REDUCTION IN CABLES AND INTERCONNECTIONS

Many of the techniques discussed for reducing interference (or coupling) between components are also applicable to wiring the interconnections. Thus, the simplest way to reduce coupling between various wiring interconnections is to physically separate, as much as possible, all wires carrying widely different signal levels (voltage, current, or power). When it is topologically impossible to separate the interconnections, a significant advantage is obtained by running wiring which carries different signal levels at right angles, or at least by avoiding situations where the wires run parallel and close together for any appreciable length.

In balanced circuits [i.e., two-conductor circuit (return path via second conductor rather than by ground) in which both conductors are electrically symmetrical with respect to ground], a considerable reduction in coupling between circuits can be obtained by twisting the wire pairs together for each circuit. A twisted pair in a time-varying magnetic field will have induced voltages in successive twists that oppose each other. The net interfering effect at the end of a length of cable will be the algebraic sum of the individual induced voltages. Actually, a perfect balance or exact cancellation of voltages is never realized; there is always some residual interfering effect which increases with frequency. For frequencies at which single twists approach an appreciable fraction of a wavelength, twisting loses effectiveness and is not used.

Two twisted-pair cables running parallel to each other will have less coupling if they have a random length of twist rather than the same length of twist. In this case, the accumulation of unbalance will increase as the square root of the length of the circuits. If the pairs all have the same length of twist, there is a tendency for the pairs to repeat the same relative relationship with each twist length along the cable so that the induced voltages increase on a systematic basis directly as the length of the circuits.

For still further reduction in the amount of coupling between twisted pairs, a conducting shield is often placed around the twisted pair. A copper or aluminum tube is an effective shield at frequencies above about 100 kHz. Such a shield will attenuate both the electric and magnetic fields around the cables. At the lower frequencies (below 100 kHz), the effectiveness of the conducting shield for magnetic fields becomes much less. At these frequencies, the only effective shield is a material of high permeability, such as steel conduit.

In many applications, cables must be bent to small radii, which requires that the shield be constructed of a flexible braid. Electrostatic fields are usually shielded about as effectively with a braided shield as with a solid conduit. The suppression of a magnetic field depends strongly on inducing currents in the shield that will produce an opposing magnetic field. If the wires of a braided shield do not make good electrical contact at each crosspoint, the effective resistance increases and the effectiveness of the shield decreases. Even with perfect connections at the crosspoints, the shield is not as effective as a solid conductor because the possible current paths in the braided shield are limited, whereas in a solid shield they are not. As a result, one can expect a braided shield to be several tens of decibels less effective in shielding magnetic fields than a solid shield of the same thickness.

Many circuits in communication equipment are unbalanced in that they use a ground return, are grounded, or otherwise are unsymmetrical with respect to ground. A coaxial cable is an important example of an unbalanced structure. The advantage of coaxial cable is that the outer conductor or sheath serves both as a return path for the signal currents and as a shield. The shielding results from the skin effect which causes the signal current returning along the outer conductor of the coaxial to flow on the inside surface. Consequently, as one approaches the outer surface of the sheath, the magnetic field due to the signal current approaches zero. If a time-varying magnetic field is present in the vicinity of the cable, the current flow due to the induced voltage will tend to stay at the outside surface of the sheath and thus not seriously affect the currents flowing in the cable.

A solid-sheath coaxial cable affords a degree of shielding several tens of decibels better than a braided sheath. In instances where the shielding effectiveness of a solid-sheath coaxial cable is needed, but where the flexibility of the braided sheath is desired, a braided double-shielded coaxial structure is often used. This consists of a conventional coaxial structure with an additional sheath surrounding it. The additional sheath is completely insulated from the inner sheath (in essence, it is a triaxial structure). The center conductor and inside sheath are used as the signal leads in a conventional manner. The outside sheath is then connected to chassis ground at each end of the cable. However, because of skin effect and the way the connections are made, the outside sheath carries an insignificant portion of the return signal current. As a result, the degree of shielding is improved by several tens of decibels. Thus, a well-shielded flexible cable can be obtained at the expense of a more complicated cable configuration and a somewhat more difficult task in making connections.

Other transmission line configurations, such as those shown in Fig. 9-19, are frequently used. In general, these other configurations do not provide the degree of shielding at high frequencies that is obtainable using coaxial cable or shielded twisted pair. The strip-line configuration is an approximation to the coaxial cable; as such, it provides a reasonable degree of shielding if the different conductors are spaced at somewhat greater distances than the spacing between the ground planes. Other strip configurations provide somewhat less shielding; this is sometimes improved by running grounded strips on each side of the "hot" conductor.

The crosstalk characteristics of various types of cables will, of course, depend to a great extent on their details of construction. As an order of magnitude measure of performance, Fig. 10-20 lists values of mutual inductance for several typical cables (parallel, closely spaced conductors in the MHz frequency range). Note the advantage of both the twisted pair and the coaxial cable over the other configurations, and the order of magnitude advantage of coaxial cable over twisted pair. At low frequencies, however, where the coaxial outer conductor is a poor shield, the twisted pair will give better crosstalk performance than will the coaxial cable.

An example of an application of partial shielding to a microstrip delay line

| Wiring system | Mutual inductance ($\mu$H/m) |
|---|---|
| Standard cabling | 5 |
| Wiring over ground plane | 0.5 |
| Twisted pair | 0.05 |
| Coaxial (braided outer conductor) | 0.005 |

**Fig. 10-20** Mutual inductance between typical wiring systems of parallel, closely spaced conductors in the MHz frequency range.

occurred in the design of a pulse code modulation parallel-to-series converter. Parallel pulses entering at equally spaced intervals along the delay line are converted to a serial pulse train. The need for signal taps along the line precluded the use of coaxial cable in favor of an exposed microstrip line which permitted easier connection without introducing appreciable discontinuities in the line. To achieve the maximum amount of delay for a printed circuit board of a given size, it is necessary to "coil" the conductor in some geometry on the board to make it as long as possible. Obviously, if this is done, there will be coupling between parts of the delay line that come physically close to each other. After trying various geometries, it was found that even the best arrangement did not give adequate performance because of the amount of coupling present. The solution to the problem came in surrounding the conductor on the board with grounded conductors in the same plane as the wiring, in addition to the ground plane on the back of the board. The additional shielding obtained in this way was adequate, so that, with a good geometrical layout, the performance of the line compared favorably with that obtainable with coaxial cable. The resulting delay line used in the parallel-to-series converter is shown in Fig. 10-21.

**Fig. 10-21** A partially shielded delay line.

Printed circuit boards have been made in which the board consists of a lamination of an insulator on each side of a conducting sheet. Circuit conductors can be run on both sides of such a board. The conducting sheet in the center of the board, if adequately grounded, provides a fair degree of shielding between the circuits on one side of the board and those on the other side.

A unique solution was found for a pulse access cable used in a store for a large digital system. Groups of eight wires in this cable have the property that only one wire of the eight is energized and carrying a current pulse at any one time (with ground return). The problem was to prevent coupling between one group of eight wires and other groups in the same (or parallel) cable. Coupling to wires in a particular group was not critical. The coupling could be reduced to a tolerable level by making each wire and ground return circuit a twisted pair. This would require eight twisted-pair lines for each group. A more economical solution was achieved by wrapping each group of eight conductors with a single ninth conductor which serves as a common ground return. When one conductor of such a group is activated, the configuration looks very much like a twisted pair (admittedly with the dielectric somewhat cluttered with other inactive wires). As a result, the crosstalk or interaction between groups was reduced to an acceptable level without the expense of separate twisted pairs.

## 10-6. GROUNDING TECHNIQUES TO REDUCE INTERFERENCE

The use of the term "ground" is often misleading in that it has more than one meaning. Ground is used to refer to the potential of the earth, which often is used as a reference for voltage measurements. It is also common practice to call any conducting medium that serves as a common connection of electrical circuits a "ground." Such a ground could be a metal chassis, a rack of equipment, a ground strip on a printed wire board, or the structural metal of a building. The circuit ground need not be at the same potential as earth ground and, indeed, may not even be connected to earth. However, it is common practice to connect equipment to earth ground as a means of avoiding dangerous potentials between different pieces of equipment and between equipment and the building housing it. In addition to safety of personnel and equipment, the establishment of a common reference voltage for proper system operation and the prevention of noise coupling through the ground network are primary considerations in grounding electronic equipment.

For lightning protection, most buildings are connected to earth ground. The building ground paths must be capable of carrying currents of hundreds of amperes with relatively fast rise times (on the order of 10 milliseconds). To avoid dangerous potentials, the resistance in the ground path must be less than about 0.1 ohm with inductance less than about 0.1 millihenry. The requirements for ground leads are usually covered in wiring codes for buildings. A detailed discussion of earth grounding for lightning and power protection is covered in Ref. 11.

The connection of electronic equipment to earth ground can be made in two ways: the multipoint or grid system and the single-point or tree system. The multipoint ground system, shown in Fig. 10-22, requires the existence of an equipotential ground plane or grid for the system. This could be the structural steel of a building or a ground grid embedded in a concrete floor at earth potential. Electronic equipment is then connected to this ground plane at multiple points, with the usual requirement that lead lengths be short as possible.

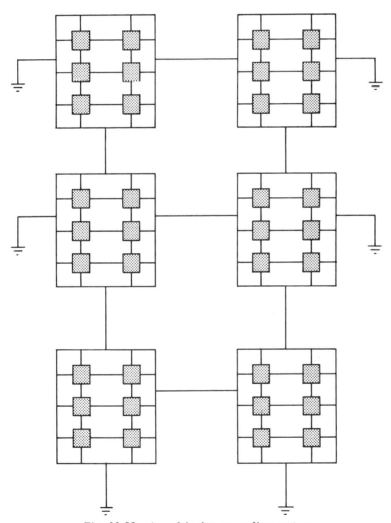

**Fig. 10-22**  A multipoint grounding system.

Equipment cabinets are connected to the ground plane. Chassis are then connected to equipment cabinets, and all grounded components and leads are connected to the chassis. This procedure invariably results in ground loops in that there are several paths from any one point to the ground plane. The ground plane will be truly equipotential only if the grounding system has virtually no resistance or if the currents in it are held to low values.

In the single-point ground system shown in Fig. 10-23, all pieces of equipment are referenced to a single earth ground through a tree network in which there is only one unique path to ground from any point. In a cabinet, all

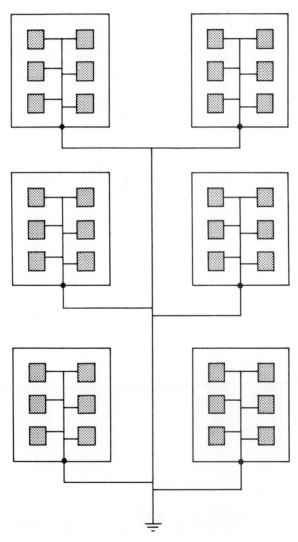

**Fig. 10-23** A single-point or tree grounding system.

electronic circuits are referenced to a common point or bus which is insulated from the cabinet and building. This common point is then connected to the reference point. This, of course, prevents any circulating currents in the building from producing potential drops within the equipment. Also, no circulating currents are introduced into the building from the equipment. This system has the advantage that the equipment structure is not relied upon to carry ground currents, so that the bonding requirements between pieces of equipment are relaxed. Another advantage of the single-point system is the ease with which one can control the exact paths of the various ground currents. The disadvantage, of course, is the difficulty in maintaining low-impedance ground paths throughout the tree when all ground connections must go to a common point and, consequently, may be of considerable length.

Systems that are entirely multipoint or entirely single-point, as shown in Figs. 10-22 and 10-23, respectively, rarely occur in practice. Instead, a hybrid combination of the two schemes is usually used. For example, a system consisting of many isolated bays within a room may connect the bays to earth ground via a single-point system but ground all equipment in a bay as a multi-point subsystem using the bay structure as an equipotential surface. Many printed wire boards contain a multipath ground "grid" or a ground plane and can thus be considered multipoint grounded boards, but they may connect to earth ground through a single lead so that a system of boards is single-point grounded.

The presence of voltages between the various grounds in a system is a source of considerable interference. One possible interference mode is that due to the common impedance in the ground path of various circuits. This can become especially serious in single-point grounding systems where several circuits may share the same ground bus. Logic circuits, for example, may be falsely operated as a result of ground lead inductance. When unbalanced logic gates share a common ground path (as they would on a printed wire board), a rapidly switched gate can produce an inductive voltage drop in the ground path that may act as an input signal to another gate. The inductance of a single wire in free space[1,2] (length $\gg$ diameter) is approximately 0.8 $\mu$H/m. Thus, a sudden change in current of 30 mA with a rise time of 30 ns would produce a noise voltage spike in a 1-meter length of line of

$$\Delta V \approx L \frac{\Delta I}{\Delta t} = (0.8 \times 10^{-6}) \frac{30 \times 10^{-3}}{30 \times 10^{-9}} = 0.8 \text{ V}$$

Actually, some effects of the inductance are canceled by lead capacitance to ground. However, this limitation frequently imposes restrictions on maximum lead length in digital systems and requires the design of circuits that are not highly susceptible to changes in ground voltage (often called common mode voltage).

Frequently, an attempt is made to provide a ground path through structural fastenings and members that have painted contact surfaces or that can corrode or work loose with time. It is good design practice to have all equipment electrically bonded together through connections that perform no mechanical or structural function.

Clean metal-to-metal bonds should be made on equipment mounting plates, racks, shelves, and mating surfaces in order to form a continuous low-impedance path to ground. To effect good bonding, jumpers should be avoided (high impedance). Their use should be restricted to situations like crossing non-metallic areas such as shock mounts. To prevent corrosion, bonds should always be made between the structures of the same metal or, if this is impossible, between metals close together in the electrochemical series. Both electrolytic and galvanic corrosion are accelerated by moisture, so that care should be taken to keep bonds between different metals dry. It is also good practice to have bonds of different materials accessible for inspection, so that any corrosion with time is readily detectable. The use of high-frequency gaskets should not be overlooked. Several types are available in a wide variety of shapes, sizes, and materials.

Even with utmost care, it is impossible to obtain zero-impedance ground paths. However, the effects of ground path impedance can be minimized by minimizing the current flow through the ground path. This can be done by providing a return circuit for all currents rather than by relying on the ground path. Also, some isolation can be obtained by providing separate ground paths for low-level and high-level circuits. Many problems will be avoided by attempting to visualize where the various ground currents will flow (each will flow to its destination by following the minimum-impedance path) and by avoiding situations where both high and low currents interact or share the same path.

Even with zero-impedance grounds, interference and coupling can exist in multipoint ground systems through the presence of ground loops. These consist of conducting loops formed by ground and conductors which are grounded on both ends. Such an arrangement is like a closed loop of wire. Recalling Eq. (9-30), we see that a time-varying **B** field within this closed conducting loop will induce a voltage in the loop. This voltage depends upon the time rate of change of the field, the area of the loop, and the strength of the field.

Small ground loops formed in a subsystem are obviously less significant than the larger loops associated with the entire system. Thus, the multipoint method is frequently used within small subsystems where it is important to minimize ground lead impedance, and the single-point method is used to ground the subsystems. Ground loops enclosed by a shield (chassis or cabinet) are also much less susceptible to interference from outside the shield.

It is often very difficult to avoid ground loops in a system because of the nature of the signal interconnections and the need for compatibility with power wiring and safety codes. For example, a coaxial interconnection between two points in a system, where the outer conductor connects to ground at each end, shorts two branches in the ground tree and thus forms a ground loop. Removing the ground connection on one end would break the signal return path in the coaxial outer conductor and force the return current to flow through the ground tree, nullifying the effectiveness of the coaxial interconnection. Transformers can be used to break the ground loop, as will be discussed later. A more common and simpler procedure is to accept the existence of the ground loop and to minimize its area by dressing all grounded signal interconnections along the grounding tree.

Compatibility of a single-point ground system with ac power distribution mains also presents a problem. Since power lines are highly susceptible to lightning strikes, safety considerations require that earth ground be provided through a low-impedance path at the power entry point of the building. This results in two grounding systems—a "power ground" and a "system ground" which, if they are crossed, will form ground loops.

Surprisingly, ground loops are not usually serious problems at high frequencies, where coaxial cable is used, in spite of the fact that the time rate of change of the magnetic field is high. The reason is that, because of the skin effect, high-frequency induced currents in the ground loop will tend to flow on the inside surface of the loop (outer surface of the coaxial structure). Signal current at high frequencies will flow on the inside surface of the outer coaxial conductor. Thus, the induced current and the signal current are isolated from each other by the thickness of the outer conductor. At lower frequencies, where skin effect is not so significant, such a shielding advantage is not available. In fact, the most troublesome induced loop current is usually due to the field produced by the ac power lines (usually 60 Hz). As a result, circuits that are sensitive to these frequencies are usually wired with no closed loops in the ground system (i.e., using a single-point ground system).

As an example of a single-point grounding system, we will consider a grounding plan for a transmission terminal. The terminal consists of multiplex equipment (modulators, filters, etc), power supplies, and maintenance facilities which are mounted for the most part in duct-type bays. The system operates in the frequency range of 0.5 to 6.5 MHz.

In the past, similar systems have been susceptible to interference from broadcast transmitters because of the presence of ground loops in the equipment. To minimize susceptibility to broadcast interference, a single-point grounding system, shown in Fig. 10-24, was proposed. This plan isolates equipment frames from the building steel and thus eliminates the possibility of ground loops between the equipment and building. Since coaxial and twisted-pair interconnections (including a ground lead) must be made between various pieces of equipment, ground loops cannot be avoided within the equipment.

However, the effective area of these loops can be decreased considerably by requiring that all interconnections be cabled along the ground leads, as illustrated in Fig. 10-24. This technique requires somewhat longer interconnections than would otherwise be necessary.

The arrangement in Fig. 10-24 poses a potential safety problem. For example, if the structural steel of the building is struck by lightning at point A, the voltage from A to reference ground could be substantial due to the inductance and resistance of the path. This high voltage could be a safety hazard for a man in contact with the building steel at A and the nearby grounded equipment. To minimize this problem, the reference ground point is placed near the middle of the equipment and is connected to the structural steel of the building at that point. If the building is not too large, such a scheme will satisfy safety requirements. In addition, to avoid problems with power system grounds being at different potentials due to lightning or faults, the power system ground should also be connected to the reference point. This implies that the power should be brought into the building physically close to the reference point [safety requirements dictate that the power ground (neutral) be connected to earth ground upon entering a building]. Leads leaving the building should also be brought out near this reference ground point.

As an example of multipoint grounding, consider the so-called "ring" scheme used in some microwave radio installations. These systems usually have a high antenna structure which is particularly vulnerable to lightning hits. For reasons of safety and protection of equipment, the objective is to ground the system so that large potential differences do not develop between equipment units and between equipment and the building when lightning hits a part of the system. This is achieved through the use of multiple earth grounds as

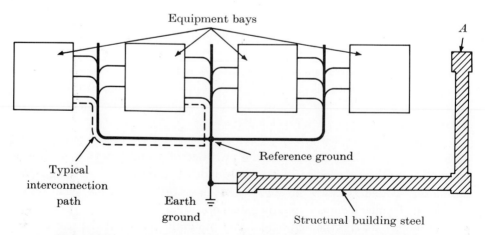

**Fig. 10-24**  Proposed single-point grounding system for transmission terminal.

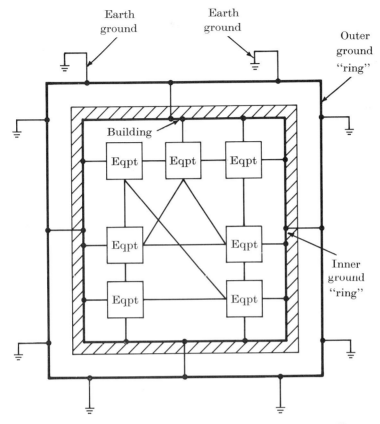

**Fig. 10-25**    Multipoint grounding system for microwave radio.

shown in Fig. 10-25. Equipment is connected to earth ground through the grounding rings as shown. This technique minimizes impedance to earth ground from any point by providing short paths to ground.

The system is ideal from a safety point of view, but many ground loops are present. Cross connections to ground help to reduce the area of these loops somewhat. In addition, the high operating frequencies and special design techniques employed to minimize 60-Hz induced pickup compensate for ground loop susceptibility. However, large external sources of interference such as EMP (electromagnetic pulse) arising from a nuclear explosion would present a problem at sites that are to be hardened to withstand nuclear attack.

A common method of ground isolation is to use a transformer, as shown in Fig. 10-26(a). This is very useful at audio and low frequencies, but it becomes ineffective at higher frequencies because of other coupling through stray capacitances of the transformer. Transformers have been built which give reasonably good isolation up to about 5 or 10 MHz. Instead of using a transformer,

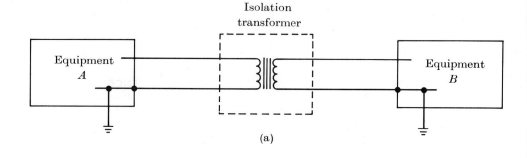

(a)

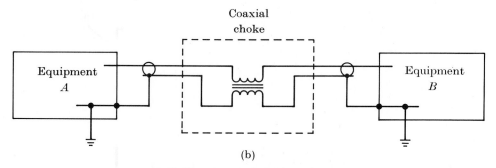

(b)

**Fig. 10-26**   Ground-isolation schemes.

isolation can be achieved by using active circuits. Such schemes, however, are relatively complex and too specialized to be included here.

An interesting modification of the isolation transformer is shown in Fig. 10-26(b). Here the isolation transformer is turned on its side and acts like a coaxial choke. If a single coaxial cable is wound around a core, then one winding of the transformer is the center conductor and the other winding is the outer conductor. High-frequency signal currents will pass through the coaxial cable with the current remaining on the inside surface of the outer conductor. Thus, as far as the signal currents are concerned, the fact that the coaxial cable is wound around a magnetic core is of no consequence. Any ground current flowing on the outside of the outer conductor (without an opposite flow through the center conductor) will look upon the "winding" of the cable as an inductor or choke. As a result, any high-frequency spurious ground currents (longitudinal currents) will encounter a high-impedance path. The advantage of such a choke arrangement over a transformer is its usefulness at frequencies up to the GHz range.

The comparative effectiveness of several methods of shielding leads and grounding transmission lines is shown in Fig. 10-27. The data[12] were taken at low frequencies where skin effect is negligible, and the circuit shown in part (a) was used as a reference. Since the wire in the reference condition was surrounded by a grounded shield, the effects of electric or capacitive coupling were minimized. Therefore, the numbers indicate the effectiveness of each scheme with respect to an interfering magnetic field.

The reference circuit is very susceptible to a time-varying magnetic field since a closed loop is formed by the conductor, the two resistors, and the ground plane (assumed to be an equipotential surface). If the shield is grounded at

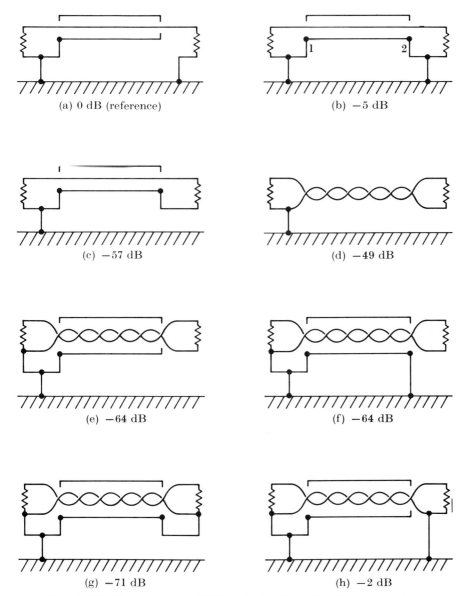

(a) 0 dB (reference)

(b) −5 dB

(c) −57 dB

(d) −49 dB

(e) −64 dB

(f) −64 dB

(g) −71 dB

(h) −2 dB

**Fig. 10-27**  Relative susceptibility of circuits to low-frequency interference.[12]

both ends, as shown in Fig. 10-27(b), the low-frequency shielding is improved very little because a significant ground loop is present. This causes a voltage between points 1 and 2 which will also appear across the resistors. It should be noted that at higher frequencies where skin effect becomes very important, the scheme shown in part (b) is much more attractive due to the isolation obtained between the induced loop current (flowing on the outside of the outer sheath) and the signal current (flowing on the inside of the outer sheath). In fact, at high frequencies, scheme (b) is often used very successfully in conjunction with coaxial cables. If the ground loop is broken, as shown in Fig. 10-27(c), the interference susceptibility of the circuit is considerably reduced.

We noted earlier that the use of twisted-pair cable is very advantageous in low-frequency circuits. The twisted cable shown in Fig. 10-27(d) gives a 49-dB improvement over the reference circuit. This comes about through the absence of a ground loop and the breaking up of the circuit loop from twisting the wires. Obviously, still better performance could be obtained if the twist rate were increased. If the twisted pair is surrounded by a conducting shield, as shown in part (e), the susceptibility is still further reduced. By grounding the shield at each end, Fig. 10-27(f), the shielding properties are further improved at high frequencies because the shield is more nearly an equipotential surface (better electrostatic shielding). At low frequencies, this additional grounding makes little difference.

If the shield is connected to the low side of the load, Fig. 10-27(g), the best low-frequency performance is obtained. The reason for the improvement over that shown in (f) is that the ground loop was broken. Whether or not this loop is broken is not too important at high frequencies for reasons previously discussed. The scheme shown in part (h) is almost as undesirable as the reference condition, and for the same reason—the presence of a ground loop.

It should be emphasized that the susceptibilities shown in Fig. 10-27 are for low frequencies. At high frequencies, the relative susceptibilities change considerably. It was previously pointed out that the circuit shown in (b) would be much better at high frequencies. The circuit shown in (f) would be even better if the frequencies are not so high that the effectiveness of the twisting is lost.

## 10-7. DC POWER DISTRIBUTION

Problems encountered in dc power distribution are similar to those encountered in the transmission of signals throughout a system, except that power is usually more widely distributed. Since power distribution is closely related to system grounding, it is appropriate to consider problems related to power distribution at this point.

Power for the circuits comprising a system is provided by a power converter (power supply) which converts power from the ac mains to a suitable dc voltage. Usually, the circuits require that this voltage be nearly constant under conditions of varying ac line voltages and varying dc load currents. For economy, regulation is usually achieved within the power converter although regulation at each critical circuit eases the power distribution problem. The problem consists of studying means of transmitting dc voltages from the power converter to the circuits without seriously affecting the regulation. A typical

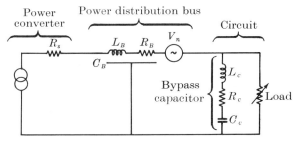

**Fig. 10-28**    A typical power distribution system.

power transmission system is shown in Fig. 10-28. As can be seen from the figure, there are three sources of voltage change at the load; specifically:

1. Static drops in the distribution system and poor converter regulation due to $R_B$ and $R_s$, respectively.
2. Transient changes because of the finite impedance of the distribution bus, characterized by the characteristic impedance ($Z_0 = \sqrt{L_B/C_B}$).
3. Crosstalk from signal leads and other power leads into the dc distribution system, as shown by $V_n$.

The static voltage drop is reduced to an acceptable level by minimizing $R_s$ and $R_B$. $R_s$ is a function of the regulation of the power converter and may be less than 0.01 ohm if necessary. The bus resistance, $R_B$, is a function of the cross-sectional area of the bus although, if fuses are used, a substantial part of $R_B$ may be due to the resistance of the fuse and holder. A knowledge of the maximum current excursions and maximum allowable voltage variations will enable one to determine a maximum value for $R_s + R_B$ from Ohm's law.

Transient changes on the distribution line are produced by a sudden current demand by a circuit or group of circuits. The magnitude of the resulting noise voltage is a function of the characteristic impedance of the line ($Z_0 = \sqrt{L/C}$). Thus, we desire a line with low inductance and high capacitance. From Fig. 9-19, we note that inductance per unit length is reduced by increasing line width and by providing a return path in close proximity to the power conductor. The line capacitance is increased in the same manner and also by using a high-dielectric insulating material. A convenient power bus arrangement involves the use of rectangular, parallel copper conductors as shown in Fig. 10-29. The characteristics of this configuration are (neglecting fringing—$\epsilon_r \gg 1$ or $w \gg d$):

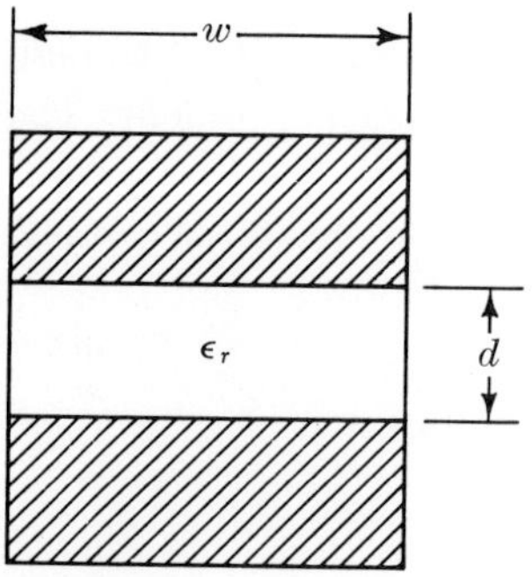

$$C \approx \epsilon_0 \epsilon_r \frac{w}{d}$$

$$L \approx \mu \frac{d}{w}$$

$$Z_0 \approx \sqrt{\frac{L}{C}} \approx \frac{377}{\sqrt{\epsilon_r}} \frac{d}{w} \qquad (10\text{-}28)$$

**Fig. 10-29** Cross section of a typical power bus.

Practical values of characteristic impedance below 1 ohm are difficult to obtain, and a common means of reducing this impedance is to add additional shunt (bypass) capacitors along the power bus. Unfortunately, such a solution is suitable for only a limited frequency range because of the series inductance associated with each lumped capacitor. For this reason, the low-impedance transmission line is favored for power distribution to pulse circuits containing a broad spectrum of frequency components. It should be added that commercial bus bars are available with the conductors and insulators molded as a single unit. A typical bus bar is shown in Fig. 10-30 along with its electrical characteristics at 10 MHz.

The effect of crosstalk is also reduced by most of the means already described. Basically, if all power bus impedances are kept low compared to the load impedance, and if areas of power loops are minimized, the crosstalk problem should not require more than an occasional bypass filter at particularly troublesome points.

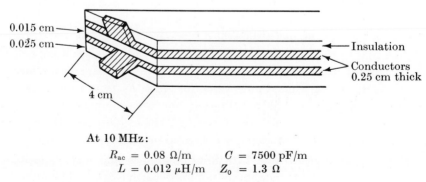

At 10 MHz:

$R_{ac} = 0.08 \ \Omega/\text{m}$     $C = 7500 \ \text{pF/m}$
$L = 0.012 \ \mu\text{H/m}$    $Z_0 = 1.3 \ \Omega$

**Fig. 10-30** A typical commercial bus bar.

**Fig. 10-31** Proposed layout of a large communication system.

**Example 10.3.** We wish to develop a grounding and power distribution plan for a modern communication system. On the basis of a tentative layout, we will assume that the system consists of nine bays arranged in a single row, with a capacity of eight shelves of circuitry per bay, as shown in Fig. 10-31. Each shelf holds twenty plug-in printed wire master boards, as shown in

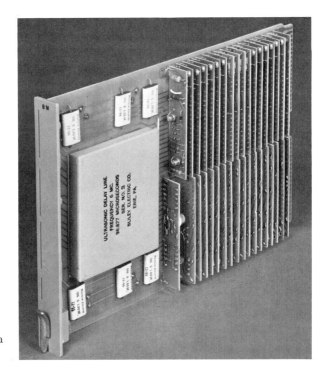

**Fig. 10-32** A typical shelf in the system of Fig. 10-31.

Fig. 10-32. All connections to each master board are made through a multipin connector at the back of the shelf. The solid state circuits (both discrete and integrated) are mounted on modules soldered to the mother board. The arrangement of modules, mother board, and connector is shown in Fig. 10-33.

The digital circuits comprising the system have a noise margin of approximately 2 V and require that precautions be taken to minimize susceptibility to

**Fig. 10-33**   A board from the shelf of Fig. 10-32.

interference. The circuits are designed to operate on +6 V, +24 V, or both. Power consumption estimates are 200 A maximum at 6 V (50 A maximum per bay) and 150 A at 24 V (25 A maximum per bay). The maximum voltage drop from the power supplies to any particular circuit has been established at 0.2 V. It is also necessary to install 120-V ac receptacles near the bays to provide power for auxiliary test equipment (oscilloscopes, oscillators, etc.).

In view of the noise susceptibility and possible formation of large ground loops in a system of this size, a single-point grounding system is highly desirable. The type of construction chosen makes this relatively simple since the ground paths on the master boards must pass through the rear connector and can easily become part of a tree without introducing ground loops. The ground paths on the rear connectors of each shelf can be attached to a horizontal ground bus. These busses can then be attached to vertical busses or "branches" of the tree which, in turn, are connected to a ground bus or "trunk" running along the base of the nine bays. Connecting the trunk to earth ground at a single point (ground rod or water pipe) gives a true single-point system.

The common ground impedance inherent in single-point or tree grounding systems can, however, cause serious coupling problems. For example, consider two circuits that are separated by 2 m of ground path (the circuits may be in adjacent bays and physically much closer than 2 m). If the circuits are inter-connected by a single point-to-point signal lead, the ground lead inductance could be as high as 1.6 $\mu$H. In the worst case of a 10-ns rise-time pulse of 60 mA, the ground path voltage becomes

$$\Delta V = L\frac{\Delta I}{\Delta t} = (1.6 \times 10^{-6})\left(\frac{60 \times 10^{-3}}{10 \times 10^{-9}}\right) \approx 10\text{ V}$$

which is unacceptable. However, if the signal lead is instead run along the ground path, not only is the inductance reduced (reduced area of loop) but the capacitance from the signal lead to ground is increased, and the connection behaves like a transmission line. This reduces the effect of the ground inductance by as much as an order of magnitude (depending upon specific lead dress). In this example, with proper lead dressing, single-conductor wiring is acceptable for connections separated by up to about 2 m of ground path. For longer runs, two-conductor transmission lines carrying the ground with the signal lead are required. For economy, twisted pair is preferable; however, in cases where improved shielding is needed, coaxial cable can be used. The grounded inter-connections (coaxial and twisted pair), of course, introduce undesirable ground loops in the system; to minimize this effect, the interconnections should be dressed along the ground grid as well.

Up to this point, we have ignored the grounding of the metal bay frames and shelves. These must be grounded for safety reasons, and an apparently simple way of doing this is to connect the metal frame to the ground tree. Theoretically, such a connection should be made at only one point to preserve the single-point ground concept. As a practical matter, the ground bus can be in contact with the metal frame at many points without introducing ground loops of significant area.

The introduction of 120-V ac receptacles in the bays poses another problem. Receptacles are normally wired with a third safety ground wire (green wire). To satisfy safety codes, this power ground wire is connected to the metal box enclosing the receptacle. If the receptacles are mounted in the equipment bays, this results in connecting the power ground to the system ground, forming ground loops, and introducing noise into the system. There are three possible solutions to this problem:

1. Keep power receptacles separate from the equipment. This has the additional advantage of keeping ac out of the bays and avoiding potential 60-Hz coupling problems.
2. Use special power receptacles which do not connect the metal box to power ground. The safety wire would be connected to power ground while the enclosing box connects to signal ground.
3. Insulate the system ground from the metal bays, and connect the bays to the power ground instead.

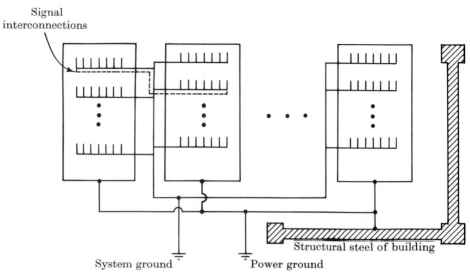

**Fig. 10-34**   Grounding plan for multibay system.

In this particular example, the first alternative was dropped since there was no other convenient location for the receptacles. The second alternative requires special receptacles. The last alternative requires that the power and system ground grids be isolated from each other, but this is not difficult to implement in this system. Employing the third alternative results in a grounding plan as shown in Fig. 10-34.

When using test equipment powered from ac mains, one must not connect between the chassis of the equipment and system ground unless special means are used to prevent the connection of the test equipment to power ground. One of the most serious aspects of shorting the two grounds is the relative undetectability of a short. Except for the possibility of much more noise on the system ground, the shorting of the two grounds is undetectable unless the system ground is removed from earth ground—a procedure usually possible only when the equipment is inoperative.

The problem of power distribution is complicated by the unusually large currents required in a system of this size and by the precise voltage regulation necessary for proper operation of the solid state circuits. Since it is desirable not to transmit high current for any greater distance than necessary, an obvious location for the power supplies is in the center of the bay lineup. In Fig. 10-31, the power converters occupy the bottom third of the middle three bays. From this location, the longest power bus is only about 4 m in length. It is proposed to use rectangular copper bars as power busses. The main bus will run along the bottom of the bays, while branches connected to this will run vertically between the bays. A small bus serving each shelf will connect to the vertical bus through a fuse accessible from the front panel. Of the allowable 0.2-V drop between converter and circuit, 0.1 V will be allowed for the fuse and shelf wiring drop, and 0.1 V for the drop from the converter to the fuse. For simplicity, we will assume the same type of conductor bus for horizontal runs, vertical runs, +6 V, +24 V, and ground return. As a result, the current densities in the various busses will not be constant, but will vary from a maximum of about 175 A (half of the total current requirement) in the ground bus (carrying return for both +6 and +24 V) on each side of the converters to nearly zero at the top ends of the vertical busses. For this example, we estimate an average bus current of about 100 A and obtain a maximum bus resistance of $R = V/I = 0.1/100 = 0.001\ \Omega$. The total length of a power bus (including ground return) is about 8 m; thus, the required minimum cross-sectional area of each copper conductor ($\rho = 1.724 \times 10^{-8}\ \Omega$-m) is given by:

$$A = \frac{\rho L}{R} = \frac{(1.724 \times 10^{-8})(8)}{0.001} = 1.38 \times 10^{-4}\ \mathrm{m^2}$$

To minimize the characteristic impedance, we would like to use a rectangular bus as wide as possible (Eq. 10-28). However, physical limitations in this example force the maximum width to be no more than 3 cm and result in a minimum thickness of $1.38/3 = 0.46$ cm. Again, to minimize impedance, it would be desirable to place the power bus and ground return as close as possible. Because of the two supply voltages, an obvious arrangement is as shown in cross section in Fig. 10-35.

Initial mechanical considerations favored 0.16-cm phenol-fiber insulation. For a dielectric constant of $\epsilon_r \approx 5$, Eq. (10-28) gives:

$$Z_0 = \frac{377}{\sqrt{\epsilon_r}}\frac{d}{w} = \frac{377}{\sqrt{5}}\frac{0.16 \times 10^{-2}}{3 \times 10^{-2}} = 9\ \Omega$$

To further reduce transient noise voltages to within acceptable limits, a 0.01-cm mylar film dielectric ($\epsilon_r = 5$) decreases this impedance to $0.56\ \Omega$. The ground conductor in the power distribution bus is, of course, the system ground.

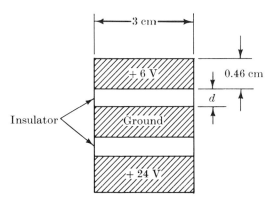

**Fig. 10-35**    Cross section of system power bus.

By careful engineering of the grounding and power distribution, a very large communication system can be developed that is practically free of noise in the power and ground paths of the system. Not only will such a system meet its noise requirements, but the troubleshooting and debugging effort saved by judicious layout in the conceptual stages of the design makes such approaches very worthwhile.

## 10-8. INTERFERENCE MEASUREMENTS

Interference measurements are of value in pinpointing sources of interference, in measuring the shielding effectiveness of materials, and in evaluating final designs. The intent of this discussion is to acquaint the physical designer with some of the possibilities and limitations of interference measurements.

Losses through various coupling paths have been described in some detail in other sections of this chapter. Several test sets are available for making transmission measurements versus frequency for frequencies up to several hundred megahertz. These sets usually consist of an oscillator or source with an impedance of 50, 75, or 600 ohms and a sensitive detector with the same impedance. The reference condition of zero decibels is obtained when source and load are connected together. The insertion loss of any two-port network placed between the source and the load can then be read directly. Such sets are usually capable of measuring losses up to about 60 to 80 dB without trouble. Higher loss readings can be obtained below 10 MHz by using auxiliary equipment (such as amplifiers), but the upper limit is around 120 to 140 dB. For losses above these values, the techniques and equipment become very specialized.

To measure the crosstalk loss between two cables, it is only necessary to excite one of the cables by the source and have the other cable connected to the detector. The measurement of shielding effectiveness of various shield materials is somewhat more difficult. The scheme generally used is shown in Fig. 10-36. If small loop antennas are used at the source and load, as shown in Fig. 10-36(a), the magnetic shielding of the material is obtained. If small probe antennas are used instead, as shown in Fig. 10-33(b), the electric shielding is obtained. Since the electric shielding of most materials is much better than the magnetic shielding, the scheme shown in part (a) is usually used. When the reference measurement is made without the sample, care must be taken that the spacing between the two antennas is accurately maintained, since the coupling is very dependent upon that spacing.

Radio frequency interference (RFI) is simply energy radiated by equipment that interferes with other equipment. Since the useful electromagnetic spectrum is limited and must be shared by many users, it was long ago recognized that certain requirements should be imposed to minimize possible interference. As a result, the Federal Communications Commission (FCC) has defined minimum

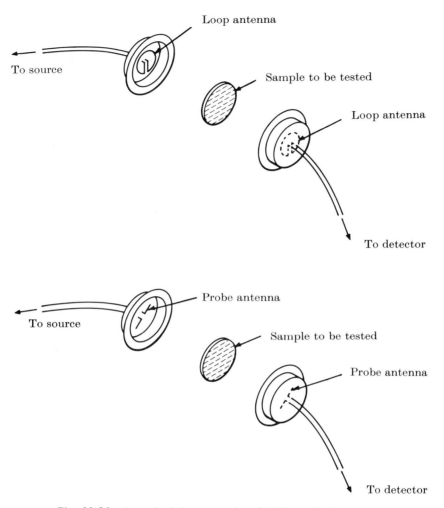

**Fig. 10-36** A method for measuring shielding effectiveness.

requirements, which are covered in FCC Rules and Regulations, volume 2, part 15.

The military services, which often have large concentrations of electronic equipment in a confined space (such as a ship or aircraft), have additional requirements for electromagnetic compatibility, such as MIL-I-6181B, MIL-I-16910A, and MIL-I-17623. These are generally (though not necessarily) more exacting than the FCC specifications and include specifications on susceptibility of equipment. Furthermore, there are applications where the military services are interested not only in reducing interference to the point of not affecting nearby equipment, but also in reducing (or disguising) the radiated energy from a particular piece of equipment to make its location undetectable by interception of any significant radiated energy. This last requirement is much more stringent than the others and, of necessity, much more expensive to implement.

To determine whether equipment meets the foregoing specifications and requirements, several RFI meters have been developed by various manufacturers. These meters are simply sensitive, calibrated radio receivers capable of being tuned over a wide frequency range. They are usually used with calibrated probes or antennas so that the field strength can be read directly on a meter. Earlier units were made to be sensitive only on the electric field and gave the intensity in volts (or microvolts) per meter. Newer RFI meters can also use a loop as a pickup device and thus can measure the magnetic field strength. This is useful when probing near the source of interference where the ratio of **E** to **H** may be much less than 377 ohms, so that only magnetic fields are significant. RFI meters are very handy for probing around equipment that is generating interference, since we can quickly determine specific sources of interference and determine where it is "leaking out" of the system.

Unfortunately, the RFI meter must be tuned to the frequency of interest. In many cases (such as pulse circuits), the interfering frequency is not necessarily unique and may be impossible to determine. In such cases, probing with an oscilloscope allows us to observe waveforms as functions of time. This can often prove useful in determining the approximate interfering waveform and frequency components.

A still more useful tool is the wave analyzer. It allows us to observe energy versus frequency over a wide frequency range. This capability is valuable when analyzing all of the electromagnetic energy in a given part of a circuit. Modern spectrum analyzers cover frequencies from audio to microwave frequencies with sensitivities of about 1 to 3 microvolts.

## 10-9. SUMMARY FOR ELECTRICAL INTERACTIONS

As noted in the introduction to this chapter, two aspects of interference must be considered in system design: first, a tolerably low level of interference within the system to permit reliable operation, and second, compatibility with surrounding equipment to avoid interference between one system and another. To achieve these objectives requires careful design of signal characteristics, impedance levels, transmission media and routing arrangements, placement of components and subsystems, and grounding.

The choice of signal levels in a system has an important bearing on interference coupling between components and circuitry. High-level signals may interfere with the operation of nearby equipment. On the other hand, low-level signals may cause undue susceptibility to interference. Thus, wherever possible, it is desirable to avoid extremely high- or low-level signals. Extreme high- or low-impedance values should also be avoided. High impedance increases susceptibility to capacitive coupling, while low impedance increases susceptibility to magnetic or inductive coupling. Consideration must also be given to the need for matching impedances on long leads in order to avoid signal reflections. Signal transmission within subsystems and between subsystems is not only a potential interference problem but also a significant economic consideration. There is a great incentive to use inexpensive interconnections and employ special suppression techniques to obtain adequate isolation, rather than to use more expensive cable with better shielding qualities.

An astute layout of equipment can do much to avoid interference problems between subsystems and in system cabling. Physical separation and shortened length of exposure to interfering signals are perhaps the least expensive methods of controlling interference and, consequently, should be employed to the greatest extent possible. A power distribution and grounding plan should be established early in the development effort. This includes methods of bypassing or filtering to be used and general wiring rules to cover lengths of unbypassed power leads. The grounding plan should provide for adequate lightning protection as well as protection for operating and maintenance personnel.

Obviously, these factors require close collaboration between the physical design, circuit design, and system design. To achieve satisfactory results requires, in general, that interference considerations be included in the initial design plan and that they be reviewed throughout the design process. Finally, experimental evaluation is required on subsystems, and eventually on the entire system, to ensure that interference objectives are met.

## REFERENCES

1. Terman, F. E., *Engineers' Handbook*, New York, McGraw-Hill Book Co., 1943. Section 2 is a reasonably complete empirical treatment of circuit components, coupling, and shielding.

2. *Handbook of Chemistry and Physics*, Cleveland, Ohio, Chemical Rubber Publishing Co., 1954. Includes a section of mathematical tables that is available separately. Several formulas are given for inductance and capacitance of various configurations of conductors.

3. *Radio Instruments and Measurements*, U.S. Department of Commerce Circular C-74, National Bureau of Standards, 1937 (U.S. Government Printing Office, Washington, D.C.). A handy collection of radio formulas including a reasonably large set of capacitance and inductance formulas.

4. Gray, H. S., *Digital Computer Engineering*, Englewood Cliffs, N.J., Prentice-Hall, Inc., 1963. Chapter 9 gives a good treatment of crosstalk problems encountered in digital systems.

5. Grover, F. W., *Inductance Calculations*, Princeton, N.J., D. Van Nostrand Co., Inc., 1946. Many formulas for calculating self- and mutual inductance.

6. Smythe, W. R., *Static and Dynamic Electricity*, New York, McGraw-Hill Book Co., 1950. An advanced text on field theory with particular emphasis on electrostatics.

7. Papoulis, A., *The Fourier Integral and Its Applications*, New York, McGraw-Hill Book Co., 1962. A modern and complete treatment of the use of the Fourier integral for time and frequency transformations.

8. Kaupp, H. R., "Pulse Crosstalk Between Microstrip Transmission Lines," *Symposium Record*, Seventh International Electronic Circuit Packaging Symposium, 1966. Figures 10-7, 10-8, 10-9, and 10-10 by permission.

9. Bunk, D. S., and T. J. Donovan, "Electromagnetic Shielding," *Machine Design*, **39**, 102–117, July 6, 1967. Figure 10-12 by permission.

10. Cowdell, R. B., "Nomograms Solve Tough Problems of Shielding," *Electronics*, **40**, 92–99, April 17, 1967. Figure 10-15 by permission.

11. Ficchi, R. F., *Electrical Interference*, New York, Hayden Book Co., 1964. One of the few books available on the subject of interference. Strong emphasis on grounding at the expense of other subjects, with an excellent bibliography.

12. Milton, R. T., *Design Handbook Electromagnetic Compatibility*, Schenectady, N.Y., General Electric Co., 1963. Covers material similar to that covered in this chapter, with a considerable number of graphs and empirical data.

*Part IV*

**HUMAN FACTORS IN DESIGN**

*Chapter 11*

# HUMAN CHARACTERISTICS

### R. Hammell

No worthwhile thing is ever built except to satisfy a human need or purpose. A machine can exist and perform fully its intended function only through the correct actions of the human beings who design, build, test, transport, install, operate, and repair it.

The physical designer of electronic systems cannot expect people to adapt themselves to a product that is too difficult to build, or is inconvenient to repair, or that stretches the operator's capabilities to the limit. Although there are many ways in which equipment can be designed, people must be taken essentially as they are. This means that the physical designer must consider people from the very earliest planning stages of any design effort.

Man-machine combinations often fail or fall short of their objectives because the designer has given too little consideration to the man. Although the designer may recognize the man as a system component, he may have a tendency to consider the man as a simple element in an otherwise complex arrangement. Also, there is too often the dangerous belief or hope that, through some magic of adaptation, the man can compensate for gross design shortcomings.

As a system building block, man cannot be described by a specification such as that used for a motor or capacitor. No two men are alike; moreover, no individual is the same from day to day because he is modified continually by all his experiences, by his learning, and by the gradual process of aging. Also, a man's performance may be affected temporarily by illness, fatigue, worry, discomfort, or distractions. The man who can perform a task easily under calm conditions may fail under stress. It is clear that the machine must be contrived to match the man who is neither wholly definable nor entirely predictable.

Because it deals with man, human factors engineering† draws heavily from the specialized knowledge and skills of psychology, anthropology, physiology, and medicine. Work had been done in this field prior to World War II, but the sudden wartime demand for huge numbers of machines of ever-mounting complexity forced the search for general principles—principles that could be applied as design rules in all man-machine situations. The results of this work fill entire bookshelves, and new information is being added constantly.

This chapter describes some human characteristics which should be understood and appreciated by the physical designer of electronic systems, including the performance of the visual and auditory senses, and the central processing of information. Other characteristics, such as the tactual, kinesthetic, and balance senses; reaction time; body movements; and strength are discussed briefly. The effects of environmental factors on man's performance are treated next, followed by descriptions of the principal methods of experimenting with people. The chapter ends with a discussion of user preference engineering, an important topic not generally treated in human engineering texts.

In Chapter 12, the interactions between man and machine are discussed. Descriptions are given of basic control and display design principles which can be used in matching machines to men. The importance of designing equipment for efficient installation and maintenance is emphasized. Finally, some fundamentals of designing for pleasing appearance are outlined.

It is hoped that this treatment will give the physical designer a better appreciation of man's complexity and the need for considering human characteristics throughout the design effort, and that it will encourage the designer to further study in those areas that bear upon his work.

## 11-1. LIGHT AND VISION

The light-sensitive screen, or *retina*, of the human eye contains some 137 million separate light receptors, many of which are connected individually to the brain by separate optic nerve fibers. This exquisitely delicate mechanism performs prodigious feats. For example, if the air is very clear and the night is very dark, the fully adapted eye can see the light from a match 10 miles away.

---

† In the United States, it is also called *human engineering* or *biotechnology*. In Great Britain, it is called *ergonomics*.

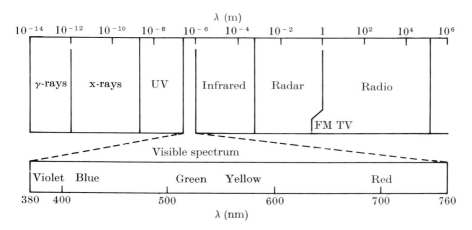

**Fig. 11-1** The relationship of the visible spectrum to the entire electromagnetic spectrum.

Understanding that we gather as much as 80 percent of all our information through the visual sense, we can appreciate the importance to the physical designer of knowing something of the eye's capabilities and limitations.

The eye is sensitive to a narrow band of radiant energy, spanning about one octave, bounded by the ultraviolet and infrared, as shown in Fig. 11-1. The unit of wavelength used by the visual scientist is the nanometer (nm), often called the millimicron, which equals $10^{-9}$ meter; the physicist uses the Angstrom unit (Å) which equals $10^{-10}$ meter. Thus, 1 nm = 10 Å.

## PHOTOMETRIC UNITS

Figure 11-2 shows the relative sensitivity of the light-adapted human eye to equal amounts of radiant energy at various wavelengths in the visible spectrum. The curve is an arbitrary one that has been standardized by inter-national agreement; it is unlikely that the vision of any individual will agree exactly with this curve.

Although it would be possible to measure light intensity in absolute units, such as joules per second (watts), it is clear from Fig. 11-2 that this would not be a measure of the resulting visual sensation. The photometric units to be described here evaluate light intensities according to the visual sensations they can produce. These units are basic tools in the evaluation and specification of visual displays and lighting arrangements, and they are useful in describing various properties of the visual sense.

The photometric units include the *luminous intensity* of a concentrated source of light, the *intensity of illumination* falling on a surface, and the *surface brightness* of a distributed light source or of a reflecting surface.

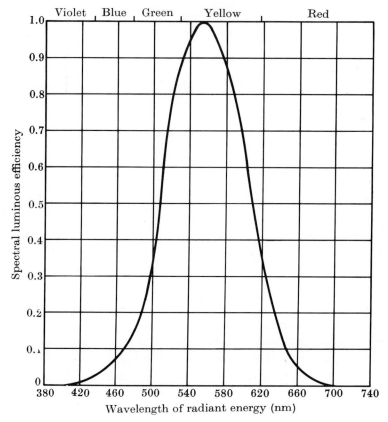

**Fig. II-2** The standard (CIE) spectral luminous efficiency curve, showing the relative capacity of radiant energy of various wavelengths to produce visual sensation.[1]

The time rate of flow of luminous energy, evaluated according to its ability to produce visual sensation, is called *luminous flux*, $\Phi$, and is measured in lumens. Thus,

$$\Phi = \frac{dQ}{dt} \text{ lumens} \qquad (11\text{-}1)$$

where $Q$ is the total effective quantity of light, or luminous energy, in lumen-seconds.

Suppose that a point source, Fig. 11-3, emits light uniformly in all directions and that an amount of light flux, $d\Phi$, passes normally through the small surface area on a sphere, $dA$, which subtends a solid angle, $d\omega$. The luminous intensity, $I$, of this light source is defined as

$$I = \frac{d\Phi}{d\omega} \qquad (11\text{-}2)$$

However, since a solid angle is related to the surface area on a sphere by

$$d\omega = \frac{dA}{r^2}$$

we may write

$$I = r^2 \frac{d\Phi}{dA} \qquad (11\text{-}3)$$

The unit of luminous intensity is the *candela*, which is arbitrarily defined as the intensity radiated by a black body $\frac{1}{60}$ cm² in area at the freezing temperature of platinum, measured in a direction normal to the surface. The candela is nearly equivalent to the older *candle*, which has been defined in various ways, but always in less-precise terms. Although a standard 1-candela source is directional in its radiation, it is convenient to think of a source which radiates with a uniform, 1-candela intensity in all directions. If such a

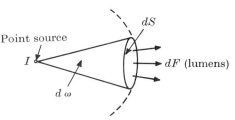

**Fig. II-3** The luminous intensity of a point source is the luminous energy radiated per unit solid angle.

source were placed at the center of a sphere, Eq. (11-3) gives the total luminous flux emitted as

$$\Phi = \frac{IA}{r^2} = 4\pi \text{ lumens} \qquad (11\text{-}4)$$

The *luminous efficacy*† of a light source is defined as the ratio of the total luminous flux (lumens) to the total power input (watts). Theoretically, if all the light from an incandescent lamp were radiated at the wavelength at which the normal eye is most sensitive (555 nm), a maximum efficacy of 680 lumens per watt would be attained. The actual efficacies of incandescent light sources are much lower than this because some of the radiation is at wavelengths outside the visible spectrum.

For the purposes of the designer, light is evaluated by multiplying the energy, $W_\lambda$, radiated at each wavelength by the spectral luminous efficiency, $K_\lambda$, of the "standardized" observer at that wavelength and summing over the visible spectrum to obtain

$$Q = \int_{380\times10^{-9}}^{760\times10^{-9}} K_\lambda W_\lambda \, d\lambda \text{ lumen-second} \qquad (11\text{-}5)$$

---

† This term should not be confused with *luminous efficiency*, a property of the eye (Fig. 11-2).

where $K_\lambda$ is 680 times the ordinate of Fig. 11-2 at any given wavelength, and is expressed in lumens per watt; $W_\lambda$ is the radiant energy per unit wavelength, at wavelength $\lambda$, and is expressed in joules per meter.

The maximum attainable efficacy of any white-light source, with its entire output distributed uniformly with respect to wavelength within the visible region, is of the order of 200 lumens per watt.

Light-measuring instruments are equipped with filters to give an overall response characteristic like the curve of Fig. 11-2. Thus, the measurements are in terms of visual sensation.

The intensity of illumination or *illuminance*, $E$, is defined as the density of light flux falling on a surface, or

$$E = \frac{d\Phi}{dA} \tag{11-6}$$

Illuminance is measured in lumens/meter², which are called *lux*. Other units sometimes used are the foot-candle (1 lumen/foot²) and the phot (1 lumen/cm²). From the definitions, it is seen that a surface one meter away from a source intensity of one candela, and normal to the direction of flux, has an illuminance of one lux. The illuminance of the earth's surface at noon on a very clear day can approach 100,000 lux.

The luminous quality of a distributed light source or of a reflecting surface may be expressed in terms of either luminous intensity per unit area (*luminance*) or luminous flux leaving the area (*brightness*). Luminance is measured in units of candela/meter², while brightness is in units of lumens/meter². It can be readily shown that a plane, 1-candela source (such as the standard source) radiates $\pi$ lumens, so that a luminance of 1 cd/m² is equivalent to a brightness of $\pi$ lm/m². As with illuminance, the brightness (sometimes called the *luminous emittance*) is determined by the expression

$$B = \frac{d\Phi}{dA} \tag{11-7}$$

where the flux measured is the flux leaving the surface in the latter case. For fresh snow in noon sunlight, $B$ is about 50,000 lm/m², indicating that about half the total incident light is reflected for this condition.

## THE HUMAN EYE

Although the human eye is complex in structure and function, simple diagrams and discussions are sufficient for an understanding of the following material. Figure 11-4 represents a horizontal section through the right eye.

The outer transparent covering of the front of the eye is called the *cornea*. There is a small, lens-shaped chamber behind the cornea that is filled with a

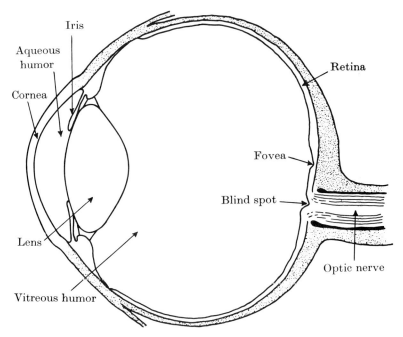

**Fig. 11-4**   Horizontal cross section of the human eye.

liquid called *aqueous humor*. Inside this chamber is a colored diaphragm, the *iris*, whose central circular aperture, the *pupil*, contracts or expands in order to control the amount of light entering the eye.

Behind the iris is the *crystalline lens*. The thickness of the lens is controlled by the *ciliary muscles* of the eye to focus light rays on the retina. When a distant object is viewed, the crystalline lens flattens and increases its focal length. For seeing a nearby object, the lens is thickened by contraction of the ciliary muscles at its periphery. The aging person develops focusing problems because the crystalline lens gradually loses its elasticity. The volume behind the crystalline lens is filled with a transparent, gelatinous material called the *vitreous humor*.

The light-sensitive retina is connected through the optic nerve to the brain. When an object is viewed, its inverted and transposed image is focused on the retina by the system of lenses (cornea, aqueous humor, and crystalline lens). The light stimulates chemical receptors in the retina which generate impulses for transmission to the brain through the optic nerve fibers.

Vertically, the retina is divided into left and right halves. As indicated in Fig. 11-5, the left sides of both retinas are connected to the left side of the brain, and the right sides of both retinas are connected to the right side of the brain. Because the received image is transposed by the lenses, an object at the viewer's right is sensed in the left side of the brain, and vice versa. Sensory and motor

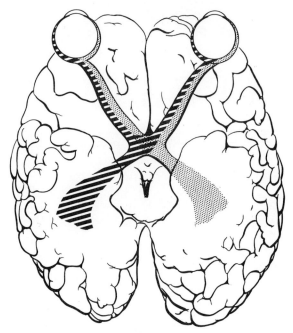

**Fig. 11-5** The pattern of nerve connections from
the two sides of each retina to the left and right
hemispheres of the brain (bottom view).

activities in the left sides of the body are controlled mainly in the right side of
the brain, and vice versa. Thus, the same side of the brain is involved in seeing
in a given direction, for receiving other sensations from that side, and for
controlling activities on that side.

A cross section of the retina reveals ten distinct functional layers; one of
these is a layer of light receptors of two types called *rods* and *cones* because of
their shapes. The system involving the cones is used for seeing in bright light,
whereas the rod system operates in very dim light. The cones are color-
sensitive and the rods produce visual sensations only of different depths of
grayness. Cone vision is called daylight or *photopic*† vision, and rod vision is
called twilight or *scotopic*‡ vision.

Figure 11-6 shows the distribution of the rods and cones in the retina. The
heaviest concentration of the 6.5 million cones is in the *fovea*, an area within 1°
of the center of the retina. The rods number about 130 million and have their
greatest density at about 20° on either side of the fovea, decreasing in density
in fairly linear fashion toward the periphery of the retina. There are no rods at

---

† From the Greek word *photos* meaning light.
‡ From the Greek word *skotos* meaning darkness.

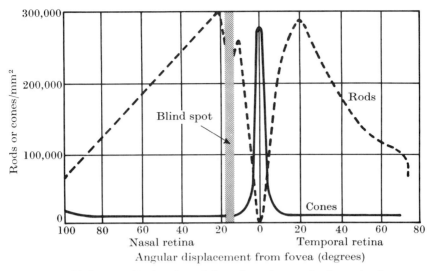

**Fig. 11-6**  The distribution of the rods and cones in the retina.[2]

the fovea, and no rods or cones at the blind spot where the nerve fibers leave the retina.

In the foveal area, each cone has a separate nerve fiber in the optic nerve; but in peripheral regions, there may be several cones linked together to a single optic nerve fiber. Rods are always linked together in groups to a single nerve fiber, and the number of rods per single fiber increases toward the periphery of the retina. The cone width varies from 2.5 to 7.5 $\mu$m. An object subtending a visual angle of about 1 minute is the minimal discriminable detail under ideal conditions.

From the foregoing description, it is clear that visual acuity should be best for head-on seeing, and poorest for peripheral seeing. Also, visual acuity should be better for high illumination than it is for very low illumination. Experiments prove these statements to be true.

The sensitivity of the retinal receptors and the diameter of the pupil must be adjusted to conform with the intensity of the illumination. The eyes are functional over a light-intensity range of 100 dB. They have a range of automatic adjustment of 72 dB which is accounted for as follows. The cone sensitivity varies through a range of 20 dB, the rods over a range of 40 dB, and the pupil contraction, through an area change of 17 $\times$, can vary the intensity of the light entering the eye over a range of about 12 dB.

The refracting power of the normal eye is about equivalent to that of a single lens of 58 *diopters*.† The crystalline lens contributes about 15 diopters of

---

† The focal length, $f$, of a lens is the distance from the "center" of the lens to the point where a distant image is brought to a focus. The power of the lens in diopters is $p = 1/f$, where $f$ is in meters.

this. In accommodating for seeing near or distant objects, a change of about 3 diopters can be made by the crystalline lens.

At low illumination levels, the sensation derived through one eye tends to add to that derived through the other. As a result, the visual brightness threshold is about 30 percent lower for binocular vision than for monocular vision.

## VISUAL ACUITY

There are several factors that influence visual acuity, or the ability of the normal eye to recognize viewed objects. These are:

1. Direction of viewing (position of the image on the retina)
2. Exposure time
3. Size of object (visual angle subtended by object at eye)
4. Brightness contrast
5. Brightness

Remembering that the greatest concentration of cones having individual nerve fibers is in the foveal region, we would expect that an object would be seen most clearly when the eye is aimed straight at it. Figure 11-7 shows the truth of this and illustrates the fast drop in acuity as the eye is turned away from the object. Although peripheral vision has poor acuity, it is relatively efficient at detecting motion and blinking lights; the effect of the blinking is similar to motion.

The ability to recognize an object depends upon the exposure time. If visibility is to remain constant, the brightness must be increased as the exposure time is reduced, as shown in Fig. 11-8, which gives measurements obtained with a standard visual test-object. This factor is becoming more important with the increasing speeds of aircraft, and it underscores the danger of high-speed night driving. It can also be a factor in limiting the rate at which data are presented on a dim cathode-ray screen whose maximum light output is a property of the phosphor material.

The effects on visual acuity of visual angle, contrast, and brightness are interrelated. The relationships shown in the following discussion are based on data obtained with a visual target known as a Cobb parallel bar, shown in Fig. 11-9. This is a black square, the central third of which has been made white, or vice versa. The actual target to be resolved by the eyes is the space between the two bars. Now suppose that the pattern is of large size and is printed with very black ink on a white card. Assume that the illumination is

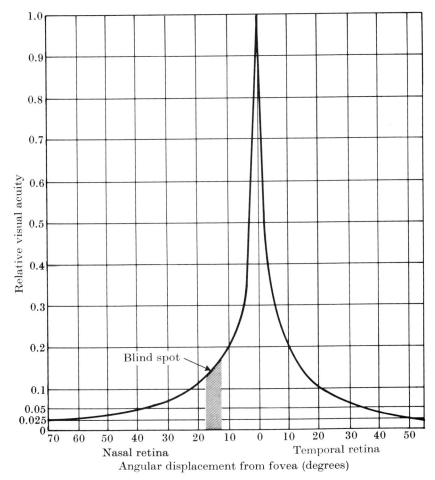

**Fig. 11-7** Variations in visual acuity for different parts of the eye in daylight. Acuity is greatest at the fovea.[3]

very high and that ample time is allowed for viewing. It is clear that the ease of recognition would be reduced if any of the following changes were made:

1. Reduce the pattern size without altering the proportions.
2. Reduce the brightness contrast by bleaching the ink or darkening the background. [This is expressed as contrast, $C = (B_1 - B_2)/B_1 \times 100$ percent, where $B_1$ is the brightness of the lightest part and $B_2$ is the brightness of the darkest part.]
3. Reduce the illumination.
4. Shorten the seeing time.

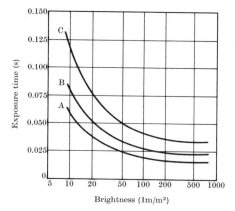

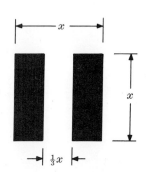

**Fig. II-8** The relationship between time of exposure and brightness for various criteria of threshold visibility. Curves A and B represent the relationship when the object is seen correctly in 50 and 80 percent of the trials, respectively. Curve C represents the relationship when the object is seen correctly almost every time it is presented.[4]

**Fig. II-9** Cobb parallel bar.

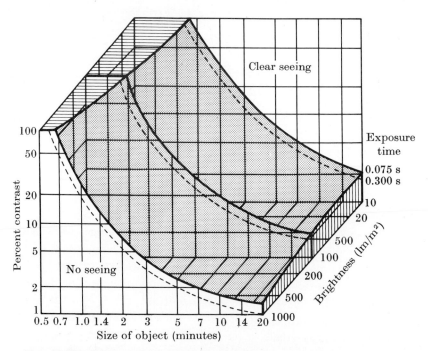

**Fig. II-10** The curved surface represents the relationship between combinations of size, contrast, and brightness for threshold visibility for constant exposure times of 0.075 and 0.300 second.[4]

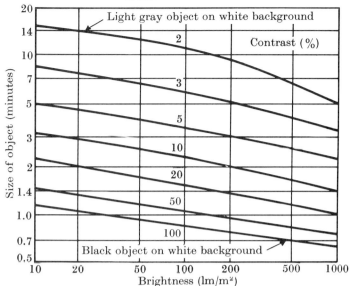

**Fig. 11-11** The relationship between size and brightness for threshold visibility of standard parallel-bar test-object of various contrasts for an exposure time of 0.17 second.[4]

For pattern recognition, it is necessary that each of these variables be above a limiting or threshold value. Psychologists and physiologists use the Latin word for threshold, *limen*, and speak of liminal values or limens. For a given seeing time, the liminal values may be represented by a curved surface with respect to the three $x$, $y$, $z$ coordinate axes. The surfaces obtained for an exposure time of 0.075 second and 0.300 second are shown in Fig. 11-10. Figures 11-11, 11-12, and 11-13 illustrate the effects of sectioning the three-dimensional solid in planes parallel to its reference planes. Before these figures are discussed, however, it is necessary to consider that eye movements consist of rapid sweeps, separated by brief pauses. The pauses, which are necessary for object recognition, have an average duration of 0.17 second.

Figure 11-11, the relationship between size and brightness for various contrast levels, represents data taken at a viewing time of 0.17 second, the mean fixation time. At maximum contrast and 1000 lm/m² brightness, the threshold of resolution is of the order of 1 minute for normal vision. Note that for 2 percent contrast and the same brightness, the object must subtend an angle of 5 minutes. Thus, the threshold size increases by about 5 to 1 when the contrast is reduced to 2 percent at the 1000 lm/m² brightness level. Figure 11-12 indicates that contrast is approximately inversely proportional to brightness for any size object, except for the very largest which can be encompassed by foveal vision. Figure 11-13 illustrates the relationship between contrast and object size, for various brightness levels.

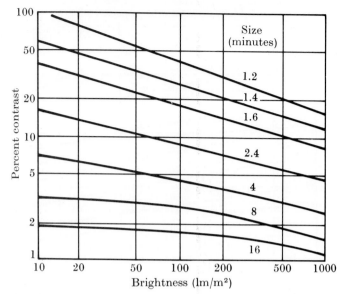

**Fig. II-I2**  The relationship between contrast and brightness for threshold visibility and a constant exposure time of 0.17 second.[4]

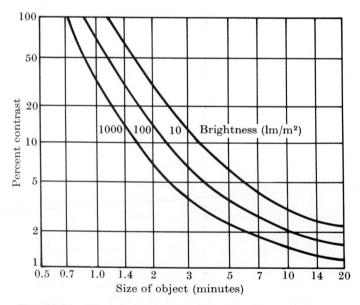

**Fig. II-I3**  The relationship between contrast and size for threshold visibility at various brightnesses with a constant exposure time of 0.17 second.[4]

It was said earlier that an object subtending a visual angle of about 1 minute is the minimal discriminable detail under ideal conditions. Seemingly at odds with this, and never satisfactorily explained, is the fact that a displaced line segment, as in a vernier scale, can be detected when the displacement subtends a visual angle as small as 5 seconds.

## VISUAL PERCEPTION

Visual perception is the overall conscious response to a visual stimulus situation.[4,5] It depends not only upon the structure and performance of the visual sense, but also on the viewer's past experiences. For example, the newborn child cannot orient his eyes and fuse the two images so as to achieve well-defined binocular vision. This aspect of perception must be learned, the development process spanning the individual's first six years.

Various aspects of perception pertain to the total experience of seeing color, form, movement, size, depth, etc. Although it is necessary to describe these aspects separately, visual experiences tend to include combinations of them. This was made evident in the discussion of visual acuity, in which the interrelations between brightness, size, illumination, and seeing time were described.

The perception of depth requires the use of both eyes and depends upon the separation between them. This sense operates at a maximum of about 100 meters. The one-eyed man has some ability to judge depth; he uses various cues such as shadows, perspective, and his memory of various object sizes. For example, an automobile appearing to be very small is judged to be far away.

The threshold of motion perception is strongly affected by the angle between the object's position and the line of sight.[4] When this angle is only 1°15', an angular motion of 1'30" per second can be perceived. When the angle is 20°, placing the image of the object nearer the periphery of the retina, the threshold increases to 34 angular minutes per second.

Perception is influenced to a marked degree by the contrast between an object and its background, being most difficult when the background has a pattern of shapes similar to the target, and close to it in color and brightness. Targets are seen best against nonuniform backgrounds when there is maximum contrast of color and brightness; they should have large areas of solid color, rather than stripes or other patterns.

Flicker is a visual response to alternations between light and dark. When the frequency of alternations is raised slowly from zero, there is no response at first. With further increase in frequency, a coarse response develops. This response becomes increasingly refined and then suddenly disappears. The frequency at which the flicker sensation disappears increases as the logarithm of the stimulus brightness and is independent of color. The peripheral regions of the retina are more sensitive to flicker than is the central region. Flicker must be considered in the design of motion picture and television equipment. It is useful in the design of visual signals for maximum alerting effect.

## COLOR AND COLOR VISION

Color sensations are produced when lights of different wavelengths enter the eye and fall on the fovea. The eye is not equally sensitive to all wavelengths in the visible spectrum. This is illustrated by Fig. 11-14, which shows the

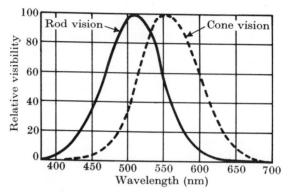

**Fig. 11-14** Visibility curves for cone vision (high intensity) and rod vision (low intensity).[6]

variation in sensitivity with wavelength for both day (photopic) vision, which is color sensitive, and night (scotopic) vision, which does not perceive color. Relatively, the eye is more sensitive to longer wavelengths in daylight, i.e., when the cones are working. At night when the rods are working, the shorter wavelengths are relatively more visible. This shift in sensitivity is called the *Purkinje effect*.

Since the transition from day to night vision is gradual as the illumination is reduced, the sensitivity shift toward the blue takes place while color impressions are still produced. If different colored lights, all of equal size, are used to provide the same initial brightness level and their intensity levels are then uniformly reduced, they will not all continue to appear equally bright. Green-blue lights outlast other colors as the brightness is reduced.

Because the color of an object depends upon the selective absorption or reflection of components of the incident light, it follows that a color sensation can be affected by changes in the illuminant. A red object would appear black under light from which all long wavelengths had been removed. A good summary of the factors affecting the color sensation is given in Ref. 5.

When the eye is stimulated by a mixture of lights of several different wavelengths, it sees only a single color sensation. In fact, there are many possible choices of light combinations which, in the proper proportions, will yield the same color sensation. Thus, the eye acts as an integrating mechanism rather than as a wave analyzer.

*Colorimetry*, the science of color measurement, is vital in today's economy. It is necessary to have means for measuring colors in terms of precisely defined standards. It then becomes possible to reproduce any specified color within tight tolerances and to establish methods for inspecting color to determine product uniformity. A brief discussion of colorimetry standards is given here because it will help to explain an important property of the eye.

Any color can be described in terms of three basic qualities called *hue*, *saturation* (or chroma), and *brightness* (or value). The double cone of Fig. 11-15

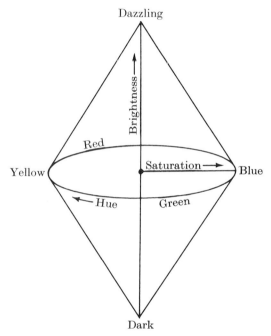

**Fig. 11-15** The color cone, illustrating the meanings of hue, saturation, and brightness.

aids in understanding these qualities and their relationships. Hue is represented on the cone's circumference; proceeding around the circle, the hue changes continuously through the entire range from blue to green, yellow, orange, red, purple, and back to blue. The saturation of the color is represented by the radius; going inward on the radius, a color is progressively less saturated, or pure. The color's brightness is shown by its position on the vertical axis; thus, colors become brighter toward the upper apex, and darker toward the lower apex. In a given horizontal plane, all colors are of equal brightness and, of course, all colors at the same radial distance from the center have the same saturation. The vertical line in the center has no hue and varies from black at the bottom, through various shades of gray, to brilliant white at the top.

The visual impressions of most spectral colors can be synthesized by combining the proper amounts of light from three primary sources of spectral red, green, and blue. However, there are some pure spectral colors that cannot be obtained in this way. In 1931, the Commission Internationale de l'Éclairage (CIE)[†] developed a system which circumvents this apparent obstacle. The CIE system makes possible the specification of any color in terms of mixtures of three theoretical primary colored lights. These primary red, green, and blue lights are imaginary, in that they do not occur in nature. However, this is not an inconvenience because a color can be analyzed in terms of the standard primaries, and the results can then be transformed into physically realizable color components.[7]

Figure 11-16 is the CIE chromaticity diagram. Note that it is plotted with respect to the red and green primaries only, omitting the blue. This is because

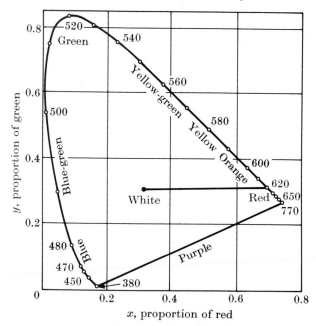

**Fig. 11-16** The 1931 CIE chromaticity diagram, showing the spectrum locus and the purple boundary. Wavelengths are indicated in nanometers. The line from white to the curve represents reds of varying degrees of purity.[7]

---

[†] The CIE is also known by the English version of its name, International Commission on Illumination, and the system is called the ICI system in many textbooks published in the United States. However, CIE is the preferred usage.

the proportions of the three primaries that must be combined to produce any desired color sensation must always add up to 1.00. Thus, the proportions of red ($x$) and green ($y$) are determined first from the chart, and the proportion of blue is then given by $z = 1 - (x + y)$. All colors in the visible spectrum lie on the upper curved contour beginning at 380 nm and moving clockwise to the 770-nm point. The straight line connecting the lower apexes contains the family of purples. Purples, which are not found in the spectrum, are formed with various mixtures of red and blue lights.

Any spectral color can be called single-hued, in that it has a specific wavelength. The spectral colors, then, represent the ultimate in purity. Colors that are made up of mixtures of various hues do not have the same pure appearance as the spectral colors. These less pure colors all fall inside the curve. White, in the center of the diagram, is matched by very nearly equal proportions of the three primaries.

Consider the line which has been drawn from white to 620-nm red. Along this line away from white, people with normal color vision would see a series of pinks, beginning with an extremely "washed out" or pastel appearance, becoming darker, and terminating finally at pure red. Such radial lines are called lines of constant hue. The hue is called "washed out" near the white end and "saturated" at the boundary end.

It is important to realize that equal displacements in the chromaticity diagram do not represent equal color differences. In Fig. 11-17, the ellipses are drawn so that the distances from the center of any ellipse to points on its boundary represent equally noticeable color differences. The eye is most sensitive at detecting color differences where the ellipses are small. This principle is of great importance in the design of color codes, the selection of colors for signal lamps, color coding of displays and controls, etc. Colors should be chosen from ellipses having the maximum separation.

A person having normal color vision is called a *trichromat* because he can match any color with a mixture of lights of three colors. There are wide ranges of color sensitivity among trichromats, i.e., some have much greater ability to make fine color distinctions. Persons with normal color vision can distinguish about 150 different hues. For any hue, many differences in saturation can also be distinguished. The minimum perceptible difference in saturation varies with hue and is around 1 percent to 2 percent, in general.

It has been estimated that, taking hue, saturation, and brightness into account, the normal eye can distinguish between about 7,500,000 colors in the light reflected from surfaces. Because emitted light has greater ranges of saturation and brightness than reflected light, the total number of discriminable colors has been estimated at 10,000,000.

The color-normal human eye does not always respond in the same way to a given color, there being many factors that affect the response. For example,

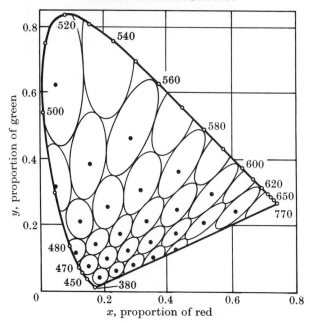

**Fig. II-17** Perceptibility scales for the standard 1931 CIE colorimetric coordinate system. Distances from the center of an ellipse to the boundary of the ellipse represent equally noticeable color differences. The smaller the ellipse, the more sensitive the eye is at detecting color differences.[8]

variations in the angular size of an object can cause a change in color; up to an angular size of 20° or so, an object's color appears more saturated with increasing size. However, further increases in object size give the effect of reduced saturation. The relative positions of colored objects can affect their colors. Thus, when objects of high and low brightness are placed side-by-side, the eye tends to accentuate the difference between their brightnesses.

Total color blindness is found very rarely; most people who are called "color-blind" are more properly called "color-deficient."[7] Commonly, the color-deficient person can match a given color by mixing colored lights from two sources; thus, he is called a *dichromat*. The dichromat can distinguish between light and dark and also between yellow and blue or red and green. He is more likely to have the yellow-blue capability.

The totally color-blind person, or *monochromat*, can distinguish only between light and dark. This person has defective cones and thus his visual acuity is poor. Because he is dependent upon his rod vision, which is not suitable for high illumination, he tends to have "day blindness," a condition in which vision is painful and inefficient in strong light. About 8 percent of the male population is said to be color-deficient to some degree. Females seldom have this difficulty;

it is a sex-linked hereditary trait which may pass from a color-deficient man, via his daughter (who has normal color vision), to his grandson.

Frequently, designers must standardize and specify colors for finishes, inks, dyes, etc. Object-color systems having large numbers of standardized color samples are more convenient than the CIE system for this purpose. There are a number of these systems in common use. The Munsell color system uses 40 equally spaced hues and 10 equally spaced brightness intervals. The number of steps in the saturation scale depends on hue and brightness, the intervals being chosen to represent equal differences in saturation. The *Munsell Book of Color*[9] contains over 1200 removable color chips, available in glossy or matte finish. The Ostwald system[10] provides 680 color samples.

> **Example 11.1.** Suppose that indicator lamp caps are available in four colors. The color sensations from these caps are equivalent to pure colors of the following wavelengths: 500 nm, 520 nm, 540 nm, and 620 nm.
>
> A control panel is being designed for a critical application and the lamp colors must not be confused. Two colors are required for indicating different functions.
>
> (a) Which two colors would be best? Explain.
> (b) Of the remaining two colors, which one would be best if a third color were required for use with the first two choices?
>
> *Solution.* Refer to Fig. 11-17. To be distinguishable with maximum certainty, colors should not be selected from within the same ellipse. The best color choices are from ellipses with maximum separation.
>
> Consider the following pairs:

| Pair | Separation | Result |
|---|---|---|
| 500, 520 nm | Same ellipse | Poor |
| 500, 540 nm | Adjacent ellipses | Fair |
| 500, 620 nm | Nine ellipses apart | Good |
| 520, 540 nm | Adjacent ellipses | Fair |
| 520, 620 nm | Nine ellipses apart | Good |
| 540, 620 nm | Seven ellipses apart | Good |

> (a) Apparently, either the 500, 620 pair or the 520, 620 pair would be good because they have the largest separations. The final choice of 500, 620 was made because it has a greater wavelength spacing than 520, 620 does.
> (b) The third color selected was 540 nm because it is one and one-half ellipses away from 500 nm and eight ellipses away from 620 nm.

## DARK AND LIGHT ADAPTATION

If a person has been in a brightly lighted environment and is then plunged into relative darkness, he has difficulty in seeing. However, changes in the state of the retina then begin, causing a lowering of the threshold brightness. An increasing amount of detail can be seen as time passes, until very dimly lighted objects can be seen. This increase in visual sensitivity is called *dark adaptation*.

As a person enters a dark place, his visual threshold depends upon the brightness to which he has been previously adapted, as shown in Fig. 11-18.

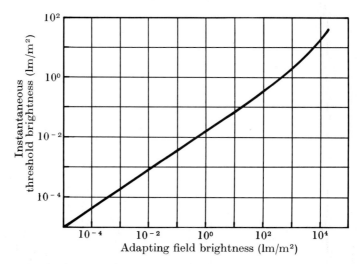

**Fig. 11-18**   The brightness that can just be seen after the eye has become adapted to a higher brightness.[11]

The general slope of this curve is less than 1, showing that as the adapting brightness increases, the difference between it and the instantaneous threshold also increases. This relationship is important in any situation in which a person must perform a task under dim lighting while his eyes are still accustomed to a high brightness.

Dark adaptation proceeds through two phases, according to the curves of Fig. 11-19. The first phase involves a rapid increase in sensitivity. Then there is a kink at the point where a transfer from cone to rod vision occurs. The second phase involves a large adjustment which takes a relatively long time. As the series of curves suggests, it takes longer to adapt for a wide field of seeing than for a narrow field. The explanation for this is that the increase in sensitivity begins at the center of the retina and proceeds outward toward the periphery as time passes.

The time required for dark adaptation depends upon the *preadapting brightness* and upon the length of time that the eye has been adapted to a high intensity. Thus, a radar operator would not greatly impair his dark adaptation if he were to use a dim light for chart reading, especially if the exposure were brief. The eyes adapt to darkness independently. Thus, one eye can be closed

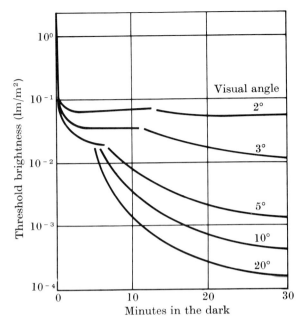

**Fig. 11-19** The threshold during dark adaptation for centrally fixated areas of different size.[12]

or covered to retain its dark adaptation while the other eye is exposed to bright light.

Night vision occurs in the brightness range over which the rods function as light receptors. It was shown in Fig. 11-6 that there are no rods at the fovea and that the rod density increases rapidly at either side of the fovea. Thus, we see most acutely in low brightness by looking somewhat off to the side, rather than head-on.

**Example 11.2.** In 45 minutes, a sailor must go on watch as a night lookout. His duties will require that his eyes be thoroughly dark-adapted so that he will be able to detect very dim lights. Can anything be done to enable the man to engage in recreational activity in a brightly lighted area until it is time for him to go on watch?

*Solution.* Equip the man with tight-fitting red goggles. His rods will become dark-adapted while he continues to use his cones for seeing detail. Of course, he will not have color vision during the adapting period. This phenomenon can be explained with the aid of Fig. 11-20.

The two upper curves represent the relative sensitivities of the rods, $S_R$, used in night vision and of the cones, $S_C$, used in day vision. When a lighted

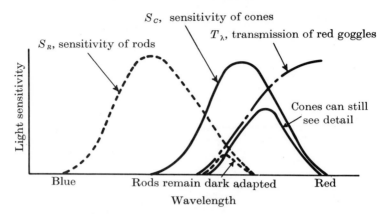

**Fig. II-20**   Dark adaptation in red light.

surface is viewed, the apparent brightness at any wavelength, $\lambda$, is

$$B_\lambda = E_\lambda S_C \qquad \text{(day vision)}$$

$$B_\lambda = E_\lambda S_R \qquad \text{(night vision)}$$

for a monochromatic radiant power density $E_\lambda$ leaving the surface.

Suppose that the surface is viewed through a filter whose transmission is $T_\lambda$. The brightness is then $B_\lambda = E_\lambda S_C T_\lambda$ or $B_\lambda = E_\lambda S_R T_\lambda$. Assume that the light is white and that the filter transmits red. Then the brightnesses at the rod and cone systems are as indicated by the smaller curves. The rods become dark-adapted, and the brightness at the cone system is adequate for seeing detail.

**Example 11.3.** After becoming accustomed to an apparent brightness level of 10,000 lm/m², an automobile driver suddenly enters a dimly lighted tunnel. What brightness level would make seeing just barely possible for the driver?

*Solution.* From the curve of Fig. 11-18, the corresponding instantaneous apparent threshold brightness is about 20 lm/m².

Note that, in this instance, the instantaneous threshold brightness is about $\frac{1}{500}$ of the brightness to which the driver's eyes were accustomed. Of course, safety requires that the tunnel be lighted to a much higher brightness than this.

Whereas complete dark adaptation requires 30 to 45 minutes, the reverse process, *light adaptation*, proceeds much more rapidly. When a dark-adapted person enters daylight, his eyes are nearly light-adapted after the first minute, and completely adapted after about ten minutes. Light adaptation is slower at lower illumination levels.

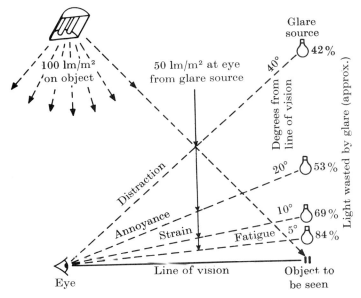

**Fig. 11-21** The reduction in visibility due to a moderately glaring light source, at various degrees from the line of vision, is represented in terms of the waste of light which illuminates the object.[13]

## GLARE

Glare effects are readily explained by reference to Fig. 11-21. The eye is directed toward an object that is illuminated to 100 lm/m² by a fluorescent fixture. Suppose that a source of glare, above the object, delivers 50 lm/m² at the eye. When the angular separation between glare source and object is only 5°, there is an 84-percent reduction in the visibility of a standard test object, and the observer experiences fatigue. When the separation is increased to 40°, there still is a 42-percent reduction in visibility, and the observer is distracted.

Figure 11-22 shows that the lowest amount of glare that is just perceived as

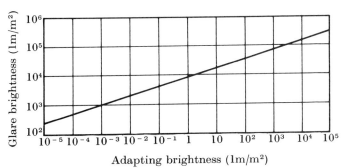

**Fig. 11-22** Glare brightness for incipient discomfort versus adapting brightness.[11]

uncomfortable depends upon the brightness to which the eye has been adapted. For example, if the eye is adapted to a brightness of $10^{-5}$ lm/m², an interfering brightness of only about 200 lm/m² would be noticed. This is what happens to a driver on a very dark road when he suddenly encounters oncoming headlights. At the upper extreme, eyes adapted to a brightness of $10^5$ lm/m² are just bothered by a glare brightness of about $3 \times 10^5$ lm/m².

## 11-2. HEARING, SPEECH, AND SOUND

In man's interaction with machines, the auditory sense is generally second in importance only to the visual sense. This section describes the workings of the hearing mechanism and some of its characteristics.

### HEARING MECHANISM

The hearing mechanism, Fig. 11-23, has three distinct divisions: the outer ear, the middle ear, and the inner ear. The visible ear flap, or *pinna*, helps in gathering sound, and the auditory canal, or *meatus*, protects the eardrum from temperature and humidity extremes. In addition, the meatus, acting somewhat like a resonant organ pipe, provides a pressure amplification of 5 to 10 dB in the range from 2000 to 5500 Hz.

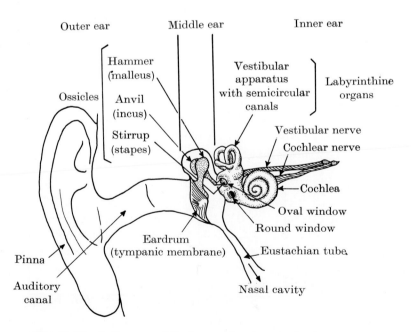

**Fig. 11-23**  A diagram of the human hearing mechanism.

The middle ear contains three tiny bones, or *ossicles*: the *malleus* (hammer), the *incus* (anvil), and the *stapes* (stirrup). The ossicles form a mechanical linkage which acts as an impedance transformer to permit sound waves to pass readily from the compressible air to the incompressible liquid which fills the *cochlea* in the inner ear. As shown in Fig. 11-23, the hammer is attached by its "handle" to the center of the eardrum. Its upper end is connected by a joint to the anvil, and this, in turn, is joined to the stirrup which carries the vibratory motion through the oval window to the fluid in the cochlea.

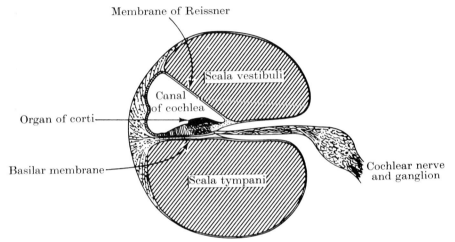

**Fig. 11-24**   Transverse section of the cochlea.[14]

The bony linkage reduces the motions at the eardrum by a factor between 1.3 and 3. Furthermore, the area of the oval window is much smaller than that of the eardrum. The combined effects result in a pressure multiplication of 15 to 30 times (about 20 to 30 dB).

To equalize static air pressure on both sides of the eardrum, the middle ear is connected to the upper part of the throat by a small passage called the *eustachian* tube. This tube is normally collapsed, and it is opened by the act of swallowing.

The cochlea is a tube about $3\frac{1}{3}$ cm long, coiled like a snail. It contains the wave-analyzing mechanism which enables man to hear the separate components in a complex sound. In cross section, (Fig. 11-24), the tube of the cochlea is divided by two longitudinal membranes, the *basilar membrane* and the *membrane of Reissner*, into three parallel canals: the *scala vestibuli*, the *scala tympani*, and the *canal of cochlea*. The canal of cochlea is closed at the innermost end by the junction of the two membranes. Beyond this point, there is a small opening (the *helicotrema*) that joins the scala vestibuli and the scala tympani to form a continuous passage from the oval window to the round window; this space is filled with a viscous liquid. Within the canal between the two membranes and lying atop the basilar membrane is the *organ of Corti*, which contains the auditory nerve endings. The membrane of Reissner is very thin and flexible and does not take a major part in the hearing process.

Suppose that the ear is stimulated by a sound. The pumping action of the stapes at the oval window causes displacement of the liquid through the scala vestibuli, the helicotrema, and the scala tympani. The membrane in the round window moves correspondingly to accommodate the motion of the liquid. Vibratory energy is communicated from the liquid to the basilar membrane. The basilar membrane varies in width, being narrowest at the end nearest the round window and widest at the far end, near the helicotrema. The wide end responds most readily to low frequencies. A displacement at some location on the basilar membrane results in excitation of the corresponding auditory nerve endings. The mechanism whereby pressure waves are converted to auditory sensation is not perfectly understood. The interested reader can find discussions in several of the references.[14,15,16,17,18]

## SOUND

*Sound* has two definitions. To the physicist, sound means waves of air pressure; to the psychologist, sound is a sensation. The distinction is important because the hearing mechanism is nonlinear and, thus, sensation is not directly proportional to air pressure variations. Also, sound components that do not exist in the air pressure wave are sometimes heard. For instance, when a person listens to a pure tone of high intensity, e.g., 50 dB, he hears the tone and a series of its harmonics. When two intense, pure tones are presented, the listener hears these tones, their sum and difference, harmonics of each tone, and sums and differences of the harmonics.[14]

For physical measurements of air pressure waves, the terms frequency and intensity are used. *Frequency* is a measure of the number of complete air pressure cycles per second in a sound wave. *Intensity* is a measure of the air pressure change.

For subjective measurements, or measurements of what is actually heard, the terms pitch and loudness are used. *Pitch* refers to the tonal quality of a sound (high or low). Pitch is governed primarily, but not entirely, by the frequency of the sound wave. If the frequency of a pure tone is held constant, a change in intensity can result in a change in pitch. *Loudness* is the measure of the strength of a sensation and is produced mainly by intensity. If the intensity is held constant, however, a change in frequency can result in a change in loudness.

The minimum detectable sound intensity is limited by background noises originating within the body from blood circulation, breathing, muscle tremors, and head movements. These noises can be heard under conditions of absolute quiet.

The ratio of the intensities of the strongest tolerable sounds to the weakest detectable sounds is somewhere between $10^6$ and $10^7$. Because this range is so large, the decibel is used in sound intensity measurements in order to compress the numbers to manageable size. The decibel, or dB, is defined by

$$N_{dB} = 10 \log \frac{P_1}{P_0}$$

where $P_1$ and $P_0$ are two power levels being compared.

Sound intensity measurements, however, are made in terms of pressure. Power is proportional to the square of pressure; therefore,

$$N_{dB} = 20 \log \frac{p_1}{p_0}$$

where $p_1$ and $p_0$ are two pressure levels being compared.

The standard reference pressure for sound intensity measurements is $2 \times 10^{-5} \, \text{N/m}^2$ (or $2 \times 10^{-4} \, \text{dyne/cm}^2$), which is equivalent in power to $10^{-12} \, \text{W/m}^2$.

The term *intensity level* is the number of dB by which a sound intensity exceeds the standard reference. The intensity levels of some common sounds are as follows:

| *Sound* | *Intensity level* (dB)† |
|---|---|
| Threshold of pain | 130 |
| Loud thunder | 120 |
| Subway train | 100 |
| Average auto | 70 |
| Normal conversation | 60 |
| Quiet office | 40 |
| Whisper | 25 |
| Threshold of hearing in quiet | 0 |

## NOISE

The term *noise* is defined in a number of ways. Generally, noise is described as sound having no definite pitch; this definition applies to nearly all sounds other than speech or music. Extraneous sounds appearing in amplifying

---

† Whenever an intensity is given in dB, without further qualification, the meaning is "dB above standard reference pressure."

systems or communication links also are called noise.[14] *White noise* is a mixture of many widely distributed frequencies, all of the same intensity. It is named for its similarity to white light. A hissing air jet makes this kind of noise.

Noise has a variety of effects on human beings. Some noises are merely irritating; others impair working efficiency in marked degree, and some can cause permanent damage to the sense of hearing. Intermittent noises are more distracting than steady noises. The irritating effect of a noise is not necessarily related to the loudness of the noise. A man may work all day in a very noisy factory without adverse reaction to the high noise level. Yet this same man may lie awake at night, driven to distraction by the faint sound of a dripping faucet.

High-frequency tones and extremely low frequency tones are most annoying, and tones in the middle range are relatively less annoying. The annoyance value of the overall noise field has, in some cases, been greatly reduced by simply eliminating the very high frequency noises, even though the reduction in total noise power has been very slight. In other cases, means have been found to shift the dominant noise frequencies to less annoying values, without significantly reducing their amplitudes.

The most serious effects of some noises are the tendencies to cause temporary or permanent damage to the hearing mechanism. The ear's sensitivity is seriously reduced by exposure to very intense noise. Generally, this hearing loss is temporary, and the sensitivity returns to normal although it may take several days. It has been found that the higher-frequency tones have a more serious effect on hearing acuity than do low tones of the same intensity. The impairment is greater for long exposures than it is for short exposures.

## EQUAL-LOUDNESS CONTOURS

The ear is most sensitive to frequencies between about 500 and 4000 Hz; these are the frequencies of greatest importance in the understanding of speech. Higher or lower frequencies must be more intense to be audible. Young people can hear frequencies from about 20 Hz to as high as 20,000 Hz; the upper limit drops progressively as a person ages.

In Fig. 11-25, the lowest curve represents the threshold of hearing. The intensity for just hearing a 1000-Hz tone was arbitrarily set at 0 dB as a reference for all other points on the curve. The sound pressure intensity level at this point is $2 \times 10^{-5}$ N/m$^2$, the standard reference. The intensities of all the other frequencies were adjusted to the point of being barely audible. Note that a 30-Hz tone is just audible when it has an intensity of about 65 dB above reference; at the upper end of the scale, the just-audible intensity for 10,000 Hz is about 10 dB.

The curves of Fig. 11-25 are called *equal-loudness contours*. To obtain these curves, a 1000-Hz reference tone was set first to a given intensity level, such as 10 dB. Another tone was then adjusted to the intensity level where an observer judged it to have the same loudness as the 1000-Hz reference tone. Thus, all tones on a given curve appear to have the same loudness. The uppermost contour is called the *threshold of feeling* or the *threshold of pain*. Permanent

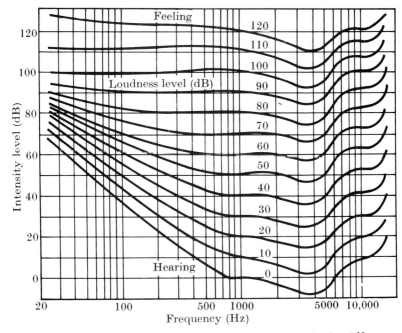

**Fig. 11-25**  Loudness level contours versus intensity level.[19]

injury is likely to result from continued exposure to intensities above these values. Note the tendency of the higher curves to become increasingly flat, indicating that all high-intensity tones tend to be equally loud.

In summary, the *loudness level* of any tone equals the intensity level of a 1000-Hz tone which has been adjusted to sound as loud as the tone in question. The term *phon* is used for loudness level. A tone having a loudness of 20 phons has the same loudness as a 1000-Hz tone having an intensity 20 dB above the standard reference.

**Example 11.4.** Under ideal conditions, the eye can just see a 1-candela source at a distance of 13 miles. At the dominant wavelength of 589 nm, 1 watt = 621 lumens. The threshold sensitivity of the ear is about $10^{-12}$ W/m². 

(a) What is the threshold sensitivity of the eye in W/m²?
(b) Which is more sensitive, the eye or the ear?

*Solution.*

(a) From Eqs. (11-3) and (11-6), the threshold intensity of illumination is

$$E = \frac{d\Phi}{dA} = \frac{I}{r^2} \; \text{lm/m}^2$$

$$= \frac{1}{(13 \times 5280 \times 12 \times 0.0254)^2(621)} \; \text{W/m}^2$$

$$= 3.7 \times 10^{-12} \; \text{W/m}^2$$

(b) The ear has the lower threshold, in the ratio of about 1 to 3.7.

**Example 11.5.** At the threshold of hearing, what is the amplitude of air "particle" motion? How does this amplitude compare with the wavelengths of visible light?

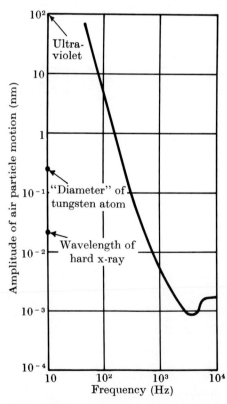

**Fig. 11-26** Amplitudes of air particle motion at sound pressures along the threshold of hearing.

*Solution.* When the air carries a sound, the amplitude of air particle motion is given by

$$A = \frac{p}{2\pi f \rho v_s}$$

where:

   $A$ is the air particle amplitude (m);

   $p$ is the pressure of the transmitted wave (N/m²);

   $f$ is the frequency (Hz);

   $\rho$ is the air density (1.205 kg/m³ at 20°C and 760 mm Hg);

   $v_s$ is the velocity of sound (344 m/s under standard conditions).

(The quantity $\rho v_s = 414$ N·s/m³ under standard conditions is called the characteristic impedance of air.)

In referring to the equal-loudness contours, it should be remembered that the reference pressure at 1000 Hz is $2 \times 10^{-5}$ N/m². The pressures at other frequencies along the threshold of hearing can then be found from

$$N_{dB} = 20 \log \frac{p}{p_0}$$

On rearrangement,

$$p = p_0 \log^{-1} \frac{N_{dB}}{20}$$

Results are tabulated below and are plotted in Fig. 11-26. The amplitudes are converted to nm for ready comparison with the wavelengths of visible light.

| Frequency (Hz) | dB above reference | Pressure (N/m²) | Amplitude (m) | (nm) |
|---|---|---|---|---|
| 50 | $+53$ | $8.9 \times 10^{-3}$ | $6.9 \times 10^{-8}$ | 69 |
| 100 | $+38$ | $1.6 \times 10^{-3}$ | $6.1 \times 10^{-9}$ | 6.1 |
| 1,000 | 0 | $2 \times 10^{-5}$ | $7.7 \times 10^{-12}$ | $7.7 \times 10^{-3}$ |
| 3,500 | $-8$ | $8 \times 10^{-6}$ | $8.8 \times 10^{-13}$ | $8.8 \times 10^{-4}$ |
| 6,000 | $+1$ | $2.2 \times 10^{-5}$ | $1.4 \times 10^{-12}$ | $1.4 \times 10^{-3}$ |
| 10,000 | $+8$ | $5 \times 10^{-5}$ | $1.9 \times 10^{-12}$ | $1.9 \times 10^{-3}$ |

It is interesting to see that the largest amplitude is comparable to the wave length of ultraviolet, about one-fourth the shortest visible light wavelength.

## DIFFERENTIAL THRESHOLDS OF INTENSITY AND FREQUENCY

Because intelligence is conveyed by changes of sound intensity and/or frequency, we need to know what changes of intensity or frequency are just detectable. Figure 11-27 shows the just-detectable changes in intensity for various pure tones over a wide range of loudness level. Note that the minimum detectable change tends to be constant for high intensities (high loudness levels) but increases rapidly as the intensity falls toward the threshold of hearing. At the most favorable frequency and amplitude, a change of about $\frac{1}{4}$ dB can be detected. However, these measurements were made under ideal quiet conditions; the just-detectable change is closer to 1 dB under normal listening conditions.

Figure 11-28 illustrates the minimum perceptible percentages of frequency change versus frequency for constant loudness levels between 5 and 60 dB.

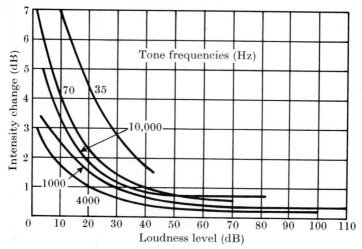

**Fig. 11-27** Minimum detectable intensity changes versus loudness level for various frequencies.[20]

Frequency changes are detected most easily in the middle and upper ranges. Above 1000 Hz, the ear can just detect a frequency change of about $\frac{1}{4}$ percent, and below 1000 Hz, the minimum detectable change is about 2.5 Hz. The ability to detect small frequency changes increases as the loudness level is raised to about 40 dB, but it does not increase much at higher levels.

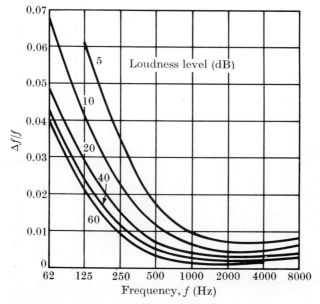

**Fig. 11-28** Minimum detectable frequency changes versus frequency for various loudness levels.[21]

## MASKING

The hearing characteristics that have been described were measured under conditions of ideal quiet. Of course, the usual listening situation involves various unwanted sounds or noises. These tend to distract the listener's attention and to hide or mask the sounds he would like to hear.

First, consider the effect of a pure tone on a listener's ability to hear another pure tone. Suppose that A is the wanted tone and B is an unwanted, disturbing tone. Regardless of the frequency relationship between A and B, the threshold intensity of A is always higher when B is present than when B is absent. The extent of the upward shift in threshold for A is a measure of the masking effect of B.

Figure 11-29 shows two examples of pure tone masking. In the first case, a 400-Hz masking tone is present, at loudness levels varying from 20 dB to

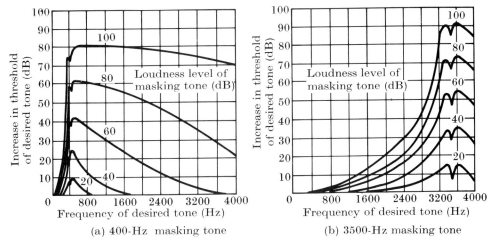

(a) 400-Hz masking tone        (b) 3500-Hz masking tone

**Fig. 11-29**   The masking effects of pure tones on other pure tones.[14]

100 dB. As the sensation level of the masking tone is raised, it affects the thresholds of progressively higher wanted frequencies. When it reaches 100 dB, there is a nearly uniform effect on hearing all higher-frequency tones. In the second case, where a 3500-Hz masking tone is used, the effect on hearing tones of lower frequency is much less severe. Even when the masking sensation level is at 100 dB, there is little effect on the threshold for signals below about 800 Hz.

The dips in these curves in the regions of the masking frequencies are explained by the phenomenon of *beats*. The presence of the masked tone is revealed by the beats produced between it and the masking tone.

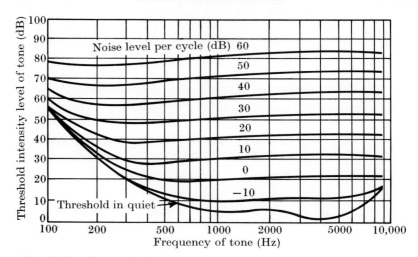

**Fig. 11-30** Monaural thresholds for pure tones when masked by white noise at various intensities.[22]

It is a general rule that intense low-frequency noises make higher frequencies hard to hear, but the reverse effect is much less severe. This explains why low-frequency noises are used for radio jamming and why the pickup of power-line frequencies must be carefully avoided in voice communication systems.

In normal situations, listeners are more likely to encounter masking by noise than by pure tones. Figure 11-30 shows how various intensities of white noise affect the threshold intensity levels of pure tones. Note that, as the masking noise level is increased, all tones tend to have the same threshold of audibility. There is a marked similarity between these curves and the equal-loudness contours of Fig. 11-25. Apparently, all tones tend to sound equally loud at high intensities, regardless of whether the background is noisy or quiet.

**Example 11.6.** A manufacturing operation generates a 2000-Hz tone at an intensity level of 50 dB. The tone shifts downward by 100 Hz when the machine goes out of adjustment; this is the operator's only warning of trouble. Under which of the following background noise conditions will the operator detect the frequency shift?

    (a) No background noise.
    (b) A buzz of predominantly 400 Hz at 90-dB intensity.
    (c) A 3500-Hz tone at 100-dB intensity.
    (d) Escaping compressed air at 60-dB intensity.

*Solution.*

    (a) Figure 11-25 shows that, for a frequency of 2000 Hz, a 50-dB intensity level corresponds to a loudness that is also 50 dB. From Fig. 11-28, a

frequency change of about 0.2 percent is just detectable at this loudness and frequency. Therefore, the 5-percent frequency change is
easily observed.

(b) From Fig. 11-29, the 2000-Hz tone will not be heard at all.

(c) From Fig. 11-29, the tone will be heard easily. Figures 11-25 and
11-28 show that the change in frequency can also be detected.

(d) From Fig. 11-30, the tone will not be heard. A 2000-Hz tone in the
presence of 60 dB of white noise has a threshold intensity of about
83 dB.

## CHARACTERISTICS OF SPEECH

Speech is a mixture of "voiced" and "unvoiced" sounds. In the production of a voiced sound, air passes through the *glottis* (a slit) between the
vocal cords and causes them to vibrate. This imposes a harmonic-rich modulation on the air stream. The fundamental frequency averages about 125 Hz
for men and 250 Hz for women.

The relative amplitudes of the harmonics are modified by the vocal cavities,
which can be adjusted by the changing positions of the tongue, lips, and teeth
to form the articulate sounds of speech.

The vocal cords are drawn aside and do not vibrate during the production
of unvoiced sounds as in S or F. For this reason, they do not have the harmonic
structure of voiced sounds. Sibilant sounds are made by the flow of air through
apertures formed by the tongue, lips, and teeth. Although the unvoiced sounds
are generally of lower intensity than the voiced sounds, they probably are more
important to the understanding of speech than are the voiced sounds.

Figure 11-31 shows the ranges of frequency and intensity of conversational

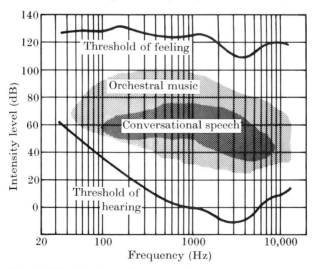

**Fig. 11-31**  The intensity versus frequency spectrum of
conversational speech and orchestral music.

speech and orchestral music. The lower and upper curves are the thresholds of hearing and feeling, respectively. Figure 11-32 shows the relative intensities of frequencies in speech. This curve represents averages of measurements made

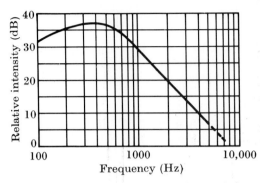

**Fig. 11-32** The relative intensities of frequencies in male and female speech.[23]

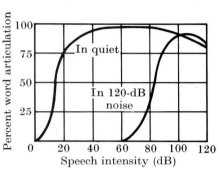

**Fig. 11-33** The relationship between speech intelligibility and speech intensity for quiet conditions and for the extreme case where there is 120 dB (above reference level) of white noise present.[24]

on many subjects. Speech frequencies range from a low of about 100 Hz to a maximum of around 9000 Hz. The energy is greatest at a frequency of about 400 Hz and falls rapidly as frequency increases beyond 600 Hz.

## ARTICULATION TESTING

Articulation testing is a tool for evaluating the performance of speech circuits. In 1910, it was proposed that lists of spoken syllables be used to measure the intelligibility of received speech. During the next several decades, this testing system was brought to a high degree of refinement. Lists of spoken sounds, syllables, words, or simple sentences are transmitted through some medium by people with good diction. At the receiving end, the listener records what he actually hears. If a list of words is used, the percentage of words received correctly is called the *percent word articulation* for the medium.

Figure 11-33 shows the relationship of word articulation to speech intensity in conditions of quiet and very intense noise. When it is quiet, the articulation score mounts rapidly as the intensity is increased. Beyond the 30-dB intensity point, the intelligibility rises slowly, reaches a maximum at about 60 dB, and then drops as speech intensity is increased beyond this point.

The right-hand curve indicates that the listener has a serious problem in understanding speech in the presence of high background noise. The effect of the intense noise is to reduce the usable speech intensity by about 70 dB. Note that as in quiet the articulation curve reaches a peak and then drops if the speech intensity is increased beyond the optimum point.

In the foregoing illustration, the practical extremes of listening conditions have been used, with 120 dB of noise at the threshold of feeling. Therefore, all usual listening situations must be on curves somewhere between these two. The masking effects of noise are of serious concern, especially in the design of complex communication systems. Practical methods have been devised for improving intelligibility in the presence of noise, for various conditions which will be described.

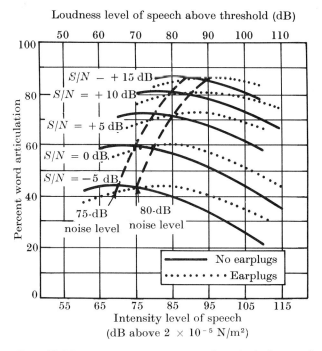

**Fig. II-34** Relation between word articulation and speech level with signal-to-noise ratio (solid and dotted lines) and noise level (dashed lines) as the parameters.[25]

The speech-to-noise or signal-to-noise ratio $(S/N)$ is a much better indicator of intelligibility than is speech or signal intensity alone. Consider the family of solid curves in Fig. 11-34. Suppose first that the $S/N$ ratio is held constant while speech intensity is raised. For a constant $S/N$ ratio of 0 dB, increasing the speech level from 65 dB to 75 dB gives little change in word articulation. Further increases in speech (and noise) level yield a marked reduction in word articulation. Now suppose that the speech level is held constant, but the $S/N$ ratio is improved. At a 75-dB speech level, an increase in $S/N$ level of only 5 dB, from $-5$ dB to 0 dB, gives about 17 percent improvement in word articulation. For any given speech level, raising the $S/N$ ratio always improves intelligibility; but for a constant $S/N$ ratio, there is a single speech level at which intelligibility is optimum.

Consider a noisy radio circuit in which the speech and noise are inextricably mixed. Although the $S/N$ ratio is fixed, a gain setting can be found that will give the best intelligibility for that $S/N$ ratio. For example, with an $S/N$ ratio of 10 dB, the best gain setting would give an intensity level of about 80 dB.

On the other hand, suppose that the radio circuit is quiet, but there is high ambient noise. In this instance, the best gain setting is the one that gives the highest $S/N$ ratio. Ear plugs can be used to raise the intelligibility when the ambient noise level is very high. The dotted curves in Fig. 11-34 represent the hearing experience under this condition. It is seen that the dotted articulation curves are higher than the solid curves everywhere to the right of the 80-dB noise level contour, giving improvements of up to about 10 percent in word articulation. At lower noise levels, the ear plugs reduce the intelligibility. Specially designed ear plugs are often worn in tanks, military aircraft, and some industrial environments.

## DISTORTION

Many experiments have been made to establish the hearing mechanism's sensitivity to various kinds of distortion. These show not only that the ear is quite tolerant of some types of distortion, but also that the deliberate use of distortion can sometimes be beneficial.

*Amplitude distortion* occurs in a nonlinear system in which the output is not directly proportional to the input; this introduces harmonics and intermodulation products. *Phase distortion* occurs when the original phase relations between the component frequencies of a sound are not preserved. *Frequency distortion* exists when the various component frequencies of a sound are amplified unequally.

In speech, the maximum energy in the vowels may be five to ten times as great as the energy in the consonants. However, the much weaker consonants are essential to intelligibility. If the vowel sounds are greatly suppressed, the fidelity is impaired, but there is little effect on intelligibility. Therefore, when speech intelligibility is the primary consideration, a form of deliberately introduced distortion called *peak clipping* can pay large dividends.

Suppose that a speech wave is subjected to increasingly severe peak

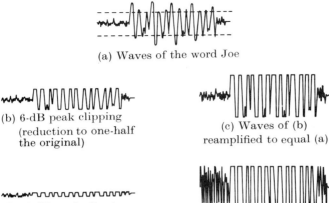

(a) Waves of the word Joe

(b) 6-dB peak clipping
(reduction to one-half
the original)

(c) Waves of (b)
reamplified to equal (a)

(d) 20-dB peak clipping
(reduction to one-tenth
the original)

(e) Waves of (d)
reamplified to equal (a)

**Fig. 11-35**   Diagram illustrating peak clipping.[26]

clipping and that the output of the clipper is reamplified to the original peak-to-peak amplitude, as illustrated in Fig. 11-35. The effect on word articulation is given in Fig. 11-36, which shows that as much as 24 dB of peak clipping and reamplification can be very beneficial.

The effect of this signal "tailoring" is to boost the peak-to-peak amplitude of the essential consonant sounds so that they load the channel more nearly to its capacity. This use of distortion is destructive if there is nonimpulsive noise mixed with the speech, ahead of the clipper. It is effective when the speech is mixed with sharp, high-amplitude pulses, or when the listener's environment is noisy.

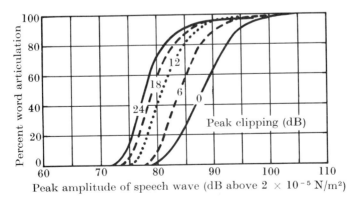

**Fig. 11-36**   Curves showing that clipped speech is more intelligible than unclipped speech if the waves are equated in terms of peak instantaneous amplitude.[27]

The importance of the consonants is emphasized further by the fact that only 2 dB of center clipping reduces the articulation score considerably. With center clipping, all signals below a given level (2 dB in this instance) are discarded.

Phase distortion is not very serious in most acoustical systems; however, it can become important in a long circuit having many networks in tandem. Phase-distortion effects are more readily noticed in speech than in music transmission.[28]

Figure 11-37 summarizes an interesting experiment in which the effects of frequency distortion on speech intelligibility were determined. The curves

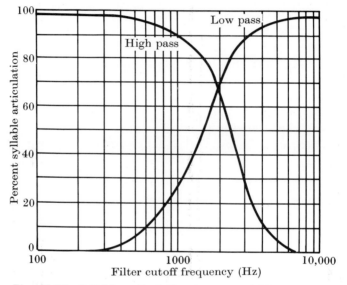

**Fig. II-37**  Syllable articulation versus variable cutoff frequencies of high-pass and low-pass filters.[23]

represent the loci of the variable cutoff frequencies of high-pass and low-pass filters. For example, if the high-pass filter eliminates all frequencies below 1000 Hz, the articulation score is 90 percent. As was shown in Fig. 11-32, most of the energy is in the frequencies below 1000 Hz; yet it now appears that the low frequencies are relatively unimportant. If, on the other hand, the low-pass filter eliminates all frequencies above 1000 Hz, the articulation score drops to about 25 percent. Thus, it is the high frequencies that are essential to the understanding of speech, even though they are relatively weak.

Remember that speech patterns contain mixtures of fundamental and harmonic frequencies. It is the pattern of harmonic frequencies that must be transmitted if the sound is to retain its distinct meaning.

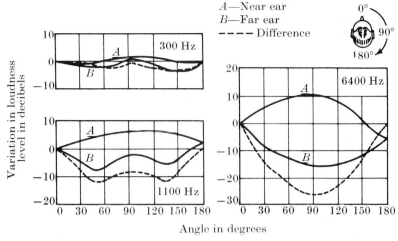

**Fig. 11-38**  Variation in loudness level as a sound source is rotated in a horizontal plane around the head.[18]

## LOCALIZATION

The directive effect of the hearing sense is called *localization*. It is the process by which a listener determines the location of a sound source. For a plane progressive sound wave, assuming that the listener's head position is fixed, there are three factors that assist in angular localization. These are phase difference, loudness difference, and quality differences in the sounds received by the two ears.

Figure 11-38 shows how the loudness level of sounds varies at the separate

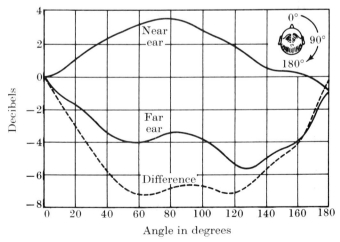

**Fig. 11-39**  Variation in loudness as a speech source is rotated in a horizontal plane around the head.[18]

ears, for pure tones, as the sound source is moved in a horizontal plane around the head. The same effect for speech is shown in Fig. 11-39. When the quality of sound is different from various loudspeakers, localization tends toward the source giving the most natural reproduction.[18]

## AUDITORY ADAPTATION, FATIGUE, AND IMPAIRMENT

When any human sense has been exposed to a stimulus for a certain length of time, it tends to become less sensitive to the stimulus. This phenomenon is known as *adaptation*.[17] When a pure tone is presented to the ear, there is a rapid decrease in the apparent loudness of the tone, followed by a gentle decrease requiring several minutes. Recovery is usually rapid when the tone is removed.

Prolonged exposure to a sound can produce a condition in which the auditory sense takes a long time to recover its initial sensitivity. This condition is called *auditory fatigue*.[17] Experiments have shown that it is a function of frequency, intensity, and duration of the stimulus. Auditory fatigue is greater for high than for low frequencies, and it affects the ability to hear frequencies higher than that of the fatiguing sound.

High sound intensities and long exposure times, as in some industrial environments, can produce permanent hearing impairment. Sound intensities of the order of 130 dB produce temporary hearing losses lasting for a day or more. It is well known that exposure to very intense sounds (160 dB), as from cannon fire or explosives, can produce permanent hearing damage, even though the sound is of short duration. Typically, there is severe hearing loss in the 3000- to 6000-Hz range.

## 11-3. CENTRAL PROCESSES

There are a number of basic functions involved in any complex human activity. Information is received, or sensed. It is stored in the memory or retrieved from it during all phases of the activity. Information is processed and judgments are formed; the judgments lead to decisions which result in action functions, either physical control or communication.[29] The functions of storing, retrieving, and processing information, called *central processes*, have been under intensive study in recent years. Results of this work are providing better guides to designing equipment and operating procedures for optimum overall performance.

Containing of the order of $10^{10}$ neurons, the central nervous system is far more elaborate and complex than any mechanism man has ever developed. There are no definitions of what the central nervous system is supposed to do, there are no circuit diagrams for it, and it does not lend itself to direct measurement. Faced with a difficult challenge at best, the experimenter may have the further problem of separating the man's performance from that of a man-machine combination being observed.[30]

## INFORMATION THEORY

The concept of information theory has proved useful in the measurement of information and the rates at which man can receive and use it. In this theory, information is measured in binary digits or *bits*. If a signal can have a number of alternative states, and if these states are equally probable, the amount of information in bits is given by

$$H = \log_2 n,$$

where $n$ is the number of alternative states. To illustrate, suppose that the message is conveyed by lighting either of two lamps. Then, $n = 2$, and $H = \log_2 2 = 1$ bit of information. Similarly, four alternative states carry two bits of information, and eight alternative states give a three-bit message. Reference 29 describes the method for determining the total amount of information when the probabilities of the alternative events or signal states are unequal.

The following paragraphs describe some interesting estimates and measurements of human capacities which have been facilitated by information theory.

## ESTIMATES OF HUMAN CHANNEL CAPACITIES

The *channel capacity* of a human sense can be defined as the upper limit of the rate at which information can be received by that sense. Studies in this field can suggest better ways of presenting information to people and for setting the upper limits on information rates.

The variable properties of a stimulus, such as the loudness of a sound or the hue of a light, are called *stimulus dimensions*. Human judgments of stimulus dimensions can be made either on a relative basis, as when one musical tone is compared with another, or on an absolute basis. An absolute judgment, with no reference for comparison, is far more difficult than a relative one. People can detect huge numbers of color differences on a relative basis when the stimulus dimensions of hue, brightness, and saturation are varied; however, information usually is presented in practical systems in ways requiring absolute judgments.

Figure 11-40 summarizes estimates of the numbers of levels of various stimulus dimensions which people can identify on an absolute basis, and the corresponding amount of information in bits. Note that, in general, people can identify about 4 to 9 levels of single stimulus dimensions; but the number of levels identified can be markedly greater when combinations of dimensions are used, reaching 150 when 6 dimensions of sound are involved.

An estimate has been made of the amount of information conveyed in speech.[31] Measurements were made of the reading rates of people who read at various speeds, using lists of words drawn from vocabularies containing from 2 to 5000 words. The highest observed information rate was 43 bits/second. It is known from other experiments that reading aloud is the means by which man can communicate fastest—faster, for example, than by typing, playing the piano, or tracking. This seems to be the upper limit for the processing of information by a human channel.

| Sensory modality and stimulus dimension | No. of levels which can be discriminated on absolute basis | No. of bits of information transmitted (H)* |
|---|---|---|
| Vision: single dimensions | | |
|    Pointer position on linear scale | 9 | 3.1 |
|     Short exposure | 10 | 3.2 |
|     Long exposure | 15 | 3.9 |
|    Visual size | 7 | 2.8 |
|    Hue | 9 | 3.1 |
|    Brightness | 5 | 2.3 |
| Vision: combinations of dimensions | | |
|    Size, brightness, and hue† | 17 | 4.1 |
|    Hue and saturation | 11–15 | 3.5–3.9 |
|    Position of dot in a square | 24 | 4.6 |
| Audition: single dimensions | | |
|    Pure tones | 5 | 2.3 |
|    Loudness | 5 | 2.3 |
| Audition: combination of dimensions | | |
|    Combination of six variables‡ | 150 | 7.2 |
| Odor: single dimension | 4 | 2.0 |
| Odor: combination of dimensions | | |
|    Kind, intensity, and number | 16 | 4.0 |
| Taste | | |
|    Saltiness | 4 | 1.9 |
|    Sweetness | 3 | 1.7 |

**Fig. 11-40** The amounts of information in absolute judgments of various stimulus dimensions.[29]

---

    * Since the number of levels is rounded to the nearest whole number, the number of bits does not necessarily correspond exactly.

    † Size, brightness, and hue were varied concomitantly, rather than being combined in the various possible combinations.

    ‡ The combination of six auditory variables included frequency, intensity, rate of interruption, on-time fraction, total duration, and spatial location.

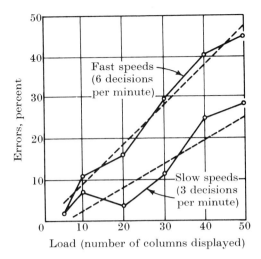

**Fig. 11-41** Effects of increasing load (number of channels used) upon errors, for two decision rates.[29]

## EFFECTS OF LOAD AND SPEED ON ERROR RATES

A number of experiments have been done to determine error rate versus load (the number of information channels to be scanned), error rate versus speed of presentation, and error rate versus load and speed combined.[29] Figures 11-41 to 11-43 summarize results from some of these studies.

Figure 11-41 shows the relationship between error rate and load, as

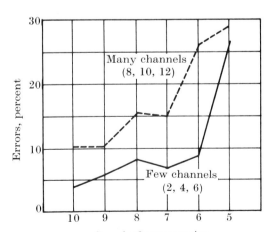

**Fig. 11-42** Effects of speed of presentation upon errors, for two load levels.[29]

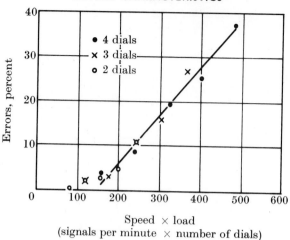

Speed × load
(signals per minute × number of dials)

**Fig. II-43**   Relationship between error rate and the product of speed and load.[29]

represented by the numbers of columns (containing numerical counters) which were scanned visually by the test subjects, for two decision rates.

Figure 11-42 shows error rate versus speed of presentation, for two load levels. Studies have shown that the relationship between error rate and the product of load and speed is linear, as in Fig. 11-43.

## TIMING

The timing of signals has been found to be a significant factor in human response. Suppose that an operator has just responded to a signal and then is presented with another signal. If the second signal follows the first response by a very short interval, e.g., less than 0.5 s, it is likely that the operator will give a delayed or incorrect response, or that he will miss the signal entirely. It has been found that some operators perform better under these conditions if they are given a means of regulating the interval between signals—lengthening the very short intervals, and shortening the very long ones. It might be impossible to provide such a feature in a practical system.

## MULTIPLE INPUTS

Although the foregoing descriptions relate mainly to visual inputs occurring singly, typical work situations may involve a number of inputs to either the visual or auditory sense, or to both. Some results of studies of the effects of multiple inputs[32] are outlined next.

When two auditory inputs of the same intensity arrive simultaneously, the listener's efficiency in detecting a desired message is less than 50 percent.

However, if one message begins slightly later than the other, the listener is most likely to identify the first one. When there is a distinct intensity difference, the listener will favor the more intense signal, even though it may arrive later.

Performance of subjects presented with two simultaneous visual tasks suggests that they tend to devote their attention to one of the tasks and to ignore the other. Where there are competing inputs to the auditory and visual senses, the auditory sense is affected adversely to a lesser degree than the visual sense.

A number of investigators have found that an operator performs better when the same information is presented simultaneously through visual and auditory channels than when it is presented through only one of these channels. Furthermore, performance holds up very much better throughout a long session with the dual inputs. In an experiment involving visual (color-coded) and auditory (tone-coded) signals, there were 89 percent correct responses to visual signals, 91 percent to auditory signals, and 95 percent to the combined signals.[33]

## INTERACTIONS BETWEEN ENVIRONMENT AND MULTIPLE-TASK PERFORMANCE

As in this chapter, human engineering texts describe the performance of the senses in terms of threshold stimulus levels, the thresholds being measured under ideal conditions with subjects having only one task. Handbooks generally give tables of recommended minimum lighting levels and maximum noise levels, as well as limits for other environmental factors. These, too, are based on the concept of a person with a single task. With these references, physical designers are likely to produce work arrangements and routines in which the operators cannot give adequate performance in complex tasks.

There has been a growing appreciation among researchers that the performance of complex tasks can be enhanced through use of higher lighting intensities, lower noise levels, etc., compared to those now listed. Of fundamental importance to the success of complex man-machine systems, this discovery is so new that it is not mentioned in the current references for equipment designers. As an example of the findings in this field, suppose that a man performs a visual task, and that the lighting intensity has been raised to a value permitting error-free work. At this point, the man is given an additional task, such as listening to a voice signal on a noisy channel. Although the man's performance of the visual task may drop due to the interfering effect of the second task, raising the illumination intensity still further brings the visual performance up toward the original level.

An important conclusion from the study of multiple tasks is that the operator's channel capacity should be kept fully occupied when tests are being made, for example, to determine which of two displays is the best.

It should be emphasized that each element of a complex job should be made as simple, straightforward, and "natural" as possible—natural in the sense that there should be an expected or obvious relationship between an action and its result.[30] More is said about the last point in Chapter 12.

## JUDGMENTS

In recent years, a great deal of effort has been devoted to the study of judgmental processes most likely to yield optimum decisions. This is an inter-disciplinary effort with psychologists, mathematicians, operations analysts, economists, and others playing active roles. Findings from these studies should be useful to system planners and to designers of complex displays and operating procedures. Suppose, for example, that there are a number of input data available, perhaps of different degrees of dependability. The planner may have to determine which of these data to use and how to present them. The operating procedures may have to be tailored to weight the inputs according to their relative reliabilities.

Decision theorists use a number of logics. These include programming, the theory of games, and Bayesian decision making which involves statistical methods in the study of thought processes.[34]

## 11-4. OTHER HUMAN CHARACTERISTICS

In the development of any device, machine, or system, it is essential that the designer consider all man-machine interfaces with respect to human body dimensions, speed and range of motion of body members, and muscle strength. In other words, the machine must be designed to fit its users. This is not only a matter of personal comfort; it also may be a serious factor in the proper operation of the system, customer satisfaction, efficiency of the man-machine combination, and even the health and personal safety of the operator.

Although the foregoing statements would seem obvious, this basic design necessity is often overlooked entirely, or the designer misapplies the under-lying principles or uses the wrong data. In consequence, a myriad of man-machine situations have not met their original goals. It is easy to find examples. A bomber was designed with an escape hatch too small for a man wearing a parachute. In the manufacture of communications equipment, a repetitive operation performed by women using long-nose pliers resulted in numerous complaints of sore hands because the tool had been designed for use by men. An aircraft gun-charging handle was designed so that a large, bare hand would fit easily inside the grip opening. However, the handle grip opening was not large enough for a gloved hand, although heavy gloves are often needed by military fliers at high altitudes.

There is considerable evidence that many motor vehicle accidents are more the result of designer failure than operator error in that the designer may not have considered an important human body dimension, or he may not have provided adjustments for the range of this dimension among the population. Of course, there are many situations in which some humans do not have sufficient muscular strength to avert disaster.

## HUMAN BODY MEASUREMENTS

The field of *anthropometry* is concerned with the measurement of human body dimensions, speed and range of body movements, and muscle strength.

Body dimensions vary widely between different racial groups. A fighter aircraft designed for American pilots is difficult for the smaller Asiatic pilots to operate unless it is extensively modified. The overhead (ceiling) height inside Japanese naval vessels is uncomfortably low by American standards.

Body measurements tend to become larger from generation to generation. The average World War II soldier was 1.8 cm taller and 6 kg heavier than his World War I predecessor. This trend is continuing, with a projected increase of almost 5 cm in the height of young adults of the year 2000, as compared with those of 1940, as shown in Fig. 11-44. Current dimensions are in about the center of the ranges shown.

Men in different occupations do not have the same dimensions. College men tend to be larger than those who do not go to college. Bomber pilots average 1.5 cm taller and 3 kg heavier than fighter pilots. In the same age group, truck drivers have quite different measurements from research workers. In any large occupational group, a given measurement has a normal, Gaussian distribution, Fig. 11-45.

The designer must avoid committing a blunder that has ruined many designs—that of designing for a man having average body dimensions. There is no man having all average measurements. It is claimed that less than 4 percent of the population are "average" in as many as three uncorrelated dimensions, such as height, hand breadth, and eye spacing.[36] Only about 1 percent of the population are "average" in as many as four dimensions, even when correlated dimensions such as height, weight, and chest circumference are examined. The body measurements of any selected group, specialized trade, or occupation are not representative of measurements taken on the population as a whole.

Figure 11-44 is an example of some of the detailed measurements which are frequently needed by equipment designers. The changes shown in the figure emphasize the necessity of using recent measurements. Reference 35 contains extensive compilations of current anthropometric data. Chapter 12 includes discussions of how these data are used in equipment design.

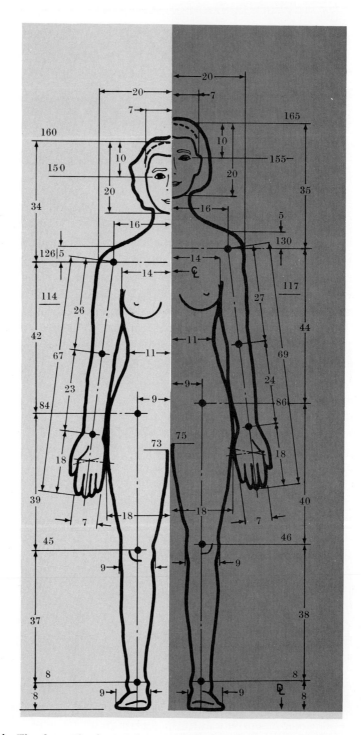

**Fig. 11-44** The dramatic changes in average male and female body dimensions over the

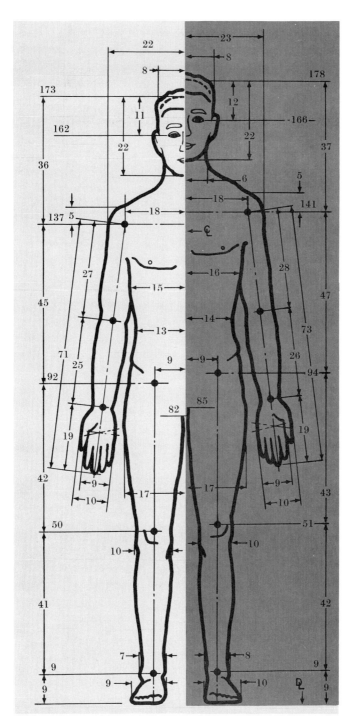

period from about 1940 projected to the year 2000. All dimensions are in centimeters.[37]

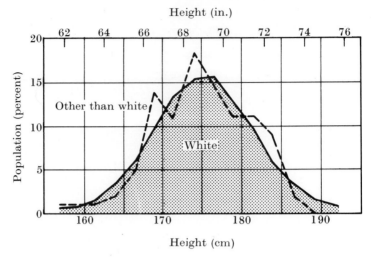

**Fig. 11-45**   The "normal" bell-shaped curve for heights of 5911 white and 173 nonwhite Navy recruits.[35]

## THE TACTUAL SENSE

The touch or tactual sense yields four separate sensations: pressure, pain, cold, and warmth. It appears that the skin contains specific neural receptors for each of these senses. For example, the fingertips rank with the tip of the tongue as the most pressure-sensitive spots of the body, but they are relatively insensitive to pain.

Normally, we are interested in the tactual sense primarily in its capacity as an identifier of the shape, size, texture, etc., of objects and surfaces. The palms of the hands, undersurfaces of fingers, the tip of the tongue, and the lips are especially sensitive in this regard.

## THE KINESTHETIC SENSE

The kinesthetic sense provides a feedback mechanism to give us knowledge of the movements and positions of various parts of the body. It is the sense that makes it possible for a person to lift a spoon to his lips with his eyes closed, or for an expert tennis player to serve faultlessly, time after time. The visual sense, and other senses, provide some of the information, but the principal source is kinesthesis, or "muscle sense." This sense gives us information about our posture, position of limbs, etc., and provides impulses that coordinate all of the body parts involved in complex actions such as walking or running.

## THE SENSE OF BALANCE

Equilibrium is an essential sense which functions with kinesthesis to maintain body posture under static and dynamic conditions. The labyrinthine organs in the inner ear (Fig. 11-23) provide the sensory data for this function. Each labyrinth has three branches, called *semicircular canals*, which lie at approximately right angles to each other, giving a three-dimensional coordinate system. The canals contain a watery fluid that flows through one or more canals when the head is moved. This flow causes bending of tiny hair-tuft nerve endings, causing the initiation of nerve impulses. The semicircular canals respond only to acceleration.

Two structures called the *vestibular sacs*, also located in the inner ear, are important to the maintenance of posture. The sacs contain hairlike nerve endings, which have tiny crystals of calcium carbonate at their ends, embedded in a gelatinous mass. Apparently, the "loaded" hair cells are sensitive to gravitational pull and, thus, provide static posture information.

## REACTION TIME

*Reaction time* is the interval between the presentation of a stimulus and the completion of the operator's response. It is the sum of the times required for sensing the stimulus, for deciding what response to make, and for making the response.

Sensing time is affected by the strength and duration of the stimulus and by which human input channel is used. The time required for decision is short, e.g., 0.2 s, when the decision is simple, becoming longer when the decision is complex. Response time depends upon the complexity of the response and upon the body member involved.

Figure 11-46 lists typical reaction times to various single stimuli of intermediate intensity. This is defined as *simple reaction time*.

There is a marked increase in reaction time when a person must give a

| *Stimulation* | *Reaction time* (ms) |
|---|---|
| Visual | 180 |
| Auditory | 140 |
| Tactual | 140 |
| Pain | 900 |
| Cold | 150 |
| Warmth | 180 |
| Taste | 300 to 1000 |

**Fig. 11-46**  Simple reaction times for various senses.

different response to each of several alternative stimuli. Generally, the time increases as the logarithm of the number of choices which must be made.

Reaction time is shorter for a person who is highly motivated. When a stimulus is preceded by a warning signal, there is also a marked shortening of reaction time. For example, reaction time may be lowered by about 50 ms when a warning signal precedes the stimulus by one to two seconds.

Reaction time is essentially constant for mature people until they reach the age of 60 or so; then it begins to increase slowly. Generally, men tend to have slightly faster reactions than do women.

## MOVEMENTS

Muscles spanning a joint or controlling a limb usually are arranged in two opposing groups, one of which moves the limb in one direction, and the other in the opposite direction. There are primitive nervous connections that link these opposing muscle groups in pairs, so that when one group is contracting, the other automatically relaxes. There are also overriding controls that can cause both muscle groups to contract simultaneously, thus fixing the joint or limb.

This gives rise to two broad types of motion:

1. *Moving fixations*—In motions of this kind, the opposing muscles are in tension. This causes a waste of energy, but it tends to smooth the motion. Practice reduces the tension and makes the motion less tiring.

2. *Ballistic movements*—These motions are typified by rapid, often reciprocating, movements of a limb, in which there are alternate bursts of activity in two opposing muscle groups. These actions are separated by intervals in which the limb is swinging under its own momentum. These features can be recognized in many complex, skilled movements, such as hitting a baseball, swinging a sledge hammer, or kicking a football.

The briefest contraction of a muscle lasts for about 0.05 s, and about the same time must elapse after the muscle has relaxed before it can contract again. This puts a limit of about 10 per second on the frequency with which a repetitive movement, such as tapping a finger or opening and closing the lips, can be performed. Cranking movements can be performed at about 0.6 times the rate for a reciprocating movement of the same amplitude.

Visual positioning movements are nonrepetitive ones in which a person moves an object from one position to another. The operator can see the results of his movement, compared to the target location, and eventually will be exactly on target. Driving an automobile requires a continuous sequence of visual positioning movements.

The total time required to execute a visual positioning movement has three

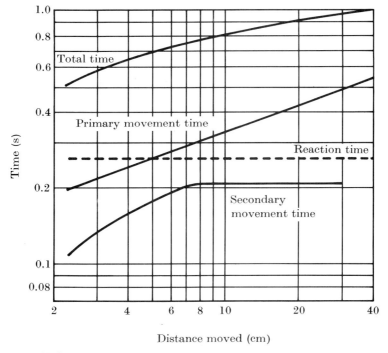

**Fig. 11-47** Time taken for visual-positioning movements through various distances.[38]

components: the *reaction time* to a starting signal, the *primary movement time* required to make the major movement toward the goal, and the *secondary movement time* which is necessary for making small final adjustments. Figure 11-47 shows the results of an experiment in which a subject was required to move a knob laterally in a slot from one mark to another in the least time. Note that the reaction time is independent of the distance between marks, the primary movement time increases with extent of movement, and the secondary movement time increases for small movements and then becomes independent of the extent of movement. Note especially the relatively small increase in the total time required when the extent of movement changes from 2 to 40 cm.

Figure 11-48 shows the times required (for different distances) for an

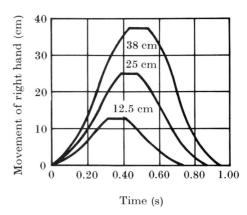

**Fig. 11-48** Movement of the right hand through varying distances between mechanical stops.[39]

operator to move his hand from an initial position to some other position, pick up a small object, and return his hand to the starting point. This is typical of many control panel operations, such as operation of a toggle switch. (Note that the maximum distance is still within easy reach.) As with the straight-line motion discussed earlier, the total time for this operation does not increase very much as the range becomes greater.

## WEIGHT-HANDLING CAPACITY

Figure 11-49 shows the relationship between the maximum weight of an object and the height to which it can be lifted without a feeling of possible injury and when fatigue is not a factor. The data represent young men of the 5th percentile in lifting strength and, therefore, would be a safe guide for use with all young men. The curve can be used with regard to objects of any convenient size and shape, as long as there is ample clearance around the man.

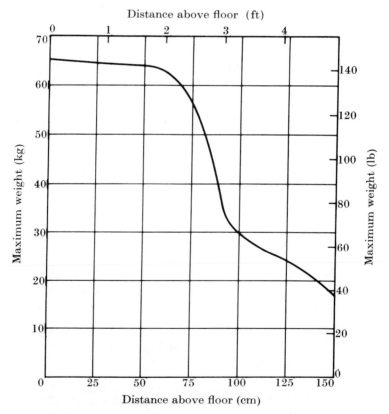

**Fig. 11-49**  Maximum weight of an object versus the height to which it can be lifted comfortably.[40]

However, for maximum comfort and safety, and especially when fatigue may be a factor, it is recommended that an upper limit of about 22 kg (50 pounds) be used.

## FORCES THE BODY CAN EXERT

There are many situations in man-machine systems in which the man must move levers, turn wheels, or depress foot pedals. Of course, the design must not require the man to overtax his strength. Men vary widely in physical strength. In addition, the force a man can exert depends upon the relative direction in which the force is to be applied and upon the body posture. Generally, a man can pull a control toward his body with considerably more force than he can push it; this is because his biceps muscle comes into play. The reverse may be true, however, if maximum use is made of body weight and the back or leg muscles.

With the arm alone, a man can lift greater weights with the palm up than with the palm down. Twenty-seven kilograms (270 newtons, or 60 pounds) is the maximum weight that can be lifted by the arm alone. Legs can exert greater forces in extending than in bending. By itself, the leg can exert a force of about 180 newtons (40 pounds), but this rises to about 2000 newtons (450 pounds) for short periods if a backrest is provided and other body components are used. A man's maximum squeezing or gripping force is about 450 newtons (100 pounds). It is greater for the "skilled" hand (i.e., the right hand for a right-handed man) than for the other hand.

## 11-5. EFFECTS OF ENVIRONMENT ON MAN

Although machines can be designed to work in severe environments, human performance may be badly degraded when critical environmental factors vary beyond some rather narrow limits. Before planning any man-machine system, the designer must know in detail what the working environment will be. An obvious reason is that special measures may be needed to modify the external environment to make the man's situation tolerable. In most situations, the environmental factors of principal concern to the physical designer are lighting, noise, vibration, temperature, and humidity.

## TEMPERATURE AND HUMIDITY

When engaged in light activity, the human body dissipates between 100 and 200 watts. Walking up a flight of stairs can increase the dissipation to over 1000 watts.

The body normally regulates its internal temperature at about 37.0°C (98.6°F). Heat generated in the body is being continually lost through the skin and lungs. When the air temperature has risen to the point where it equals the skin temperature, the body is no longer able to lose heat by conduction and convection, but must depend instead upon the evaporation of sweat. If, in addition, the humidity is increased until the air is saturated, sweat no longer evaporates, and the body begins to store its heat. This results in an increase in body temperature, first to a point of marked discomfort, then to a point of inefficiency, and finally to the point of death.

Figure 11-50 is helpful in describing the interrelated effects of temperature and relative humidity on human comfort and efficiency. The terms to be used here are defined as follows. *Temperature, air temperature, ambient air temperature, and dry-bulb temperature* all have the same meaning. All of them will

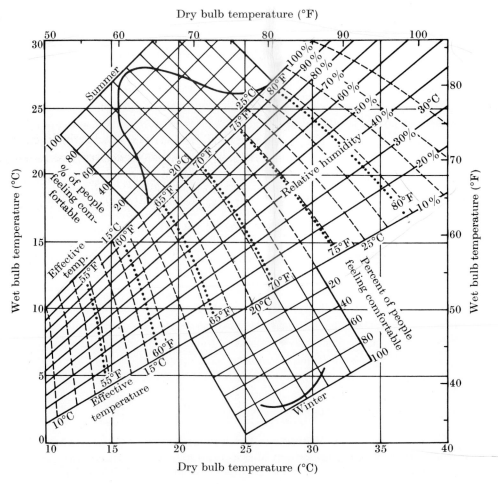

**Fig. 11-50**  The revised ASHRAE comfort chart, adapted for use with the Celsius temperature scale.[41]

be encountered in discussions of atmospheric effects and their control. *Wet-bulb temperature* is indicated by a thermometer whose bulb is surrounded by a water-soaked wick. The water is evaporated by fast-moving air, and the indicated temperature depends upon the rate of evaporation. Therefore, wet-bulb temperature must be the same as dry-bulb temperature when the air is saturated with water, that is, when the humidity is 100 percent. *Humidity, absolute humidity*, and *moisture content* are measures of the amount of water vapor in a specific volume of air. *Relative humidity* (RH) is the ratio between absolute humidity and the saturated value at a given temperature, expressed in percent. The amount of water required to saturate the air increases with dry-bulb temperature.

The straight lines in Fig. 11-50 that slant upward toward the right are the loci of constant relative humidity. On the uppermost line, the dry-bulb and wet-bulb temperatures are the same, so that this line represents 100 percent relative humidity. The American Society of Heating, Refrigerating and Air-Conditioning Engineers conducted extensive experiments on test subjects with various combinations of temperature and relative humidity. From these tests came the dashed and dotted *effective temperature* lines, those that slant downward toward the right. It was found that a person feels about the same at all combinations of temperature and relative humidity that lie on the same effective temperature line. As shown, the effective temperature is the same as the actual temperature at 100 percent RH. At the top and bottom of the chart are shown the regions of greatest comfort for summer and winter, respectively. This chart, as well as the temperature-humidity index to be discussed next, have been developed in the United States using the Fahrenheit temperature scale. To be consistent with SI units, they are adapted here for use with the Celsius scale with cross-references to Fahrenheit values where appropriate.

Suppose that we wished to regulate the conditions in an office to secure an effective temperature of 22°C (71.6°F). We note that this could be obtained with combinations ranging from a dry-bulb temperature of 22°C at 100 percent RH, to a dry-bulb temperature of almost 29°C at 10 percent RH. A good choice would be a combination in the region of 25°C and 50 percent RH. Note that as the humidity is reduced below 50 percent, additional heating units are required to maintain the effective temperature. Of course, if the environment is naturally dry, attainment of 50 percent RH may also be costly. It is clear that air-conditioning engineers are often required to make trade-offs between the costs of heating and of humidifying, while maintaining the combination within limits that are acceptable to most people. The effective temperature has been criticized because it does not take into account the subjective effects of radiation into or out of wall surfaces.

Related to the effective temperature is the *temperature-humidity index*, or THI, which is often stated in summer weather summaries. The THI may be calculated from the following empirical relations:

$$\text{THI} = 0.4\,[T_d(°\text{C}) + T_w(°\text{C})] + 5 \quad \text{in degrees Celsius}$$

or

$$\text{THI} = 0.4\,[T_d(°\text{F}) + T_w(°\text{F})] + 15 \quad \text{in degrees Fahrenheit}$$

$$(11\text{-}8)$$

where $T_d$ and $T_w$ are the dry- and wet-bulb temperatures, respectively. More accurate but less convenient expressions are

$$\text{THI} = T_d(°\text{C}) - 0.55\,[1 - \text{RH}]\,[T_d(°\text{C}) - 14.4]$$

or

$$\text{THI} = T_d(°\text{F}) - 0.55\,[1 - \text{RH}]\,[T_d(°\text{F}) - 58]$$

$$(11\text{-}9)$$

It can readily be seen that the THI is about the same as the effective temperature. For example, suppose we have

$$T_d = 30°\text{C}$$
$$T_w = 20°\text{C}$$

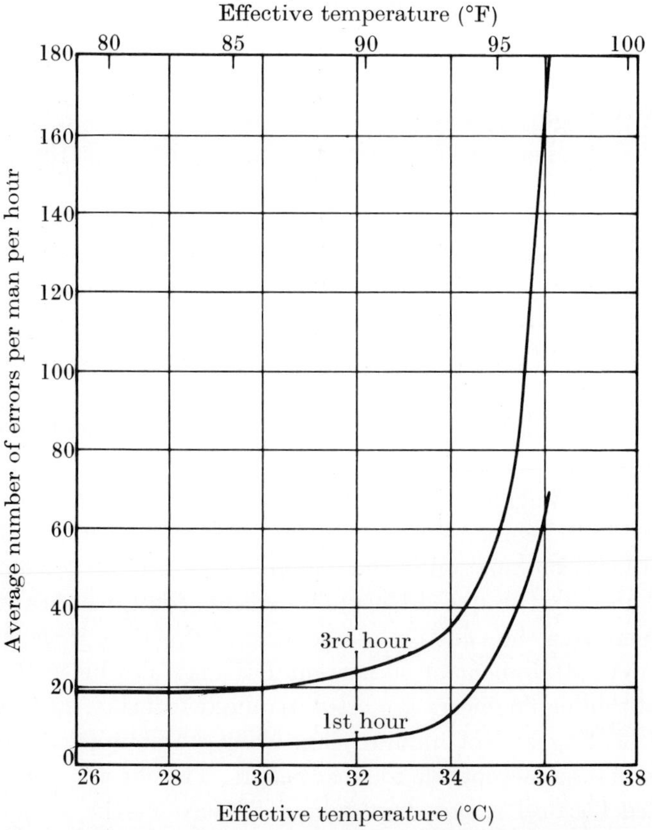

**Fig. 11-51** Performance of radio operators following the first and third hours of operation at various fixed effective temperatures.[42]

Figure 11-46 shows that these temperatures correspond to a relative humidity of 39 percent and an effective temperature of 25°C. For the temperature-humidity index, Eq. (11-8) gives

$$\text{THI} = 0.4(30 + 20) + 5 = 25°C$$

and Eq. (11-9) gives

$$\text{THI} = 30 - 0.55(1 - 0.39)(30 - 14.4) = 24.8°C$$

The temperatures will not always check this closely, but the similarity of results is clear.

Note that the optimum summer conditions fall at slightly higher temperatures than for winter. This is because we become somewhat accustomed to the new conditions as the seasons change. When people move from one location to another having a quite different climate, their bodies adapt gradually. The adaptation process may require several months if the climatic change is large.

Although the comfort zones are of interest, it is of more real importance to the designer to know the effects of temperature and humidity extremes on an operator's efficiency. Figure 11-51 is from a classic experiment by Mackworth, who measured the performance of radio operators working at various constant effective temperatures for long time periods.[42] When the effective temperature was held at 26°C, the average error rate was about 5 per man per hour after the first hour, and 20 per man per hour after the third hour. Note how rapidly both curves rise when the effective temperature is increased above 33°C. Above this temperature, there is a rapid collapse of the operator's performance from the very outset of the task. Further, the progressively greater deterioration, as shown by the skyrocketing upper curve, illustrates the serious effect of high effective temperatures on human endurance.

Figure 11-52 shows the outcome of research into the effects of temperature and humidity on soldiers who marched at 3 mph for 4 hours while carrying 9-kg

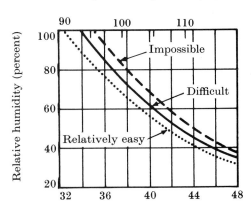

**Fig. 11-52** Relative difficulty of performing a marching task under various temperature and humidity conditions.[43]

packs.[43] The task was judged as relatively easy at elevated temperatures if the air was kept dry, because the body was able to cool itself by the evaporation of sweat. However, when this final cooling mechanism was disabled by 100 percent relative humidity, the task became impossible at an air temperature of about 35°C. Under these conditions, it would not have taken long for the internal body temperature to reach the danger point. Another interesting observation from this figure is that only a few humidity percentage points separate "impossible" from "easy" at the higher temperatures.

Man's efficiency is degraded not only by elevated temperatures, but also by depressed temperatures. When the temperature is reduced to 13°C, there is a slight drop in manual dexterity.[44] The effect is more severe when the temperature drops below 10°C. As might be expected, lowered temperatures raise the accident rate. Munitions workers have been found to have the fewest accidents at 19°C.[45] The accident rate was higher not only at reduced temperatures, but also at higher temperatures. The increases were 37 percent at 11°C and 23 percent at 25°C.

## OTHER ATMOSPHERIC FACTORS

Air motion is an important factor in human comfort and efficiency because it tends to dissipate odors, water vapor from perspiration, and carbon dioxide from breathing. It is recommended that the carbon dioxide content of room air be kept below 0.5 percent. Although people may not notice a concentration of 1 to 2 percent, it does affect their efficiency. Above 3 percent, breathing requires more effort; 5 to 10 percent causes heavy breathing and rapid fatigue; and prolonged exposure to more than 10 percent is fatal.

Reduction of the supply of oxygen to the lungs, even for a short time, has a serious effect upon human comfort and efficiency. At 4900-m (16,000-ft) altitude, a person requires $2\frac{1}{2}$ times as much light for seeing as he does on the ground. He also is affected by hand tremors, and he has difficulty making precise hand movements. Simple exercises and talking become difficult, and speech level drops. The effects of oxygen deficiency, or anoxia, are insidious in that the affected person is not aware of the deterioration in his performance; to the contrary, test subjects say that they feel fine. There is a progressive narrowing of the visual fields and a gradual lowering of light sensitivity when altitude reaches about 1800 m (6000 ft), but the auditory sense is not affected until the altitude reaches about 4600 m (15,000 ft). Pressurization or the supplying of extra oxygen is required to avoid these effects.

Of the many noxious gases which may be found in the air, carbon monoxide is the most important because it is produced, in ever greater quantities, by so many of the tools of civilization. Carbon monoxide goes directly into the blood stream where it enters into chemical combination with the red cells, preventing them from carrying oxygen. For this reason, the effects are similar to those of anoxia due to high altitudes. Five percent carbon monoxide in the blood reduces the visual threshold as much as does an altitude of 2400 to 3000 m (8000 to 10,000 ft). When there is 1 part carbon monoxide in 10,000 in the air, people show no symptoms for about 2 hours; however, 1 hour's exposure to 4 parts in 10,000 is unsafe. At 6 or 7 parts in 10,000, headaches and other symptoms, such as weakness, nausea, and collapse, occur within an hour. Exposure to 35 parts in 10,000 is generally fatal in less than an hour.

## MOTION AND VIBRATION

Experiments indicate that speed alone has little effect on reaction time or on human behavior in general, but accelerations produce dramatic effects. The effects of vibration on human beings are to lower their physiological well-being and, often, to reduce their physical and mental abilities. Both acceleration and vibration effects have been measured.[46]

## INTERRELATION OF ENVIRONMENTAL FACTORS

In dealing with environmental factors, the designer should be wary of so-called "comfortable levels," "tolerable levels," etc., which may be given for the individual factors. In a real man-machine situation, a particular environmental factor, such as the loudness of a sound or the vibration of an instrument panel, may be small and still be unacceptable to the operator. This is because the operator is affected by the interaction of all existing environmental quantities and the complexities and stresses stemming from his task. Thus, the designer must consider the effects of individual variables on the affected human functions and the total effect of all sources of distraction and discomfort within the context of the man's assignment.

## FATIGUE

Although fatigue cannot be classed as an environmental factor, it is affected by environment. Therefore, the physical designer should have some understanding of it. Because fatigue causes a lowering of human efficiency, the designer should limit the load in order that the man's performance will be adequate throughout the operating period.

A number of characteristics of human behavior are called fatigue. With *receptor fatigue*, the sensitivity of a particular receiving channel is reduced by prolonged, intense stimulation. *Muscle fatigue* results from heavy or sustained muscular activity. A point is reached where the muscles can no longer function until they have been rested. Although neither the receptors nor the muscles are tired, a person who has performed a monotonous task for a long time may find it difficult to continue; this is known as *fatigue due to boredom*. Emotional stress can produce deterioration in performance which has been called fatigue; "combat fatigue" is an example of this *fatigue due to stress*.

## 11-6. EXPERIMENTING WITH PEOPLE

Despite the large amount of experimentation which has been done with man-machine situations, much of the recorded information applies only to the specific experimental conditions and cannot be generalized. The designer with a man-machine problem should always examine the literature to see what others may have done in the area of interest. He is likely to find information that will provide some insight and guidance. Usually, he will have to perform his own experiments before he has all of the essential design data.

Experimenting with people is extremely difficult because man is so complex and variable. Man changes continually through his experiences and may be affected further by his emotional state or his health. Another difficulty with man as an experimental subject is that he is affected by the social setting of the experiment. Consciously or unconsciously, he may try to bias the result in the direction in which he believes the experimenter wants it to go. Man is an inconsistent and unreliable observer and finds it difficult to be objective. For example, consider the unlikelihood that two observers of an automobile accident would give independent accounts agreeing in all important details. The wide differences between people in the keenness of their senses, such as taste, color vision, and the hearing of tones, add further to the difficulty.

The more important methods of studying people include methods of direct observation, methods for the study of accidents and near-accidents, and the experimental method. These methods and some of their subdivisions will be described briefly. Reference 47 contains detailed discussions and numerous interesting examples.

### STUDY BY DIRECT OBSERVATION

The method of direct observation, involving the study of actual situations, may reveal trouble sources, indicate ways of making improvements, or provide essential data for use in a new design. One type of direct observation is the *study of operator opinions*, which can provide valuable insight into problem areas and suggest possible solutions. Caution is necessary on the experimenter's part because an operator may become so accustomed to a system that he is blind to its defects; furthermore, some complaints may reflect personal problems or conflicts having nothing to do with equipment or work methods. Finally, it is difficult to write questions which elicit the desired information without "leading" the subject or suggesting a specific kind of response.

Another kind of direct observational method, called *activity sampling*, requires the recording of what an operator is doing at the ends of equal time intervals, say, every five seconds. It is then possible to plot the distribution of the operator's time among the various parts of the job. This may show that a disproportionate amount of time is devoted to a relatively unimportant work element, or that one of the operator's hands is overburdened while the other is nearly idle, etc.

A highly precise form of activity sampling, called *memomotion study*, employs a motion picture camera. Thus, the activity samples can be much closer together, and the observer can make repeated examinations of each work element. This method can have serious disadvantages in that special preparations must be made, lighting may be too dim for picture taking, and it may be impossible to follow an operator who must move from place to place in doing his work.

Other forms of direct observation employ *process charts, flow diagrams*, and *link analysis*. The process chart employs special symbols to show the various steps, in sequence, which make up a complex operation. The flow chart is a geographical diagram, in two or three dimensions, which follows the physical movement of men and materials through a process.

To the designer of electronic systems, link analysis is perhaps the most useful type of process analysis. In contrast with process charts and flow charts, which apply to sequences in which the same things are always done in a definite order, link analysis applies to complex activities having variable patterns. Automobile driving, aircraft piloting, and many kinds of factory operations are examples. Link analysis uses a chart which expresses the linkages between components according to their relative frequencies. Suppose that an aircraft instrument panel is the object of study. A motion picture can be made of the pilot's eye motions during all phases of an entire flight. From careful study of the pictures, the observer can plot, on a diagram of the panel, the relative frequencies with which the pilot shifts attention from compass to altimeter, or from fuel gauge to airspeed indicator, etc. This may suggest a way in which the instruments can be rearranged for greater pilot efficiency and less fatigue. Another illustration is a work space containing a number of operating positions and men, including operators and various command and liaison personnel. On a floor plan of the room, the observer indicates the relative frequencies with which the people move between pairs of locations in the room. Study of the chart may indicate that a rearrangement of operating positions can reduce lost time and motion, and also minimize the number of path crossings which cause collisions between people.

When it is necessary to reduce operating time to a minimum in a repetitive operation, *micromotion techniques* (time and motion study) may be helpful. The operation usually is filmed with a motion picture camera so that it can be observed repeatedly. The sequence is analyzed in terms of basic work elements, such as searching, selecting, grasping, transporting, holding, etc., and the duration of each element is timed. A careful study of the work pattern is used for redesign of the job, to eliminate unnecessary work elements, or to redistribute the work more efficiently among the hands and feet.[39]

Although operational observation can be very useful, it has the following limitations:

1. The process of observing may influence the person being observed.
2. Operational observing may yield a tangle of data from which it is difficult to extract significant relationships.
3. The observer may examine irrelevant operations because he does not know what is worth observing.
4. Operational observation is usually expensive and time consuming.
5. The findings usually cannot be reduced to general principles for application to other situations. They are valid only for the specific combination that was tested; therefore, the tests must be repeated when a change is made.

A classic experiment,[48] which was initiated in 1927 at the Western Electric Co. in Chicago, illustrates the effects of the observing process on the person being observed. The purpose of the experiment was to answer such questions as: Are rest periods desirable? Is a shorter working day desirable? What effects do wrong or right methods of supervision have on a worker's effectiveness and morale? What are some of the factors that determine an employee's mental attitude?

In the experiment, all working conditions were held as nearly constant as possible, with introduction from time to time of a single variable. Different methods of payment were used. Rest periods were introduced and eliminated. Midmorning meals were introduced. The working day was shortened and lengthened. Some of the test results were startling in that productivity of the group tended to increase no matter what changes were introduced. Changes that would have been objectionable under ordinary circumstances brought higher performance. The inference from these studies was inescapable: the dominant factor in the performance of these employees was their mental attitude. The overshadowing factor of influence on the members of the test group was the fact that someone was interested in them.

## STUDY OF ACCIDENTS AND NEAR-ACCIDENTS

Sometimes called the study of malfunctioning systems, this method can be helpful in locating trouble sources in man-machine systems. For any accident or near-accident, the investigator assembles all available information about the event. Careful study may reveal a factor or pattern leading to discovery of the cause. A variation on this method is the critical-incident technique, in which many people who have used a given equipment or system are asked to recall the details of accidents or near-accidents which they have had with it. The study of malfunctioning systems has limited effectiveness because of the difficulty of reconstructing prior events and because it may depend upon people's recollections.

## STUDY BY THE EXPERIMENTAL METHOD

This method is the best for studying people because it permits precise control of the pertinent variables. The traditional approach to controlled experiments is to hold all factors constant except one, to vary that one in a precisely controlled way, and to record the effect of the variation. A newer approach to controlled experiments uses the simultaneous controlled variation of several factors, making it more applicable to systems research problems.[49,50] This *design of experiments* approach is relatively difficult to plan, but it is closer to realism and can be performed much faster than a series of single-variable experiments.

Obviously, the planning of either single-variable or multivariable experiments must be done in such a way as to suppress or eliminate effects that could bias or invalidate the results. The problem is further complicated by the unpredictability and complexity of people. The following are some of the factors or principles which must be considered.

1. The group of people chosen as test subjects should be representative of the population who will use or operate the final product.
2. In some experimental situations, control groups should be used as checks on the validity of the test results. Suppose, for example, that the effect of a change in working environment on productivity is to be evaluated. Subjects would be divided into two groups: a test group and a control group. Both groups would be put to work in identical environments until they had fully learned the work. A single change would then be made in the environment of the test group, the environment of the control group being held constant. Beyond this point, any change in test group performance, relative to that of the control group, probably would be the result of the change in environment. The word "probably" is used because of possible unanticipated effects. Members of a test group may raise their outputs merely because they know that they are objects of interest, as illustrated by the Western Electric Co. experiment previously cited.

3. The tasks to be performed by test subjects must be clearly defined. In tests of experimental dial designs, quite different results were obtained from use of these three instructions: (1) "Read the dials as accurately as you can." (2) "Read the dials as rapidly as you can." (3) "Read the dials as accurately *and* rapidly as you can."

4. The engineer must decide how closely to duplicate real-life conditions. Simulation in the laboratory offers the advantages of relative ease, economy, and speed. In addition, it provides surer control over the experimental conditions. It is always possible, however, that some real-life factors that would materially affect the results may be inadvertently omitted. On the other hand, the real-life situation is the most expensive and may contain many uncontrolled sources of variance that contaminate the data. The final judgment of how much realism to use must be based on careful consideration of what factors are essential to a useful conclusion. It is reassuring to know that the relative values obtained from well-planned simulation in the laboratory will generally apply to the real-life situation.

5. An experiment can easily be invalidated by overlooking the fact that a person's performance of a specific assignment tends to improve through learning. For instance, if we wanted to compare a number of different hand tools, each designed for the same function, we should try to plan the experiment so that the inevitable effects of learning on test subject performance would not make a real comparison impossible. To minimize the effects of learning or other extraneous variables, the experimenter would select a quantity of test subjects and would have each subject use all tools in different sequences. There are two approaches to developing the sequences: the extraneous effects may be distributed evenly over the experimental conditions, or they may be distributed randomly. In planning an even distribution, the experimenter might use a *Latin square*, such as the following 5 × 5 array:

$$A \quad B \quad C \quad D \quad E$$
$$B \quad A \quad E \quad C \quad D$$
$$C \quad D \quad A \quad E \quad B$$
$$D \quad E \quad B \quad A \quad C$$
$$E \quad C \quad D \quad B \quad A$$

Note that each letter appears only once in each row and column. The letters may be rearranged in many ways without violating this rule. In the hand-tool evaluation, the letters A through E could represent the different tools. The rows would give the sequences in which the tools are to be given to the individual test subjects.

**Example 11.7.** A newly designed radar indicator is to be evaluated by comparing it against four standard equipments. The criterion is the time required for operators to read target range and bearing information from this indicator in comparison with the standard models.

*Solution.* In planning the experiment, the engineer elects to use five operators and five sequences of tape-recorded targets. Each operator is to use each equipment and all five of the target sequences. The engineer appreciates the importance of arranging the tests so that no two operators will be exposed to the five sets of targets in the same sequence. Furthermore, each operator should use the five indicators in a different sequence. These precautions will prevent the operators from using the equipments in I through V order, in ever better states of practice.

The following table shows the experimental plan. A through E are the operators, a through e are the target sequences, I through IV are the standard indicators, and V is the experimental model.

| Operator | I | II | III | IV | V |
|---|---|---|---|---|---|
| A | 9 b | 11 c | 13 e | 3 d | 12 a |
| B | 15 c | 8 e | 21 a | 1 b | 25 d |
| C | 6 a | 7 d | 22 b | 20 e | 17 c |
| D | 19 d | 18 b | 5 c | 24 a | 4 e |
| E | 23 e | 16 a | 10 d | 2 c | 14 b |

The target sequences (a through e) are arranged in a 5 × 5 Latin square. The sequence of test steps is indicated by the numbers 1 through 25, assigned in a random sequence.

The next table gives the observed times in seconds for the tests.

| Operator | I | II | III | IV | V | Average |
|---|---|---|---|---|---|---|
| A | 4.2 | 4.4 | 4.2 | 4.7 | 2.8 | 4.1 |
| B | 4.3 | 4.3 | 4.5 | 4.3 | 2.9 | 4.1 |
| C | 4.5 | 4.7 | 4.8 | 4.3 | 3.0 | 4.3 |
| D | 4.0 | 4.1 | 4.0 | 4.2 | 3.1 | 3.9 |
| E | 4.9 | 5.0 | 5.4 | 5.5 | 2.8 | 4.7 |
| Average | 4.4 | 4.5 | 4.6 | 4.6 | 2.9 | |

In comparing results of this kind, it is important to establish whether the differences are statistically significant. In this case, when the data for the separate indicators are plotted, the times for the new indicator appear markedly lower and more tightly grouped than those for the other indicators. Moreover, an analysis of variance confirms that the differences are, indeed, significant. In other words, it is unlikely that the difference in averages is caused by pure chance.

As suggested earlier, the experimenter's obligations do not end with running the experiment. This is true regardless of the experimental method used. Generally, the mass of recorded data will contain variations from many sources, some relevant and some irrelevant to what is being studied. Unless a thorough and competent evaluation is made of the data, the considerable expense and time used for constructing and doing the experiment go for naught. In most instances, the expensive item is the design and construction of the equipment. Next is the cost of conducting the experiment; this may be the most expensive item when the experiment is lengthy and complex. The analysis of data is typically the least expensive phase in that it usually requires few people and little equipment.

Results in the form of averages are usually insufficient when dealing with the variability of human beings. Statistical methods and various techniques for evaluating experimental data are given in Vol. IV, Chapter 3, and in the references.[24,49-53]

## 11-7. USER PREFERENCE ENGINEERING

Very simply, user preference engineering is the art of determining in an economical manner what people prefer. No competitive business can long survive if its products are not pleasing to the public. User preference is equally important in business situations in which the equipment is provided by the owner for use by his employees. Here, user preference may materially affect the success or efficiency of a man-machine combination, the worker's comfort, or his satisfaction with the job.

A classic example of the neglect of user preference concerns the colors of automobiles. Henry Ford said that the public could have a car of any color "as long as it is black." General Motors then took command of the market by offering a variety of colors.

There is another story of a vacuum cleaner manufacturer who developed a quiet machine. To his consternation, women would not buy it because they had learned to associate noisy vacuum cleaners with good results. Disaster may await the electronic equipment manufacturer who does not check user preference with care before making large quantities of a new item for use by customers.

To determine economically what people prefer, user preference engineering employs the various methods of experimenting with people. Pioneers in this field soon discovered that people cannot give dependable opinions without some actual experience. For example, people were asked whether they would like to have a lighter telephone handset. They indicated general satisfaction with the rather heavy handset then in use. However, when people were asked to try a series of dummy handsets of various weights, they tended to prefer a much lighter one than the then current standard.

Some years ago, someone asked if people would like to have voice dialing. This would be a means whereby a person could speak digits into the telephone and secure a direct response from automatic equipment. Because the necessary equipment was not available (and it still is not), user preference was tested by use of simulation.[54] A number of telephones were connected to a special switchboard, and an operator who could not talk to the caller was trained to perform in a mechanical sequence. The users were told only that their phones had been equipped with voice dialing. Voice dialing was accepted with enthusiasm, even by people who had speech difficulties. These people had less trouble with a "machine" than with human operators, apparently because the speech difficulties were related to confrontations with other people.

In 1955, there were eight colors for telephones being offered on a limited basis. It was important to know what the potential market might be for color telephones, and to obtain data on users' color preferences. A preference study was conducted to determine the most-wanted colors for color telephones in the home. P. D. Bricker gives an interesting table in which the survey results for the original colors are compared to the actual colors ordered from the operating telephone companies during 1955. The apparent overestimation of the demand for yellow was actually a real prediction. Just after the survey was ended, deliveries began to reflect an increase in the demand for yellow.

| | Percent of market | |
| Color | Anticipated | Actual |
| --- | --- | --- |
| Ivory | 37 | 38 |
| Yellow | 16 | 7 |
| Beige | 14 | 16 |
| Green | 13 | 15 |
| Red | 9 | 9 |
| Blue | 6 | 5 |
| Grey | 4 | 6 |
| Brown | 2 | 4 |

A number of careful experiments preceded the design of the pushbutton telephone set.[55] The experiments were designed to answer such questions as: How does pushbutton design influence user speed, accuracy, and preference in keying telephone numbers? What design specifications will maximize these three quantities, and how critical is it to achieve these maxima?

Specially designed universal pushbutton switches, adjustable through a range of force-displacement characteristics, were used in order to determine optimum design. The experimental equipment was arranged to record errors by comparing the keyed number against a punched tape containing the correct number, and to record the elapsed time between the keying of the first and

| Arrangement | Keying time (s) | Percent errors | Ranking for | Ranking against |
|---|---|---|---|---|
| 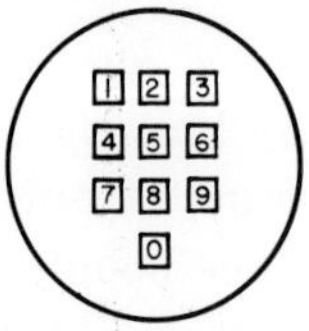 Three-by-three plus one | 6.01 | 2.5 | 3rd | 2nd |
| 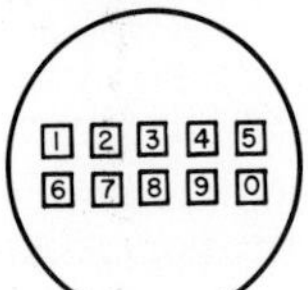 Two horizontal rows | 6.17 | 2.3 | 1st (most) | 4th |
| 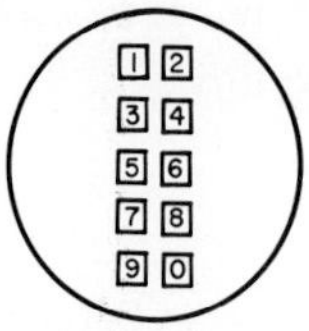 Two vertical columns | 6.12 | 1.3 | 5th (least) | 1st (most) |
| 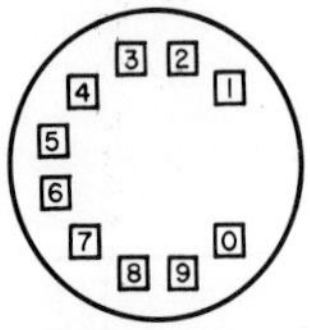 Telephone | 5.90 | 2.0 | 2nd | 5th (least) |
| 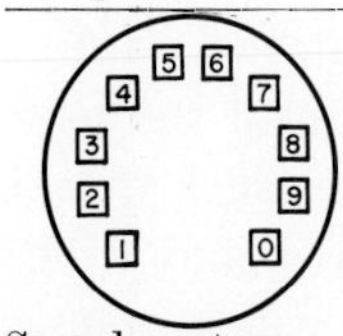 Speedometer | 5.97 | 3.0 | 4th | 3rd |

**Fig. 11-53**  The five arrays of pushbuttons that were studied in the second phase of testing.[55]

seventh digits. The most satisfactory pushbutton switches were found to have a force of 1 to 2 newtons and 0.32 cm of travel. There was no significant improvement in performance when either a slight snap-action or an audible click was provided.

Two sets of tests were made in determining the most satisfactory arrangement of the ten pushbuttons. In the first series, a group of five preferred arrangements were selected from a group of sixteen contenders. Among those eliminated were circular, semicircular, diagonal, triangular, and several block-shaped configurations. In the second phase of testing, comparisons were made of the five preferred arrangements, shown in Fig. 11-53. The differences between the keying times were found to be insignificant; this is also true of the differences in error rates. It is interesting that the arrangement with two horizontal rows of pushbuttons received the largest number of "for" votes and next to the smallest number of "against" votes. On the other hand, the arrangement with two vertical columns was the least preferred and the most opposed. Perhaps this extreme difference in preference is related to the fact that it is easier for the eye to scan a given distance horizontally than vertically, and, of course, people are accustomed to reading in this direction. The "three-by-three plus one" and the two horizontal rows were subjected to further tests because these arrangements offered engineering advantages. The final choice of the three-by-three plus one was made because of its compactness.

An important point emerges from this last illustration. User preference is one of many factors which must be weighed and cross-compared in securing a reasonably balanced design. The best compromise between user preference and, say, mechanical feasibility may necessitate some sacrifice of either or both.

## REFERENCES

1. *IES Lighting Handbook*, 4th ed., New York, Illuminating Engineering Society, 1966. Standard reference on light measurement and design of illumination facilities.

2. Osterberg, G., "Topography of the Layer of Rods and Cones in the Human Retina," *Acta Ophthalmologica*, **13**, Suppl. 6, 103, Copenhagen, Holger Ehlers, 1935. Figure 11-6 by permission.

3. Wertheim, T., "Über die indirekte Sehschärfe," *Zeitschrift für Psychologie*, **7**, 172–187, 1894.

4. Luckiesh, M., and F. K. Moss, *The Science of Seeing*, Princeton, N.J., D. Van Nostrand Co., Inc., 1937. Workings of the visual sense, light measurement, lighting design principles. Figures 11-8, 11-10, 11-11, 11-12, and 11-13 by permission.

5. Burnham, R. W., R. M. Hanes, and C. J. Bartleson, *Color: A Guide to Basic Facts and Concepts*, New York, John Wiley & Sons, Inc., 1963. A compact, concise summary of basic information on the physical nature of color and related subjective effects.

6. Hecht, S., and R. E. Williams, "The Visibility of Monochromatic Radiation and the Absorption Spectrum of Visual Purple," *J. Gen. Physiol.*, **5**, 1–34, 1922, New York, Rockefeller University Press.

7. Judd, D. B., and G. Wyszecki, *Color in Business, Science and Industry*, New York, John Wiley & Sons, Inc., 1963. A clear treatment of color, color vision, color standards, and measurement. Figure 11-16 by permission.

8. Judd, D. B., "Estimation of Chromaticity Differences and Nearest Color Temperature on the Standard ICI Colorimetric Coordinate Systems," *J. Opt. Soc. Amer.*, **26**, 421–426, 1936. Figure 11-17 by permission.

9. *Munsell Book of Color*, Baltimore, Md., Munsell Color Co., 1941. Contains over 1200 removable color chips, based upon the Munsell color system.

10. Jacobson, E., W. C. Granville, and C. E. Foss, *Color Harmony Manual*, 3rd ed., Chicago, Ill., Container Corp. of America, 1948. Contains 680 color samples based upon the Ostwald color system.

11. Nutting, P. G., "Effects of Brightness and Contrast in Vision," *Trans. Illum. Eng. Soc.*, **11**, 939–946, 1916. Figures 11-18 and 11-22 by permission.

12. Hecht, S., C. Haig, and G. Wald, "The Dark Adaptation of Retinal Fields of Different Size and Location," *J. Gen. Physiol.*, **19**, 321–339, 1935, New York, Rockefeller University Press. Figure 11-19 by permission.

13. Luckiesh, M., *Light, Vision and Seeing*, Princeton, N.J., D. Van Nostrand Co., Inc., 1944. A simplified presentation of the relationships and importance of light, vision, and seeing in human efficiency and welfare. Figure 11-21 by permission.

14. Fletcher, H., *Speech and Hearing*, Princeton, N.J., D. Van Nostrand Co., Inc., 1929. Classic text based on early research at Bell Telephone Laboratories. Characteristics of speech, music, and noise; hearing; and perception of speech and music. Figure 11-29 by permission.

15. Pierce, J. R., and E. E. David, Jr., *Man's World of Sound*, Garden City, N.Y., Doubleday and Co., Inc., 1958. An easily read collection of material on speech and hearing and their use in language.

16. von Békésy, G., *Experiments in Hearing*, New York, McGraw-Hill Book Co., 1960. Collection of classic papers by a world-renowned authority on the hearing mechanism.

17. Littler, T. S., *The Physics of the Ear*, New York, The Macmillan Co., 1965. Explanations of the behavior of the hearing mechanism in mathematical terms.

18. Fletcher, H., *Speech and Hearing in Communication*, Princeton, N.J., D. Van Nostrand Co., Inc., 1953. Based on the earlier work, *Speech and Hearing*. Updated in the light of further research. Figures 11-38 and 11-39 by permission.

19. Fletcher, H., and W. A. Munson, "Loudness, Its Definition, Measurement and Calculation," *Bell System Tech. J.*, **12,** 1933, New York, American Telephone and Telegraph Co. Figure 11-25 by permission.

20. Riesz, R. R., "Differential Intensity Sensitivity of the Ear for Pure Tones," *Phys. Rev.*, **31,** 867–875, 1928, New York, American Institute of Physics. Figure 11-27 by permission.

21. Shower, E. G., and R. Biddulph, "Differential Pitch Sensitivity of the Ear," *J. Acoust. Soc. Amer.*, **3,** 275–287, 1931, New York, American Institute of Physics. Figure 11-28 by permission.

22. Hawkins, J. R., and S. S. Stevens, "The Masking of Pure Tones and of Speech by White Noise," *J. Acoust. Soc. Amer.*, **22,** 6–13, 1950, New York, American Institute of Physics.

23. French, N. R., and J. C. Steinberg, "Factors Governing the Intelligibility of Speech Sounds," *J. Acoust. Soc. Amer.*, **19,** 90–119, 1947, New York, American Institute of Physics.

24. Chapanis, A., W. R. Garner, and C. T. Morgan, *Applied Experimental Psychology*, New York, John Wiley & Sons, Inc., 1949. Application of experimental psychology to the design of machines for use by men. Figure 11-33 by permission.

25. Kryter, K. D., "Effects of Ear Protective Devices on the Intelligibility of Speech in Noise," *J. Acoust. Soc. Amer.*, **18,** 413–417, 1946, New York, American Institute of Physics.

26. Licklider, J. C. R., D. Bindra, and I. Pollack, "The Intelligibility of Rectangular Speech Waves," *Amer. J. Psychol.*, **61,** 1–20, 1948, Austin, Texas, University of Texas. Figure 11-35 by permission.

27. Licklider, J. C. R., "Effects of Amplitude Distortion Upon the Intelligibility of Speech," *J. Acoust. Soc. Amer.*, **18,** 429–434, 1946, New York, American Institute of Physics.

28. Steinberg, J. C., and W. A. Munson, "Effects of Distortion on Speech and Music," *Electrical Engineer's Handbook*, edited by H. Pender and K. McIlwain, New York, John Wiley & Sons, Inc., 1950.

29. McCormick, E. J., *Human Factors Engineering*, New York, McGraw-Hill Book Co., 1964. Detailed treatment of human characteristics and man-machine relationships. Research investigations and experimental procedures are covered. Emphasis on systems aspects of design. Figure 11-40 by permission of McGraw-Hill Book Co.

30. Poulton, E. G., "Engineering Psychology," *Annual Review of Psychology*, edited by P. R. Farnsworth, Palo Alto, Calif., Annual Reviews, Inc., 1966.

31. Pierce, J. R., and J. E. Karlin, "Reading Rates and the Information Rate of a Human Channel," *Bell System Tech. J.*, **36,** 1957, New York, American Telephone and Telegraph Co.

32. Mowbray, G. H., and J. W. Gebhard, "Man's Senses as Information Channels," *Report CM-936*, 1958, Silver Spring, Md., Johns Hopkins University, Applied Physics Laboratory.

33. Klemmer, E. T., "Time-Sharing Between Frequency-Coded Auditory and Visual Channels," *J. Exp. Psychol.*, **55**, 229–235, 1958.

34. Shelly, M. W., and G. L. Bryan, editors, *Human Judgments and Optimality*, New York, John Wiley & Sons, Inc., 1964. A broad introduction to the study of human judgments, containing articles by 21 authors who work in a number of disciplines. Extensive bibliographies.

35. Damon, A., H. W. Stoudt, and R. A. McFarland, *The Human Body in Equipment Design*, Cambridge, Mass., Harvard University Press, 1966. Application of anthropometrics and biomechanics in equipment design. Tables of anthropometric and biomechanical data. Figure 11-45 by permission.

36. Daniels, G. S., and E. Churchill, "The 'Average Man'?" *Technical Note WCRD 53-7*, Wright Air Development Center, Air Research and Development Command, USAF, Wright-Patterson Air Force Base, Ohio, 1952.

37. Dreyfuss, H., *Industrial Design Vol. 5*, New York, published by the author. Figure 11-44 by permission.

38. Brown, J. S., and A. T. Slater-Hammel, "Discrete Movements in the Horizontal Plane as a Function of Their Length and Direction," *J. Exp. Psychol.*, **39**, 84–95, 1949.

39. Barnes, R. M., *Motion and Time Study*, 5th ed., New York, John Wiley & Sons, Inc., 1963. The study and measurement of work. Design of tools, methods, and work situations. Figure 11-48 by permission.

40. Emanuel, I., J. W. Chaffee, and J. Wing, "A Study of Human Weight-Lifting Capabilities for Loading Ammunition Into the F-86H Aircraft," *WADC Technical Report 56-367*, 1956, Aero Medical Laboratory, Wright Air Development Center, Wright-Patterson Air Force Base, Ohio.

41. *ASHRAE Guide and Data Book, Fundamentals and Equipment*, New York, Am. Soc. of Heating, Refrig. and Air-Cond. Engrs., Inc., 1963. Exhaustive compilation of data on atmospheric effects; descriptions and applications of equipment for heating, refrigerating, and air-conditioning. Figure 11-50 by permission.

42. Mackworth, N. H., "Effects of Heat on Wireless Telegraph Operators Hearing and Recording Morse Messages," *Brit. J. Industr. Med.*, **3**, 143–158, 1946, London, British Medical Ass'n.

43. Eichna, L. W., W. F. Ashe, W. B. Bean, and W. B. Shelley, "The Upper Limits of Environmental Heat and Humidity Tolerated by Acclimatized Men Working in Hot Environments," *Journal of Industrial Hygiene and Toxicology*, **27**, 59–84, 1945, Detroit, Amer. Indus. and Hygiene Ass'n.

44. Clark, R. E., "The Limiting Hand Skin Temperature for Unaffected Manual Performance in the Cold," *PB Report 29*, U.S. Army Quartermaster Research and Engineering Center, Oct., 1959.

45. Vernon, H. M., *Accidents and Their Prevention*, Cambridge, Cambridge University Press, 1936. Factors which make accidents likely, and how to control them.

46. Morgan, C. T., J. S. Cook, III, A. Chapanis, and M. W. Lund, *Human Engineering Guide to Equipment Design*, New York, McGraw-Hill Book Co., 1963. Thorough and authoritative guide to human factors engineering design practices.

47. Chapanis, A., *Research Techniques in Human Engineering*, Baltimore, The Johns Hopkins Press, 1959. Detailed treatment of the principal methods of experimenting with people.

48. Pennock, G. A., "Industrial Research at Hawthorne," *Personnel Journal*, **8,** 296–313, 1930, Chicago, Western Electric Co., Inc.

49. Cox, D. R., *Planning of Experiments*, New York, John Wiley & Sons, Inc., 1958. Written to help the experimental worker in the sound planning of experiments. Avoids statistical and mathematical technicalities.

50. Davies, O. L., *The Design and Analysis of Industrial Experiments*, New York, Hafner Publishing Co., Inc., 1954.

51. Davies, O. L., *Statistical Methods in Research and Production*, New York, Hafner Publishing Co., Inc., 1957.

52. Hoel, P. G., *Introduction to Mathematical Statistics*, 3rd ed., New York, John Wiley & Sons, Inc., 1962. A first course in probability and statistics. Contains numerous examples of various degrees of difficulty.

53. McNemar, Q., *Psychological Statistics*, New York, John Wiley & Sons, Inc., 1949. Statistical techniques of particular usefulness in psychological experimenting.

54. Karlin, J. E., and R. K. Potter, "Preference Research," *Bell Laboratories Record*, **32,** 161–166, May, 1954.

55. Deininger, R. L., "Human Factors Studies of the Design and Use of Push-Button Telephone Keysets," *Bell System Tech. J.*, **39,** 995–1012, 1960, New York, American Telephone and Telegraph Co. Figure 11-53 by permission.

*Chapter 12*

# MAN-MACHINE INTERACTION

## S. Glazer and R. Hammell

The preceding chapter emphasized that, if it is to be entirely successful, an equipment or system must be matched to the characteristics of the various people who will work with it. The human characteristics of general importance to most design efforts have been described. This chapter discusses the interactions of men and machines and describes some principles, methods, and examples of good design.

The term *man-machine system* is used in this chapter in a broad and general way. It applies to any combination of man and machine, simple or complex. In this sense, one man with a shovel fits the term. Although the physical designer is concerned with more complex situations, he will find that the larger design problem consists mainly of a multitude of small ones. However, the degree of difficulty may increase more rapidly than the number of separate small problems.

In its most general form, the man-machine system is described in Fig. 12-1. The machine has an input and an output. The input may be one signal or it may be a large family of signals from many sources. The machine communicates with man by activating appropriate displays that may produce patterns of light, sound, motion, vibration, etc. The man's sensors (eyes, ears, tactual sense) receive the displayed data and transfer them to the brain. Here

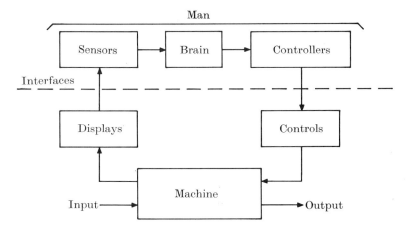

**Fig. 12-1**   The man-machine system.

information is interpreted, weighed, and compared, and decisions are made to operate controls that affect the machine.

Man-machine systems can be categorized as manual, semiautomatic, or automatic, and as either open-loop or closed-loop.[1] A manual system is one in which the man's action is entirely unassisted; there may or may not be corrective feedback. A man throwing a baseball represents a manual, open-loop system because the man has no control over the ball's path after the ball has left his hand. On the other hand, a man driving an automobile with a basic steering mechanism is in the class of manual, closed-loop systems because the man is continually correcting his steering in response to visual feedback cues.

A semiautomatic system involves human control of a machine. A man firing a rifle is an example of a semiautomatic system because the man's action of pulling the trigger initiates a machine action. This is an open-loop system. A man driving an automobile equipped with power steering constitutes a semiautomatic, closed-loop system.

In the automatic system, the entire action is performed by the machine. Generally, automatic systems have closed loops, the machine being arranged to compare its own performance against a reference (which may be either fixed or varying) and to derive its own corrective signals to keep the output within the prescribed error limits.

It might appear that, with the advent of automatic systems, the man has been eliminated; but this is far from true. Man continues to be an essential element because no system can be made totally reliable. There must be men to be aware of malfunctions and to initiate corrective actions. Moreover, there are many automatic systems whose tasks are so complex that they cannot have built-in means of dealing with everything that might happen. For these systems, the man performs a monitoring task; equipped with the proper displays and controls, he can modify the machine's workings to cope with emergencies. A dramatic illustration of this principle developed during the moon landing of the Apollo 11 module, on July 20, 1969. The computer-guided module was descending into a boulder-filled crater. Except for the manual intervention by the command pilot, who steered to a clear, flat area, the module could never have been returned to earth.

A fundamental task in man-machine system planning is the allocation of the various tasks to man or machine in keeping with their respective abilities and strengths, with efficient and economical operation as the constant goal. Despite intensive experimentation in the human factors field, especially in the past 25 years, there are no generalized rules of procedure for making these allocations; however, a good overall result depends upon the designer's understanding of human characteristics.

There are some things that man can do better than machines, and, of course, there are things that machines can do better than man. There are some things that one of them can do exclusively, and there are many things that either one can do.[1]

Man is more efficient than machines in the ability to detect dim lights or weak sounds and to organize patterns of light or sound. In a welter of noise, man can extract one message to the exclusion of others, and he can derive information from incomplete or garbled messages. Man can reason inductively and use judgment. He can create and improvise to meet nonstandard or unforeseen situations. Although his recall time is long compared to that of a computer, man can draw generalized patterns of previous experience from his memory in order to solve new problems; a computer cannot do this.[1,2]

Machines excel over man in rapid responses to control signals and in exerting great force smoothly and accurately. They can compute rapidly and perform repetitive routine tasks. Machines can do many different things at the same time. Stored information can be erased completely from a machine's memory. Of course, machines are not subject to the effects of boredom, anxiety, etc., and they can be designed to function in environments that man cannot tolerate.

The successful design of a man-machine system depends upon methodical studies and careful judgments. First, of course, the designer must have a clear understanding of what the system is to do. Then he must determine what operations are required and must allocate them to men or machines.

When the allocations of tasks have been tentatively determined, the man-machine interfaces (Fig. 12-1) must be considered. By proper choices and designs of displays and controls, the engineer matches the machine to the man. Considerable care may be needed here to avoid overloading human input or output channels. Matching the machine to the man can be likened to the impedance matching of electrical circuits. Displays must be contrived to exploit our knowledge of the human senses; controls must be convenient for the operator to locate and use; and, of course, the decisions and actions required of the man must be well within the limits of normal human performance. The designer must continually review his work to be sure that the equipment can be readily manufactured, installed, and maintained. Another matter which is often overlooked is that the final appearance of the product, its form, colors, and textures, cannot readily be applied as an afterthought. The most successful and pleasing overall result requires careful planning.

This chapter begins with a short discussion of man's role as an element of closed-loop, or "tracking," systems. Consideration is then given to designing for the operator, first in the design of displays, then in the selection and design of controls, and, finally, in the combination of these elements in comfortable and efficient operating positions. A number of essential design factors, including illumination and safety, are also outlined. The next section emphasizes the need for advance study and planning of the installation and maintenance aspects of equipment. Some design philosophies and equipment features for enhancing these characteristics are outlined. Finally, emphasis is given to the importance of good appearance to the overall success of a design. The subjective effects of color, line, form, proportion, and texture are described, together with some illustrations of ways in which these principles have been utilized in successful designs.

## 12-1. MAN AS A SYSTEM ELEMENT

There is an important class of man-machine system in which the man is employed within a closed loop in an activity generally called *tracking*. Figure 12-2 illustrates this situation. In *pursuit tracking*, the operator sees both the target, or a symbolic representation of the target, and the controlled element, or a representation of it. In *compensatory tracking*, the operator is shown only the tracking error—the difference between the positions of the target and the controlled element. In either case, the operator senses the error and operates a control mechanism in a way to minimize the error at the machine's output. Either the machine's output or the difference between this quantity and the system input is displayed continuously to the operator. Typical inputs to the system include constant velocity (ramp) functions, step functions, and sinusoidal or complex waveforms.

Human beings are most successful in those tracking operations that require them to judge and react to changes of position only. They are less successful when differentiation, the judging of velocity or acceleration, is required. A man finds it nearly impossible to perform a task requiring combinations of two or more complex processes such as differentiation, integration, multiplication, or

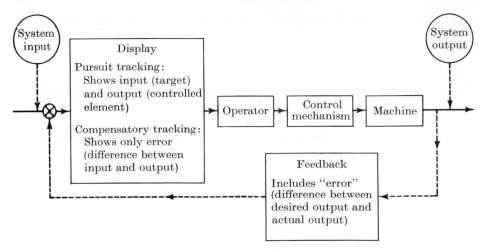

**Fig. 12-2** Generalized illustration of a continuous closed-loop, man-machine system. Such systems are usually referred to as tracking systems.[1]

addition. Sometimes these complex activities can be delegated to elements of the controls and machine.

It seems paradoxical that when man is performing a function that cannot be realized in any other way, the man's characteristics may set the upper limit on system capability. For example, human reaction time causes a phase lag in tracking-type activities. Increasing linearly with frequency, this phase lag sets the upper limit on a man's response rate to error signals. When there is a man in a closed-loop system, the system cannot reproduce input signals whose frequency spectra extend above about 3 Hz.

Successful design of a closed man-machine system loop, such as that shown in Fig. 12-2, depends upon the designer's ability to characterize the man in the same way as any other system building block. To be a manageable system element, the man should have a linear transfer function. In other words, there should be a linear relationship between human output and input.

In recent years, intense efforts have been made to find satisfactory expressions for the human transfer function. The search is made difficult by the fact that man is not a truly linear element, especially near the limits of input stimulus ranges. However, a number of different linear transfer functions have been found which apply, at least approximately, to men in various relatively simple tasks.

When the input to the man can be expressed as a time-varying function, $i(t)$, its Laplace transform, $I(s)$, can be derived.[3] If the human-operator transfer function is $H(s)$, the Laplace transform for the operator's response is

$$O(s) = I(s)\,H(s) \qquad (12\text{-}1)$$

and the expression for the time-varying output is the inverse Laplace transform of $O(s)$.

An accepted, generalized human-operator transfer function is[4]

$$H(s) = \frac{Ke^{-\tau s}(T_L s + 1)}{(T_l s + 1)(T_N s + 1)} \tag{12-2}$$

where:

$K$ is the gain of the human-operator model;

$\tau$ is the man's reaction time;

$(T_L s + 1)$ is a lead term that anticipates and contributes to high-frequency stability;

$(T_l s + 1)$ is a lag term that contributes to low-frequency stability;

$(T_N s + 1)$ is a neuromuscular lag term related to the human body's inertia.

When the controlled element is designed to respond instantly to the operator's control movements, $K$ has been found to have values from 1 to 100, depending on the bandwidth of the stimulus. Also, $\tau$ is approximately 0.2 s ($\pm 20$ percent), $T_L$ is usually between 0 and 2.5 s, $T_l$ ranges from 0 to 20 s, and $T_N$ is estimated as about 0.1 s ($\pm 20$ percent).

**Example 12.1.** A man is engaged in compensatory tracking. The display, Fig. 12-3, has two indications: point C (control) is fixed in the center of the screen, and point T (target) moves about the screen to indicate the amount and direction of error in the system output. The man's task is to manipulate a control in order to move point T into coincidence with point C and to keep it there.

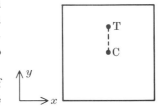

Figure 12-4 is a simplified block diagram of the tracking system. The system input $i(t)$ is the signal representing the target path. The system response is $o(t)$, and the input to the operator (the tracking error) is $e(t) = i(t) - o(t)$. The time-varying expression for the operator transfer function is $h(t)$, and the control transfer function is $y(t)$.

**Fig. 12-3** Compensatory tracking display.

The operator uses a handheld "light gun" of negligible mass. Further, the

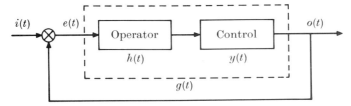

**Fig. 12-4**  Block diagram of compensatory tracking system.

machine acts as a linear amplifier of unity gain and has negligible lag compared to that of the man. At time $t_0$, the target path begins to follow a constant-velocity ramp in the $y$ direction as shown in Fig. 12-5, which corresponds to a system input voltage rate of 1 V/s. What is the system response to this input?

Use the generalized human-operator transfer function. Assume that the following values for the human gain and lag parameters have already been established:

$$K = 100$$
$$\tau = 0.2 \text{ s}$$
$$T_L = 0.09 \text{ s}$$
$$T_l = 20 \text{ s}$$
$$T_N = 0.1 \text{ s}$$

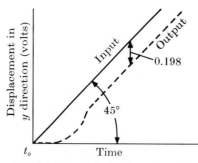

**Fig. 12-5** Comparison between target track (solid line) and operator's response (dashed line) in compensatory tracking problem.

*Solution.*

$$e(t) = i(t) - o(t)$$
$$g(t) = h(t) * y(t)$$
$$o(t) = e(t) * g(t)$$

where the asterisk denotes "convolved with." For the stated conditions, the Laplace transform of the machine transfer function, $Y(s)$, is 1. Thus, the solution will show only the effects of the human-operator gain and lag parameters. Therefore,

$$G(s) = H(s)$$
$$O(s) = E(s)H(s)$$
$$= [I(s) - O(s)]\,H(s)$$
$$= \frac{I(s)H(s)}{1 + H(s)}$$

which is the Laplace transform of $o(t)$.

The Laplace transform for the input ramp function is

$$I(s) = \frac{1}{s^2}$$

Therefore,

$$O(s) = \frac{1}{s^2}\left[\frac{Ke^{-\tau s}(T_L s + 1)}{(T_l s + 1)(T_N s + 1) + Ke^{-\tau s}(T_L s + 1)}\right]$$

With omission of many steps, the time-varying expression (or inverse transform) for the system output is

$$o(t) = (0.99t - 0.198 - 6.49e^{-19.2t} + 26.8e^{-26.3t}) \text{ volts}$$

This is indicated by the dashed line in Fig. 12-5. After a short time, the response becomes constant along a line of the same slope as the input and with a constant lag of about 0.198 V.

It is possible to build combinations of controls and machines to perform the more complex mathematical operations encountered in some tracking tasks, leaving the man to make simple position corrections. This is called *aided tracking*. As an example, suppose that an operator tracks by using a lightweight, handheld photocell light gun, and that his task requires him to perform the operations of amplification and integration. Remembering that integration is relatively difficult for a man, the designer can delegate it to the machine by changing the control to a joy stick having viscous damping, because the displacement of this control is proportional to the time integral of the applied force.

In *rate-aided tracking*, a change in control position results in changes of both position and rate within the machine. This feature has proved useful in some, but not all, tracking situations. The ratio of the position change to the rate change is called the aided-tracking time constant. The optimum value for this time constant is different from one system to another, in those cases in which rate-aid is beneficial. Values between 0.25 and 1.0 s are typical.

In the earlier example of compensatory tracking, the tracking of the ramp function is a constant-rate process. With rate-aiding, the machine would derive the rate from the initial movements of the control. The output would then follow at this established rate until the operator made a further change in the control position.

A process called *quickening* can be helpful in some tracking situations.[5] Quickening is especially useful in systems where there are appreciable delays between control actuations and system responses. It requires a system modification whereby the eventual effects of the operator's current control actions are displayed immediately to him. This ensures that, after a long delay, the operator will not find that he has done the wrong, and perhaps dangerous, thing.

This very brief discussion of tracking systems is merely an introduction to the topic. McCormick[1] gives a more thorough treatment and lists many useful references.

## 12-2. DESIGN FOR THE OPERATOR

In general, designing for an operator involves the selection and design of appropriate display and control devices; the combination of these into comfortable, efficient, and safe operating arrangements; and control of the significant environmental factors, when possible. Before the detailed work in these areas is begun, it is essential that the man-machine situation be studied with care. The designer must know the number of signals to be presented, their relative importance, their unique meanings and characteristics, and their rates of arrival and durations. He must understand the decisions, operating sequences, and physical activities required of the operator. Finally, the operating environment must be defined in detail. The designer must work around those factors, such as vehicular motion, which he cannot control. Other factors, such as temperature or the general lighting level, may be adaptable to the needs of an optimum design.

This section contains discussions of principles, procedures, and philosophies that should underly any design effort. It has not been the intent to reproduce the multitude of "how to" details which can be found in a number of excellent handbooks.

## DISPLAYS

Considered first are displays, the machines' means of communicating with man. Used in a broad sense, the word "display" is not limited to the presentation of visual information. A display can be any contrivance for exciting a human sensory channel.

In a complex situation, thorough study is needed before the machines' outputs are assigned to definite human input channels. Of course, some kinds of signals are especially suited to visual presentation, while others may be more suited to auditory presentation. The tactual sense may be a useful input channel when the others are thoroughly occupied.

In general, displays should present all of the essential information at the right time and place. Operators should not be burdened with unessential information, nor should the same information be presented in more than one way except with good reason.[6] Compared to the auditory and other senses, the visual sense is the most suitable input channel for most information. The auditory channel may be more suitable for some messages that are simple and brief, especially those of an urgent or emergency nature; moreover, it may be useful for directing an operator's attention toward a display outside his usual field of attention. It is often necessary to augment visual displays with auditory signals in order to prevent visual overload. Auditory displays are essential when the situation does not permit the use of visual displays; for example, the receiving location may be too bright, or it may be necessary to preserve the operator's dark adaptation, or the operator may be continually moving about.[2] For maximum clarity, the designer should choose the best "dimension" of each sensory stimulus. The sensory discriminations required, as between colors or the pitches of sounds, should not tax the operator's capabilities.[6] The following discussion is limited to some basic factors in the design of visual displays.

**Visual Displays.** The designer of a visual display must determine its purpose, the conditions under which it will be used, and the way in which the operator will use the displayed information. The purpose may suggest the kind of display to use, either symbolic or pictorial. The use conditions which must be considered include the viewing distance, illumination, angle of view, presence of other displays, and compatibility with related controls. The method of use may involve quantitative reading, qualitative reading, check reading, setting, tracking, or spatial orientation.

The *symbolic display* presents information in encoded form. Meter dials, thermometers, indicator lamps, and teletypewriter messages are symbolic displays. Such displays are suited for presenting almost any kind of information such as speed, pressure, or flow rate, which the user needs in quantitative form. They are often helpful in providing compactness and simplicity of display equipment.

The *pictorial display* gives a more or less realistic picture of a situation. Photographs and television pictures are among the most faithful pictorial displays. Other pictorial displays, such as wiring diagrams, may include elements of symbolic displays. Although it generally requires more complex devices, the pictorial display is good for showing relative locations, relative motions, and space orientation. The cathode-ray tube is an especially versatile basis for pictorial indicators. A common radar display, the Plan Position Indicator, places the operator at the center of the screen. A radial sweep, from center to screen edge, rotates in synchronism with the radar antenna and is intensified at each target position.

A display panel which also contains manual controls should be designed for a maximum reach distance of 71 cm (28 in.) because this is the reach distance of the 5th percentile man.† The recommended dimensions for scale markings and characters should be chosen for good legibility at this distance. For shorter or longer reading distances, marking dimensions should be multiplied by (distance in cm)$7/1$.

The best viewing angle is at 90° to the display surface, but it is not possible for the designer to adhere to this when large areas are used or when the same display is viewed by more than one operator. In these cases, the designer must ensure that all details can be seen (no blocking) and that there are no excessive parallax effects. If there is a tendency for the upper portion of a panel to reflect light from luminaires or bright ceiling surfaces, it may be helpful to tilt that position slightly (several degrees) toward the operator.

If reflected light is essential to a display's legibility, the size of display

---

† In a plot of the distribution of reach distances for all members of the using population, the 5th percentile man has a reach distance that just equals or exceeds that of the smallest 5 percent of the population.

details must be consistent with the lowest expected light level. Consideration must also be given to anything unnatural about the color of the panel illumination which would affect the use of color coding.

Where there are a number of displays, it is essential that they be consistent in their manner of presentation; this minimizes operator errors and maximizes reading speed. Each display must be well identified, especially when the displays are of similar appearance.

As far as possible, the design and relative placement of displays and controls should make it easy for the operator to select the right control and operate it in the proper manner.

Having considered the operator's working conditions, the designer must then determine what the operator is going to do in response to the displayed information. This generally has an important bearing on the choice of indicating device and its special characteristics. For example, precisely calibrated dials and scales are used for quantitative reading. Counters and other types of digital devices are also useful for this purpose. Often, however, the operator needs only a qualitative or approximate value, trend, rate, or direction of change, rather than a precise numerical value. The auto engine temperature indicator with cold, normal, and hot ranges is an example. The scale does not need numbers. Similarly, an on-off indicator for a check reading gives the operator a go or no-go signal, indicating that a quantity is or is not present (or within a desired range).

Displays are also used for setting and tracking. For setting, the indicator is watched while the operator adjusts a control to a desired value. In tracking, the operator makes intermittent or continuous adjustments to maintain a desired value.

Three very common symbolic indicators are shown in Fig. 12-6; their relative advantages and disadvantages, with respect to the way they are used, are listed in Fig. 12-7. Indicators of this type may be designed in a variety of

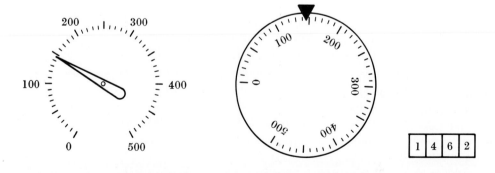

(a) Fixed scale with moving pointer    (b) Moving scale with fixed index    (c) Counter

**Fig. 12-6**   Some basic types of symbolic indicators.

| Method of use | Fixed scale | Moving scale | Counter |
|---|---|---|---|
| Quantitative reading | Fair | Fair | Good (requires minimum reading time with minimum reading error) |
| Qualitative and check reading | Good (location of pointer and change in position are easily detected) | Poor (difficult to judge direction and magnitude of pointer deviation) | Poor (position changes not easily detected) |
| Setting | Good (has simple and direct relation between pointer motion and motion of setting knob; pointer-position change aids monitoring) | Fair (has somewhat ambiguous relation between pointer motion and motion of setting knob) | Good (most accurate method of monitoring numerical settings, but relation between counter motion and motion of setting knob is less direct) |
| Tracking | Good (pointer position is readily monitored and controlled; provides simple relationship to manual-control motion, and provides some information about rate) | Fair (not readily monitored and has somewhat ambiguous relationship to manual-control motion) | Poor (not readily monitored, and has ambiguous relationship to manual-control motion) |
| General | Good (but requires greatest exposed and illuminated area on panel, and scale length is limited) | Fair (offers saving in panel space because only small section of scale need be exposed and illuminated, and long scale is possible) | Fair (most economical in use of space and illuminated area; scale length limited only by number of counter drums, but is difficult to illuminate properly) |

**Fig. 12-7**   Relative evaluation of basic symbolic indicators.[2]

ways. In addition, there are many types of digital displays, other than the counter, that are available.

**Indicator and Warning Lights.** Lights are often used to convey routine information and to signal alarms, warn of dangerous conditions, or to announce malfunctions. The effectiveness of a signal light depends more upon color and brightness than upon size. Of course, there must be adequate contrast between the light and the ambient illumination. The total number of colors used for lights should be kept small, and the designer must avoid choosing combinations, such as red and orange, which could be confused. Recommended colors are green, amber, red, white, and blue. Although it is not readily possible to obtain spectrally pure colors, the colors should be selected with care so that they will be readily identifiable. For example, an orange-red might be confused with yellow, or a blue-green might be confused with blue. In any design for use by the general population, the prevalence of color blindness should be considered, and colors should be chosen for maximum discriminability.

It is recommended that, in general, colors and functions be related as shown in Fig. 12-8. Note that the categories of information conveyed by green,

| Color | Function |
| --- | --- |
| Red | Stop; danger (e.g., safety interlocks shorted); blown fuse alarm (power OFF); emergency, urgency, alerting, warning; complete casualty (to a major function) |
| Green | Go; power ON; OK; last event in an important sequence |
| Amber | Conditions intermediate between red and green; power in STANDBY condition; partial equipment casualty (having relatively minor effect) |
| White | Routine operating data |
| Blue | If a fifth color is needed |

**Fig. 12-8**  Recommended color and function relationships for indicator lamps.[7]

amber, and red lights are similar to those associated with highway traffic lights. Of course, if colors have acquired special meanings for special situations, as in telephone offices, these should be used. In determining any feature of a display or control arrangement, the designer should try to match the user's previously established habits.

Because most annunciator and alarm lights are normally extinguished, a convenient means (momentarily operated button or toggle switch) should be provided for testing all the lamps. This feature is essential when safety or urgency requires that signals not be missed.

Generally, every signal light should be clearly identified. Ideally, legends should be on the indicator faces if space permits. If the ambient illumination is sufficiently high, however, the legends may be on a panel near the lights. Special problems may require special solutions, as discussed later.

**Scales and Labels.**  The design of displays requires careful attention to the selection of scales and labels. It is important that scales be designed for reading only to the necessary degree of precision. The operator's time and energy are wasted if the scale is overdesigned. The display must also give information in a directly usable form that does not require mental conversion.

Planning of a scale requires the careful selection of the scale range, numbered interval value, and the graduation-interval value. Figure 12-9 shows some

| Graduation interval value | Recommended scales | Numbered interval value | Graduation marks | | |
|---|---|---|---|---|---|
| | | | Major | Intermediate | Minor |
| 0.1, 1, 10 | 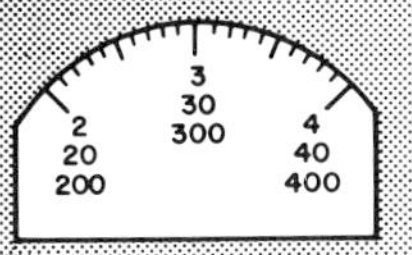 | 1, 10, 100 | X | X | X |
| | 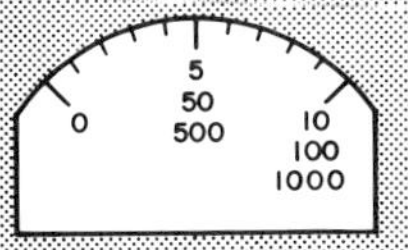 | 5, 50, 500 | X | | X |
| | 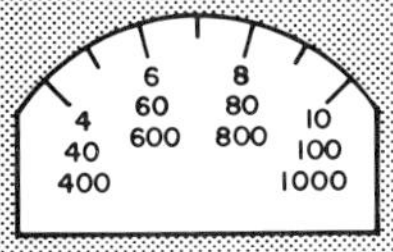 | 2, 20, 200 | X | X | |
| 0.2, 2, 20 | 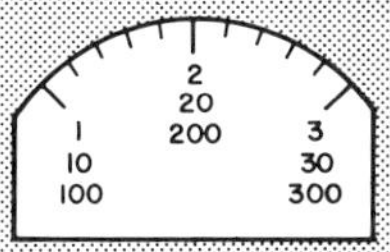 | 1, 10, 100 | X | | X |
| | 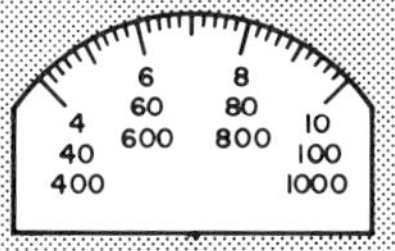 | 2, 20, 200 | X | X | X |
| 0.5, 5, 50 | 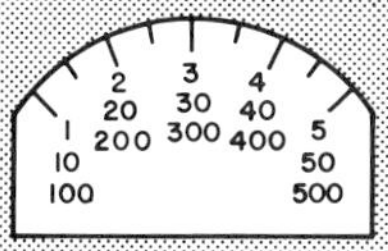 | 1, 10, 100 | X | X | |
| | 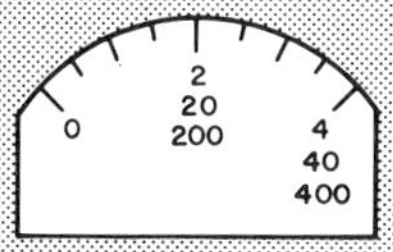 | 2, 20, 200 | X | X | X |
| | 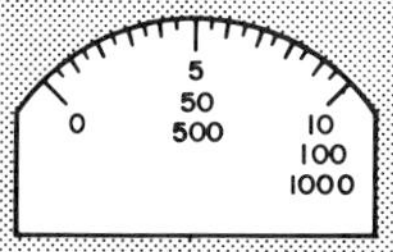 | 5, 50, 500 | X | X | X |

**Fig. 12-9**  Recommended combinations of graduation-interval values and scale-numbering systems.[2]

recommended combinations of graduation-interval values and scale numbering systems. The graduation-interval values should be 1, 2, 5, or decimal multiples of these; however, values of 2 are less desirable than 1 or 5. There should be no more than 10 graduation intervals (9 graduation marks) between numbered graduation marks. Scales numbered by intervals of 1, 10, 100, etc., and sub-divided by 10 graduation intervals, are usually preferable.

There are different recommended standards for scale design, depending on whether the scale is to be read under normal illumination or in dim light. Figure 12-10(a) gives recommended minimum standards for scale design for use under favorable viewing conditions. Figure 12-10(b) gives minimum standards

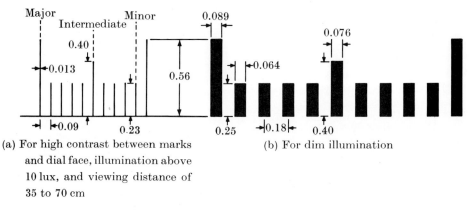

(a) For high contrast between marks
and dial face, illumination above
10 lux, and viewing distance of
35 to 70 cm

(b) For dim illumination

**Fig. 12-10**   Recommended minimum standards for scale design (all dimensions in centimeters).[2]

for the design of scales for use under dim illumination. In each case, the width of the pointer should be similar to the scale line widths.

Of course, the sizes and spacings of graduation marks must be increased proportionally with greater viewing distances, and the number of marks must be decreased on a dial of fixed diameter, as viewing distance increases. Some quantitative recommendations are available for these cases.[8]

Various research efforts have been made to determine what factors give the greatest legibility of printed material, signs, labels, etc. Although the results of these efforts are not entirely consistent, it is possible to list some general recommendations which give satisfactory results. Brief labels, captions, or instrument markings should be made entirely with capital letters. However, lower-case lettering should be used for printed material or captions of any length, such as complete sentences or paragraphs.

The legibility of characters is affected by contrast between character and background, character height, ratio of character height to width, and ratio of height to stroke width. The following recommendations are given for good legibility:

1. Panels and dials should have white lettering on a dark background if the operator's task requires dark adaptation. However, black labels on a light background are preferred when dark adaptation is not necessary. If the background area is small and protected from dirt, as on some dials, a matte white is usually best. For larger areas or where dirt is a problem, a 20-percent-gloss light gray might be preferred.

2. Figure 12-11 gives recommended minimum character heights for different illumination levels over a wide range of viewing distances (for

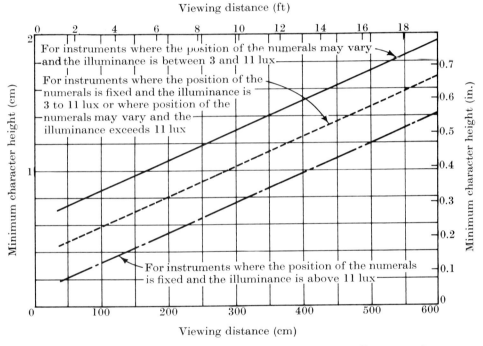

**Fig. 12-11** Minimum character height versus viewing distance and illumination level.[8]

characters with fixed positions as well as for those whose positions may vary).

3. A height-to-width ratio of 3 to 2 is recommended for characters on panels and scales.

4. For black characters on a white background, the highest legibility is given by a stroke width of about one-sixth the character height. White characters on black backgrounds, however, should have thinner strokes

of one-seventh to one-eighth the character height. Characters for back-lighted or edge-lighted panels should have a stroke width of about one-eighth the character height; a visual phenomenon called *irradiation* makes the strokes appear thicker than they really are.

## CONTROLS

Considered next are the controls which man uses to communicate his decisions or actions to the machine. Considerable study may be required in allocating the various control tasks to the operator's hands and feet and in selecting the best control device for each task. These allocations and selections must be made within the constraints of environment, space, and related displays. Of course, the tasks allotted to the various body control members should be appropriate ones for these members. The total load should be distributed evenly among the available members so that no single member is given an excessive burden.

In specifying the controls and their characteristics and locations, the designer must also consider the ranges of operator size and strength and the effects of any heavy clothing (especially gloves and boots). Further, the designer must take into account the effects of environmental extremes and prolonged operating periods on human efficiency, strength, and endurance.

The systematic selection of a control for a specific purpose requires first that the function and requirements of the control be defined. The purpose of the control, what it controls, and the relative importance of the control action must be considered, as well as the task requirements in terms of precision, speed, range, and force. Thought must also be given to the information needed by the operator in locating, identifying, and using the control, and to any limitations imposed by constraints of the work space.

After consideration of these requirements, the designer should be guided by the following general principles:

1. Assign to the hands those control tasks which must be done with speed and accuracy. Control tasks involving large or continuous forward application of force are appropriate for assignment to the feet. Do not assign more than two controls to either foot. Distribute the controls among the hands and feet so as to avoid overloading any one member.
2. Select controls having motions compatible with those of the associated displays.
3. Select either a linear control or a rotary control for making a small adjustment over a short range. If the range of adjustment is large, however, a multirevolution rotary control is desirable; a trade-off

between high precision of adjustment and reasonably short operating
time may be necessary.

4. For adjustments which are made in a limited number of discrete steps,
   select multiposition, detented control devices to make the operation
   swift and easy.

5. Consider combining functionally related controls if this gives advantages
   such as fewer or shorter reaching movements or a saving of space (e.g.,
   the combined channel selector and fine tuning control on a TV set).

6. Select controls for ease of identification. Consider shape coding, size
   coding, and location coding where vision is restricted.

7. Select controls of the right type and size for the combination of function
   and required force.

One of the important considerations in the relationship between displays
and controls is the control-display ratio. This is the ratio of control motion to
resulting display motion. There are various ways of defining this ratio, depending
upon the types of controls and display motions. For example, it is cm/cm if
the control motion and display response are both linear. For other arrangements,
it could be revolutions per cm or revolutions per revolution.

The discussion of movements in Sec. 11-4 describes the primary and
secondary movements that an operator makes in slewing and setting a control.
Figure 12-12 shows the results of an experiment to find the best control ratio
for a control knob linked to a moving pointer.[9] Note how the primary movement time decreases with decreasing control ratio. At the same time, the time
required to make the secondary movement (the final adjustment of the pointer
to the index mark) increases with decreasing control ratio because the adjustment is becoming increasingly difficult. The optimum control ratio, for which
the total adjustment time is a minimum, is about 0.1–0.2 knob revolutions per
cm of pointer travel. It is interesting and useful to know that a change in the
knob diameter cannot compensate for an unfavorable control ratio, and furthermore, as long as the knob diameter exceeds 1.3 cm, the actual diameter has little
effect on the setting time. For much different ranges of pointer motion or for
other kinds of controls and displays, the designer should set up an experiment
to determine the best control ratio.

Numerous experiments have shown that, for a majority of test subjects,
displays should move in specific ways in response to certain control motions.
These relationships should be maintained in equipment design because they
have a significant effect on operating time, efficiency, and learning time. They
become increasingly important as the amount of detail increases in the operator's
overall job. An additional point is that an operator who is under heavy stress
may forget an "unnatural" relationship and revert to the "natural" one,
perhaps failing in his task. Some of the more basic preferred control-display

relationships are shown in Figs. 12-13 and 12-14. An operator who will have to work with a number of similar equipments should be given consistent control-display relationships in all these equipments.

There are some control-display combinations that pose special problems. An especially troublesome one involves a rotary display having a moving dial

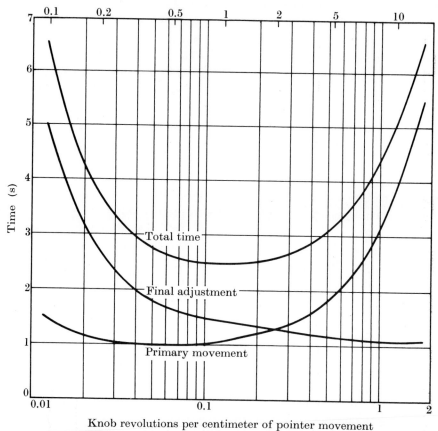

Knob revolutions for 8 cm point movement

Knob revolutions per centimeter of pointer movement

**Fig. 12-12**  Knob revolutions per cm of pointer movement.

and fixed pointer. The operator's dilemma may be that he cannot sense whether a clockwise knob rotation should cause the dial to move clockwise or the quantity marked on the dial to increase. The most effective design solution is to use a fixed dial and moving pointer.

All controls offer resistance to the operator. To a degree, the designer can control this resistance so as to suppress undesirable effects and to enhance those that will aid the operator. Also, as stated previously, control characteristics can sometimes be exploited to relieve operators of difficult tasks such as

| Control action | Response |
|---|---|
| 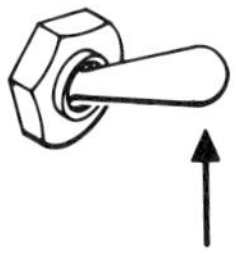 Switch thrown up | Lamp lights; motor starts, etc. |
| 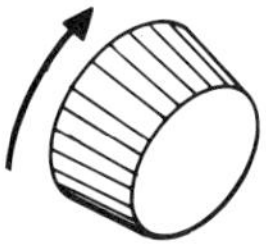 Knob turned clockwise | Volume or other quantity increases; something turns on, or lamp becomes brighter |
| 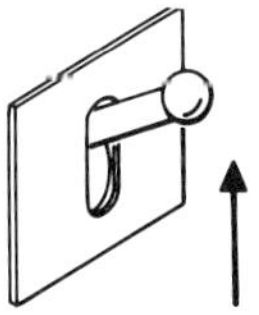 Lever moved upward | Load hoisted; vehicle moves forward (accepted but not preferred) |
| 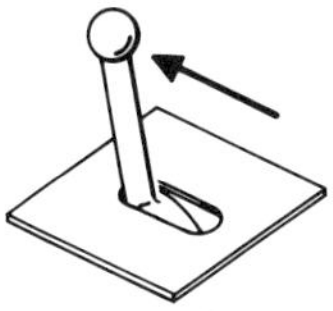 Lever moved forward | Vehicle moves forward; liquid flow increases |

**Fig. 12-13**   Some preferred control-display relationships.

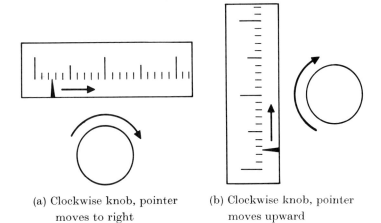

(a) Clockwise knob, pointer moves to right

(b) Clockwise knob, pointer moves upward

**Fig. 12-14**   Preferred dial-pointer relationships.

integration. Generally, control resistance is a combination of two or more of the following kinds:

1. Elastic resistance—This increases with control displacement, in a manner determined by the control mechanism and its materials.
2. Viscous damping—The operator encounters an opposing force which is proportional to control speed.
3. Static and sliding (Coulomb) friction—These two components cannot be exploited easily by the designer, because they are not related systematically to control displacement, speed, or acceleration.
4. Inertia—This is proportional to the control acceleration.

Controls are coded so that they may be identified correctly. They may be coded by shape, size, color, location, operation mode, or captions. Control captions or labels should be carefully designed for clarity and brevity. The operator should not require special training in order to read them. A cardinal rule is that the caption should not give the name of the control (e.g., lamp rheostat), but it should state what quantity is controlled (e.g., brightness). It is often desirable to use more than one method of coding on a control.

The designer should use the maximum number of coding methods for each control, within the limitations of the environment. It has been determined experimentally that both size and shape coding can be used on the same controls, but neither one is much good if the operator wears heavy gloves. Of course, color coding is useless in darkness or in an unnatural lighting environment, such as red lighting for maintenance of dark adaptation. For dimly lighted or dark areas, control captions must be lighted from within.

There are some kinds of controls which must not be operated except at the right moment. Examples include those whose inadvertent operation would have serious effect on system operation or on the safety of property or human life. Controls of this kind can be guarded by recessing, by use of hinged safety covers, by careful location or orientation, or by employing locking devices.

## OPERATING POSITIONS

Broadly defined, an operating position provides input signals for human sensory channels, and it provides controls whereby the user can communicate his decisions or reactions to a machine. Control consoles, airplane cockpits, telephone booths, and communications receivers are such positions. After the designer has selected appropriate means for fulfilling each separate display and control requirement, and has determined that their combination provides a reasonably balanced load for the operator, he must combine them in a comfortable and efficient operating position. This can be a challenging exercise.

Extensive treatments of the principles and methods of operating position design are found in various texts.[2,6,8] Reference 8 also contains detailed check lists which provide some insurance against overlooking the "obvious."

**Control and Display Arrangements.** In the design of operating positions, the important displays must be placed for best seeing, and the important controls must be placed for easy reaching and operating. When a number of displays and controls must be accommodated, the designer will find that compromises are necessary to achieve a reasonable balance between the ideal and the feasible.

The development of a complex display and control position may require several stages of revision, rearrangement, and refinement. The designer should strive for a "self-explanatory" arrangement and the elimination of unnecessary visible detail. In general, the highly refined design tends to have a fine appearance, which gives a feeling that it also will perform well. The following example, which is adapted from a real-life situation, may give some insights into the procedures used in designing display and control positions.

**Example 12.2.** A television network switching center is to fulfill the following requirements:

1. Number of separate inputs: ten program sources.
2. Number of separate outputs: ten TV stations.
3. It must be possible to connect any single input to any number of the outputs.
4. It must be impossible to connect any output to more than one input at a time.
5. The shortest program will last 15 minutes. Therefore, it may be necessary to change some connections every 15 minutes.
6. The operator must make all required changes in connections within 20 seconds after receiving a cue.
7. At the beginning of each day, the operator is given a tabulation of all required connections and the times when they are to be established.
8. Environment: air-conditioned room; noise level about 65 dB above reference (from loudspeakers and operating personnel); lighting adequate for reading panel captions.
9. Viewing distance: 71 cm.

Design a display and control position to meet these requirements, and describe the operating principles and rules which the operator must follow.

*Solution.* The requirements state that the operator will have a long time, at least 15 minutes, to prepare for the change of connections. However, the actual changing may require a burst of activity in which up to ten connections are made, broken, or rearranged in 20 seconds. This suggests that some of the operator's waiting time be devoted to setting up a visual cue for each of the next changes, with the purpose of minimizing the time needed to make the changes. It is desirable that there be a visual indication that each required connection has been established. Moreover, there should be an instant warning when an undesired connection is initiated, because improper connections cannot be tolerated.

The 20-second limit dictates that there be a fast means for breaking, making, or rearranging the connections without having to go through sequences of unwanted switch points. The arrangement to be described takes advantage of the fact that both of the operator's hands are available for use in the switching operation.

Figure 12-15 is a preliminary sketch of the proposed panel. Arranged vertically at the left edge of the panel are ten input pushbuttons. These represent the program sources. Each pushbutton is marked with a single letter at least 0.4 cm high. The letters are black on a white background. Near the bottom of the panel is a row of output pushbuttons. These represent the TV stations. Each pushbutton is marked with a number, from 1 to 10. The numerals are the same height as the letters on the input buttons and are also black on a white background. At the intersections of the ten rows and ten columns (100 crosspoints) are 100 white lamps which are normally extinguished.

The panel has a dark, nonreflecting background. Thin white lines on the panel connect the pushbutton and lamps in each row and in each column. Two pushbuttons marked RELEASE appear at the ends of the row of station buttons. These buttons do not contain lamps. Directly beneath each numbered output button is a special "cueing indicator." Each one has a knurled thumb-wheel whose edge appears through a slot in the panel. Beneath the panel, there is a small rotating drum mounted on the thumb-wheel. The drum is made of clear plastic and contains a green lamp and a red lamp which are normally extinguished. The periphery of the drum is divided into twelve segments. The first ten are marked with the letters A through J, the eleventh is marked RLS (release), and the twelfth segment is not labeled. Adjacent to each thumb-wheel is a window of such size that the label on a single segment is visible.

At the top of the panel is a clock with sweep-second hand. The clock is equipped so that the second hand can be set accurately. Next to the clock is a large green CUE lamp which is normally extinguished. To ensure that the operator will not miss signals because of dead lamp bulbs, a LAMP TEST pushbutton is mounted in a convenient location on the panel. When this button is pressed, all lamps on the panel will light.

Effort has been made to design a fail-safe arrangement in which it is unlikely that the operator will establish wrong connections, or that he will break connections inadvertently or prematurely. The establishment of a connection requires simultaneous operation of one input button and one output button. When remotely controlled switching has operated to establish the desired connection, the corresponding crosspoint lamp lights. This provides feedback to the operator, so that he will know that the entire switching chain has operated

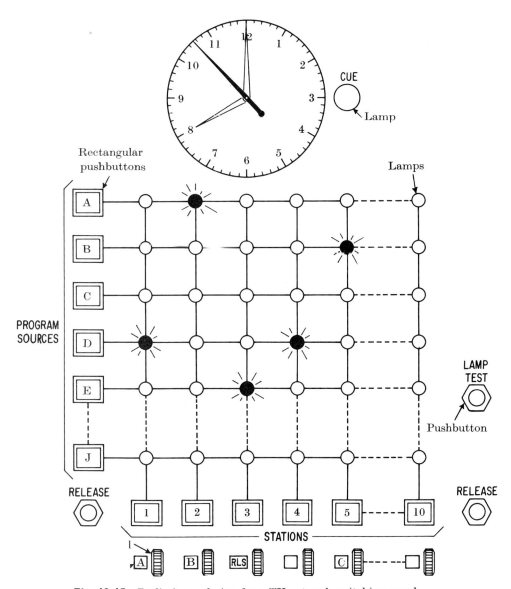

**Fig. 12-15** Preliminary design for a TV network switching panel.

properly. To shift a given station from one input to another, the operator
presses the station button and the button for the new input channel. This
breaks the existing connection and establishes the new one. To release an
existing connection without making a new one, the operator must simultaneously
operate the station button and either RELEASE button. Two RELEASE
buttons are provided so that the operator can use either hand. During the long
interval between cues, the operator refers to the tabulation sheet and sets the

"cueing indicators" to show the actions he will have to take when he receives his next cue. For example, Fig. 12-15 shows that on the next cue, the operator should connect station No. 1 to input channel A, and No. 2 to input channel B. The input to station No. 3 is to be released. Number 4 is to be left undisturbed, and No. 5 is to be shifted to input C. The cue is delivered to the operator by lighting the green ("go ahead") lamps in the cueing indicators, together with the large CUE lamp beside the clock. The operator proceeds to make the changes as recorded in the cueing indicators. If he presses an input button other than the one called for by the cueing indicator, the green light in the cueing indicator is replaced by a flashing red light. When the correct connection has been made, the light in the cueing indicator is extinguished.

As described above, this constitutes a rough, preliminary design. The next step would be construction of a mock-up and simulation of real operation. Operating tests would answer such questions as these:

1. Can the operator easily perform the required switching (maximum possible number of changes) in the 20-second interval?
2. Is it worthwhile to provide two RELEASE buttons? Do most operators tend to use the same one?
3. Are the horizontal and vertical white lines useful to the operator?
4. Is the cueing indicator design satisfactory? Is there a better location for the cueing indicators?
5. Considering that the operator may leave the console for long periods, perhaps to perform other tasks, should there be an audible warning near the end of each 15-minute interval? What kind of signal is appropriate? By what interval should it precede the lighting of the large CUE lamp? Would the signal bother other operators in the room?

This example illustrates the importance of considering the human factors as a prerequisite to all other design work. The task of the electrical designer, as well as that of the physical designer, is defined in large measure by the panel's operating principles. For instance, the need for a LAMP TEST pushbutton dictates that the lamp transformer be rated to supply all lamps on the panel for a short time, not just the maximum number of lamps that would be lighted during normal use.

**Use of Anthropometric Data.** The successful designer is careful to obtain all pertinent body dimensions of the using population, and the ranges of these dimensions. If the designer cannot locate published data suitable for the specific application, he should arrange for a competent organization to obtain the data for him.[10] After a preliminary design has been laid out according to these data, it is advisable to build a full-size model or mock-up. The mock-up should be evaluated by a number of test subjects, some of whom are near the smallest and largest of the height and weight distributions of the user group.

The smallest persons should be dressed in light clothing, and the largest persons should wear the bulkiest clothing and personal equipment planned for the final operating environment. One of the advantages of such tests is that the model is evaluated for both *static fit* and *dynamic fit* of the operator. The conditions for static fit are usually easy to achieve from the anthropometric data; but the fit of the operator during all necessary motions in three dimensions is more easily determined with the model. The model also helps to assure that the operator is not required to tax his physical strength, or to strain to reach controls, or to perform an awkward or confusing pattern of movements. These people should operate the model for full-length operating periods to ensure the discovery of any difficulties or sources of discomfort that may appear only after extended operation.

The designer should evaluate each discovered design shortcoming in terms of the percentage of the using population who will be inconvenienced or otherwise affected by it. Obviously, a deficiency which seriously affects all operators must be corrected; on the other hand, something that causes minor discomfort to 5 percent of operators may not merit attention. Preferably, a high proportion (say 98 percent) of the using population should be accommodated without penalty. In practice, the proportion may be as low as 90 percent, depending on other design features (such as overall size and weight) that would otherwise be sacrificed. The proportion accommodated will also vary with the extent of the penalty incurred by those outside the limits, and on the availability of people within limits to operate the equipment.

The following two examples illustrate the use of anthropometric data in designing for the operator.

***Traffic service position console.*** This console is used by an operator who assists customers making certain kinds of calls, such as person-to-person, coin toll, third party charge, etc. Important design goals included speed, operating efficiency, and comfort over long operating periods. The design minimizes operator fatigue by providing for unrestricted movement of the legs, arms, and head.

In Fig. 12-16, we can see how the maximum reach requirement of the small operator was met in order to permit satisfactory operation of the farthest row of keys on the key shelf. Ample leg room is supplied for the large operator, leg fatigue is relieved by an adjustable footrest, and chair height is variable. If footrests were not used, the shelf and chair heights would usually be lower than shown here.

The experimental technique called *link-analysis* (Chapter 11) was used to find a suitable arrangement for the 76 keys and lamps that are required on the keyshelf. An efficient and functional grouping resulted, Fig. 12-17, and what might have been a difficult operational job became routine. Horizontal eye

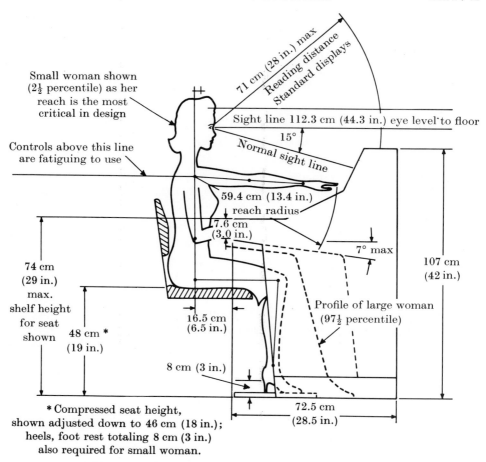

Small woman shown
(2½ percentile) as her
reach is the most
critical in design

71 cm (28 in.) max
Reading distance
Standard displays

Sight line 112.3 cm (44.3 in.) eye level to floor

15°

Normal sight line

Controls above this line
are fatiguing to use

59.4 cm (13.4 in.)
reach radius

7.6 cm
(3.0 in.)

7° max

74 cm
(29 in.)
max.
shelf height
for seat
shown

48 cm *
(19 in.)

16.5 cm
(6.5 in.)

107 cm
(42 in.)

Profile of large woman
(97½ percentile)

8 cm (3 in.)

72.5 cm
(28.5 in.)

* Compressed seat height,
shown adjusted down to 46 cm (18 in.);
heels, foot rest totaling 8 cm (3 in.)
also required for small woman.

**Fig. 12-16** The traffic service position console designed with the operator in mind. Variance in arm and leg dimensions of operators was one of the most critical points of the design.[11]

scan for maximum retention dictated a 24-cm wide digital readout with characters large enough for easy identification, but small enough to permit a quick scan. Disturbing glare was reduced by the inclusion of an amber polarized filter behind the face shield of the digital readout. The filter rejects reflected light originating from the front, but allows normal light originating from the display to pass through to the viewer. The polarized filter is curved so that all frontal light is reflected down to the horizontal, where it is absorbed by a dull black surface.

*New telephone booths.* A second example of the application of anthropometric data is the design of a new line of telephone booths which are engineered with a strong emphasis on satisfying human requirements. From

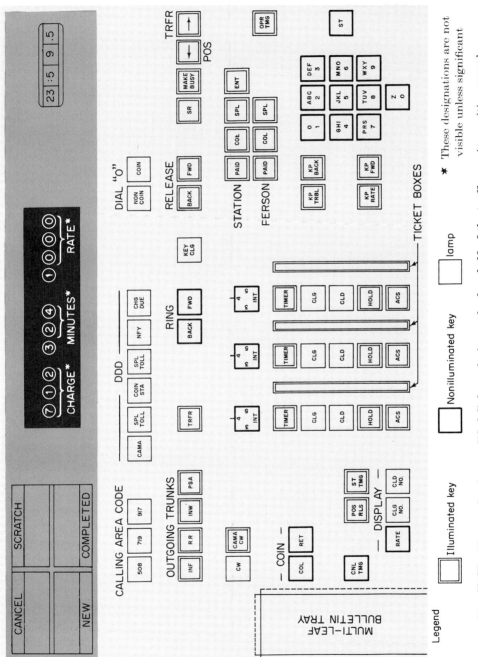

**Fig. 12-17** The result of a modified link analysis on the keyshelf of the traffic service position console.

547

available anthropometric data,[10,12] the space requirements for the new booths were established as shown in Fig. 12-18. The data were selected to represent about 97.5 percent of the population, excluding only the smallest $2\frac{1}{2}$ percent of the women and largest $2\frac{1}{2}$ percent of the men. The way people sit and move, the clothes they are likely to be wearing, and the packages they may be carrying were studied to determine the dimensional relationships between such things as telephone, seat, shelf, doors, and walls. Comfort was assured by the inclusion of ample lighting, ventilation, a contoured padded seat, soundproofing, nonreflective surfaces, and ample storage on the floor and on a shelf. The doors of these new booths, Fig. 12-19, can be operated with minimum inconvenience to the user and will allow an almost unimpeded use of floor space. If someone

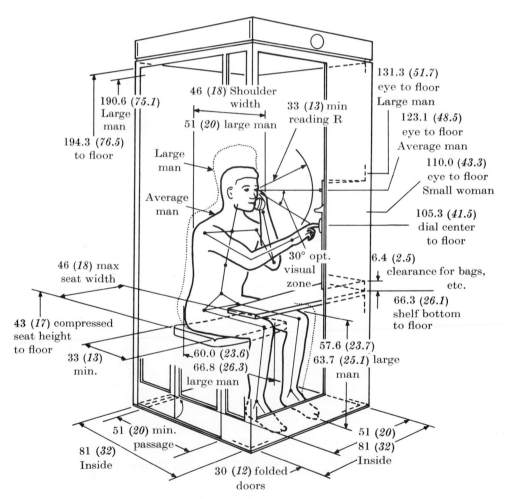

**Fig. 12-18**  Anthropometry applied to the new square phone booth. (Dimensions are in centimeters, with inches in parentheses.)[13]

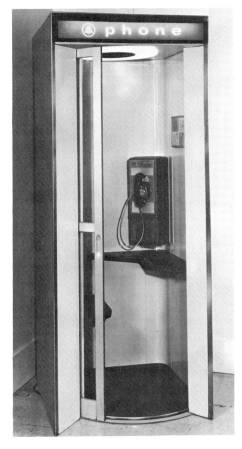 

(a) Curved-door booth                    (b) Square booth

**Fig. 12-19**  Modern telephone booths.

should become ill while in the booth, the door can be opened from the outside—an important safety feature not found in older booths.

## ILLUMINATION

During eons of evolution, man's visual sense developed to match the spectral distribution and lighting intensities that nature provided. Thousands of years after he moved indoors, man invented the candle, with a luminous efficiency of about 0.1 lumen per watt. Today, we have light sources with efficiencies approaching 100 lumens per watt and, someday, we may come close to the highest possible efficiency with which white light can be produced (200 lumens per watt).[14]

This discussion outlines the characteristics of modern lighting equipment, describes some basic practices of importance to physical designers, and lists a few of the minimum illumination levels currently recommended for various visual tasks. The word "minimum" is emphasized because our best lighting arrangements usually do not approach the illumination levels found in nature. Visual tasks are increasingly fatiguing to the entire body as the illumination level is reduced.

When the system being designed includes the equipment and the spaces within which it is to be used, the designer can achieve an optimum result. On the other hand, many systems must be designed without advance knowledge of the lighting conditions that will be used. For these cases, the designer must anticipate poor lighting. He should consider the possibility that the illumination will sometimes be too high, as well as the more usual one in which it is too low. Examples are modern telephone dials which can be seen in dim light, and the PICTUREPHONE® set which must be usable under a wide range of lighting conditions.

**Interior Lighting.** In the discussion of the visual sense, it was shown that the eye sees clearly within a 2° central cone and that there is a 60° cone within which the eye has some sensitivity. Because the eye is in almost constant motion, these cones of vision sweep over large areas on and around the object of interest. This explains why it is desirable to obtain a reasonable balance between the brightness of the object, its surroundings, and anything else in the immediate field of view.

A few definitions will aid in a general discussion of interior lighting.[15]

*Luminaire*—A complete lighting unit consisting of a lamp or lamps, together with the parts designed to distribute the light, to position and protect the lamps, and to connect the lamps to the power supply.

*General lighting*—Lighting designed to provide a uniform level of illumination throughout the area involved.

*Supplementary lighting*—Lighting used to provide a specific amount or quality of illumination which cannot readily be obtained by the general lighting system, and which supplements the general lighting system.

*Local lighting*—Illumination provided over a relatively small area or confined space without any surrounding general lighting.

*Glare*—The effect of brightnesses or brightness differences within the visual field sufficiently high to cause annoyance, discomfort, or loss in visual performance. Glare is of two types: *direct*, which results from high brightness or insufficiently shielded light sources in the field of view, or

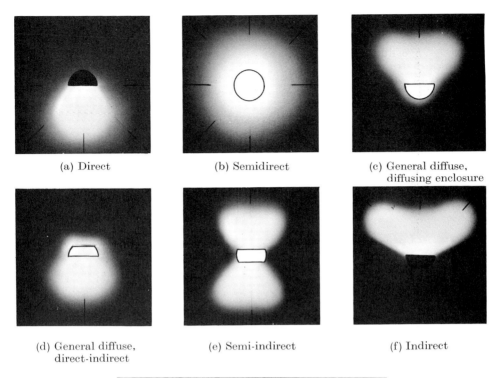

(a) Direct       (b) Semidirect       (c) General diffuse, diffusing enclosure

(d) General diffuse, direct-indirect       (e) Semi-indirect       (f) Indirect

| Classification | *Approximate distribution of luminaire light output (percent)* | |
| | Upward | Downward |
| --- | --- | --- |
| Direct | 0 to 10 | 90 to 100 |
| Semidirect | 10 to 40 | 60 to 90 |
| General diffuse* | 40 to 60 | 40 to 60 |
| Semi-indirect | 60 to 90 | 10 to 40 |
| Indirect | 90 to 100 | 0 to 10 |

* General diffuse luminaires which produce little light in angles near the horizontal are termed direct-indirect.

**Fig. 12-20** The CIE luminaire distribution classifications.[15]

reflecting areas of high brightness and large area; and *reflected*, which results from specular reflections of high brightness sources in polished surfaces in the field of view.

There are five basic classifications of luminaires, with light distribution characteristics as indicated in Fig. 12-20. Within these classifications, there are many kinds of fixtures.

Of the many kinds of light sources, the incandescent filament lamp and the fluorescent lamp are of the greatest usefulness in most equipment designs. Fluorescent lamps are available in many colors and have high efficiency; they can be dimmed over a restricted range by using autotransformers, and over the entire range from maximum to zero output by means of special circuits. They can produce annoying stroboscopic effects around machine parts moving at critical speeds; however, this effect can be minimized by connecting different lamps to the separate phases of a two- or three-phase circuit. Unless handled carefully, the fluorescent lamp can be a potent generator of radiofrequency interference. Bypassing and shielding may be necessary when these lamps are used near radiation-sensitive equipment.

Some words of caution about some other light sources are in order. Arc lamps such as those containing mercury, xenon, or sodium vapor emit light at a number of discrete frequencies, rather than as continuous bands of frequencies. There is experimental evidence that the line type spectrum can cause physical discomfort (headaches, disorientation, nausea). Fluorescent lamps have continuous spectra that do not give these undesirable effects.

A few of the illumination levels currently recommended for specific tasks are listed in Fig. 12-21. These illumination levels are intended to be minimum

| *Location or task* | *Lux on task* |
|---|---|
| Inside switchboards, rear of vertical switchboard panels | 100 |
| Battery rooms, telephone equipment room, corridors, stairways | 200 |
| Rough, easy-seeing assembly work, office tasks not involving critical or prolonged seeing | 300 |
| Control rooms | 300 to 500 |
| Ordinary inspection work, rough bench and machine work, general testing | 500 |
| Electrical manufacturing, laboratories | 500 to 1,000 |
| Medium assembly work, metal layout and template work, difficult inspection work, medium bench and machine work, regular office work | 1,000 |
| Clerical, keypunch, business machine operation, reading | 1,500 |
| Extra-fine instruments, scales, etc.; detailed drafting | 2,000 |
| Fine bench and machine work | 5,000 |
| Most difficult inspection work, extra-fine assembly work, extra-fine bench and machine work | 10,000 |
| Cloth inspection | 20,000 |
| Hospital operating rooms | 25,000 |

**Fig. 12-21**   Recommended minimum illumination levels. (Figures are rounded; values listed in Reference 15 indicate lighting levels about 8 percent higher than shown here.)

on the task irrespective of the plane in which it is located. They also apply after any correction for losses.

In practice, the nominal illuminance is multiplied by a *coefficient of utilization* and a *maintenance factor*. The coefficient of utilization represents that portion of the generated lumens that reaches the work plane, and the maintenance factor takes into account the gradual lessening of light output as lamps deteriorate or become dirty.[15]

The illumination on vertical planes is, in general, considerably lower than on horizontal planes. For luminaires with narrow distribution patterns, the ratio of vertical-to-horizontal illumination is about 1 to 3; this increases to about 1 to 2 if the distribution is wide. When normal arrangements of luminaires do not provide enough light on vertical surfaces, it is necessary to use special arrangements or additional luminaires for the critical areas.

**Example 12.3.** A small light source of 500 candlepower (candela) is mounted 5 m above the center of a surface 0.4 m wide by 0.6 m long. Above the lamp, there is a dull black ceiling that does not reflect light.

(a) What is the intensity of illumination on the surface?
(b) If this surface is to be used for doing work involving the reading of large print, will there be enough light?
(c) If this surface reflects 10 percent of the incident light, what is the surface brightness (measured normal to the surface)?

*Solution.* From the geometry given, assume that the intensity of illumination is the same at all parts of the flat surface.

(a) The light flux falling on the surface is found from Eq. (11-3):

$$I = r^2 \frac{\Phi}{A}$$

The intensity of illumination at the surface, from Eq. (11-6), is

$$E = \frac{\Phi}{A}$$

Therefore,

$$E = \frac{I}{r^2} = \frac{500}{5^2} = 20 \text{ lux}$$

(b) The recommended minimum illumination level for office tasks not involving critical or prolonged seeing, from Fig. 12-21, is 300 lux. There will not be enough light.
(c) The surface brightness becomes

$$B = 0.1 \times 20 = 2 \text{ lm/m}^2$$

**Glare Control.** Light sources located behind persons wearing eye glasses can cause disturbing reflections (see Fig. 12-22). The light source must be 30° or more above the line of sight, 40° or more below it, or outside the two 15° zones indicated at the sides.

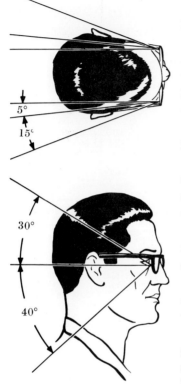

To aid in minimizing glare, shiny finishes should not be used on flat work surfaces, table tops, sloping control panels, etc. Because non-reflecting, matte finishes are easily soiled, the designer may have to accept a finish that reflects 20 to 40 percent of the incident light. When the function of an object requires a smooth finish (e.g., the safety glass cover over a cathode-ray screen), special care must be taken to locate light sources so that reflected light cannot enter the observer's eyes.

In large work spaces, a high level of general illumination and the proper control of room surface reflectance are useful in minimizing glare. "Egg crate" barriers mounted beneath fluorescent lamps serve to block all except essentially vertically incident light.

The provision of local lighting is often of special concern. In deeply shadowed areas inside equipment, consideration should be given to building the work lighting into the equipment. An example is mentioned in Sec. 12-3.

**Fig. 12-22** A person wearing glasses may receive glare from a light source behind his head if the source is within the indicated angles.

**Panel Lighting.** There are a number of techniques used for lighting display and control panels. The choice depends upon the ambient illumination level, upon whether or not the operator's dark adaptation must be maintained, and upon the intended service life of the equipment.

Large panel areas can be floodlighted by use of small fixtures about 20 cm apart. These can be equipped with red filters which can be rotated into place when needed. Very small luminaires can be obtained for floodlighting single instruments; there will be shadows if instrument faces are recessed far below the panel surface.

Edge lighting and back lighting are especially effective in low ambient illumination, although they are relatively complex and costly. In either case, the outer surface of a transparent plastic panel has bright translucent characters with an opaque surrounding background.

The most expensive means of panel lighting employs *electroluminescence*. The panel, constructed similarly to a capacitor, acts as its own light source. The intensity is initially low, and diminishes very slowly as the panel ages. Descriptions of the panel construction are readily available.[8]

**Special Lighting.** Occasionally, the designer may be confronted with a set of inconsistent lighting needs, in that one requirement may be in conflict with another. This situation arises in airport control towers and in radar plotting rooms. In the radar room, the detection and interpretation of radar signals requires low illumination; but most other tasks require moderate to high illumination levels.

It is important that the ambient illumination not be reflected from the radar screen. There is a 1- to 4-dB loss in signal visibility when the reflected light equals the screen brightness.[16] Nevertheless, a small amount of diffuse illumination around the radar screen may actually enhance signal visibility. Radar screens with P7 phosphor are reported to have better signal visibility with about 1 lux of surrounding illumination than they do in complete darkness.[17]

> **Example 12.4.** Radar displays in a naval shipboard equipment are equipped with cathode-ray tubes having P19 screens. This phosphor has long persistence and an orange fluorescence and phosphorescence.
>
> For best viewing of the P19 screen, there should be good contrast between the orange blips and the screen. This contrast is ordinarily attained by keeping the radar room dark. In conflict with this requirement, room illumination of moderate intensity is desirable for the comfort and safety of other personnel. Some men have tasks that cannot be performed easily in darkness.
>
> How is this apparent dilemma resolved to the satisfaction of everyone?
>
> *Solution.* The solution to this problem is the use of *selective spectrum* lighting. The visible spectrum is divided into two "channels"; the orange cathode-ray tube blips are assigned to one channel and the room lighting to the other channel. Of course, means must be found for barring the room lighting from the cathode-ray screen, where it would degrade the contrast between signals and their background.
>
> In Fig. 12-23, curve 1 is the relative sensitivity of the light-adapted eye to various wavelengths. Curve 2 represents the distribution of wavelengths in the blips on the P19 screen. The general room lighting is provided by "daylight white" fluorescent lamps, each surrounded by a cylindrical blue filter having the transmission characteristics shown by curve 3. The lighting system can be dimmed over a wide range.
>
> An amber-colored plastic sheet is mounted in front of the cathode-ray screen, in place of the usual clear window. The light transmission of this filter is shown by curve 4. Within its passband, this filter transmits orange light

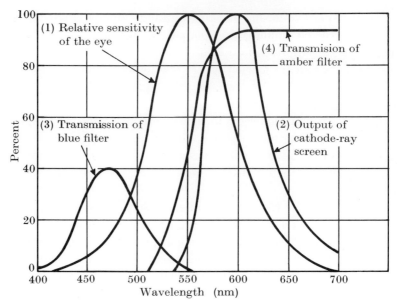

**Fig. 12-23** The relationships in a selective spectrum lighting system.[7]

about as well as does clear glass; the 10 percent light loss is due mainly to reflections from the upper and lower surfaces.

Luminaires were equipped with egg-crate barriers so that all light rays would be essentially vertical. They were located with great care to prevent the operator from receiving either direct glare or glare reflected from the top surface of the amber filter.

Because the blue room light is blocked from the radar screen by the amber filter, the screen appears to be jet black with bright orange spots representing the radar targets. These spots are bright enough that the operator's eyes require little or no dark adaptation.

The lighting is bright enough that a man can enter the room, directly from bright sunlight, and easily recognize nearby people. This aids in avoiding collisions, speeds the man's adaptation to the room environment, and to a limited degree even permits messages to be written and read.

This system, first described by Kraft[18] for use in radar approach control centers, was later adapted to fit the naval shipboard environment.

## SAFETY

Of overriding importance in all designs is the consideration of safety—not only of personnel, but also of equipment and the area in which it is used. The attainment of safety in a design may involve the solution of problems in electrical, thermal, chemical, and mechanical areas. Specific examples are dangerous voltages or currents, extremes of temperature, toxic gases or materials, and sharp corners or rough edges. Mechanical hazards are by far the most common and also the most readily avoidable. Designers should make use of check lists[19] when considering safety in order to assure themselves that nothing has been overlooked. This is one place where "second-best" cannot be tolerated.

The physiological monitor, Fig. 12-24, is an interesting study in hazards. The instrument is used to monitor the heart and brain activity of patients by displaying either the electrocardiogram (ECG) or the electroencephalogram (EEG) during surgery, recovery, and intensive care. Of course, the instrument must not pose a hazard to users or patient. Beyond this, however, is the possibility that the patient's life would be endangered if the instrument should perform imperfectly, or if it should fail at a critical moment.

The human factors criteria for this instrument are extensive. The National Fire Prevention Association requires that, when used in a hospital operating room, the physiological monitor should be operated at least 1.5 meters (5 feet) above the floor, because there may be flammable gases at lower levels. Uninterrupted monitoring is required while the patient is being moved to a recovery area; so the monitor had to be fully portable, free of mechanical hazards, and usable in a variety of positions and environments. Environmental lighting varies from very intense, surrounding the surgical table, to low ambient light in peripheral areas where the anesthetist is located. Yet, the waveforms must be presented so clearly on a large screen (together with function and sweep data) that the possibility of misinterpretation by any of the personnel involved is avoided. An audible "beep" signal further reduces any chance of error. Side mounting of controls, placed in descending order of importance, front-to-rear, allows maximum front-panel area for presentation of information.

## OTHER DESIGN CONSIDERATIONS

Some additional design techniques and considerations are discussed briefly in the following paragraphs. These include the use of biomechanical data, important factors in the design of desk-top equipment, some notes on user expectations, and some cautions regarding equipment-generated noise, the re-use of compromised designs, and the importance of avoiding obnoxious materials.

**Use of Biomechanical Data.** Biomechanical data cover the range, strength, and speed of human movements, as well as body composition and response to such physical forces as acceleration and vibration. These data are essential to the design of hand tools and controls, to the layout of work spaces and tasks, and in the protection of personnel against mechanical force.[10] Biomechanical data and techniques are used extensively in the design of new

(a) Basic monitor

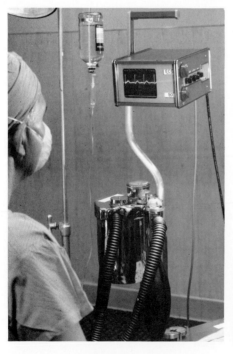

(b) Used in surgery

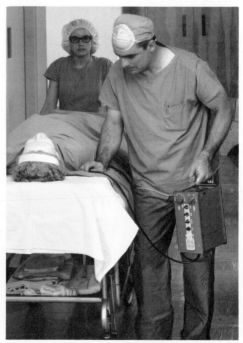

(c) Used during transport

**Fig. 12-24** Physiological monitor. (Permission to reprint courtesy of Tektronix, Inc., Beaverton, Ore.)

facilities, or in the improvement of existing facilities, as illustrated by the two examples that follow.

The first example, the design of a work chair for electronic equipment assemblers in Western Electric Company plants, is given to emphasize the amount of detail involved in what might at first seem to be a very simple exercise.

The seat width and depth must be adequate for those users having the maximum dimensions when seated, and the seat height should be adjustable through a range that will accommodate 95 percent of the using population. This adjustment eliminates the need for footrests for most short people.

The seat should be designed to counteract the operator's tendency to slide forward. Without aid, people oppose this tendency by tightening their leg muscles, with consequent fatigue. This tendency can be eliminated by use of seat padding, which also adds to comfort. An aerated (perforated or woven) seat covering would add to the operator's comfort under warm and humid conditions; however, small, sharp objects could become embedded in the holes or mesh of the weave. Thus, it may be better to use unperforated vinyl sheeting for reasons of safety.

The need to make gross side-to-side or rotational trunk movements dictates that the chair have a swivel. This also lessens the tendency to fatigue that would otherwise result if extreme retraction of an elbow is required.

A backrest is necessary. It should swivel to permit deviation from the vertical plane and, thus, adjust to the vertical contour of the operator's back. It should be adjustable in height through a range to fit the majority of male and female operators. A forward-and-backward adjustment will allow for the wide variation in spinal curvature among operators, and will permit a comfortable adjustment for the operator whose work requires that he sit in a forward position. This adjustment is especially beneficial to female operators during menstrual periods and to any operator who must work for long periods in a fixed position. There should be backrest padding for the lumbar region, but its width should be restricted to prevent interference with retraction of the elbows.

Adjustable and/or detachable armrests should be provided for use when either arm of the operator is motionless or infrequently moved. Casters should be specified where considerable change of position of the body, with respect to the work, is required; they cannot be used, of course, if the feet perform a part of the operation cycle.

The design of a good work chair is but one example in the area of biomechanics. Another is the long-nose pliers used extensively throughout the electronics industry. Medical groups associated with factory operations reported that many of the shop assemblers using the standard, commercial pliers were experiencing a soreness in the palm of the hand and in the forearm.

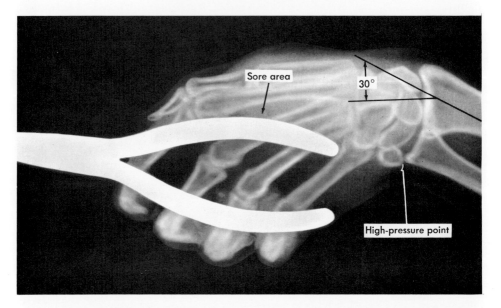

**Fig. 12-25(a)**  X-ray showing the trouble regions caused by using the standard long-nose pliers.

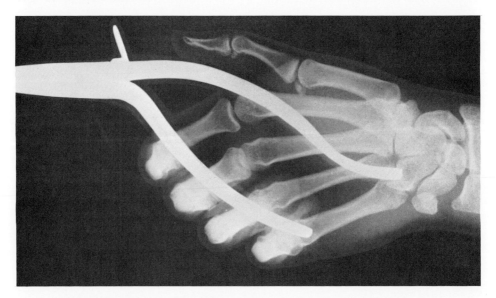

**Fig. 12-25(b)**  X-ray showing a new design long-nose pliers with the troubles eliminated.

The soreness in the palm was found to be caused by the operators' using the pliers with one handle pressing in the tender area of the palm. An X-ray, Fig. 12-25(a), showed that, under normal wiring and assembly conditions, the operators were holding the pliers in such a way that the hand and the forearm were at an angle of approximately 30°. This was creating excessive tension in some of the forearm muscles and compression in others. With the cause of the complaints clearly established, the solution was not difficult, as shown in Fig. 12-25(b).

**Desk-Top Equipment.** Desk-top equipment is an important category because there is so much of it. The requirement that it be convenient to operate while causing a minimum of interference with normal desk activities often poses difficult design problems. Studies have shown that the user is most concerned that desk width be conserved. Next in importance is the front-to-back dimension. The principal restriction on height is that all controls be within comfortable reach.

The PICTUREPHONE® set, Fig. 12-26, which was developed to provide face-to-face communications, poses an exceptional variety of desk-top equipment problems. Many human factors were encountered in the development effort. Perhaps the most interesting one is the difficulty of keeping the subject on screen and seeming to look at the viewer. When user A is viewing his screen and talking to B, he is not looking directly into his own camera. This is because

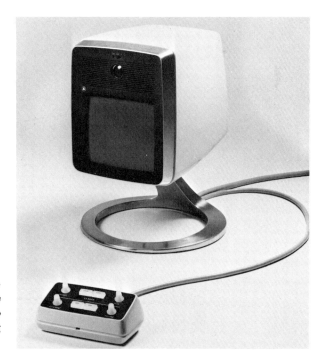

**Fig. 12-26** The PICTURE-PHONE® visual telephone set with camera adjacent to and just above the viewing screen.

the viewing screen and camera cannot occupy the same space. If A's eyes are directed more than 3° away from the camera, B receives the impression that A is being inattentive. The solution was to place the camera as close to the screen as possible, and to establish a minimum separation of 90 cm, the desk depth, between user and camera lens.

Another design problem is created by restless people who will not remain in front of the screen. The user who has a swivel chair equipped with casters is bothersome. One solution would be to widen the screen, but this would require an uneconomical increase in bandwidth.

Many suggestions have been made to resolve this problem. The screen and camera can be placed back in a large hollow cylinder, compelling the viewer to remain in front of the camera in order to see the screen; but this wastes too much valuable desk space. A self-view feature was introduced which consisted of a button the user pressed to see if he was on screen, but this was not successful and violated other operational criteria. Some additional methods which were tried were the use of a small convex mirror placed beneath the camera lens, and another centering device consisting of two concentric overlapping rectangles which have to be lined-up for the subject to be on camera. In the former case, when the viewer sees himself, then he is in view. The most promising solution is to provide an adjustable field of view in conjunction with a wide angle camera lens. This would provide the additional feature of permitting one or two other persons to be "on camera" at the same time.

**User Expectations.** Most people expect certain specific things to happen in some situations. These expectations are usually based on previous training, experience, or intuition. Equipment designed without consideration of these factors will always fall somewhat short of the designer's goal. Although retraining or reindoctrinating the operator is sometimes necessary, there is always the danger that under stress of emergency conditions, the operator may revert to previous habits, possibly endangering personnel and equipment.[20]

For example, a dial tone is always anticipated when a telephone user picks up a handset and prepares to place a call. With conventional telephone switching systems, it informs the user that the switching equipment is ready for dialing to begin. In electronic switching systems, however, there is no functional need for a dial tone. Designers had the alternatives of furnishing a dial tone or retraining the public. Of course, a dial tone was provided.

People usually assume that the purpose of ear plugs is to keep out foreign material and also to reduce noise in a high-noise environment. Although these assumptions are true, ear plugs are also used to protect the ears against damage by high-intensity sounds and to improve the hearing of messages in noisy surroundings, as described in Chapter 11. At one time, a military jet engine had a noise spectrum with a discrete frequency that was above the audible spectrum but of harmful intensity. Special ear plugs were issued to personnel working near these engines, with the sole purpose of preventing inner ear damage. However, nobody thought to give information or instruction about the ear plugs. The users looked for noise reduction which they did not hear. They then concluded that the plugs were no good, discarded them as a poor design, and continued going to sick call. This device, although functionally good, did not achieve its objective because no steps had been taken to educate the users in its purpose.

**Noise.** The designer should be on the lookout for sources of objectionable noise within equipment when it is under development. If strenuous efforts are made to minimize equipment-generated noise, external means of noise suppression can often be avoided. Even if external suppression should still be required, a greater effect can be realized.

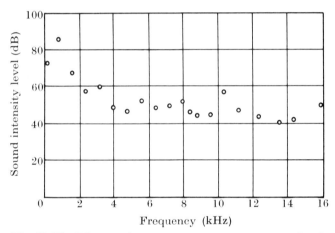

**Fig. 12-27** Discrete frequency spectrum at one point in Florida City terminal.

At a submarine cable terminal in Florida City, station personnel were exposed to an annoying and uncomfortable noise which originated in the 400-Hz power plant. As shown in Fig. 12-27, the sound contained fairly intense components throughout the audible spectrum. Various components in the power circuit convert electrical energy into acoustical energy.

Protective devices were used successfully in the Florida City terminal to muffle the noise to a more comfortable level. To prevent recurrence of this trouble in new systems, a power inverter frequency of 20 kHz was adopted. This frequency is well above the normal hearing range.

**Design Compromises.** Sometimes there are circumstances which necessitate compromises with the best design practices. Designers should be wary of basing new equipment designs on others which may contain these compromises. The following example will illustrate this point.

Ideally, a display panel should be oriented so that the user's line of sight is perpendicular to the surface. For a seated operator, the recommended panel slope for a single, unbroken plane is about 60° above the horizontal.[21] In a target selection and tracking console, Fig. 12-28, used in military shipboard

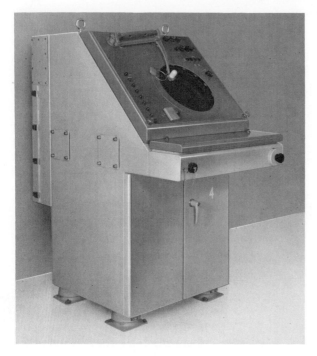

**Fig. 12-28**  Target selection and tracking console for shipboard use.

quipment, the control panel is at an angle of only 45°. This was made necessary (compromised) because there is a very long cathode-ray tube that would project through the back of the console if the panel were nearer to the vertical. The maximum depth of the cabinet was limited by the size of the access hatches in the ship. The resulting compromised design was very successful because it met all of the user requirements and performed well. However, in a new project where similar equipment was needed, a decision was made to use the same console slope of 45°. The results were disastrous because the operators saw strong reflections of the overhead lights in their screens. This problem never existed in the original application because the room illumination level was low.

Figure 12-28 shows other operator features of this equipment that are worth mentioning. The display and control panel was designed to have no unessential visible details. The only protuberances present are those things the operators must manipulate. For example, the lamp caps are mounted under the panel surface. The panel is a plastic sheet lighted from inside so that light is emitted through translucent captions. In the upper right corner of the panel, the adjusting knobs are made of transparent plastic with the visible surfaces painted black, except for a white ring on the top of each knob. Light is coupled into the knob from the main panel; this illuminates the ring, making the knob easy to find in the dark.

**Objectionable Materials.** Sometimes an apparently good design falls short of expectations because of some seemingly trivial detail that annoys the user. A case in point was an early telephone handset which was molded of cellulose butyrate. Users found that it was easily stained by tobacco smoke, kitchen grease, lipstick, etc., and sometimes had a repulsive odor. Later handsets were made from an ABS (acrilonitrile-butadiene-styrene) compound which has an acceptable "kiss resistance." Additional advantages of the new material are that it is easily cleaned with a damp cloth and is less expensive.

Some materials have characteristic odors which can be unpleasant, especially in closed environments. Leather and some plastics, such as the cellulose butyrate cited before, are examples. Another pertinent fact is that odors cling more tenaciously to dark materials than to light ones.[22]

## 12-3. DESIGN FOR INSTALLATION AND MAINTENANCE

Design objectives should not be limited to operational aspects but, just as important, must include features for installation and maintenance. These features often facilitate manufacture as well, but the broader subject of design for manufacture is beyond the scope of this chapter. In all cases, however, the principal costs are related, directly or indirectly, to the cost of work performed by people. The original manufacturing costs are often considered the principal costs, with subsequent costs of secondary importance. However, the installation and maintenance costs incurred during the service lives of many systems are currently running as high as 20 times the manufacturing costs. Moreover, as systems become more complex and as packaging densities increase, the proportionate costs of these functions could further increase unless adequate consideration is given to these factors early in the design and development process.[23] To accomplish this, it is necessary to have a knowledge of the capabilities and characteristics (both mental and physical) of the people who will install and maintain the system, as well as those who will operate it.

Generally, installation begins when the equipment is delivered to the site and terminates when a working system is turned over to a customer. Installation includes such operations as unpacking, handling, erecting, mounting, mechanical aligning, interconnecting, fastening, testing, trouble recognition, diagnosis and correction, and electrical adjusting. On subsequent occasions, the installation personnel are again involved when equipment is functionally expanded or modified for design improvements.

Maintenance, or equipment maintainability, relates to the ability to restore equipment to, or retain it in, serviceable operation. It is a function of parts accessibility, internal layouts, repair and use environment, time, tools, personnel skill, and instructions. There are two primary types of maintenance: routine or preventive, and corrective. The former includes such things as adjusting the terminal equalizer of a submarine cable system for the seasonal temperature changes of the ocean, oiling the bearings of a stepping switch, recalibrating a bridge circuit, cleaning, making amplifier gain adjustment, etc. The latter type is a restorative process necessitated by equipment malfunction.

Although installation and maintenance routines are different with respect to the people and conditions involved, they are considered together since the design features for each overlap. In both cases, craft personnel have similar tasks to perform, and it is these tasks that influence design. This section discusses first the important steps of planning, task analysis, and evaluation, followed by a number of pertinent design considerations, including automatic maintenance facilities, usability of test equipment, accessibility, design options, division of work between the field and shop, growth, and parts minimization. To make equipment more easily installed and maintained requires attention to many major items and a profusion of little ones. Check lists[1,2,8,19,24] offer convenient listings of these items to assist the designer in avoiding the more common pitfalls.

## PLANNING, TASK ANALYSIS, AND EVALUATION

In a broad sense, planning is used to define a system and to assure that it will meet the need for which it is being created; task analysis is a part of this planning which determines how men and machines should work together to fill this need; and evaluation is used to determine what is accomplished and how efficiently. These subjects are discussed here very briefly and only as related to installation and maintenance. More complete treatments are available in the literature.[1,2,8]

Once the installation and maintenance tasks have been identified through planning and task analysis, the design features needed to support these tasks can be established. The success of the resulting design can then be determined by evaluation of either models or working systems. Some of the problems and techniques for their solution are illustrated in the following two examples. The first involves a redesign of communication equipment used in business locations, and the second example applies these processes to the design of a new mass communication system.

Businesses today make widespread use of data sets furnished by the telephone companies. These sets are used in conjunction with other equipment from a variety of sources, with telephone circuits used to provide the interconnections between units at various locations. Unfortunately, experience has shown that when trouble occurs in such an arrangement, the customers find it very convenient to call their local telephone business office, complain, and wait for the repairman to arrive. More times than not, the repairman finds that the fault is not in his equipment. This situation results in unnecessary, additional downtime for the equipment, as well as in wasted man-hours on the part of the telephone company. To combat this, new-model data sets contain built-in loop-back test circuits to be used in combination with remote testing facilities. When a customer reports a trouble condition, his request is turned over to a test center which, in turn, calls the customer and instructs him to press a button on the data set. The test center can now send and receive through the customer data set and fully check out that portion of the equipment. A status report can be given to the customer sooner than was previously possible and with considerably less effort.

The establishment of design objectives for a new multiplex communication system offers a larger-scale example of the use of planning, including a maintenance task analysis. Experience with a previous system showed that there were major problems in the coordination of the test and adjustment activities of maintenance people who were in different locations separated by hundreds of miles. It also became apparent that, with the increasing complexity contemplated for the new system, fully manual maintenance methods would be inadequate. Further studies and evaluation trials, in which new features were actually appended to the previous system, demonstrated the gains to be expected by the use of automatic measurement and adjustment facilities, and by the simplification of those operations which must continue on a manual basis. By making adjustments the instant they are needed, automatic regulation minimizes the need for coordination of other adjustments. A man making a manual adjustment can feel confident that a preceding level is always being held at a proper value. In other words, the usefulness of the adjustment he has just made is not likely to be destroyed by the delayed reaction of technical personnel elsewhere in the system. This regulation also provides the obvious advantage of freeing skilled manpower for the more demanding and less predictable maintenance tasks.

Other results of these planning and evaluation studies are summarized in the following design objectives which were established to facilitate installation and maintenance:

1. In-service testing and maintenance with conveniently available test facilities.
2. Improved accessibility to all components.

3. Automatic scanning and alarm circuits to facilitate maintenance by warning of impending failures, by identifying trouble, and by indicating corrective action to be taken.

4. Active elements to be mounted in plug-in assemblies, introducing a high degree of flexibility and ease of installation and maintenance.

5. Equipment arranged to reduce wire and cabling between units.

## AUTOMATIC MAINTENANCE FACILITIES

Requirements for larger electronic systems are growing more severe. Because of the very large number of parts of which these systems are composed, individual units must be held to very close tolerances to ensure good overall performance. Also, there is an increasing need for continuity of service, which is being intensified by the high cost of equipment and by new service offerings. For instance, the telephone plant is being used more and more to transmit data outside of regular business hours. These combined requirements are placing new burdens on maintenance that can be satisfied only by special-purpose maintenance circuits designed as an integral part of the equipment. In this way, no disturbance of service is necessary for most maintenance routines, and the burden on maintenance personnel is minimized. Other advantages include centralized control and maintenance of the facilities, automatic alarms to call prompt attention to any disorder, prevention of trouble propagation, prompt restoration of service, and the resulting increased availability of the equipment to perform its intended function. Although these circuits are intended primarily for maintenance purposes, they greatly assist installation as well.

The master control center for the electronic switching system shown previously in Fig. 1-10 is an example. The teletypewriter provides two-way communication between the system and maintenance personnel. The typing of appropriate coded messages directs the system to perform a wide variety of test routines, to change the in-service or standby status of various system units, and even to change the telephone number of a customer or to provide him with special service features. The system, in turn, types out the results of various tests performed or the verification that instructions have been followed. In case of trouble, it also prints out information on the trouble location, often identifying the particular circuit pack that may be at fault, as well as any actions the system may have taken to bypass such difficulty. Two bays to the right of the teletypewriter provide a continuous display of the in-service, standby, or trouble status of the various units, a manual control for overriding the system in emergencies, and facilities for a variety of line and trunk tests.

## USABILITY OF TEST EQUIPMENT

Maintenance routines can be simplified and performed more quickly by applying to the test equipment the principles described in Sec. 12-2, which improve the efficiency of the operator or user. This is illustrated with the "Vectorscope," Fig. 12-29, which was designed to measure easily, at television broadcasting facilities, the hue, luminance, saturation, level, and phase of the

**Fig. 12-29**  "Vectorscope" used to measure color television signals. (Permission to reprint courtesy of Tektronix, Inc., Beaverton, Ore.)

National Television System Committee composite color television signal. Proper operation of this instrument is obtained by pressing only one button in each group. The screen trace intensity and focus are kept in adjustment automatically. Self-checking calibration signals are internally generated and are similarly utilized by the press of a button. Seldom-used operational controls are grouped behind the lower access doors, eliminating operator confusion and visual clutter from the front panel.

## ACCESSIBILITY

For all maintenance and installation activities, the designer's watchword should be accessibility. This is not to say that every component has to be exposed or readily accessible from behind access panels. It is important, however, that those components that are most subject to failure and those that require routine adjustment be available, both readily and safely.

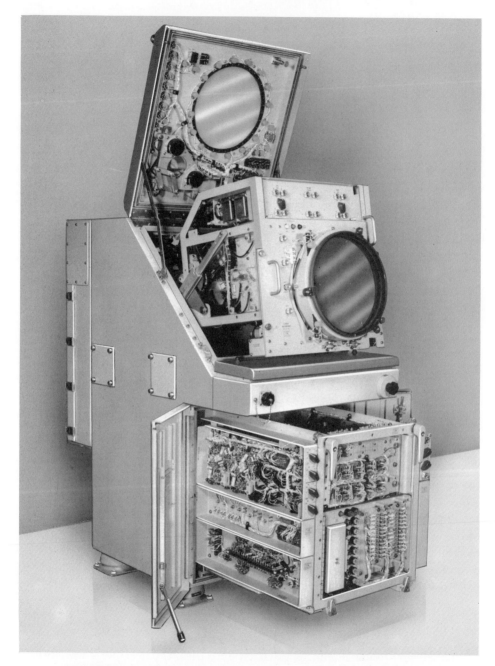

**Fig. 12-30**  Target selection and tracking console partially opened for servicing.

The shipboard radar console shown previously in Fig. 12-28 is a good example of complete accessibility when opened for servicing, as shown in Fig. 12-30. The bottom doors are opened and held against the deck with crutch-tipped sway braces. This prevents the rolling and pitching of the ship from closing the doors. The two units in the front of the bottom drawer are hinged along the left edge, giving access to all points inside the drawer; there is also complete access to all wiring on the sides. The heavy top drawer containing the cathode-ray tube is counterbalanced by strong coil springs, which relieve the operator's arms of most of the weight when he opens it. After this drawer is fully withdrawn, it can be tilted down as shown. The wide unit at the upper front of this drawer is also hinged so that it can be turned completely upside down for complete in-service testing without removing it or disabling its function. Another portion of this system is housed in an equipment cabinet. With the main cabinet doors opened and secured on the sides, the front edges of four main drawers are exposed; the drawers contain the maintenance support equipment, e.g., fuses and spares, tube pin straighteners, meters, switches, test jacks, indicator lights, etc. The lower portion, Fig. 12-31, swings open, giving

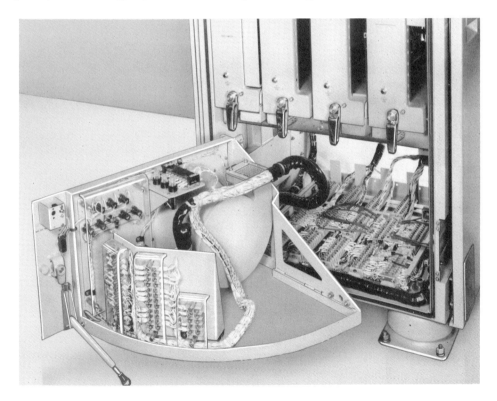

**Fig. 12-31**  Equipment cabinet with local lighting in the installation region.

complete access to the large terminal field in the floor of the cabinet. All incoming cables terminate here, easing and limiting the installation process to this area. This section also contains its own built-in (local) lighting.

An interlock switch used in the radar console equipment offers a convenient way for servicing with due consideration to personnel safety. The switch is placed behind door or access panels in such a way that the plunger is depressed to the position in Fig. 12-32(a) when the doors or panels are closed, applying power to the system. If an entry is made into any region by the opening of a door or panel, then the switch would open-circuit the applied voltages [Fig. 12-32(b)]. When maintenance has to be performed on a working circuit, the craftsman needs only to pull the plunger fully out [Fig. 12-32(c)] and the system again becomes activated. Closing the panel automatically resets the switch to its normal mode. An interlock switch of this type is a good solution for many systems which require access to components with power on during troubleshooting or testing. When the hazards are too great, the system must be designed to avoid the need for such activity. In this case, a switch with a "cheat" position should not be used.

## DESIGN OPTIONS

When equipment has to be utilized in various ways in order to satisfy the different requirements of various applications, the designer has a special challenge. He can determine the features needed for each application, specify those which are common to all as part of the basic design and list the remainder as a number of special options to be provided only where needed. This is a relatively easy and common procedure, but it often results in high manufacturing cost for those features needed in small quantities, high administration costs, and limited versatility of the equipment. Also, installation becomes more

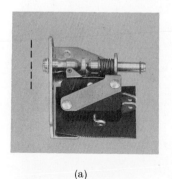 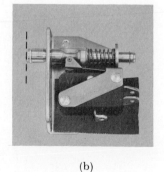 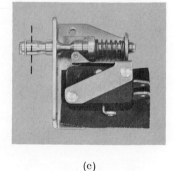

(a)                           (b)                           (c)

**Fig. 12-32**  Interlock switch for personnel and equipment protection. (a) Door closed, circuit complete, normal conditions. (b) Door opened, circuit opened. (c) Door opened, switch in "cheat" position, circuit complete, maintenance conditions.

difficult because of the larger variety of parts to be assembled and tested, and maintenance becomes more involved since each application may require specially tailored procedural instructions, stocking of spare parts, and specially trained personnel.

A far superior approach is to minimize or eliminate options by use of a single, "universal" design which satisfies all requirements, including cost. The additional cost of providing unneeded features can often be more than off-set by savings of the kinds suggested above  The following is a very simple example of a design for universal mounting arrangements.

Stimulated by a growing need for a coin telephone that could be installed in various quantities and be adaptable to its surroundings, telephone designers developed a unique "versatel" unit designed around a 45° right triangle, as shown in Fig. 12-33.[25] The applications of this telephone are almost unlimited,

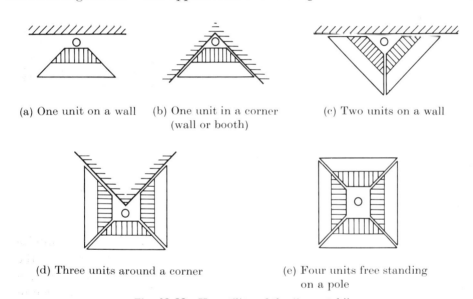

(a) One unit on a wall      (b) One unit in a corner          (c) Two units on a wall
                                (wall or booth)

(d) Three units around a corner        (e) Four units free standing
                                          on a pole

**Fig. 12-33**    Versatility of the "versatel."

and the installation procedures are almost universal. Not only do they satisfy the design objectives, they also find increased use in situations where space is limited. For example, four units arranged around one point in a space only 82 cm square, Fig. 12-34, occupy the same space that would normally be required for a single, full-sized telephone booth. The "versatel" is used either as a walk-up unit or as a drive-up unit. To minimize downtime and maintenance require-ments, consideration was given to such things as vehicular damage and the weight of children who might climb on top of the units to watch a passing parade.

The principle illustrated here is broadly applicable throughout system and device design. Overall costs, as well as installation and maintenance effort, can often be minimized by concentrating demands on a few standard building

**Fig. 12-34** Four-station walk-up installation.

blocks of maximum versatility, minimizing the varieties and codes to take advantage of economies inherent in large volume production.

### FIELD VERSUS SHOP EFFORT

As a general rule, electronic equipment should be designed so as to minimize field installation effort. Any work that can be done as well or better in the factory should be done there, rather than in the field. This results in both shorter installation time and lower overall cost. In addition, an improvement in quality can often be achieved. For instance, shop wiring ensures that a consistent cabling plan will be followed; this avoids unexpected crosstalk or other interference caused by a variety of field cabling techniques. It also becomes possible to test the wiring with production-type test equipment in order to detect errors that would otherwise require extensive field investigation. This is not to say that the field installer could not perform these functions satisfactorily. As pointed out earlier, however, the quality of human output is a function of (among other things) his tools and environment, and the conditions in the shops are more ideal than those in the field for these functions. The principle outlined here is illustrated by the following examples.

During installation of a system for automatic identification of telephone numbers, installers were required to make 4000 wire connections per frame using cross-connection lists issued for each location. These lists were based on class-of-service listings, that is, private line, two-party, four-party, multiparty, or private branch exchange. A study of this problem showed that over 70 per-cent of all connections made were of one variety of strapping. It was then decided that the shop should strap all positions with that particular variety of strapping. This required the installer to remove and restrap only those terminals involved in some other class of service. As a result, wiring errors were greatly reduced, and installation intervals were shortened. Further, even though the total amount of wire connecting and disconnecting was increased, an annual net saving of $208,000 was achieved.

As another example, consider a multiplex system developed for use either in the telephone company Community Dial Offices or in customers' business locations. The basic unit is mounted in a unitized, double-width frame about 2 meters high. To avoid options within the equipment, this frame arrangement is provided for both applications. When used in telephone offices, a 60-cm bay extender is provided to increase the bay height in order to use the overhead framing in the office. The additional space is used to mount auxiliary equip-ment needed for office use but not on the customers' premises. The basic unit is shop-wired and shipped with the plug-in units needed for each particular installation. All external (installer) connections are made to terminal strips at the top of the bay. Although plug-in units may be ordered separately as needed, the factory provides all intrabay wiring for all packages. Even though some of this wiring may never be needed, this procedure eliminates the greater expense of recalling the installer to add channels up to the capacity of the design.

Plug-in techniques are increasingly used to reduce total costs by facilitating both installation and maintenance, and reducing downtime. These savings often greatly outweigh any increase in shop cost associated with the con-nectors. When many codes of plug-in modules are available, however, there is the possibility that units may be plugged into the wrong positions. This can occur when modules look alike, which they usually do when a designer mini-mizes, as he should, the variety of piece-parts used. This difficulty can be avoided, however, by keying the modules and mating frame connectors. Color-coding schemes can also be used. Such techniques avoid improper orientation of modules, as well as their insertion in the wrong locations.

## GROWTH

Many of the problems that arise in central offices and other terminals result from changes in circuit assignments and normal growth. These problems not only result in higher expense for installation and maintenance, but often cause cable congestion and other cable-related problems, e.g., connectors and splicing.

The problems associated with growth can be handled best when the design is in the development stage by making provision for growth via plug-in modules or cables in preallocated space. The technique of growth in increments of completely wired bays, as discussed earlier, makes it possible to have the greatest flexibility with the least installation effort. The cost of carrying the initially unused equipment is usually more than compensated by the cost savings in installation time, tools, and waste. To facilitate changes that may be needed on a periodic basis, changeable circuit assignments can be handled by use of a distributing frame in lieu of permanent-type connections.

## PARTS MINIMIZATION

Customers have increased confidence in equipment when there is a minimum of effort and time spent on installation. In addition to benefiting from low installation costs, they feel that if the equipment goes together easily it must be well designed and therefore will perform better. A striking example of this is the typical combination distributing frame, which is used for the routing of a variety of cables. This relatively simple unit, formerly shipped in 18 boxes containing a total of 689 loose parts, required 17 man-hours to assemble. The unit was redesigned to permit shipment to the installation site in one piece.

As another example, difficulty was encountered in a large, new switching system with regard to the duct-closing and other details used for junctioning of adjacent frames. The main source of the difficulty was the large quantity and variety of the details and the even larger numbers of machine screws needed for assembly. It was a complex job for the installer to sort out and assemble these many thousands of parts and an equally arduous task to remove and reassemble many of then during maintenance.

A design change was introduced which replaced the loose screws and sheet metal details with captive screws and preassembled panels. Other details were also made captive, or packaged with the frames on which they were to be used, greatly reducing the effort required in searching for and identifying the parts needed at the various stages of installation. These simple changes simplified both installation and maintenance, with attendant time savings and a substantial reduction in parts.

## 12-4. DESIGN FOR APPEARANCE

The final evaluation of a product is usually based on its performance in the environment of use, and it is made by the people whom it is to serve, not the designer. This evaluation is highly subjective. If the product performs poorly, it is obviously unsatisfactory. On the other hand, a product that performs well, or even moderately well, may be judged largely by its appearance, and the initial impression often depends entirely on this factor. A good appearance leads to confidence in good performance. Installers are known to take better care of equipment that "will work better because it *looks* like it will work better." Finally, there is the simple psychological satisfaction a person receives when operating a well-engineered, esthetically pleasing piece of equipment rather than a poorly designed one.

Although good appearance can be appreciated by most people, qualities that are attractive to one person may not be so to another, since each of us holds individual, subjective judgments of what he observes. There are, however, some basic principles that can be applied which will cause no major disagreement. The first of these is that good appearance is a natural result of the design process and not something that is added on at the end. Industrial designer Henry Dreyfuss[22] has said, "If . . . design goals have been realized, then the product will automatically approach good appearance. The designer must consider line and form, proportion, texture, and color, and integrate them into a pleasing whole." To accomplish the latter requires an understanding of the psychological effects of these factors on people. All objects contain these factors, and depending on what effect a designer is trying to create, there is a combination that can help to achieve his goal.

In addition to the variations among people, the public view as to what is attractive is continually changing. This is nowhere more evident than in the automotive industry, where designers each year try to anticipate what people will be buying. At the same time, the standards and tastes of customers are considerably influenced by what is available. This helps with sales but also places a responsibility upon designers to raise the level of taste and to improve standards.

Fortunately, changes in what is considered attractive proceed more slowly with most electronic equipment. Even so, some trends are clearly discernible. For instance, the round pushbuttons and rounded cabinet edges of the recent past have given way to a preference for square buttons and square edges—in some applications. Such trends can be anticipated by industrial designers who specialize in this field, and if equipment is to last over a period of years without appearance obsolescence, these professionals should be consulted. Some of the basic principles for good appearance will be briefly described in this section. However, it is clear that these form only the framework within which appearance preferences may fluctuate.

## COLOR

Color is the first thing we see when we look at anything and the thing remembered longest. It can create in people both illusory and emotional effects. For example, color can make people gay or sad, disrupt their digestion or make them ill, relax them or produce fatigue, suggest youth or age, and suggest intimacy or hostility. The impact of color in the industrial scene has an enormous influence emotionally and even physically.[26]

The color associations of people fall into familiar patterns. For example, yellow or yellow on black indicates caution and implies striking hazards such as low beams, stairways, and the edges of platforms. Orange and red warn of immediate danger, and green indicates go or safety.

By the use of contrasting colors on adjacent walls and ceilings, the apparent width and height of rooms can be altered. Dark or heavy colors can create a sense of security or a sense of heaviness. On the other hand, light colors suggest a lack of weight. For example, the grilles on room air-conditioners typically have a dull finish and are of lighter color than the case. This is done to give the impression of a smaller unit size and weight.[22]

Colors can influence each other favorably or otherwise. Because color exists only in its relation to the color or colors next to it, it is essential to understand and make use of these color relationships. The ideal background color for use in displaying small areas of light color, with minimal distortion, is pale, neutral gray or white. If the color samples are glossy, then the background finish should be dull, and vice versa. Dark colors look dramatic, and their richness is enhanced when displayed against a black or dark gray ground.

Certain colors have a definite affinity for certain designs, shapes, contours, and textures in much the same way that colors complement and harmonize or distort and clash with each other. Line and color interrelate with remarkable finesse, and it takes a practiced eye, long experience, and understanding to minimize mistakes in this highly specialized area.[27]

The use of color as a design tool is usually done for one or more of the following purposes:

1. Create an appropriate psychological atmosphere.
2. Minimize eye adjustment if there is constant eye motion.
3. Call attention to tasks and hazards.
4. Call attention to or conceal physical features.
5. Improve visibility.
6. Conceal dirt.

Greater in-plant color coordination has been recognized as a basic objective by many companies. Even in areas where the public was heretofore barred, new public relations policies are making plants and industrial complexes more accessible, thus increasing the need for attention to appearance. Of even greater importance is the requirement for an attractive working environment for the personnel normally in these areas.

In the design of frame lineups for an electronic switching system, much

**Fig. 12-35** Equipment frame lineup for an electronic switching system.[28]

attention was given to appearance; the results are shown in Fig. 12-35. Missing from this illustration, however, is an important feature—the attractive color scheme. Cable rack enclosures at the top, end covers, and the frame bases are a dark shade of textured blue-gray, which makes an attractive contrasting border around the light glossy blue-gray equipment within each lineup. Although the covers at the ends of the lineups contain maintenance features, their main purposes are to protect and to dress-up the lineup. The light-colored equipment is thus enclosed within a darker frame, and the eye rests on a complete entity.

## TEXTURE

Texture complements color as a means for either accentuating or subduing physical features and for providing harmonious contrast. It also plays important roles in the "feel" of a product and in concealing surface blemishes.

Textures can be applied either to the metal itself, in a rolling, perforating, etching, or brushing process, or in paints applied to the surface after fabrication. In the latter case, the rougher textures are often produced by controlled spraying of viscous paints, by using paints consisting of small globules suspended in water, or by spraying the partially hardened surface with solvents which selectively attack various small areas. The wrinkle paints, which obtain their texture by surface expansion during drying, have lost most of their popularity because of their dust-catching qualities, poor cleanability, and reduced abrasion resistance as compared with some newer finishes now available. In any case, texturing must be done with care because it affects the apparent color as well as surface structure, and poor control can result in very objectionable mismatches.

The traffic service position console discussed previously provides a rather specialized example of the use of textured finishes. In addition to the requirements that the finish be durable, nonglaring, and attractive, the designers were required to create a "warm feeling" to the touch. Because of their high heat conductivity, metals do not usually have this characteristic, and since the operators were in constant contact with the console, this shortcoming had to be resolved. The use of textured vinyl finishes in substantial thickness remedied the situation.

## LINE, FORM, AND PROPORTION

The psychological effects that can be achieved with the application of line, form, and proportion are comparable with those mentioned for color and texture; indeed, the overall effect depends strongly on the manner in which these factors are combined. No attempt will be made here to cover the philosophies associated with use of line, form, and proportion, since numerous books are available on this subject.[29-32] A brief discussion is necessary, however, to show their importance.

The optical illusion in which the eye is fooled into believing something different from what truly exists is simply the effect of the interrelations of line and form.[33] Geometric patterns can similarly create these effects. For example, the designer adds shading to a plane surface to create the illusion of a third dimension. The desk-type telephone set which is in most common use today was contoured in a particular way to make the set look lower than it really is by minimizing surface reflections.[22]

Some geometric patterns have been found to be pleasing or restful to the eye, while others create restlessness. Rectangular shapes are more pleasing than squares. Shapes that are nearly square tend to be misread as square, with resulting eye discomfort in trying to make them conform.

If a square or nearly square shape is needed, a pleasing result can often be obtained by sectionalizing the area so as to remove attention from the main proportions. However, sectionalizing can cause a competition for attention, causing an uncomfortable eye decision, unless one area is made to dominate.

The storage display unit, Fig. 12-36, is a good example. Here, a nearly square shape (30.2 cm high and 29.6 cm wide) was properly masked by sectionalizing the area into three rectangles. The primary purpose of this equipment is to display alphanumeric and graphic data; the dominance of the viewing screen is therefore functionally correct, as well as convenient. The eye rests comfortably on this well-proportioned area since there is no competition for attention from the other areas or from the whole.

Possibly the most esthetically pleasing rectangle, as established by subjective testing and used widely from the time of ancient Greece, is the

**Fig. 12-36** Storage display unit. (Permission to reprint courtesy of Tektronix, Inc., Beaverton, Ore.)

"golden section," a rectangle whose length-to-width ratio is approximately 1.618. Many rectangles in our daily life are very close to the golden section, i.e., the 3 × 5 index card, the 11 × 17 painting, etc.

The design of most equipment usually contains form combinations and, in particular, nested forms. Whether or not the nesting array contains two, three, or many of the basic shapes, i.e., squares, rectangles, circles, etc., the rule to follow for better eye appeal is that the center should shift progressively upward and/or the spacing should be progressively smaller as the center is approached; see Fig. 12-37.[29,34]

## CLEANLINING

Today, the process of combining color, texture, line, form, and proportion to make a harmonious, esthetically appealing whole has been called

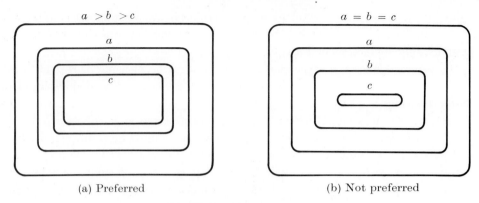

(a) Preferred                    (b) Not preferred

**Fig. 12-37**   Nesting areas.

*cleanlining,* possibly in contrast to streamlining so diligently practiced in times past. To call a design "clean" is perhaps the most common way to compliment it. A basic feature of cleanlining is the absence of irrelevancies. The design is purged of nonessentials, distractions, obscurities, and ambiguities. This applies not only to the display and control areas discussed earlier, but also to those additive elements like decorations and trimmings that are supposedly used to dress-up a design.

In the electronic switching frames, shown previously in Fig. 12-35, clean-lining is achieved by designing and grouping components to obtain regional uniformity within the frames of a lineup. That is, the components and equip-ment of similar depth are located together in planar regions, or groupings, in order to avoid the eye-irritating effect of haphazard surface contouring. This clean surface effect, when combined with color and texture, achieves a good overall appearance without the use of covering-up techniques. Indeed, the interest associated with a well-ordered display of functional elements makes this a preferred approach if covers are considered only for appearance value.

With high-speed systems requiring minimal lengths of connecting wires, function often dictates component placement. When this is combined with the fact the component design is sometimes beyond the system designer's control, then another alternative must be found in order to enhance the system's appearance. One of the more common methods is to enclose functional groupings of components within building blocks of uniform external appearance and mounting arrangement. This was the approach followed in the master-group multiplex equipment, Fig. 12-38. Recognizing the limitations, appearance was considered during the talking stage of the development program. Artists' renditions were made in order to paper-test the esthetic features of the design. This allowed all concerned the opportunity to offer constructive suggestions while there was ample time to implement changes. In the figure, the artist's rendition can be compared with a photograph of the finished product.

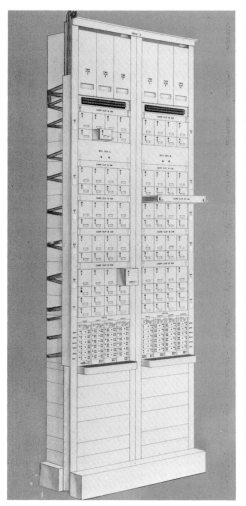

(a) Artist's rendition　　　　　(b) Actual equipment

**Fig. 12-38**　Mastergroup multiplex equipment.

Sometimes considered the last resort, but not necessarily so, is the covering-up technique, used when the system objectives can be met with a heterogeneous assortment of existing functional blocks and when the number of systems needed is too small for redesign to be feasible. In this case, each functional block has its own form and perhaps color, independent from the others. An example of this is found in a submarine cable terminal where liberal use is made of existing components combined with some newly designed ones. To make this functionally satisfactory system presentable, covering-up techniques were employed, as shown in Fig. 12-39.

**Fig. 12-39** Four-bay lineup of submarine cable terminal equipment (artist's rendition).

On many occasions, covering-up techniques are specified in the design objectives. This may be due to harsh external environments, i.e., for protection, or for purely esthetic reasons where the design is required to blend with surroundings such as typical office furniture, Fig. 12-40. In the latter case, the designer can choose from a standard offering of modular wall- or floor-mounted

**Fig. 12-40** Equipment cabinet for a communication system designed to blend and harmonize with typical office furniture.[35]

equipment cabinets. The user is usually not interested in what is contained in these cabinets, just as long as the equipment performs its required functions, blends harmoniously with its environment, and is easily maintained. Many manufacturers offer a variety of modular cabinets which are designed to be flexible in use and attractive to the eye. Harmonious blending with a variety of surroundings can be achieved by maintaining a soft neutrality of any exposed display and control areas, and by using such finishes as dull, satin-anodized aluminum, matte or textured paints of subdued colors, and plastic materials with nonglare surfaces.

## CUSTOMIZING

With an increased standard of living has come an increased public sensitivity to esthetic values. This has been accompanied by a growing demand among architects for commercial equipment that harmonizes with, and esthetically contributes to, the decor of the surrounding environment, for use in prime locations such as airport terminals, shopping center malls, and the foyers of public buildings. With this growing market for new designs having an increased emphasis upon appearance, it has become urgent for the telephone companies (among others) to make new offerings to satisfy these needs. The undesirable alternative would be to exclude public telephone facilities from the direct view of the public in these prime locations.

Toward this end, designers have embarked on a limited program of working with local architects. One result of this endeavor is known as the "circular serpentine," Fig. 12-41. The first of these units was located in a new shopping center known as Plymouth Meeting Mall in suburban Philadelphia, where it was required to present a "gay appearance compatible with the warm atmosphere created by the use of soft materials throughout the shopping center." A metallic, machine-like appearance was to be avoided.

The installed facility consists of six walk-in, partially enclosed modules in a circular array about a central supporting column with a disc-type canopy and light overhead. The modules are attached to a central structure which, in turn, is bolted to a column. This cantilever mounting arrangement eliminates the need for a cluttered array of supporting legs, greatly enhancing the soft, flowing lines of the modules. These lines are accented by the flared contour of the shrouds covering the center post and white caps on the topside and underside of the modules. The modules are tapered toward the outside so that the white caps on top and bottom are tangent to imaginary conical surfaces centered about the post. The perforated metal sheet covering the module is painted soft blue, the module caps are white, and the central support structure and canopy tops are charcoal blue. All other surfaces are stainless steel.

The effective outside diameter of the assembled facility is 2.7 meters (9 feet), which was selected with due consideration given to human factors

**Fig. 12-41**  Six-station "circular serpentine" in use at Indianapolis Airport.

criteria.  Each module contains a panel telephone, a directory compartment for two books, recessed lighting above the telephone and directory compartment, and a writing shelf.  Acoustically treated surfaces are provided to minimize the effect of ambient noise.

## SUMMARY

This chapter has briefly described some of the principles of man-machine interaction, with emphasis on those factors that contribute to the comfort, efficiency, and safety of people.  The need to consider all people—those who install and maintain electronic equipment as well as those who use it—has been indicated.  Also, recognizing that functional and esthetic objectives are of comparable importance, some of the principles concerning each have been sketched.

Application of these principles often requires new and different approaches which reflect creativity and imagination.  These should be undertaken with confidence that change will produce exciting results in the future, as it has in the past. Although the physical designer cannot hope to become expert in all the areas that contribute to good human factors design, he can enlist the help of specialists to achieve designs which satisfy both functional and cost objectives, while retaining a vitality and freshness of appearance.

## REFERENCES

1. McCormick, E. J., *Human Factors Engineering*, New York, McGraw-Hill Book Co., 1964. Detailed treatment of human characteristics and man-machine relationships. Research investigations and experimental procedures are covered. Emphasis on systems aspects of design. Figure 12-2 by permission.

2. Morgan, C. T., J. S. Cook, III, A. Chapanis, and M. W. Lund, *Human Engineering Guide to Equipment Design*, New York, McGraw-Hill Book Co., 1963. A very thorough and current guide to human factors engineering design practices. Figures 12-7, 12-9, and 12-10 by permission.

3. Gardner, M. F., and J. L. Barnes, *Transients in Linear Systems*, New York, John Wiley & Sons, Inc., 1942. Treatise on the analysis of linear, lumped-constant systems by means of the Laplace transformation.

4. Mitchell, M. B., "Systems Analysis—The Human Element," *Electro-Technology*, **77,** No. 4, April, 1966. A survey of recent efforts to define the human element in man-machine closed-loop control systems. Extensive bibliography.

5. Birmingham, H. P., and F. V. Taylor, "Why Quickening Works," *Automatic Control*, **8,** No. 4, 16–18, April, 1958.

6. McCormick, E. J., *Human Engineering*, New York, McGraw-Hill Book Co., 1957. Good basic text on the use of human factors in design.

7. Hammell, R., "Displays for Weapon Direction Equipments," *Bell Laboratories Record*, **39,** 367–369, Oct., 1961. Figures 12-8 and 12-23 by permission.

8. Woodson, W. E., and D. W. Conover, *Human Engineering Guide for Equipment Designers*, 2nd ed., Berkeley, University of California Press, 1964. A detailed guide to human engineering design practices. Excellent chapter on the systems approach to design. Figure 12-11 by permission.

9. Jenkins, W. L., and M. B. Connor, "Some Design Factors in Making Settings on a Linear Scale," *J. Appl. Psychol.*, 395–409, 1949, The Amer. Psychol. Ass'n.

10. Damon, A., H. W. Stoudt, and R. A. McFarland, *The Human Body in Equipment Design*, Cambridge, Mass., Harvard University Press, 1966. Application of anthropometric and biomechanical data to equipment design.

11. Funck, R. H., "Designing the Traffic Service Position Console," *Bell Laboratories Record*, **42,** 210, June, 1964. Figure 12-16 by permission.

12. Dreyfuss, H., *The Measure of Man*, 2nd ed., New York, Whitney Library of Design, 1967. A compilation of anthropometric data including full-size charts of the human body.

13. Bartley, K. D., "The New Look in Public Telephone Stations," *Bell Laboratories Record*, **44**, Jan., 1966, Bell Telephone Laboratories. Figure 12-18 by permission.

14. Luckiesh, M., *Light, Vision and Seeing*, Princeton, N.J., D. Van Nostrand Co. Inc., 1944. A simplified presentation of the relationships and importance of light, vision, and seeing in human efficiency and welfare.

15. *IES Lighting Handbook*, 4th ed., New York, Illuminating Engineering Society, 1966. Standard reference on light measurement and design of illumination facilities. Figure 12-20 by permission.

16. Morgan, C. T., *Theory and Problems of Radar Visibility*, NRL Report 3965, April, 1952, Washington, D.C., Naval Research Laboratory.

17. Hanes, R. M., and S. B. Williams, "Visibility on Cathode Ray Tube Screens: The Effects of Light Adaptation," *J. Opt. Soc. Amer.*, pp. 363–377, 1938.

18. Kraft, C. L., *A Broad Band Blue Lighting System for Radar Approach Control Centers: Evaluation and Refinements Based on Three Years of Operational Use*, WADC Technical Report 56-71, Aug., 1956, Wright Air Development Center, Wright-Patterson Air Force Base, Ohio.

19. Truax, et al., *Human Engineering Design Criteria Study*, Technical Report No. N66-21824, NASA, 1966. For use by design engineers on the subject of human engineering application of control-display interactions, human capabilities, human responses, anthropometry, work space, illumination, vibration, noise, temperature, clothing, safety and maintainability; contains many check lists, scales, and references.

20. Javitz, A. E., "Engineering Psychology and Human Factors In Design," *Electro-Technology*, **67**, No. 5, May, 1961.

21. Ireland, F. H., and J. L. Hanna, "Graphic Aids for Console Designers," *Industrial Design*, **12**, No. 2, Feb., 1965.

22. Dreyfuss, H., *Designing for People*, New York, Paragraphic Books, 1967. Very interesting reading on the industrial design story with an emphasis on the user.

23. Chapanis, A., *Man-Machine Engineering*, Belmont, California, Wadsworth Publishing Company, 1965. A comprehensive treatment of man-machine engineering, written in a nontechnical format for the layman.

24. Tolcott, M. A., A. N. Chambers, P. Preusser, and Staff of Dunlap & Associates, Inc., "Human-Factors Engineering—Design Standards," *Electro-Technology*, **68**, No. 2, Aug., 1961.

25. Ericsson, J. W., "Walk-up, Drive-up Coin Telephone Mounting," *Bell Laboratories Record*, **43**, May, 1965.

26. Ketcham, H., "Color in Marketing," *Industrial Design*, **12**, No. 7, July, 1965.

27. Birren, F., *New Horizons in Color*, New York, Reinhold Publishing Corp., 1955. Industrial applications of color and illumination are discussed.

28. Ferguson, J. G., et al., "No. 1 ESS Apparatus and Equipment," *Bell System Tech. J.*, **43**, No. 5, Part 2 (2355), 1964, The American Telephone and Telegraph Co. Figure 12-35 by permission.

29. Van Doren, H., *Industrial Design*, New York, McGraw-Hill Book Co., 1954. A full discussion of industrial design with a thorough treatment of line, form, and proportion.

30. Read, H., *Art and Industry*, London, Faber & Faber Ltd., 1953. Discusses the relationships between art, technology, and esthetic values with the objective of creating esthetic standards for new technologies.

31. Teague, W. D., *Design This Day*, New York, Harcourt, Brace & World, Inc., 1949. A method of approach outlining the techniques toward solution of any problem in industrial design. Well illustrated, covering the panorama from products to human environments.

32. Hambidge, J., *Practical Applications of Dynamic Symmetry*, New Haven, Conn., Yale University Press, 1932 (also New York, The Devin-Adain Co., 1960). A series of lectures on the theory of dynamic symmetry (as contrasted to static symmetry), its relationship to natural forms, rhythmic composition, and design. Some mathematical support is also presented.

33. Luckiesh, M., *Visual Illusions*, Princeton, N. J., D. Van Nostrand Co., Inc., 1922 (also New York, Drew Publications, 1965). A thorough introduction to visual illusions in layman's language. Virtually all known types are categorized, with examples.

34. Hornung, C. P., *Handbook of Designs and Devices*, New York, Drew Publications, 1946. A thoroughly illustrated handbook, with commentary, on the geometry of space division as a foundation for decorative design.

35. Abbott, H. H., "Sixty Years of PBX Development, "*Bell Laboratories Record*, **46**, 8, Jan., 1968, Bell Telephone Laboratories, Inc. Figure 12-40 by permission.

# APPENDICES

*Appendix A*

# SUPPLEMENTAL TABLES AND CHARTS
# FOR PART I—
# STATICS AND DYNAMICS OF STRUCTURES

| Material | Condition | Young's modulus (GN/m²) | Young's modulus ($10^6$ psi) | Poisson's ratio | Yield strength, 0.2% offset (MN/m²) | Yield strength, 0.2% offset ($10^3$ psi) | Tensile strength (MN/m²) | Tensile strength ($10^3$ psi) | Elongation % in 5.08 cm (2 in.) | Hardness Bhn = Brinell R = Rockwell |
|---|---|---|---|---|---|---|---|---|---|---|
| Steel, structural | Typical | 207 | 30 | 0.292 | 207–276 | 30–40 | 345–448 | 50–65 | 30–40 | 75$R_B$ |
| Steel, AISI 1040, med. carbon | Normalized | 207 | 30 | 0.292 | 379 | 55 | 586 | 85 | 31 | 93$R_B$ |
| Steel, AISI 4130, alloy | Quenched and tempered (750°F) | 207 | 30 | 0.292 | 1173 | 170 | 1373 | 199 | 10 | 43$R_C$ |
| Steel, AISI 4340, alloy | Quenched and tempered (450°F) | 207 | 30 | 0.292 | 1483 | 215 | 1860 | 270 | 10 | 52$R_C$ |
| Steel, AISI H11, tool | Quenched and tempered (100°F) | 207 | 30 | 0.292 | 1655 | 240 | 2070 | 300 | 6 | 54$R_C$ |
| Steel, Type 302, stainless | 30% cold work | 190 | 27.6 | 0.305 | 963 | 140 | 1206 | 175 | 15 | 34$R_C$ |
| Steel, Type 17-7PH, stainless | Heat treated condition TH1050 | 200 | 29 | 0.305 | 1275 | 185 | 1380 | 200 | 9 | 43$R_C$ |
| Cast iron, malleable ASTM A-47, GR. 35018 | | 172 | 25 | 0.17 | 241 | 35 | 365 | 53 | 18 | 80$R_B$ |
| Cast iron, gray ASTM A-48, Cl. 50 | | 124 | 18 | 0.211 | — | — | 345 | 50 | — | 24$R_C$ |
| | | | | | | | 1130* | 164* | | |
| Copper, E.T.P., CDA 110 | Annealed | 117 | 17 | 0.33 | 69 | 10 | 221 | 32 | 45 | 45$R_F$ |
| | Hard drawn | 117 | 17 | 0.33 | 276 | 40 | 331 | 48 | 6 | 50$R_B$ |
| Brass, 70-30 | Annealed | 110 | 16 | 0.331 | 113 | 15 | 331 | 48 | 62 | 65$R_F$ |
| | Hard drawn | 110 | 16 | 0.331 | 379 | 55 | 483 | 70 | 15 | 80$R_B$ |
| Phosphor bronze, Gr. A | Annealed | 110 | 16 | 0.349 | 131 | 19 | 324 | 47 | 60 | 26$R_B$ |
| | Hard drawn | 110 | 16 | 0.349 | 517 | 75 | 558 | 81 | 10 | 81$R_B$ |
| Monel, INCO Alloy 400 | Annealed | 179 | 26 | 0.315 | 241 | 35 | 517 | 75 | 40 | 125Bhn |
| | Hard drawn | 179 | 26 | 0.315 | 552 | 80 | 690 | 100 | 25 | 190Bhn |
| Nickel silver, 12% Gr. D | Hard drawn | 117 | 17 | 0.3 | 448 | 65 | 704 | 102 | 3 | 90$R_B$ |
| Beryllium copper, CDA 170 | Heat treated | 124 | 18 | 0.3 | 963–1105 | 140–160 | 1135–1240 | 150–180 | 1–3.5 | 35–40$R_C$ |
| Titanium, alloy 6 AL-4V | Annealed | 110 | 16 | 0.3 | 895 | 130 | 963 | 140 | 10 | 30$R_C$ |
| | Hard drawn | 110 | 16 | 0.3 | 1068 | 155 | 1105 | 160 | 7 | 40$R_C$ |
| Magnesium, alloy ASTM AZ31B | Annealed | 45 | 6.5 | 0.35 | 152 | 22 | 255 | 37 | 21 | 55Bhn |
| | Hard drawn | 45 | 6.5 | 0.35 | 228 | 33 | 289 | 42 | 11 | 72Bhn |
| Aluminum, alloy AA 1100 | Annealed | 69 | 10 | 0.33 | 35 | 5 | 90 | 13 | 35–45 | 23Bhn |
| | Hard drawn | 69 | 10 | 0.33 | 152 | 22 | 165 | 24 | 5–15 | 43Bhn |
| Aluminum, alloy AA 6061-T6 | Heat treated | 69 | 10 | 0.33 | 241 | 35 | 289 | 42 | 10 | 95Bhn |
| Aluminum, alloy AA 7075-T6 | Heat treated | 72 | 10.4 | 0.33 | 503 | 73 | 572 | 83 | 11 | 150Bhn |
| Aluminum, alloy A-360-F | As die cast | 71 | 10.3 | — | 166 | 24 | 317 | 46 | 5 | 75Bhn |
| Zinc, alloy AG40A | As die cast | 52 | 7.5 | — | — | — | 283 | 41 | 10 | 82Bhn |

* Compressive strength.

| Material | Condition | Impact strength (Charpy) (ft-lb)* | Endurance limit, $10^8$ cycles (MN/m²) | Endurance limit, $10^8$ cycles ($10^3$ psi) | Electrical resistivity, room temp. (nΩ·m) | Thermal coefficient of expansion ($10^{-6}$/°C) | Thermal coefficient of expansion ($10^{-6}$/°F) | Density ($10^3$ kg/m³) | Density (lb/in.³) |
|---|---|---|---|---|---|---|---|---|---|
| Steel, structural | Typical | 25–50 | 172 | 25 | 120 | 12.1 | 6.7 | 7.84 | 0.283 |
| Steel, AISI 1040, med. carbon | Normalized | — | 242 | 35 | — | 12.1 | 6.7 | 7.84 | 0.283 |
| Steel, AISI 4130, alloy | Quenched and tempered (750°F) | — | 786 | 114 | 223 | 12.1 | 6.7 | 7.84 | 0.283 |
| Steel, AISI 4340, alloy | Quenched and tempered (450°F) | 19 | 758 | 110 | 300 | 12.1 | 6.7 | 7.84 | 0.283 |
| Steel, AISI H11, tool | Quenched and tempered (100°F) | 16 | 828 | 120 | — | 12.1 | 6.7 | 7.73 | 0.279 |
| Steel, Type 302, stainless | 30% cold work | 40 | 552 | 80 | 720 | 18.0 | 10.0 | 7.87 | 0.284 |
| Steel, Type 17-7PH, stainless | Heat treated condition TH1050 | 35 | 567 | 82 | 850 | 18.0 | 10.0 | 7.87 | 0.284 |
| Cast iron, malleable ASTM A-47, GR. 35018 | | 16 | 172 | 25 | — | 10.8 | 6 | 7.34 | 0.265 |
| Cast iron, gray ASTM A-48 Cl. 50 | | — | 152 | 22 | 500–2000 | 10.8 | 6 | 7.02 | 0.253 |
| Copper, E.T.P., CDA 110 | Annealed | — | 69 | 10 | 17.1 | 17.7 | 9.8 | 8.92 | 0.322 |
| | Hard drawn | — | 103 | 15 | — | 17.7 | 9.8 | 8.92 | 0.322 |
| Brass, 70-30 | Annealed | 14 (Izod) | 97 | 14 | 61.6 | 20.0 | 11.1 | 8.37 | 0.302 |
| | Hard drawn | 50 (Izod) | 138 | 20 | — | 20.0 | 11.1 | 8.37 | 0.302 |
| Phosphor bronze, Gr. A | Annealed | 10 | 172 | 25 | 115 | 17.8 | 9.9 | 9.20 | 0.332 |
| | Hard drawn | 14 | 221 | 32 | — | 17.8 | 9.9 | 9.20 | 0.332 |
| Monel, INCO Alloy 400 | Annealed | — | — | — | 482 | 13.5 | 7.5 | 8.98 | 0.324 |
| | Hard drawn | — | 276 | 40 | — | 13.5 | 7.5 | 8.98 | 0.324 |
| Nickel silver, 12% Gr. D | Hard drawn | — | 193 | 28 | 216 | 16.2 | 9 | 8.70 | 0.314 |
| Beryllium copper, CDA 170 | Heat treated | — | 276 | 40 | 68 | 16.7 | 9.3 | 8.23 | 0.297 |
| Titanium, alloy 6 AL-4V | Annealed | — | — | — | 1840 | 10.4 | 5.8 | 4.43 | 0.160 |
| | Hard drawn | 20 | — | — | — | 10.4 | 5.8 | 4.43 | 0.160 |
| Magnesium, alloy ASTM AZ31B | Annealed | — | 76 | 11 | 92 | 26.1 | 14.5 | 1.77 | 0.064 |
| | Hard drawn | 3 | 90 | 13 | — | 26.1 | 14.5 | 1.77 | 0.064 |
| Aluminum, alloy AA 1100 | Annealed | — | 35 | 5 | 29 | 23.6 | 13.1 | 2.72 | 0.098 |
| | Hard drawn | — | 62 | 9 | — | 23.6 | 13.1 | 2.72 | 0.098 |
| Aluminum, alloy AA 6061-T6 | Heat treated | — | 103 | 15 | 40 | 23.4 | 13.0 | 2.72 | 0.098 |
| Aluminum, alloy AA 7075-T6 | Heat treated | — | 159 | 23 | 52 | 23.2 | 12.9 | 2.72 | 0.098 |
| Aluminum, alloy A-360-F | As die cast | 3.5 | 124 | 18 | — | 21.1 | 11.7 | 2.68 | 0.097 |
| Zinc, alloy AG40A | As die cast | 43 | 48 | 6.9 | 64 | 27.4 | 15.2 | 6.65 | 0.24 |

* Numbers are of comparative value only.

**Fig. A-1** Mechanical and physical properties of metals (typical values). SI units in Roman type; *equivalent English units in italics.*

| Material | Some typical trade names | Type | Hardness (Rockwell) | Tensile strength (MN/m²) | (10³ psi) | Elongation (%) |
|---|---|---|---|---|---|---|
| | | | THERMOPLASTICS | | | |
| ABS | Cycolac Kralastic Lustran | Unfilled, molded | R85 R115 | 34 61 | 5.0 8.8 | 2 60 |
| Acetals | Celcon Delrin | Unfilled, molded | M78 R120 | 61 69 | 8.8 10.0 | 15 75 |
| Acrylics | Acrylite Lucite Plexiglas | Unfilled, cast, or molded | R99 R107 | 34 76 | 5.0 11.0 | 2 50 |
| Chlorinated polyether | Penton | Unfilled, molded | R100 | 41 | 6.0 | 60 160 |
| Fluorocarbons | Halon Teflon | Unfilled, molded, or extruded | R25 R95 | 14 48 | 2.0 7.0 | 80 400 |
| Polyamides | Nylon Zytel | Unfilled, molded | R103 R120 | 48 85 | 7.0 12.4 | 60 320 |
| Polycarbonates | Lexan Merlon | Unfilled, molded | M70 R118 | 55 65 | 8.0 9.5 | 100 130 |
| Polyesters | Celanar Mylar Scotchpak | Extruded sheet | — | 138 276 | 20 40 | 50 120 |
| Polyethylenes | Alathon Fortiflex Hifax | Low density | — | 7 16 | 1.0 2.3 | 90 800 |
| | | High density | — | 21 38 | 3.1 5.5 | 50 1000 |
| Polystyrenes | Dylene Lustrex Styron | Unfilled, molded, or sheet | M20 M90 | 10 83 | 1.5 12.0 | 1 80 |
| PVC | Dow PVC Exon Geon | Unmodified, rigid | — | 34 62 | 5.0 9.0 | 2 40 |
| | | Unfilled, flexible | — | 10 24 | 1.5 3.5 | 200 450 |
| | | | THERMOSETS | | | |
| Diallylphthalate | Acme Diall Durez | Filled molding compound | M108 E87 | 34 76 | 5 11 | — |
| Epoxies | Fiberite Mesa Scotchcast | Filled molding compound | M100 M110 | 34 210 | 5 30 | <4 |
| Melamines | Cymel Fiberite Plaskon | Filled molding compound | M110 M125 | 34 90 | 5 13 | 0.3 0.9 |
| Phenolics | Bakelite Durez Plenco | Filled molding compound | E54 E101 | 21 120 | 3 18 | 0.1 0.8 |

**Fig. A-2** Typical ranges of values for mechanical properties of plastics. SI units in Roman type; *equivalent English units in italics.*

| Modulus of elasticity in tension (GN/m²) | (10⁶ psi) | Impact strength (notched Izod)‡ | Thermal coefficient of expansion (10⁻⁶/°C) | (10⁻⁶/°F) | Heat distortion temp. per ASTM D648, 1.82 × 10⁶ N/m² (°C) | (°F) | Flammability* | Density (10³ kg/m³) | (lb/in.³) |
|---|---|---|---|---|---|---|---|---|---|
| | | | | | THERMOPLASTICS | | | | |
| 1.6 | 0.23 | 1.1 | 50 | 28 | 65 | 150 | Slow | 1.00 | 0.036 |
| 2.9 | 0.42 | 12 | 105 | 58 | 118 | 245 | | 1.25 | 0.045 |
| 2.8 | 0.41 | 1.2 | 81 | 45 | 110 | 230 | Slow | 1.38 | 0.050 |
| 3.6 | 0.52 | 1.6 | 85 | 47 | 124 | 255 | | 1.41 | 0.051 |
| 1.4 | 0.20 | 0.3 | 50 | 28 | 71 | 160 | Mod. | 1.08 | 0.039 |
| 3.5 | 0.50 | 4.5 | 90 | 50 | 105 | 221 | | 1.19 | 0.043 |
| 1.1 | 0.16 | 0.4 | 80 | 44 | 85 | 185 | Self-ext. | 0.42 | 0.015 |
| 0.3 | 0.05 | 2.5 | 45 | 25 | — | — | Self-ext. | 1.77 | 0.064 |
| 2.1 | 0.30 | No break | 120 | 67 | | | | 2.18 | 0.079 |
| 0.8 | 0.11 | 1.0 | 80 | 44 | 65 | 150 | Self-ext. | 1.08 | 0.039 |
| 3.1 | 0.45 | 5.5 | 90 | 50 | 105 | 220 | | 1.16 | 0.042 |
| 2.4 | 0.35 | >12 | 66 | 37 | 129 | 265 | Self-ext. | 1.22 | 0.044 |
| | | >17.5 | | | 141 | 285 | | | |
| — | — | >7 | — | — | — | — | Slow | 1.38 | 0.050 |
| | | | | | | | | 1.41 | 0.051 |
| 0.1 | 0.01 | No break | 100 | 55 | 32 | 90 | Mod. | 0.91 | 0.033 |
| 0.3 | 0.04 | | 200 | 110 | 41 | 105 | | | |
| 0.4 | 0.06 | 0.8 | 110 | 61 | 43 | 110 | Mod. | 0.94 | 0.034 |
| 1.2 | 0.18 | 20 | 130 | 72 | 54 | 130 | | 0.97 | 0.035 |
| 1.0 | 0.15 | 0.3 | 34 | 19 | 88 | 190 | Slow | 1.00 | 0.036 |
| 4.1 | 0.60 | 8 | 210 | 120 | 113 | 235 | | 1.11 | 0.040 |
| 2.4 | 0.35 | 0.4 | 50 | 28 | 54 | 130 | Self-ext. | 1.36 | 0.049 |
| 4.1 | 0.60 | 20 | 185 | 100 | 79 | 175 | | 1.44 | 0.052 |
| — | — | — | 70 | 39 | — | — | Slow | 1.16 | 0.042 |
| | | | 250 | 140 | | | | 1.36 | 0.049 |
| | | | | | THERMOSETS | | | | |
| 4.1 | 0.6 | 0.3 | 10 | 6 | 150 | 300 | Self-ext. | 1.33 | 0.048 |
| 15 | 2.2 | 15 | 60 | 34 | 230 | 450 | | 1.77 | 0.064 |
| 21 | 3.0 | 0.3 | 11 | 6 | 120 | 250 | Self-ext. | 1.80 | 0.065 |
| | | 10 | 50 | 28 | 260 | 500 | | 2.07 | 0.075 |
| .7.6 | 1.1 | 0.2 | 15 | 8 | 130 | 265 | Self-ext. | 1.38 | 0.050 |
| 17 | 2.4 | 6 | 45 | 25 | 200 | 400 | | 2.77 | 0.100 |
| 5.5 | 0.8 | 0.2 | 8 | 4 | 120 | 250 | Self-ext. | 1.33 | 0.048 |
| 34 | 5.0 | 18 | 45 | 25 | 290 | 550 | | 2.32 | 0.084 |

\* Materials listed as slow burning may be self-extinguishing in some formulations.
‡ Numbers are of comparative value only.

**Fig. A-2**  (continued)

| Material | Some typical trade names | Type | Hardness (Rockwell) | Tensile strength (MN/m²) | (10³ psi) | Elongation (%) |
|---|---|---|---|---|---|---|
| REINFORCED LAMINATES | | | | | | |
| Epoxy laminates | | Paper base | M100 / M110 | 69 / 130 | *10* / *19* | — |
| | | Glass fabric base | M105 / M120 | 240 / 690 | *35* / *100* | — |
| Polyester laminates | | Paper base | — | 41 / 97 | *6* / *14* | — |
| | | Glass fabric base | M100 / M110 | 120 / 41 | *18* / *60* | — |
| Phenolic laminates | | Paper base | M70 / M120 | 55 / 140 | *8* / *20* | — |
| | | Cotton fabric base | M90 / M115 | 48 / 110 | *7* / *16* | — |
| | | Glass fabric base | M100 / M110 | 62 / 340 | *9* / *50* | — |

**Fig. A-2**  Typical ranges of values for mechanical properties of plastics.  SI units in Roman type; *equivalent English units in italics* (continued)

| Modulus of elasticity in tension | | Impact strength (notched Izod)‡ | Thermal coefficient of expansion | | Heat distortion temp. per ASTM D648, 1.82 × 10⁶ N/m² | | Flamma-bility* | Density | |
|---|---|---|---|---|---|---|---|---|---|
| (GN/m²) | (10⁶ psi) | | (10⁻⁶/°C) | (10⁻⁶/°F) | (°C) | (°F) | | (10³ kg/m³) | (lb/in.³) |
| REINFORCED LAMINATES | | | | | | | | | |
| 4.8 | *0.7* | 0.6 | 20 | *11* | 135 | *275* | Self-ext.† | 1.41 | *0.051* |
| 8.3 | *1.2* | 0.8 | | | | | | 1.55 | *0.056* |
| 14 | *2.0* | 5.5 | 10 | *6* | 180 | *355* | Self-ext.† | 1.69 | *0.061* |
| 24 | *3.5* | 25 | 12 | *7* | 190 | *375* | | 1.91 | *0.069* |
| 5.5 | *0.8* | — | 31 | *17* | 115 | *240* | Self-ext.† | 1.22 | *0.044* |
| 8.3 | *1.2* | | | | | | | 1.49 | *0.054* |
| 6.9 | *1.0* | 19 | — | — | — | — | Self-ext.† | 1.49 | *0.054* |
| 19 | *2.8* | 35 | | | | | | 2.10 | *0.076* |
| 5.5 | *0.8* | 0.3 | 14 | *8* | 120 | *250* | Self-ext.† | 1.27 | *0.046* |
| 14 | *2.0* | 1.1 | 30 | *17* | >160 | *>320* | | 1.41 | *0 051* |
| 3.4 | *0.5* | 0.8 | 18 | *10* | >160 | *>320* | Self-ext.† | 1.30 | *0.047* |
| 10 | *1.5* | 3.0 | 32 | *18* | | | | 1.36 | *0.049* |
| 8.3 | *1.2* | 4.0 | 15 | *8* | >160 | *>320* | Self-ext.† | 1.41 | *0.051* |
| 17 | *2.5* | 18 | 25 | *14* | | | | 1.80 | *0.065* |

\* Materials listed as slow burning may be self-extinguishing in some formulations.
† With flame retardant.
‡ Numbers are of comparative value only.

**Fig. A-2**   (concluded)

**Fig. A-3** Shock spectrum chart (SI units)

600

**Fig. A-4** Shock spectrum chart (English units).

Frequency (Hz)

Velocity (in./s)

601

*Appendix B*

# SUPPLEMENTAL TABLES FOR PART II—
# THERMAL DESIGN

| Material | Thermal conductivity at 20°C, $k$ (W/m·deg) | Density at 20°C, $\rho$ (kg/m³) | Specific heat at 20°C, $c$ (J/kg·deg) | Thermal diffusivity at 20°C, $\alpha$ (10⁻⁵ m²/s) | Thermal conductivity at 100°C, $k$ (W/m·deg) | Melting or decomposition temperature (°C) |
|---|---|---|---|---|---|---|
| **NONMETALS** | | | | | | |
| Carbon | 0.31 | 320–401 | 754 | 0.114 | 0.606 | — |
| Cements: | | | | | | |
| Phenolic rubber | 0.21 | 1234–1346 | 1382 | 0.011 | — | 104–149 |
| Polyvinyl acetate | 0.12–0.17 | 1153–1394 | 1256–1675 | 0.007 | — | 66–93 |
| Ceramics: | | | | | | |
| Beryllium oxide | 225 | 2964 | 1088 | 6.97 | 157 | 2549 |
| High alumina | 35 | 3444 | 837 | 1.20 | 22.49 | — |
| Magnesium oxide | 40.7 | 3765 | 921 | 1.18 | 32.87 | — |
| Earth: | | | | | | |
| Dry | 0.069–1.38 | 352–1922 | — | 0.054 | — | — |
| Wet | 1.38–13.8 | 1602 | — | 0.154 | — | — |
| Glass: | | | | | | |
| Bonded mica | 0.5 | 2996 | 1214 | 0.013 | — | — |
| Epoxy glass | 0.29 | 1602–1842 | 837–1047 | 0.017 | — | — |
| Fused quartz (96 % silica) | 1.0 | 2259 | 837 | 0.052 | 1.38 | 1538 |
| Plate | 0.64 | 2804 | 837 | 0.027 | 0.917 | 721 |
| Porcelain | 2.0 | 2884 | — | — | 1.90 | — |
| Paper | 0.13 | 961–1362 | — | — | — | — |
| Plastics: | | | | | | |
| Acrylics, resin sheets | 0.2 | 1185 | 1465 | 0.011 | — | 66–93 |
| Cellulose acetate | 0.17–0.33 | 1298 | 1256–1758 | 0.012 | — | 66–104 |
| Epoxide resin | 0.4 | 1041 | — | — | — | 79–121 |
| Fluorocarbon (teflon) | 0.24 | 2083–2243 | 1047 | 0.010 | — | 204–232 |
| Melamine formaldehyde | 0.29–0.35 | 1506 | — | — | — | 121–138 |
| Nylon | 0.17–0.24 | 1121 | 1675 | 0.011 | — | 121–193 |
| Phenol fabric | 0.26 | 1891 | 963 | 0.014 | — | 260–316 |
| Polyethylene | 0.32 | 945 | — | — | 0.692 | 93–104 |
| Polystyrene | 0.1–0.16 | 1041 | 1005–1130 | 0.011 | — | 60–71 |
| Polystyrene foam | 0.035 | 16–64 | — | — | — | 77 |
| Wood: | | | | | | |
| Pine ⊥ to grain | 0.1 | 497 | 2805 | 0.007 | — | 260–316 |
| Pine ∥ to grain | 0.24 | 497 | 2805 | 0.017 | — | 260–316 |

METALS

| | | | | | | |
|---|---|---|---|---|---|---|
| **Aluminum:** | | | | | | |
| Pure (99.5%) | 204 | 2707 | 921 | 8.18 | 206 | 643–657 |
| Alloy 2024 (3–5% Cu, trace Mn and Mg) | 189 | 2771 | 921 | 7.38 | 190 | 502–638 |
| Alloy 5052 (2–3% Cu, trace Cr) | 138 | 2691 | 921 | 5.57 | 145 | 593–649 |
| Alloy 6061 (1% Mg, 1% Si, trace Cr and Cu) | 171 | 2707 | 963 | 6.58 | — | 582–649 |
| Alloy 7075 (5–6% Zn, 2–3% Mg, 1–2% Cu) | 125 | 2804 | 963 | 4.62 | 137 | 477–638 |
| Alloy 43, cast (5% Si) | 147 | 2675 | 879 | 6.25 | — | 573–632 |
| Alloy 195, cast (5% Cu) | 143 | 2787 | 879 | 5.83 | — | 521–643 |
| Alloy 355, cast (5% Si; 1% Cu) | 150 | 2707 | 879 | 6.38 | 163 | 546–621 |
| **Copper:** | | | | | | |
| Oxygen free (99.9% Cu) | 407 | 8939 | 385 | 11.82 | 391 | 1083 |
| Constantan (60% Cu, 40% Ni) | 23 | 8923 | 410 | 0.619 | 22 | 643 |
| **Copper–nickel** | | | | | | |
| (68.9% Cu, 30% Ni, 0.5% Fe, 0.6% Mn) | 29 | 8939 | 377 | 0.874 | 36 | 1171–1238 |
| Copper–nickel–silver (65% Cu, 18% Ni, 17% Zn) | 33 | 8747 | 377 | 0.998 | 40 | 1071–1110 |
| Naval brass (60% Cu, 39% Zn, 1% Sn) | 116 | 8411 | 377 | 3.67 | 133 | 888–899 |
| Phospher bronze (90% Cu, 10% Sn) | 50 | 8811 | 377 | 1.51 | — | 843–999 |
| Grade A (5% Sn) | 69 | 8859 | 377 | 2.08 | — | 954–1049 |
| Low-silicon bronze (1–2% Si) | 54 | 8747 | 377 | 1.63 | 48 | 1032–1060 |
| Germanium | 61 | 5303 | 335 | 3.41 | — | 958 |
| Gold | 292 | 19272 | 126 | 12.08 | 294 | |
| **Iron:** | | | | | | |
| Pure | 73 | 7898 | 452 | 2.04 | 67 | 1535 |
| Permalloy 45 (54.5% Fe, 45% Ni, 0.5% Mn) | 16 | 7754 | 544 | 0.371 | 16 | — |
| Gray cast iron (4% C) | 59 | 7850 | 461 | 1.63 | 57 | 1371–1427 |
| Kovar (54% Fe, 29% Ni, 17% Co) | 17 | 7850 | 461 | 0.459 | 14–16 | 1393 |
| **Lead:** | | | | | | |
| Pure (99.9%) | 33 | 11294 | 126 | 2.34 | 33 | 327 |
| 4–6% antimony | — | 10878 | 134 | — | 29.4 | 252–285 |
| **Magnesium:** | | | | | | |
| Pure (99.9%) | 171 | 1746 | 1013 | 9.68 | 168 | 651 |
| AZ31B (2% Mn) | 114 | 1778 | 1005 | 6.40 | 125 | 566 |
| AZ61A (6% Al) | 66 | 1810 | 1005 | 3.61 | 62.3 | 510–616 |
| **Nickel:** | | | | | | |
| Pure (99.9%) | 90 | 8907 | 446 | 2.26 | 83 | 1452 |
| Nickel–chromium (68.5% Ni, 16% Cr, 9% Fe, 2% Si) | — | 9900 | 461 | — | 15 | 1371–1399 |
| Nickel–copper (64% Ni, 32% Cu, 2% Si, 1% Fe) Alumel | 25 | 8683 | 544 | 0.531 | 26.8 | 1316–1343 |
| | 31 | 8587 | 523 | 0.686 | 29.8 | 1399 |
| Chromel | 20 | 8731 | 448 | 0.500 | 19.2 | 1429 |

**Fig. B-1** Thermal properties of some solid materials.

METALS (continued)

| Material | Thermal conductivity at 20°C, $k$ (W/m·deg) | Density at 20°C, $\rho$ (kg/m³) | Specific heat at 20°C, $c$ (J/kg·deg) | Thermal diffusivity at 20°C, $\alpha$ ($10^{-5}$ m²/s) | Thermal conductivity at 100°C, $k$ (W/m·deg) | Melting or decomposition temperature (°C) |
|---|---|---|---|---|---|---|
| Platinum | 70 | 18247 | 134 | 2.43 | 71.6 | 1773 |
| Silicon | 128 | 2323 | 754 | 7.33 | 90 | 882 |
| Silver: | | | | — | | |
| Pure 99.9% | 406 | 10525 | 234 | 16.5 | 415 | 961 |
| Solder: | | | | | | |
| Alloy 60(40% Sn, 60% Pb) | 33 | 4404 | 167 | 2.07 | — | 171–254 |
| Stainless steel: | | | | | | |
| (16–20% Cr, 6–11% Ni) | 16 | 7818 | 461 | 0.451 | 17.5 | 1399–1454 |
| (14–18% Cr) | 18 | 7754 | 461 | 0.495 | 19.6 | 1427–1510 |
| Steel: | | | | | | |
| Carbon steel (1% C) | 43 | 7802 | 473 | 1.17 | 43.3 | 1510–1524 |
| Tantalum | 63 | 16565 | 147 | 2.57 | 64 | 2893 |
| Tin: | | | | | | |
| Tin foil (92% Sn, 8% Zn) | 59 | 7001 | — | — | | 199 |
| Tungsten | 163 | 19352 | 134 | 6.27 | 151 | 3427 |
| Zinc: | | | | | | |
| Commercial rolled | 108 | 5543 | 394 | 4.93 | — | 419 |
| 3–4% aluminum | 113 | 6648 | 419 | 5.19 | 113 | 387 |

**Fig. B-1** Thermal properties of some solid materials (concluded).

AIR

| $T$ (°C) | $T$ (°F) | $\rho$ (kg/m³) | $c_p$ (10² J/kg·deg) | $\mu$ (10⁻⁵ kg/m·s) | $\nu$ (10⁻³ m²/s) | $k$ (W/m·deg) | $N_{Pr}$ | $\alpha$ (10⁻⁵ m²/s) | $\beta$ (10⁻³/deg) | $g\beta\rho^2/\mu^2$ (1/deg·m³) |
|---|---|---|---|---|---|---|---|---|---|---|
| -17.8 | 0 | 1.38 | 10.01 | 1.65 | 0.012 | 0.023 | 0.73 | 1.67 | 3.92 | 26.7 × 10⁷ |
| 0 | 32 | 1.30 | 10.1 | 1.73 | 0.013 | 0.024 | 0.72 | 1.86 | 3.65 | 20.1 |
| 38 | 100 | 1.14 | 10.1 | 1.91 | 0.017 | 0.027 | 0.72 | 2.34 | 3.22 | 11.2 |
| 93 | 200 | 0.961 | 10.1 | 2.14 | 0.022 | 0.030 | 0.72 | 3.10 | 2.74 | 5.40 |
| 149 | 300 | 0.833 | 10.2 | 2.40 | 0.028 | 0.033 | 0.71 | 3.95 | 2.38 | 2.82 |
| 204 | 400 | 0.737 | 10.3 | 2.60 | 0.035 | 0.037 | 0.689 | 4.85 | 2.09 | 1.64 |
| 260 | 500 | 0.660 | 10.3 | 2.81 | 0.042 | 0.040 | 0.683 | 5.86 | 1.87 | 1.01 |
| 316 | 600 | 0.598 | 10.5 | 2.98 | 0.050 | 0.043 | 0.685 | 6.92 | 1.70 | 0.674 |
| 371 | 700 | 0.546 | 10.6 | 3.18 | 0.058 | 0.046 | 0.690 | 8.00 | 1.55 | 447.6 × 10⁴ |
| 427 | 800 | 0.503 | 10.7 | 3.35 | 0.067 | 0.049 | 0.697 | 9.19 | 1.43 | 316.6 |
| 482 | 900 | 0.466 | 10.8 | 3.51 | 0.076 | 0.052 | 0.763 | 10.4 | 1.32 | 228.9 |
| 530 | 1000 | 0.434 | 11.0 | 3.68 | 0.085 | 0.055 | 0.713 | 11.6 | 1.23 | 168.5 |
| 816 | 1500 | 0.324 | 11.6 | 4.46 | 0.137 | 0.069 | 0.739 | 18.6 | 0.918 | 47.4 |
| 1093 | 2000 | 0.258 | 12.0 | 5.13 | 0.199 | 0.081 | 0.753 | 26.3 | 0.731 | 18.1 |
| 1371 | 2500 | 0.213 | 12.2 | 5.49 | 0.260 | 0.080 | 0.763 | 33.8 | 0.608 | 8.96 |
| 1649 | 3000 | 0.183 | 12.4 | 5.74 | 0.315 | 0.093 | 0.765 | 41.3 | 0.520 | 5.18 |

WATER

| $T$ (°C) | $T$ (°F) | $\rho$ (kg/m³) | $c_p$ (10² J/kg·deg) | $\mu$ (10⁻³ kg/m·s) | $\nu$ (10⁻⁵ m²/s) | $k$ (W/m·deg) | $N_{Pr}$ | $\alpha$ (10⁻⁷ m²/s) | $\beta$ (10⁻⁴/deg) | $g\beta\rho^2/\mu^2$ (1/deg·m³) |
|---|---|---|---|---|---|---|---|---|---|---|
| 0 | 32 | 1000 | 42.3 | 1.79 | 0.179 | 0.552 | 13.7 | 1.31 | -0.666 | — |
| 4 | 40 | 1000 | 41.9 | 1.55 | 0.155 | 0.562 | 11.6 | 1.34 | 0.36 | 14.6 × 10⁷ |
| 10 | 50 | 1000 | 41.9 | 1.31 | 0.130 | 0.574 | 9.55 | 1.38 | 0.882 | 50.9 |
| 16 | 60 | 998 | 41.8 | 1.13 | 0.113 | 0.588 | 8.03 | 1.41 | 1.53 | 117.0 |
| 21 | 70 | 998 | 41.8 | 0.979 | 0.098 | 0.600 | 6.82 | 1.44 | 2.16 | 220.0 |
| 27 | 80 | 996 | 41.8 | 0.860 | 0.086 | 0.611 | 5.30 | 1.47 | 2.70 | 356.0 |
| 32 | 90 | 995 | 41.7 | 0.765 | 0.077 | 0.621 | 5.13 | 1.49 | 3.24 | 540.0 |
| 38 | 100 | 993 | 41.8 | 0.682 | 0.069 | 0.630 | 4.52 | 1.52 | 3.60 | 750.2 |
| 66 | 150 | 980 | 41.9 | 0.434 | 0.044 | 0.664 | 2.74 | 1.62 | 5.58 | 2797.3 |
| 93 | 200 | 963 | 41.9 | 0.305 | 0.032 | 0.682 | 1.88 | 1.69 | 7.20 | 7.06 × 10¹⁰ |
| 121 | 250 | 942 | 42.3 | 0.235 | 0.025 | 0.685 | 1.45 | 1.73 | 8.54 | 13.6 |
| 149 | 300 | 918 | 43.1 | 0.187 | 0.020 | 0.683 | 1.18 | 1.73 | 10.3 | 25.4 |
| 177 | 350 | 891 | 44.0 | 0.156 | 0.018 | 0.676 | 1.02 | 1.73 | 12.4 | 39.7 |
| 204 | 400 | 859 | 45.2 | 0.135 | 0.016 | 0.659 | 0.927 | 1.70 | 14.4 | 56.9 |
| 232 | 450 | 827 | 46.9 | 0.119 | 0.014 | 0.635 | 0.876 | 1.64 | 16.2 | 76.9 |
| 260 | 500 | 785 | 49.8 | 0.106 | 0.013 | 0.604 | 0.87 | 1.55 | 18.0 | 97.3 |
| 288 | 550 | 735 | 54.8 | 0.095 | 0.013 | 0.562 | 0.93 | 1.30 | 19.8 | 113.2 |
| 316 | 600 | 679 | 63.2 | 0.086 | 0.013 | 0.505 | 1.09 | 1.18 | 21.6 | 131.0 |

**Fig. B-2** The thermal properties of air and water at atmospheric pressures. (By permission Kreith, F.: *Principles of Heat Transfer*, Scranton, Pa., International Textbook Co., 1958.)

*Appendix C*

# SYMBOLS, UNITS, SUBSCRIPTS, AND
# PHYSICAL CONSTANTS FOR VOL. I

## PRINCIPAL SYMBOLS AND UNITS FOR VOLUME I

The relationships developed or presented in this volume may be used with any consistent system of units. However, for convenience, SI units (*le Système International d'Unités*) are used throughout, with references to other systems as appropriate.

Symbols representing dimensions, angles, etc., defined in associated figures are not listed. Also, symbols representing variables substituted for other quantities in the development of equations are omitted. When logarithms are used, the abbreviation "ln" indicates a natural logarithm to the base $e$, while "log" indicates a common logarithm to the base 10.

The unit abbreviations will frequently carry prefixes which designate the multipliers to be used. For instance, the basic units for specific resistivity are ohm-meters ($\Omega \cdot m$), but values are often expressed more conveniently in nano-ohm-meters, abbreviated $n\Omega \cdot m$. In this text, the following prefixes and abbreviations are used:

| Multiplier | Prefix | Abbreviation | Multiplier | Prefix | Abbreviation |
|---|---|---|---|---|---|
| $10^{12}$ | tera | T | $10^{-2}$ | centi | c |
| $10^{9}$ | giga | G | $10^{-3}$ | milli | m |
| $10^{6}$ | mega | M | $10^{-6}$ | micro | $\mu$ |
| $10^{3}$ | kilo | k | $10^{-9}$ | nano | n |
| | | | $10^{-12}$ | pico | p |

| *Symbol and definition* | | *Unit and abbreviation* | |
|---|---|---|---|
| $A$ | area | meter$^2$ | m$^2$ |
| $B$ | magnetic flux density | weber/meter$^2$ | Wb/m$^2$ |
| $B$ | surface brightness | lumen/meter$^2$ | lm/m$^2$ |
| $c$ | coefficient of viscosity | newton second/meter$^2$ | N · s/m$^2$ |
| $c$ | velocity of electromagnetic wave propagation | meter/second | m/s |
| $c$ | specific heat | joule/degree kilogram | J/°K·kg |
| $C$ | electrical capacitance | farad | F |
| $C$ | thermal capacitance | joule/degree | J/°K |
| $C$ | contrast | — | — |
| $D$ | electric flux density | coulomb/meter$^2$ | C/m$^2$ |
| $E$ | Young's modulus of elasticity | newton/meter$^2$ | N/m$^2$ |
| $E$ | illuminance | lumen/meter$^2$ = lux | lm/m$^2$ |
| $E$ | electric field intensity | volt/meter | V/m |
| $f$ | frequency | hertz | Hz |
| $f$ | photoelastic fringe constant | newton/meter | N/m |
| $f$ | variable force | newton | N |
| $f$ | friction factor | — | — |
| $F$ | force | newton | N |
| $F$ | body force per unit mass | newton/kilogram | N/kg |
| $F$ | body force per unit volume | newton/meter$^3$ | N/m$^3$ |
| $F$ | form factor | — | — |
| $F_{ij}$ | configuration factor | — | — |
| $g$ | acceleration of gravity | meter/second$^2$ | m/s$^2$ |
| $G$ | shear modulus of elasticity | newton/meter$^2$ | N/m$^2$ |
| $G$ | thermal conductance | watt/degree | W/°K |
| $G$ | electrical conductance | mho | mho |
| $h$ | heat transfer coefficient | watt/meter$^2$ degree | W/m$^2$ · °K |
| $h$ | Planck constant | joule second | J · s |
| $H$ | unit step function | — | — |
| $H$ | magnetic field intensity | ampere/meter | A/m |
| $I$ | area moment of inertia | meter$^4$ | m$^4$ |
| $I$ | mass moment of inertia | kilogram meter$^2$ | kg · m$^2$ |

| *Symbol and definition* | | *Unit and abbreviation* | |
|---|---|---|---|
| $I$ | tensor invariant | — | — |
| $I$ | luminous intensity | candela | cd |
| $I$ | electrical current | ampere | A |
| $I$ | radiant intensity | watt/steradian | W/sr |
| $J$ | current density | ampere/meter$^2$ | A/m$^2$ |
| $k$ | thermal conductivity | watt/meter degree | W/m · °K |
| $k$ | spring constant | newton/meter | N/m |
| $k, k_b$ | Boltzmann constant | joule/degree | J/°K |
| $K$ | bulk modulus | newton/meter$^2$ | N/m$^2$ |
| $K$ | stress concentration factor | — | — |
| $K$ | dynamic load factor | — | — |
| $K$ | luminous efficiency | lumen/watt | lm/W |
| $L$ | differential operator | — | |
| $L$ | surface luminance | candela/meter$^2$ | cd/m$^2$ |
| $L$ | electrical inductance | henry | H |
| m | mass | kilogram | kg |
| $M$ | body moment per unit mass | newton meter/kilogram | N · m/kg |
| $M$ | moment | newton meter | N · m |
| $N$ | Avogadro constant | 1/kilogram mole | 1/kg · mol |
| $N_{dB}$ | relative intensity level | decibel | dB |
| $p$ | pressure | newton/meter$^2$ | N/m$^2$ |
| $P$ | load | newton | N |
| $P$ | power | watt | W |
| $q$ | electronic charge | coulomb | C |
| $q$ | heat flux per unit area | watt/meter$^2$ | W/m$^2$ |
| $q'''$ | heat generation per unit volume | watt/meter$^3$ | W/m$^3$ |
| $Q$ | quantity of light | lumen second | lm · s |
| $Q$ | heat flux | watt | W |
| $Q$ | charge | coulomb | C |
| $Q$ | quality factor | — | — |
| $r$ | radius | meter | m |
| $R$ | reflection loss | decibel | dB |
| $R$ | radiosity | watt/meter$^2$ | W/m$^2$ |

|  | *Symbol and definition* | *Unit and abbreviation* | |
|---|---|---|---|
| $R$ | reaction force | newton | N |
| $R$ | thermal resistance | degree/watt | °K/W |
| $R$ | electrical resistance | ohm | $\Omega$ |
| $R_s$ | skin effect surface resistivity | ohm | $\Omega$ |
| $S$ | relative sensitivity | — | — |
| $S$ | voltage standing wave ratio | — | — |
| $t$ | time | second | s |
| $t_r$ | rise time | second | s |
| $T$ | temperature | degree Kelvin, Celsius | °K, °C |
| $T$ | response time | second | s |
| $T$ | period of oscillation | second | s |
| $T$ | transmissibility | | — |
| $u$ | displacement in $x$ (or $r$) direction (Part I) | meter | m |
| $u$ | velocity in $x$ direction (Part II) | meter/second | m/s |
| $\tilde{u}$ | specific internal energy | joule/kilogram | J/kg |
| $u_f$ | monochromatic radiant energy density | joule second/meter³ | $J \cdot s/m^3$ |
| $u_\lambda$ | monochromatic radiant energy density | joule/meter⁴ | $J/m^4$ |
| $U$ | displacement amplitude in $x$ (or $r$) direction | meter | m |
| $v$ | displacement in $y$ (or $\theta$) direction (Part I) | meter | m |
| $v$ | velocity in $y$ direction (Part II) | meter/second | m/s |
| $v_s$ | velocity of sound | meter/second | m/s |
| $\tilde{v}$ | specific volume | meter³/kilogram | $m^3/kg$ |
| $V$ | velocity | meter/second | m/s |
| $V$ | volume | meter³ | $m^3$ |
| $V$ | voltage | volt | V |
| $w$ | displacement in $z$ direction (Part I) | meter | m |
| $w$ | velocity in $z$ direction (Part II) | meter/second | m/s |
| $\mathbf{w}$ | total velocity vector | meter/second | m/s |
| $W$ | displacement amplitude in $z$ direction | meter | m |

|  | *Symbol and definition* | *Unit and abbreviation* | |
|---|---|---|---|
| $W$ | weight | newton | N |
| $W$ | radiant energy | joule | J |
| $X$ | reactance | ohm | $\Omega$ |
| $Y$ | admittance | mho | mho |
| $Z$ | impedance | ohm | $\Omega$ |
| $\alpha$ | thermal diffusivity | meter$^2$/second | m$^2$/s |
| $\alpha$ | direction cosine | — | — |
| $\alpha$ | linear coefficient of thermal expansion | 1/degree | 1/°K |
| $\alpha$ | absorptivity | — | — |
| $\alpha$ | loss or attenuation | neper | |
| $\beta$ | phase shift | radian | rad |
| $\beta$ | volumetric coefficient of expansion | 1/degree | 1/°K |
| $\delta$ | boundary-layer thickness | meter | m |
| $\delta$ | skin depth | meter | m |
| $\delta$ | unit impulse function | — | — |
| $\delta$ | penetration depth | meter | m |
| $\delta$ | damping constant | 1/second | 1/s |
| $\epsilon$ | normal strain | — | — |
| $\epsilon$ | emissivity | — | — |
| $\epsilon$ | permittivity | farad/meter | F/m |
| $\zeta$ | fraction of critical damping | — | — |
| $\eta$ | efficiency | — | — |
| $\theta$ | temperature rise | degree Kelvin, Celsius | °K, °C |
| $\lambda$ | wavelength | meter | m |
| $\lambda$ | first Lamé elastic constant | newton/meter$^2$ | N/m$^2$ |
| $\mu$ | second Lamé constant (equal to the shear modulus of elasticity) | newton/meter$^2$ | N/m$^2$ |
| $\mu$ | permeability | henry/meter | H/m |
| $\mu$ | dynamic viscosity | kilogram/meter second | kg/m · s |
| $\nu$ | Poisson's ratio | — | — |
| $\nu$ | kinematic viscosity | meter$^2$/second | m$^2$/s |
| $\rho$ | mass density | kilogram/meter$^3$ | kg/m$^3$ |

|  | *Symbol and definition* | *Unit and abbreviation* | |
|---|---|---|---|
| $\rho$ | reflectivity | — | — |
| $\rho$ | reflection coefficient | — | — |
| $\rho_L$ | line charge density | coulomb/meter | C/m |
| $\rho_S$ | surface charge density | coulomb/meter$^2$ | C/m$^2$ |
| $\rho_V$ | volume charge density | coulomb/meter$^3$ | C/m$^3$ |
| $\sigma$ | normal stress | newton/meter$^2$ | N/m$^2$ |
| $\sigma$ | electrical conductivity | 1/ohm meter | $1/\Omega \cdot$ m |
| $\sigma$ | Stefan–Boltzmann constant | watt/meter$^2$ degree$^4$ | W/m$^2 \cdot {}^\circ$K$^4$ |
| $\tau$ | shear stress | newton/meter$^2$ | N/m$^2$ |
| $\tau$ | characteristic loading time | second | s |
| $\tau$ | reaction time | second | s |
| $\tau$ | natural time (Fourier modulus) | — | — |
| $\Phi$ | luminous flux | lumen | lm |
| $\Psi$ | stream function | — | — |
| $\omega$ | angular frequency | radian/second | rad/s |
| $\omega$ | solid angle | steradian | sr |
| $\nabla$ | vector operator | — | — |

*Subscripts*

| | |
|---|---|
| $b$ | blackbody |
| $C$ | critical value |
| $d$ | dry bulb |
| $e$ | equivalent value, emitted, or electrical |
| $e$ | effective value |
| $f$ | value at a given frequency, or at failure |
| $g$ | refers to ground, or boundary value |
| $i$ | incident (when not used as an index) |
| $l$ | longitudinal |
| $m$ | mutual |
| $p$ | constant pressure |
| $r$ | reflected, relative |
| $t$ | transverse |
| $t$ | tensile value |

*Subscripts*

| | |
|---|---|
| $v$ | constant volume |
| $w$ | wall |
| $w$ | wet bulb |
| $x, y, z$ | value along respective coordinate axis |
| $\theta$ | thermal |
| $\lambda$ | monochromatic values |
| $0$ | reference state; free space |
| $1, 2, 3$ | principal planes, axes, stresses, or strains |

## Physical Constants

| | Symbol and definition | Value and units | |
|---|---|---|---|
| $c_0$ | speed of propagation of electromagnetic waves in vacuum | $2.9979 \times 10^8$ | m/s |
| $g_n$ | standard acceleration of gravity | $9.8067$ | m/s$^2$ |
| $h$ | Planck constant | $6.6256 \times 10^{-34}$ | J · s |
| $k$ | Boltzmann constant | $1.3805 \times 10^{-23}$ | J/°K |
| $N$ | Avogadro constant | $6.0247 \times 10^{26}$ | 1/kg · mol |
| $q$ | electronic charge | $1.6021 \times 10^{-19}$ | C |
| $\epsilon_0$ | permittivity of a vacuum | $8.8542 \times 10^{-12}$ | F/m |
| $\mu_0$ | permeability of a vacuum | $4\pi \times 10^{-7}$ | H/m |
| $\sigma$ | Stefan–Boltzmann constant | $5.67 \times 10^{-8}$ | W/m$^2$ · °K$^4$ |

# INDEX